Houghton Mifflin

Math
Expressions

Teacher's Guide • Grade 5 • Volume 1

Developed by
The Children's Math Worlds
Research Project

PROJECT DIRECTOR AND AUTHOR

Dr. Karen C. Fuson

This material is based upon work supported by the
National Science Foundation
under Grant Numbers
ESI-9816320, REC-9806020, and RED-935373.

Any opinions, findings, and conclusions or recommendations expressed in this
material are those of the author and do not necessarily reflect the views of the
National Science Foundation.

 HOUGHTON MIFFLIN   BOSTON

Credits

Cover art: (stopwatch) © Photodisc/Getty Images. (cheetah) © John Daniels/ Ardea London Ltd. (train) © Michael Dunning/Photographer's Choice/Getty Images.

Illustrative art: Dave Klug.
Technical art: Morgan-Cain & Associates

Introducing
Math
Expressions

A Fresh Approach to

Math Expressions is a comprehensive Kindergarten–Grade 5 mathematics curriculum that offers new ways to teach and learn mathematics. Combining the most powerful elements of standards-based instruction with the best of traditional approaches, *Math Expressions* uses objects,

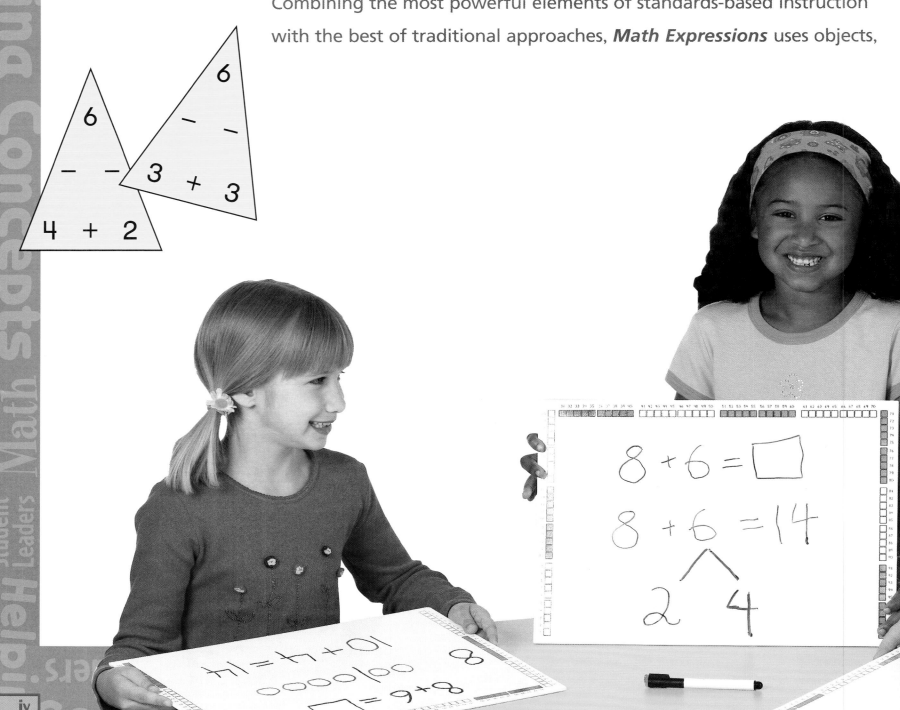

Standards-Based Instruction

drawings, conceptual language, and real-world situations to help students build mathematical ideas that make sense to them.

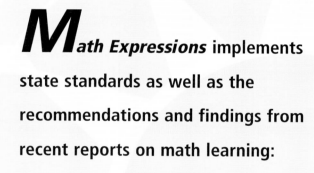

Math Expressions implements state standards as well as the recommendations and findings from recent reports on math learning:

- *Principles and Standards for School Mathematics* (NCTM, 2000)

- *Adding It Up* (National Research Council, 2001)

- *How Students Learn Mathematics in the Classroom* (National Research Council, 2005)

- *Knowing and Teaching Elementary Mathematics* (Dr. Liping Ma, 1999)

Focused on Inquiry

Math Expressions balances deep understanding with essential skills and problem solving. Students invent, question, and discover, but also learn and practice important math strategies. Through daily

and Fluency

Math Talk, students explain their methods and, in turn, become more fluent in them.

Organized for

Math Expressions is organized around five

crucial classroom structures that allow

Quick Practice
Routines involve whole-class
responses or individual
partner practice.

Math Talk
Students share strategies and
solutions orally and through
proof drawings.

Building Concepts
Objects, drawings, conceptual language
and real-world situations strengthen
mathematical ideas and understanding.

UNIT 4
LESSON
2

Explore Teen Num

Lesson Objective
• Understand how tens and ones relate to teen numbers.

The Day at a Glance

Today's Goals

Daily Routine Multi-digit Routine See page v.
Quick Practice Identify and count tens.

1 Teaching the Lesson
A1: Represent teen numbers with Secret Code Cards.
A2: Represent teen numbers by drawing circles.

2 Extending the Lesson
▶ Extra Practice
▶ Differentiated Instruction

3 Homework and Cumulative Review

Materials

Secret Co
(multiple

Math Bo

Student
pages 9

Math J

Quick Practice

⏱ 5 MINUTES   **Goal:** Identify and count tens.

Number Flashes: The Student Leader directs the clas
100 by tens, doing number flashes for each ten group
open and then close for each ten.)

10   20... and so o

The Lions' Den: The Student Leader recites this rh
responds in unison. Repeat with other decade num

40 lions in a den. Add a ten.
30 lions in a den. Add a ten.

14 UNIT 4 LESSON 2

---

1 Teaching the Lesson

Activity 1

Modeling Ten-Structured Teens

⏱ **25 MINUTES**

Goal: Represent teen numbers with Secret Code Cards.

Materials: Secret Code Cards, Math Boards, Dry-erase markers

✓ **NCTM Standards:**
Number and Operations;
Communication

Teaching Note

What to Expect from Students
Children may already know
something about place value. If so,
invite them to explain why each
teen number begins with a 1, but be
sure to make this a quick discussion.
Do not attempt a full explanation of
place value at this time. Children will
develop this understanding in the
days to come. Right now they only
need to see that each teen number
contains 1 ten.

▶ Explore Teen Numbers   WHOLE CLASS

Write the teen numbers on the chalkboard. Have t
aloud as you point to each number.

11   12   13   14   15   16   17   18

Discuss the embedded ten with the class.
• How are these numbers alike? They all begin
• Do we know what the 1 means? 1 ten.
• Yes, each number has 1 ten and something
  1 ten and some ones. We call them teen nu
• Look at the number 13. How many tens doe
• How many ones? 3.
• The 1 is in the tens place and the 3 is in the

Model Teen Numbers Line up Secret Code Car
the chalkboard, starting with the large 10-car
• We can make the number 13 with these car
  10-card.
• Which card shows how many ones are left
• So we can put the 3-card over the zero. We
  ones. We have 10 and 3 ones.

Invite two students to show the number 1
Give students the opportunity to question
who made 16.

Point out the small number in the top co
• What do these little numbers tell us ab
  a 10 and a 6. Even when you can't see
  is there.

Have the students make a few more teen
Cards. Elicit the number of tens and the number of ones f
each time.

Class Management

Organizing Materials
Keep the Secret Code Cards on the
ledge of the chalkboard throughout
the lesson as students will use the
cards in several activities.

▶ Write Equations with Teen Numbers   WHOLE CLASS
Tell the students the grouping story below. Students may use their
Math Boards if they need to. After they find the answer, write the
ten-structured equation on the board.

Kia has a bag of 10 tennis balls.
She also has 4 extra balls.
How many balls does she have altogether?

• How did you solve the problem? Encourage other students to ask
  questions about the strategies and processes used.
• Let's write the equation: 10 + 4 = 14
  Ask a student to show the total with the Secret Code Cards.
• How can the cards help you write the equation? Each card shows a
  partner to use in the equation for the total.

Activity 2

Visualizing Teen Numbers

▶ Represent 15 in Different Ways   WHOLE CLASS
Have the students position their Math Boards with the grid on the left
side as shown below.

• We will be making teen numbers on the grid.
  What does each teen number have? 1 ten.
• Let's begin by drawing 10 circles in the first
  column of the grid. Draw a rectangle around
  this ten-group to remind you not to erase it
  when you make other teen numbers.
• Now draw 5 more circles in the next column. What is the new
  number? 15. Write the equation on your boards: 10 + 5 = 15.

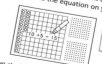

Then ask two students to make the number with Secret Code Cards.
Have students erase everything except the ten-group.
Ask students to think
of other numbers between 10 and 20. For each number they propose,
they will make the teen number with circles on their Math Boards and
write the ten-structured equation. Then two volunteers will show the
number with Secret Code Cards.

Ask questio
▶ Is 14 a te
  why not?
▶ How do y
  a teen num
▶ Draw a pic

Exploring

Classroom Success

children to develop deep conceptual understanding, and then practice,

apply, and discuss what they know with skill and confidence.

Helping Community
A classroom in which everyone is both a teacher and a learner enhances mathematical understanding, competence, and confidence.

Student Leaders
Teachers facilitate students' growth by helping them learn to lead practice and discussion routines.

Extending the Lesson

a Practice

actice solving comparison problems.
ls: Secret Code Cards, Stair Steps

TM Standards:
nber and Operations
blem Solving

al Thinking Questions

tudent Activity Book, page 94
lents begin the page, use these questions to understanding of teen numbers.

tion
Problem 1. How can you find the number
s? Count them all or start with 10 and
n.

Problem 6. Will the answer be a teen number?
you know? Yes, I am adding 6 to 10.

roblem 3. What is a quick way to count the
rt with 10, then count on 3.

roblem 9. Will the answer to this problem
ne as the answer to 10 + 4? Yes, for both
you add a 10 and 4 ones.

blems 1–5. Why will all the answers be
ers? They all show ten and some ones.

blems 6 –11. Explain how all the
l be alike in some way. They will all be
ers because some ones are being added
h problem.

t Activity Book, page 94

When students finish the page, discuss
ow students found them. Then ask why
the problems are teen numbers. All the
t adding some ones to 10.

2

Differentiated Instruction Activities for Individualizing

Intervention
for students having difficulty

PAIRS

Tens and Ones Game
Materials: Secret Code Cards

Tens and Ones Rules: First, spread the single-digit Secret Code Cards facedown. One child will choose a card. The other child will have the 10 Secret Code Card. The partners will then discuss and put the cards together to make a teen number. Replace the single-digit card and play again. Play until the partners make all the teen numbers.

10	5	10 5
1 0	5	1 5

On Level
for students having success

PAIRS

Mystery Teen Number
Materials: Secret Code Cards

One partner thinks of a teen number and draws it on the dot grid on their Math Board. The second partner makes the mystery teen number using the Secret Code Cards.

Together, the partners write two equations for the teen number. For example, if the first partner draws the number 17 on the grid, the second partner will make the number 17 using the 10 and the 7 Secret Code Cards. Together they will write the equations 10 + 7 = 17 and 7 + 10 = 17.

17
(dot grid)

10	7
1	7

10 + 7 = 17
7 + 10 = 17

Challenge
for students seeking a challenge

INDIVIDUALS

Write a Problem
Write a story for the problem 10 + 7 = □. Draw a picture of your problem and then show two ways to solve it.

Jake found 10 new shells at the beach. He had 7 old ones at home. How many shells does Jake have?

Way 1

New shells
Old shells

17 shells in all.

Way 2

10+7=17

Jake has 17 shells.

Math Writing Prompt
Intervention

Draw a Picture
Make a list of all the teen numbers that you can think of. Draw a picture of your favorite teen number. Why is this teen number so important to you?

Math Writing Prompt
On Level

Making Teen Numbers
Start by writing the teen numbers from 11 through 19 on your paper. Tell how the numbers are alike. Tell how they are different.

Math Writing Prompt
Challenge

What Goes In the Box?
Solve this problem.
10 + □ = 13

Explain how you found your answer. Now write about another way to find the answer.

Exploring Teen Numbers **17**

---

❸ Homework and Cumulative Review

Homework

Remembering
Goal: Cumulative Review

This Remembering Activity would be appropriate any time after today's lesson.

Remembering   Name

Find the missing number.

| 1. 7 | 2. 8 | 3. 9 | 4. 10 |
| 4 + 3 | 5 + 3 | 4 + 5 | 8 + 2 |

| 5. 8 | 6. 6 | 7. 10 | 8. 7 |
| 6 + 2 | 3 + 3 | 3 + 7 | 2 + 5 |

How many circles?

9.   10.

20   30

Solve.
11. There were 9 people on the train. Then 3 of them got off. How many people are still on the train?

Show your work. Use pictures, numbers, or words.

6   people
     label

96 UNIT 4 LESSON 2

Student Activity Book page 96

form numbers
ng the teen

numbers other
in some sports
than teen
ten numbers less

ix

Differentiated for

Every *Math Expressions* lesson includes intervention, on level, and challenge differentiation to support classroom needs. In addition, leveled math writing prompts provide opportunities for in-depth

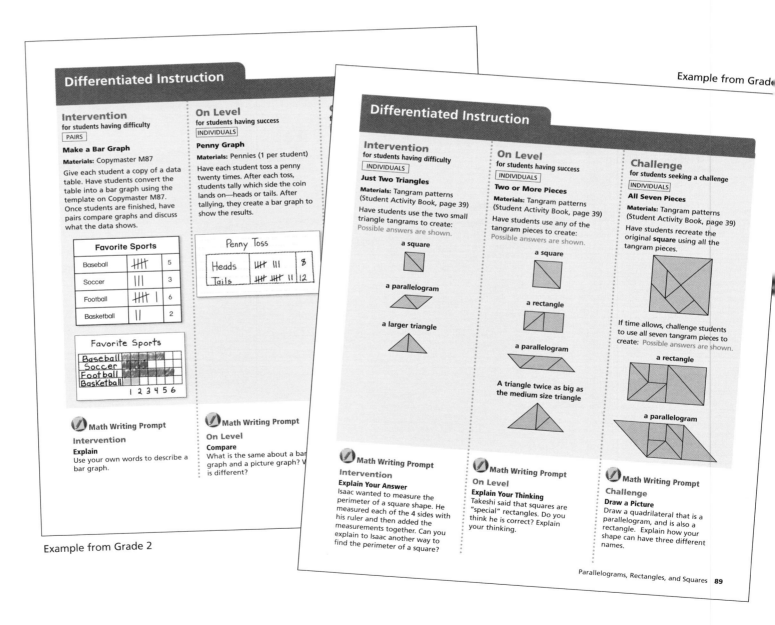

Example from Grade

Differentiated Instruction

Intervention
for students having difficulty
PAIRS

Make a Bar Graph

Materials: Copymaster M87

Give each student a copy of a data table. Have students convert the table into a bar graph using the template on Copymaster M87. Once students are finished, have pairs compare graphs and discuss what the data shows.

Favorite Sports

Baseball		5
Soccer		3
Football		6
Basketball		2

Favorite Sports

Baseball
Soccer
Football
Basketball
1 2 3 4 5 6

⊘ **Math Writing Prompt**

Intervention

Explain
Use your own words to describe a bar graph.

On Level
for students having success
INDIVIDUALS

Penny Graph

Materials: Pennies (1 per student)

Have each student toss a penny twenty times. After each toss, students tally which side the coin lands on—heads or tails. After tallying, they create a bar graph to show the results.

Penny Toss

| Heads | | 8 |
| Tails | | 12 |

⊘ **Math Writing Prompt**

On Level

Compare
What is the same about a bar graph and a picture graph? W is different?

Example from Grade 2

Differentiated Instruction

Intervention
for students having difficulty
INDIVIDUALS

Just Two Triangles

Materials: Tangram patterns (Student Activity Book, page 39)

Have students use the two small triangle tangrams to create:
Possible answers are shown.

a square

a parallelogram

a larger triangle

⊘ **Math Writing Prompt**

Intervention

Explain Your Answer
Isaac wanted to measure the perimeter of a square shape. He measured each of the 4 sides with his ruler and then added the measurements together. Can you explain to Isaac another way to find the perimeter of a square?

On Level
for students having success
INDIVIDUALS

Two or More Pieces

Materials: Tangram patterns (Student Activity Book, page 39)

Have students use any of the tangram pieces to create:
Possible answers are shown.

a square

a rectangle

a parallelogram

A triangle twice as big as the medium size triangle

⊘ **Math Writing Prompt**

On Level

Explain Your Thinking
Takeshi said that squares are "special" rectangles. Do you think he is correct? Explain your thinking.

Challenge
for students seeking a challenge
INDIVIDUALS

All Seven Pieces

Materials: Tangram patterns (Student Activity Book, page 39)

Have students recreate the original **square** using all the tangram pieces.

If time allows, challenge students to use all seven tangram pieces to create: Possible answers are shown.

a rectangle

a parallelogram

⊘ **Math Writing Prompt**

Challenge

Draw a Picture
Draw a quadrilateral that is a parallelogram, and is also a rectangle. Explain how your shape can have three different names.

Parallelograms, Rectangles, and Squares **89**

All Learners

thinking and analysis, and help prepare students for high-stakes tests. Support for English Language Learners is integrated throughout.

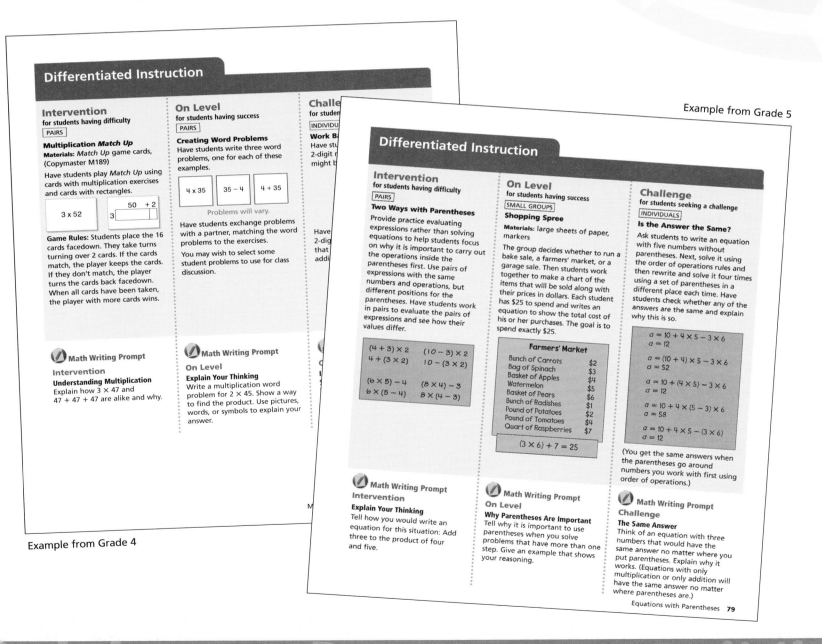

Example from Grade 5

Example from Grade 4

Validated Through Ten

For twenty-five years, Dr. Karen Fuson, Professor Emeritus of Education and Psychology at Northwestern University, researched effective methods of teaching and learning mathematics. During the last ten years, with the support of the

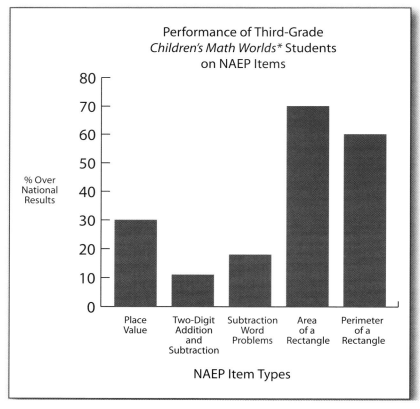

Performance of Third-Grade *Children's Math Worlds** Students on NAEP Items

NAEP Item Types

% Over National Results

Place Value · Two-Digit Addition and Subtraction · Subtraction Word Problems · Area of a Rectangle · Perimeter of a Rectangle

***Math Expressions** is the curriculum developed from the Children's Math Worlds Research Project.*

Years of Research

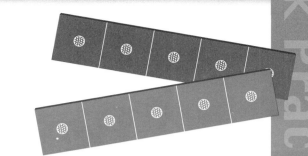

National Science Foundation for the *Children's Math Worlds Research Project*, Dr. Fuson began development of what is now the **Math Expressions** curriculum in real classrooms across the country.

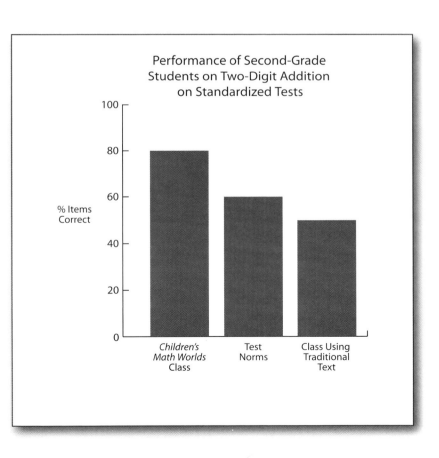

Performance of Second-Grade Students on Two-Digit Addition on Standardized Tests

"**T**he mathematical growth was tremendous and the children had a great attitude about math. I would say their overall comment about math is, 'It is fun!'"

– Grade 3 Teacher

Powered by Professional

Math Expressions incorporates a "learn while you teach" philosophy, in which elements of the Teacher's Edition—such as Mathematics Background, Teaching Tips, and the Learning Classroom—work in conjunction with the program's thoughtful, research-based content to educate both teachers and students.

Development

To further help teachers and administrators implement *Math Expressions* with the highest levels of expertise, commitment, and confidence, Houghton Mifflin also offers specialized professional institutes.

Math Expressions Institutes

- **Administrator Institute**
  For administrators with school-based curriculum responsibilities

- **Level I Institute**
  For teachers who are new to *Math Expressions*

- **Level II Institute**
  For teachers who have at least six months' experience teaching *Math Expressions*

- **Math Expressions Blended Usage Institute**
  For teachers using *Math Expressions* with *Houghton Mifflin Math*

"**I**mproving teachers' subject matter knowledge and improving students' mathematics education are ... interwoven and interdependent processes.... What is needed, then, is a teaching context in which it is possible for teachers to improve their knowledge of school mathematics as they work to improve their teaching of mathematics."

– *Knowing and Teaching Elementary Mathematics*, Dr. Liping Ma (1999), p. 147

Math Expressions
Components

	Grades					
	K	**1**	**2**	**3**	**4**	**5**
Teacher's Guide, Volumes 1 and 2	•	•	•	•	•	•
Student Activity Book, Volumes 1 and 2	•	•	•	•	•	•
Homework and Remembering, Volumes 1 and 2	•	•	•	•	•	•
Teacher's Resource Book	•	•	•	•	•	•
Assessment Guide	•	•	•	•	•	•
Manipulatives and Materials Kit	•	•	•	•	•	•
Student MathBoard		•	•	•	•	•
Teacher MathBoard		•	•	•	•	•
Blended Usage Guide	•	•	•	•	•	•
Lesson Planner CD-ROM	•	•	•	•	•	•
Test Generator	•	•	•	•	•	•
***Anno's Counting Book* Big Book**	•					

11	12	13	14	15	16	17	18	19	20
$10+1=11$	$10+2=12$	$10+3=13$	$10+4=14$	$10+5=15$	$10+6=16$	$10+7=17$	$10+8=18$	$10+19=19$	$10+10=20$

Introduction

History and Development

Math Expressions is a complete mathematics program for kindergarten through grade 5. It is a result of the Children's Math Worlds (CMW) Research Project conducted by Dr. Karen C. Fuson, Professor Emeritus, at Northwestern University. This project was funded in part by the National Science Foundation.

The project studied the ways children around the world understand mathematical concepts, approach problem solving, and learn to do computation; included ten years of classroom research; and incorporated the ideas of participating students and teachers into the developing curriculum. The research focused on building conceptual supports that include special language, drawings, manipulatives, and classroom communication methods that facilitate language competence.

Within the curriculum a series of learning progressions reflect recent research regarding children's natural stages when mastering concepts such as addition, subtraction, multiplication, and story problem solving. These learning stages help determine the order of concepts across grades, the sequence of units within grades, and the positioning of topics within units. The curriculum is designed to help teachers apply the most effective conceptual supports so that each child progresses as rapidly as possible.

The curriculum was developed within a context of both national and international mathematics education reform movements. These movements have focused on creating high standards that emphasize students' construction of mathematical knowledge. The curriculum meets the standards of the National Council of Teachers of Mathematics (NCTM) as well as various state and district goals.

Students in the ten-year field test have shown increases in standardized test scores as well as in broader measures of student understanding. These results have been found for a wide range of both urban and suburban students from a variety of socio-economic groups.

Philosophy

Math Expressions is designed to incorporate the best of both traditional and reform math curricula. The program strikes a balance between promoting children's natural solution methods and introducing effective procedures. Because research has demonstrated that premature instruction in formalized procedures can lead to mechanical, unthinking behavior, established procedures for solving problems are not introduced until students have developed a solid conceptual foundation. Children begin by using their own knowledge to solve problems and then are introduced to research-based accessible methods, which are discussed so that children understand them. In the process, many teachers discover new meanings behind their own solution methods and come to understand the methods that students use.

In order to promote children's natural solution methods, as well as to encourage students to become reflective and resourceful problem solvers, teachers need to develop a helping and explaining culture in their classrooms. Collaboration and peer helping deepen children's commitment to values such as responsibility and respect for others. *Math Expressions* offers opportunities for students to interact in pairs, small groups, whole-class activities, and special scenarios. As students collaboratively investigate math situations, they develop communication skills, sharpen their mathematical reasoning, and enhance their social awareness. Integrating students' social and cultural worlds into their emerging math worlds in this way allows them to find their own voices and to connect real-world experiences to math concepts.

Main Concept Streams

Math Expressions focuses on a few crucially important core concepts at each grade level. This is the approach taken by most international curricula. These core topics are placed at grade levels that enable students to do well on standardized tests.

The two main concept streams at all grade levels are number concepts and word problems. Breaking apart numbers, or finding the embedded numbers, is a key concept running through the number concept units. Kindergarteners and first-graders find the numbers embedded within single-digit numbers and find the tens and ones in multi-digit numbers. Second- and third-graders continue breaking apart multi-digit numbers into ones and groups of tens, hundreds, and thousands. This activity facilitates their understanding of multi-digit addition, subtraction, and story problems. Second-, third-, and fourth-graders work on seeing the repeated groups within numbers, and this awareness helps them to master multiplication and division. Fourth- and fifth-graders approach fractions as sums of unit fractions using length models. This permits them to see and comprehend operations on fractions.

Students begin working with story problems early in kindergarten and continue throughout the other grades. They not only solve, but also construct, story problems. As a result, they become comfortable and flexible with mathematical language and can connect concepts and terminology with meaningful referents from their own lives. As part of this process, students learn to make meaningful math drawings that are both easier to use and more permanent than manipulatives. Such drawings enable teachers to see student thinking, and they facilitate communication.

Concepts and skills in geometry, measurement, and graphing are woven in among these two primary streams throughout the grades. In grades two through five, geometry and measurement mini-units follow each regular unit.

Program Features

A number of special features and approaches contribute to the effectiveness of *Math Expressions*.

Quick Practice

The opening 5-10 minutes of each math period are dedicated to activities (often student-led) that allow students an opportunity to practice newly-acquired knowledge. These *consolidating activities* help students to become faster and more accurate with the concepts. Occasionally *leading activities*, prepare the ground for new concepts before they are introduced. Usually the Quick Practice activities are the same throughout each unit. In this way they become familiar routines that students can do quickly and confidently.

Drawn Models

Special manipulatives are used at key points. However, children move toward math drawings as rapidly as possible. These drawn models help children relate to the math situation. The drawings facilitate students' explanations of the steps they took to solve the problem and help listeners comprehend these explanations. The drawings also give teachers insight into students' mathematical thinking, and they leave a durable record of student work that can be examined after class.

Language Development

Math Expressions offers a wealth of learning activities that directly support language development. In addition to verbalizing procedures and explanations, students are encouraged to write their own story problems and describe their problem-solving strategies in writing as soon as they are able.

Homework Assignments

To achieve the high level of mathematical performance that is our goal, children complete homework assignments every night. Families are expected to identify a homework helper to be responsible for monitoring the child's homework completion and to help if necessary. Homework not only develops and consolidates understanding of math concepts, but also helps children become organized and self-regulatory.

Remembering Activities

Remembering Activities provide practice with the important concepts covered in all the units to date, and are ideal for spare classroom moments when children need a quick refresher of what they have learned so far. These pages are also valuable as extra homework pages that promote an on-going synthesis of concepts.

Math Talk

A significant part of the collaborative classroom culture is the frequent exchange of problem-solving strategies, or Math Talk. The benefits of Math Talk are multiple. Describing one's methods to another person can clarify one's own thinking as well as clarify the matter for others. Another person's approach can supply a new perspective, and frequent exposure to different approaches tends to engender flexible thinking.

Math Talk creates opportunities to understand errors and permits teachers to assess students' understanding on an on-going basis. It encourages students to develop their language skills, both in math and in everyday English. Finally, Math Talk enables students to become active helpers and questioners, creating student-to-student talk that stimulates engagement and community.

The key supports for Math Talk are the various participant structures, or ways of organizing class members as they interact. The teacher always guides the activity and helps students function productively, and students learn to work together as a community and also independently. Description of the most common participant structures follow.

Participant Structures

Solve and Discuss (Solve, Explain, Question, and Justify) at the Board

The teacher selects 4 to 5 children (or as many as space allows) to go to the classroom board and solve a problem, using any method they choose. Their classmates work on the same problem at their desks. Then the teacher picks 2 or 3 children to explain their methods. Students at their desks are encouraged to ask questions and to assist their classmates in understanding.

> **Benefits:** The board work reveals multiple methods of solving a problem, making comparisons possible and communicating to students that different methods are acceptable. The teacher can select methods to highlight in subsequent discussions. Spontaneous helping occurs frequently by children working next to each other at the board. Time is used efficiently because everyone in the class is working. In addition, errors can be identified in a supportive way and corrected and understood by students.

Step-by-Step at the Board

This is a variation of the Solve and Discuss structure. Again, several children go to the board to solve a problem. This time, however, a different student performs each step of the problem, describing the step before everyone does it. Everyone else at the board and at their desks carries out that step. This approach is particularly useful in learning multidigit addition, subtraction, multiplication, and division. It assists the least advanced students the most, providing them with accessible, systematic methods.

> **Benefits:** This structure is especially effective when children are having trouble solving certain kinds of problems. The step-by-step structure allows children to grasp a method more easily than doing the whole method at once. It also helps children learn to verbalize their methods more clearly, as they can focus on describing just their own step.

Participant Structures (continued)

Student Pairs

Two students work together to solve a problem, to explain a solution method to each other, to role play within a mathematical situation (for example, buying and selling), to play a math game, or to help a partner having difficulties. They are called *helping pairs* when more advanced students are matched with students who are struggling. Pairs may be organized formally, or they may occur spontaneously as help is needed. Initially it is useful to model pair activities, contrasting effective and ineffective helping. Continued discussion about how to help (for example, helping someone do it their way, not doing it for someone) can lead to improved helping by all.

> **Benefits**: Pair work supports students in learning from each other, particularly in applying and practicing concepts introduced in whole-class discussion. Helping pairs often foster learning by both students as the helper strives to adopt the perspective of the novice. Helping almost always enables the helper to understand more deeply.

Small Groups

Unstructured groups can form spontaneously if physical arrangements allow (for example, desks arranged in groups of four or children working at tables). Spontaneous helping between and among students as they work on problems individually can be encouraged.

For more structured projects, assign students to specific groups. It is usually a good idea to include a range of students and to have a strong reader in each group. Explain the problem or project, and guide the groups as necessary. When students have finished, call a pair from each group to present and explain the results of their work, or have the entire group present the results, with each member explaining one part of the solution or project. Having lower-performing students present first allows them to contribute, while higher-performing students expand on their efforts and give the fuller presentation.

> **Benefits:** Students learn different strategies from each other for approaching a problem or task. They are invested in their classmates' learning because the presentation will be on behalf of the whole group.

Whole-Class Practice and Student Leaders

This structure can be either teacher-led or student-led. When students lead it, it is usually at the consolidation stage, when children understand the concept and are beginning to achieve speed and automaticity. It is an excellent way for students to work together and learn from each other.

> **Benefits:** Whole-class practice lets the less-advanced students benefit from the knowledge of the more-advanced students without having to ask for help directly. It also provides the teacher with a quick and easy means of assessing the progress of the class as a whole.

Scenarios

The main purpose of scenarios is to demonstrate mathematical relationships in a visual and memorable way. In scenario-based activities, a group of students is called to the front of the classroom to act out a particular situation. Scenarios are useful when a new concept is being introduced for the first time. They are especially valuable for demonstrating the physical reality that underlies such math concepts as embedded numbers (break-aparts) and regrouping.

> **Benefits:** Because of its active and dramatic nature, the scenario structure often fosters a sense of intense involvement among children. In addition, scenarios create meaningful contexts in which students can reason about numbers and relate math to their everyday lives.

Unit 1 Basic Multiplication and Division

Big Idea Addition and Subtraction

Big Idea Graphing and Rounding

Big Idea Multidigit Word Problems

Unit B Circles, Polygons, and Angles

Unit 3 Fraction Concepts

Big Idea Mixed Numbers and Improper Fractions

Big Idea Equivalent Fractions

Unit C Volume, Capacity, and Weight

Basic Multiplication and Division

UNIT 1 BUILDS upon the concepts of equal groups, arrays, area, and patterns. The activities in this unit help students gain a conceptual understanding of basic multiplication and division, and the relationship between the two operations. They are expected to apply their understanding of multiplication and division to numeric calculations and real-world problem-solving situations including the use of tables, functions, and factors to solve multiplication combinations and comparisons.

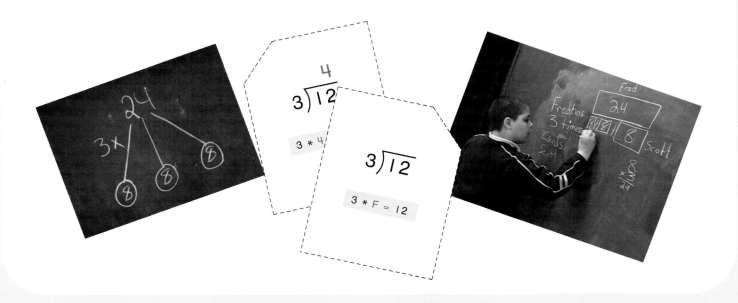

UNIT 1 CONTENTS

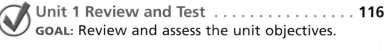

Unit 1 Assessment

✓ Unit Objectives Tested	Unit Test Items	Lessons
1.1 Recall basic multiplication and division.	1–14	1–7, 9–10, 14
1.2 Identify and write rules for a function table.	15–16	8
1.3 Solve algebraic equations involving multiplication and division.	17–20	4, 12
1.4 Identify and use the properties of multiplication.	21–22	18
1.5 Solve one- and two-step problems involving multiplication and division.	23–25	11, 13, 15

Formal Assessment

Open or Free Response Tests

- Quick Quizzes (Assessment Guide)
- Unit Review and Test (Student Activity Book pages 63–64, Teacher's Guide pages 113–116)
- Unit 1 Test Form A (Assessment Guide)
- Unit 1 Open Response Test (Test Generator)
- Test Bank Items for Unit 1 (Test Generator)

Multiple Choice Tests

- Unit 1 Test Form B (Assessment Guide)
- Unit 1 Multiple Choice Test (Test Generator)
- Test Bank Items for Unit 1 (Test Generator)

Performance Tasks

- Unit 1 Performance Assessment (Assessment Guide)
- Unit 1 Performance Assessment (Test Generator)

Informal Assessment

Ongoing Assessment

- In every Teacher's Guide lesson

Performance Assessment

- Class discussions
- Small-group work
- Quick Practice (in every lesson)
- Individual work on teacher-selected tasks

Portfolios

- See Unit 1 Review and Test for suggestions for selecting items for portfolios.
- Some Homework pages are noted as suitable for portfolio inclusion.

Review Opportunities

Homework and Remembering

- Homework pages provide review of recently taught topics.
- Remembering pages provide cumulative review.

Teacher's Guide

- Unit Review and Test (page 113-116)
- Finger Factors (multiple pages)
- Division Cards (multiple pages)
- MathBoards (multiple pages)
- Write-On and Check sheets (multiple pages)

Teacher's Resource Book

- Problem Bank

Test Generator CD-ROM

- Test Bank Items can be used to create custom review sheets.

Planning Unit 1 Unit Pacing: 26–30 days

Lesson Title	Lesson Resources	Materials and Manipulatives	
		Math Expressions	Other
1 Multiplication as Equal Groups	Student Activity Book pages 1–4 Homework and Remembering pages 1–2 Family Letter	Product Cards, Centimeter-Grid Paper (Copymaster M19)	Counters, scissors, crayons, calculator, Math Journals
2 Arrays and Area	Student Activity Book pages 5–8 Homework and Remembering pages 3–4	Inch-Grid Paper (Copymaster M1), Centimeter-Grid Paper (Copymaster M19), Digit Cards (Copymaster M2)	Crayons, Math Journals
3 Explore the Multiplication Table	Student Activity Book pages 9–10 Homework and Remembering pages 5–6	Class Multiplication Table Poster, Targets	Scissors, index cards, Centimeter-Grid Paper (Copymaster M19), calculators (optional), Math Journals
4 Make Combinations	Student Activity Book pages 11–14 Homework and Remembering pages 7–8	MathBoard materials, Inch-Grid Paper (Copymaster M1)	Tiles or counters, colored blocks, number cubes, letter cube, Math Journals
5 Understand Comparisons	Student Activity Book pages 15–19 Homework and Remembering pages 9–10	MathBoard materials	Counters, number cubes, centimeter-grid paper, markers, index cards, Venn diagram, Math Journals
6 Practice With Multiplication Situations	Student Activity Book pages 20–22 Homework and Remembering pages 11–12 Quick Quiz 1	MathBoard materials	Counters or blocks, index cards, square sheet of paper, ruler, paper clip, Math Journals
7 Discover Multiplication Patterns	Student Activity Book pages 23–26 Homework and Remembering pages 13–14	Hundred Grid	Blocks or counters, crayons or markers, index cards, Math Journals
8 Functions	Student Activity Book pages 27–28 Homework and Remembering pages 15–16	MathBoard materials	Math Journals
9 Multiplication Strategies	Student Activity Book pages 29–32 Homework and Remembering pages 17–18	MathBoard materials	Math Journals
10 Multiplication and Division Practice	Student Activity Book pages 33–46 Homework and Remembering pages 19–20	Targets, Division Cards, Factor Field	Crayons or markers, scissors, Math Journals
11 Write Word Problems	Student Activity Book pages 47–48 Homework and Remembering pages 21–22 Quick Quiz 2	MathBoard materials	Scissors, number cubes, timer or watch with second hand, centimeter-grid paper, crayons or markers, Math Journals
12 Equations With Parentheses	Student Activity Book pages 49–50 Homework and Remembering pages 23–24	Class Multiplication Table Poster	Markers, Math Journals
13 Combinations and Comparisons	Student Activity Book pages 51–52 Homework and Remembering pages 25–26	MathBoard materials	Index cards, counters, number cubes, centimeter-grid paper, Math Journals
14 Practice With Factors	Student Activity Book pages 53–58 Homework and Remembering pages 27–28	Class Multiplication Table Poster, Multiplication Tables, MathBoard materials	Small game token, index cards, centimeter-grid paper, scissors, Math Journals
15 Multiple Step Problems	Student Activity Book pages 59–60 Homework and Remembering pages 29–30	MathBoard materials	Counters, Math Journals
16 Properties of Multiplication	Student Activity Book pages 61–62 Homework and Remembering pages 31–32 Quick Quiz 3	MathBoard materials	Centimeter-grid paper, Math Journals
✓ Unit 1 Review and Test	Student Activity Book pages 63–64 Assessment Guide		

Unit 1 Teaching Resources

Differentiated Instruction

Reaching All Learners

Advanced Learners
Lesson 3, page 20

English Learners
Lesson 4, page 26
Lesson 13, page 84

Extra Help
Lesson 1, page 2   Lesson 2, page 11
Lesson 3, page 18   Lesson 4, page 26
Lesson 8, page 52   Lesson 11, page 71

Special Needs
Lesson 1, page 4
Lesson 10, page 64

Individualizing Instruction

Activities
- Intervention (in every lesson)
- On Level (in every lesson)
- Challenge (in every lesson)

Math Writing Prompts
- Intervention (in every lesson)
- On Level (in every lesson)
- Challenge (in every lesson)

Cross-Curricular Links • Home or School Activities

 Social Studies Connection
Number Systems (Lesson 15, page 104)

 Math-to-Math Connections
Greatest Product Game (Lesson 9, page 62)
Class Data (Lesson 11, page 74)

 Science Connections
Temperatures (Lesson 5, page 36)
Drinking Water (Lesson 10, page 68)
Herbivores and Carnivores (Lesson 14, page 96)

 Art Connections
Math-terpieces: The Art of Problem-Solving (Lesson 4, page 30)
Arrays and Patterns (Lesson 6, page 42)

 Sports (Physical Education) Connection
Olympics (Lesson 2, page 14)

 Language Arts Connections
The Math Machine (Lesson 8, page 56)
Parentheses and Punctuation (Lesson 12, page 80)
Letters and Words (Lesson 13, page 88)
Suffixes in Math (Lesson 16, page 112)

 Literature Connections
Math Strategies That Multiply: The Best of Times (Lesson 3, page 24)
One Grain of Rice: A Mathematical Folktale (Lesson 7, page 50)

Basic Multiplication and Division   **1E**

Teaching Unit 1

Putting Research Into Practice for Unit 1

From Our Curriculum Research Project

We found that we needed to consider affective, social, motivational, self-regulatory, and self-image aspects of learning and not just focus on building mathematical conceptions. Thus, children need to be helped to see themselves as included in the world of mathematics. They need to be taken seriously as learners so that they can begin to see themselves as learners. Mathematization (starting with children's experiences), the coconstruction of understandings in a collaborative classroom, and involvement in learning-goal setting and evaluation all contribute to students' growth.

Traditional and reform practices are usually posed as alternatives. We found many elements of value in both perspectives, especially in the context of urban schools. We wove thesee elements into a fabric of teaching-learning activities that would support teachers' and children's construction and use of mathematical meanings linked to the traditional mathematical symbols and words of the culture. In each mathematics domain the teacher connects children's experiences, words, meanings, object and drawn representations, and methods to the traditional mathematical symbols, words, and methods of that domain. These meaning connections define what we call the referential classroom: referents for mathematical symbols and words are used pervasively within the classroom.

Fuson, Karen C., et al. "Blending the Best of the Twentieth Century to Achieve a Mathematics Equity Pedagogy in the Twenty-First Century." *Learning Mathematics for a New Century, 2000 Yearbook.* Reston: NCTM, 2000. 197–212.

From Current Research:
Multiply with MI: Using Multiple Intelligences to Master Multiplication

Students can extend their understanding of multiplication and division as they consider the inverse relationship between the two operations. Another way their knowledge can grow is through new multiplicative situations such as rates (3 candy bars for 59 cents each), comparisons (the book

weighs 4 times as much as the tablet), and combinations (the number of outfits possible from 3 shirts and 2 pairs of shorts). Examining the effect of multiplying or dividing numbers can also lead to a deeper understanding of these operations. For example, dividing 28 by 14 and comparing the result to dividing 28 by 7 can lead to the conjecture that the smaller the divisor, the larger the quotient. With models or calculators, students can explore dividing by numbers between 0 and 1, such as $\frac{1}{2}$, and find that the quotient is larger than the original number. Explorations such as these help dispel common, but incorrect, generalizations such as "division always makes things smaller."

Further meaning for multiplication should develop as students build and describe area models, showing how a product is related to its factors. Using area models, properties of operations such as the commutativity of multiplication become more apparent. Other relationships can be seen by decomposing and composing area models. For example, a model for 20 × 6 can be split in half and the halves rearranged to form a 10 × 12 rectangle, showing the equivalence of 10 × 12 and 20 × 6. The distributive property is particularly powerful as the basis of many efficient multiplication algorithms.

National Council for School Mathematics. *Principles and Standards for School Mathematics* (Number and Operations Standard for Grades 3–5). Reston: NCTM, 2000. 151.

Other Useful References: Multiplication and Division

Van de Walle, John A. Paper-and-Pencil Computation with Whole Numbers *Elementary and Middle School Mathematics: Teaching Developmentally* (Fourth Edition). New York: Longman, 2001. Pages 221–234.

Math Background

Concept Building Activities

Equal Groups for Multiplication and Division

Students should now have experience working with equal-sized groups. In multiplication, equal-sized groups are combined. Division, however, is a process by which one large group is separated into equal-sized parts. Sometimes this is referred to as sharing equally. When students start to realize the relationship that occurs to groups that are combined or separated, they begin to see multiplication and division as inverse operations.

Multiplication:
Combining Equal Groups

7	7	7

3 groups of 7 = 21
3 × 7 = 21

Division:
Separating to Make Equal Groups

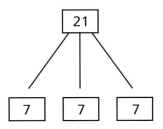

21 is separated into 3 groups of 7
21 ÷ 3 = 7

Two Types of Division The type of division that involves sharing is called partitive division and uses a known number of groups. In the second type of division, measurement division, the size of each group is known and equal but the number of groups is not known. An example is: *There are 12 apples and each child will get 2. How many children will get apples?*

Partitive Division (Sharing)

$$\frac{\text{Total Quantity}}{\text{Number of groups}} = \text{Number in each group}$$

Measurement Division (Grouping)

$$\frac{\text{Total Quantity}}{\text{Number in each group}} = \text{Number of groups}$$

Problem Solving

Real-World Problem Solving Throughout the unit, real-world situations are used as the context for problem-solving situations. Students learn to apply strategies such as Solve and Discuss to solve various word problems, including problems with multiplication and algebraic chains.

Multiplication as Equal Groups

Lesson Objectives
- Recognize multiplication as a method of finding the total of equal groups.
- Understand everyday applications of multiplication and division.

Vocabulary

equal groups
equation

The Day at a Glance

Today's Goals	Materials	123 Math Talk
1 Teaching the Lesson **A1:** Visualize equal groups to review multiplication and division concepts. **A2:** Use strategies to find the total of equal groups. **A3:** Write and solve word problems that use equal groups. **2 Extending the Lesson** ▶ Differentiated Instruction **3 Homework and Cumulative Review**	Student Activity Book pages 1–6 Counters Centimeter-grid paper or Centimeter-Grid Paper (Copymaster M19) Scissors Crayons Calculator Homework and Remembering pages 1–2 Math Journals Family Letter	In today's activities, the students are involved in discussion as they ▶ review multiplication and division concepts using visual representations of equal groups ▶ use equal group strategies to show multiplications ▶ write equations and find solutions for multiplication and division word problems

Quick Practice

This section provides repetitive, short activities that either help students become faster and more accurate at a skill or help to prepare ground for new concepts.

Quick Practice for this unit will start in Lesson 2.

① Teaching the Lesson

Visualize Equal Groups

 20 MINUTES

Goal: Visualize equal groups to review multiplication and division concepts.

 NCTM Standards:
Communication
Number and Operations
Algebra
Representation

The Learning Classroom

Helping Community By discussing multiple strategies for math problems, students become aware of other students' thinking. As students better understand other students' thinking, they become better "helpers."

Differentiated Instruction

Extra Help If students have trouble finding a strategy, ask a few leading questions to get them started. For example, ask leading questions such as, "What if we knew 3 × 6 but didn't know 4 × 6?" This will help them see that in many multiplication problems they can build on what they already know.

▶ **Concept of Multiplication**

Draw these boxes on the board. Explain that each box holds 6 yo-yos. Ask the students if they can supply a multiplication equation that shows the total number of yo-yos. (Elicit or demonstrate that there are two ways to write the multiplication sign.)

$$\boxed{6}\ \boxed{6}\ \boxed{6}\ \boxed{6}$$

$$4 \times 6 = 24$$
$$4 \bullet 6 = 24$$

Now ask students how they could find the total number of yo-yos if they didn't actually know the answer. Below are a few common strategies. At this point, it is important to encourage students to articulate what they already know and to help them think about the meaning of equal groups.

- We could add six 4 times. We call this the sixes *count-by*.

  6, 12, 18, 24   Count by six 4 times.

- If we knew 2 x 6, we could take it twice.

   $12 + 12 = 24$

- If we knew 5 x 6, we could subtract 1 six.

  $$\boxed{6}\ \boxed{6}\ \boxed{6}\ \boxed{6}\ \boxed{\cancel{6}}$$ $30 - 6 = 24$

- If we knew 3 x 6, we could add 1 six.

  $$\boxed{6}\ \boxed{6}\ \boxed{6}\ +\ \boxed{6}$$ $18 + 6 = 24$

▶ Concept of Division WHOLE CLASS

Draw this diagram on the board.

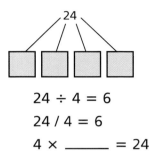

$$24 \div 4 = 6$$
$$24 / 4 = 6$$
$$4 \times \underline{\hspace{1cm}} = 24$$

Explain that now we have 24 yo-yos and 4 boxes. Ask the class to supply an equation that shows how an equal number of yo-yos can be put in each box. (Elicit or demonstrate both division signs.)

Be sure the class sees the third equation here and understands that division is unknown multiplication (4 x what number = 24).

Now ask the class what would happen if we didn't know how many boxes we needed. We know that we have 24 yo-yos, and we want to put 6 yo-yos in each box. How many boxes would we need? Put the partial drawing shown below on the board and ask a volunteer to finish it. To help students, ask, "how many times do you need to add 6 to get 24?"

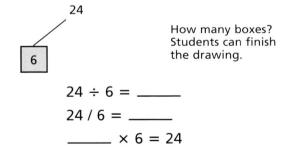

How many boxes? Students can finish the drawing.

$$24 \div 6 = \underline{\hspace{1cm}}$$
$$24 / 6 = \underline{\hspace{1cm}}$$
$$\underline{\hspace{1cm}} \times 6 = 24$$

While the volunteer is working, have the class supply the various equations that show this problem. They can use empty boxes for the unknown number.

Summarize the division review by reminding students that there are two ways to divide.

● dividing to find how many are in a group

● dividing to find how many groups

Activity 2

Strategies to Find Equal Groups

 15 MINUTES

Goal: Use strategies to find the total of equal groups.

Materials: Student Activity Book page 1

 NCTM Standards:
Communication
Number and Operations
Algebra
Representation

Differentiated Instruction

Special Needs Some students may have trouble visualizing equal groups without seeing them. Have those students draw a picture of the total amount using circles or tally marks. Guide the students to circle groups of equal amounts.

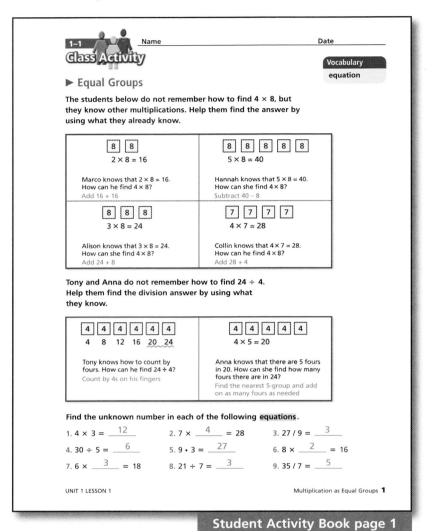

Student Activity Book page 1

► Equal Groups | INDIVIDUALS |

Have everyone turn to the first page of the Student Activity Book. Ask the class to help each of the students to find the answer to the problem 4 × 8. They can discuss how to build on what is known to find what is not known.

Encourage students to adjust the drawings to help them. For example, the two boxes of 8 shown in the first drawing can be doubled. This visual representation will help the class link the concept to the equation.

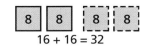

16 + 16 = 32

Be sure your students have some basic strategy for finding divisions. Adding on groups to find how many make the total is the most basic strategy. If students can count by 5, they can take a shortcut by using "fast fives."

Division Strategies

Adding-On Equal Groups
Example: 24 ÷ 4
Count by fours, using fingers to
keep track of how many groups.

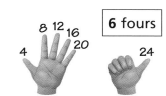

Fast Fives
Example: 24 ÷ 4
Find the nearest 5-group and add
on as many fours as needed.

20 = 5 fours
Add 1 more four to reach 24.　**6 fours**

Equations Discuss the meaning of the word equation. Emphasize that an equation must include an equals sign. It is a statement that 2 or more quantities are equal. Point out that an equation can have an unknown number in any one of three positions.

_____ × 6 = 42   7 × _____ = 42   7 × 6 = _____

Also point out to students that the answer can be written on either side of the equals sign.

7 × 6 = 42   42 = 7 × 6

Ask students to quickly give the answers to exercises 1-9. Be sure that they understand all the forms of notation shown in this section. If they get stuck on any exercise, discuss possible solution strategies based on their understanding of equal groups.

Teaching Note

What to Expect from Students In this unit students' attention is often focused on multiplication patterns and groupings. These groupings sometimes give rise to solution strategies. Awareness of patterns and groupings deepens students' number sense and knowledge of multiplicative relationships.

This is not to suggest that students should use strategies to "figure out" the answers indefinitely. Students need to become fluent in multiplication and division, and this entails considerable practice. This unit provides engaging practice materials to help your students reach this goal. You can continue to use these materials all year as your students need them.

Activity 3

Word Problems With Equal Groups

 25 MINUTES

Goal: Write and solve word problems that use equal groups.

Materials: Student Activity Book page 2

 NCTM Standards:
Communication
Number and Operations
Algebra
Problem Solving

Ongoing Assessment

Ask students:

▶ What are two ways that you could show the number 12 using equal groups?

▶ Explain how you can show 15 ÷ 3 using equal groups.

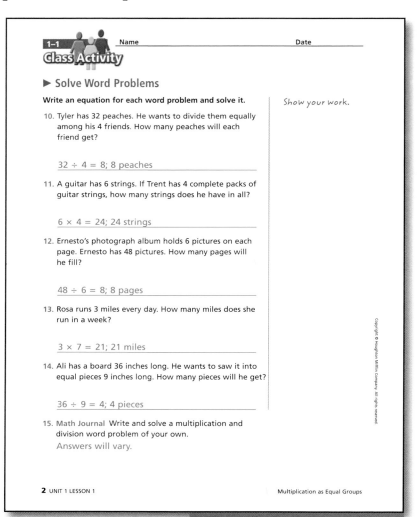

Student Activity Book page 2

Within the image (Student Activity Book page 2):

1-1 Class Activity — Name / Date

▶ Solve Word Problems

Write an equation for each word problem and solve it.

Show your work.

10. Tyler has 32 peaches. He wants to divide them equally among his 4 friends. How many peaches will each friend get?

32 ÷ 4 = 8; 8 peaches

11. A guitar has 6 strings. If Trent has 4 complete packs of guitar strings, how many strings does he have in all?

6 × 4 = 24; 24 strings

12. Ernesto's photograph album holds 6 pictures on each page. Ernesto has 48 pictures. How many pages will he fill?

48 ÷ 6 = 8; 8 pages

13. Rosa runs 3 miles every day. How many miles does she run in a week?

3 × 7 = 21; 21 miles

14. Ali has a board 36 inches long. He wants to saw it into equal pieces 9 inches long. How many pieces will he get?

36 ÷ 9 = 4; 4 pieces

15. Math Journal Write and solve a multiplication and division word problem of your own.
Answers will vary.

2 UNIT 1 LESSON 1 — Multiplication as Equal Groups

▶ Solve Word Problems WHOLE CLASS

Have students solve the word problems shown on Student Activity Book page 2. For each problem, ask two students to come to the board. Each one should write the equation in a different way. In the time that remains, invite students to make up their own multiplication and division word problems for the rest of the class to solve.

② Extending the Lesson

Intervention
for students having difficulty
PAIRS

Use Counters

Materials: counters

Give students counters. Write the number 32 on the board. Tell the first student to use the counters to make equal groups for the number 32. Have the second student write an equation that the groups represent. Repeat with the second student making the equal groups. Encourage students to write as many equations as possible. Repeat this activity several times using different numbers.

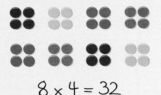

$8 \times 4 = 32$

On Level
for students having success
INDIVIDUALS

Draw Models

Materials: Centimeter-Grid Paper (Copymaster M19), scissors, crayons

Give each student a sheet of grid paper, a pair of scissors, and a crayon. List the following numbers on the board: 6, 9, 10, 16. Have the students color squares on the grid paper to make an array for each number. Next have the students cut out the arrays. Finally tell the students to cut the arrays into equal groups and record the equation that matches the array. Give students time to compare answers. Repeat this activity several times using different numbers.

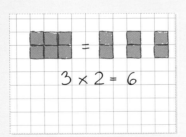

$3 \times 2 = 6$

Challenge
for students seeking a challenge
INDIVIDUALS

Look for Patterns

Materials: calculator

Give the students a calculator and ask them to solve the following:

How many groups of 2 are in 32?

How many groups of 2 are in 320?

How many groups of 2 are in 3,200?

How many groups of 2 are in 32,000?

Ask the students to explain any patterns that they discover. Have students predict whether the patterns work with other numbers. Encourage students to look for additional patterns using different numbers.

 Math Writing Prompt

Intervention

Draw a Picture
Draw a picture that shows $12 \div 3$. Write the multiplication equation that the picture represents.

 Math Writing Prompt

On Level

Explain Your Thinking
Explain how equal groups are related to both $32 \div 8 = 4$ and $4 \times 8 = 32$. Use drawings, if you need to.

 Math Writing Prompt

Challenge

Find a Strategy
Create a new strategy for finding equal groups of two digit numbers.

③ Homework and Cumulative Review

 **Homework** **Goal:** Additional Practice

✓ Use this Homework page to provide students with more practice with equal group problems.

Remembering **Goal:** Cumulative Review

This Remembering Activity would be appropriate any time after today's lesson.

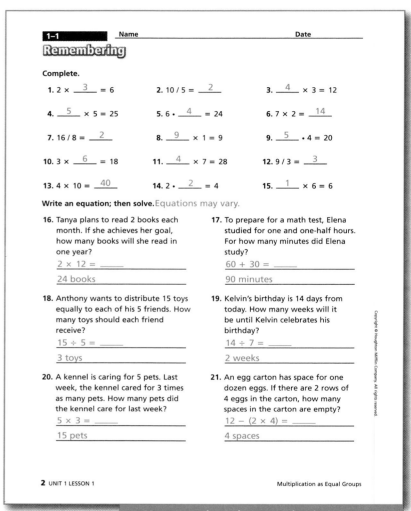

1–1 Name _____ Date _____
Homework

Solve for the unknown number.

1. $3 \times 7 = \underline{21}$
2. $32 / 4 = \underline{8}$
3. $7 \times 5 = \underline{35}$

4. $6 \times \underline{4} = 24$
5. $5 \times \underline{6} = 30$
6. $3 \times \underline{8} = 24$

7. $15 / 3 = \underline{5}$
8. $20 / 5 = \underline{4}$
9. $18 / 6 = \underline{3}$

10. $9 \cdot 2 = \underline{18}$
11. $3 \cdot 9 = \underline{27}$
12. $4 \cdot 4 = \underline{16}$

Write an equation for each word problem and then solve it. *Show your work.*

13. The Garcias have a grandfather clock that needs to be wound once a week. Starting February 1st, how many times will they need to wind it during the month of February, which has 28 days? $28 \div 7 = 4$; 4 times

14. A carousel has 40 horses. There are 4 horses in each row. How many rows are there on the carousel? $40 \div 4 = 10$; 10 rows

15. Morgan has 24 dollars. She wants to buy party hats that cost 3 dollars each. How many party hats can Morgan buy? $24 \div 3 = 8$; 8 party hats

16. There are 4 measuring cups in a set. Mr. Merton's science class has 7 sets of measuring cups. How many cups are there altogether? $4 \times 7 = 28$; 28 cups

17. There are 8 cars in a repair shop. All 8 cars need 4 new tires. How many tires will be needed in all? $8 \times 4 = 32$; 32 tires

18. Write a multiplication or division word problem of your own. Then write an equation with the answer. Answers will vary.

UNIT 1 LESSON 1 — Multiplication as Equal Groups **1**

1–1 Name _____ Date _____
Remembering

Complete.

1. $2 \times \underline{3} = 6$
2. $10 / 5 = \underline{2}$
3. $\underline{4} \times 3 = 12$

4. $\underline{5} \times 5 = 25$
5. $6 \cdot \underline{4} = 24$
6. $7 \times 2 = \underline{14}$

7. $16 / 8 = \underline{2}$
8. $\underline{9} \times 1 = 9$
9. $\underline{5} \cdot 4 = 20$

10. $3 \times \underline{6} = 18$
11. $\underline{4} \times 7 = 28$
12. $9 / 3 = \underline{3}$

13. $4 \times 10 = \underline{40}$
14. $2 \cdot \underline{2} = 4$
15. $\underline{1} \times 6 = 6$

Write an equation; then solve. Equations may vary.

16. Tanya plans to read 2 books each month. If she achieves her goal, how many books will she read in one year?
$2 \times 12 = \underline{}$
24 books

17. To prepare for a math test, Elena studied for one and one-half hours. For how many minutes did Elena study?
$60 + 30 = \underline{}$
90 minutes

18. Anthony wants to distribute 15 toys equally to each of his 5 friends. How many toys should each friend receive?
$15 \div 5 = \underline{}$
3 toys

19. Kelvin's birthday is 14 days from today. How many weeks will it be until Kelvin celebrates his birthday?
$14 \div 7 = \underline{}$
2 weeks

20. A kennel is caring for 5 pets. Last week, the kennel cared for 3 times as many pets. How many pets did the kennel care for last week?
$5 \times 3 = \underline{}$
15 pets

21. An egg carton has space for one dozen eggs. If there are 2 rows of 4 eggs in the carton, how many spaces in the carton are empty?
$12 - (2 \times 4) = \underline{}$
4 spaces

2 UNIT 1 LESSON 1 — Multiplication as Equal Groups

Homework and Remembering page 1

Homework and Remembering page 2

Home and School Connection

Family Letter Have children take home the Family Letter on Student Activity Book pages 3–4. This letter explains how the concept of multiplication and division is developed in *Math Expressions*. It gives parents and guardians a better understanding of the learning that goes on in math class and creates a bridge between school and home. A spanish translation of this letter is on the following pages in the Student Activity book.

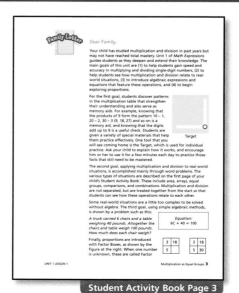

Student Activity Book Page 3

Student Activity Book Page 5

Arrays and Area

Vocabulary

array
row
column
area
length
width

Lesson Objectives

- Understand and apply the terms *array* and *area*.
- Solve word problems that involve equal groups, areas, and arrays.
- Use simple algebraic notation to show the unknown in an area situation.

The Day at a Glance

Today's Goals	Materials	Math Talk
Quick Practice Practice basic multiplications using Easy Finger Factors. **① Teaching the Lesson** **A1:** Review the difference between arrays and area, and apply knowledge to word problems. **A2:** Use simple algebraic notation and apply it to area problems. **② Extending the Lesson** ▶ Differentiated Instruction **③ Homework and Cumulative Review**	Student Activity Book pages 7–10 Inch-Grid Paper (Copymaster M1) Centimeter-Grid Paper (Copymaster M19) Crayons Digit Cards (Copymaster M2) Homework and Remembering pages 3–4 Math Journals	In today's activities, the students are involved in discussion as they ▶ review the difference between arrays and area through examples ▶ solve word problems using equal groups, arrays, and areas ▶ use letter notation to find missing numbers in area problems

Quick Practice

🕐 **5 MINUTES** **Goal:** Practice basic multiplications using Easy Finger Factors.

Easy Finger Factors Ask for three volunteers to lead the first Quick Practice. The first student leader gives a number from 0 to 5 by raising fingers on one hand and saying the number out loud. The second leader gives another number from 0 to 5 in the same way. The third leader gives a hand signal that the class will recognize as a go-signal. (This gives less advanced students time to think, ensuring that the class will answer in unison.) At that point the seated students give the product of the two numbers. Repeat with other numbers.

First Leader: 5
Second Leader: 2
Third Leader: (signal)
Class: 10

Teaching the Lesson

Compare Array and Area

 30 MINUTES

Goal: Review the difference between arrays and area and apply knowledge to word problems.

Materials: Student Activity Book pages 7–8

✔ **NCTM Standards:**
Communication
Measurement
Representation

The Learning Classroom

Building Concepts To develop connections, remember to have students summarize. Have students take turns summarizing the previous day's lesson at the beginning of math class. They can just say one or two sentences. An alternative may be to have a student summarize at the end of the lesson. Either way, if you do this regularly, students will get used to making mental summaries of the math concepts discussed and making conceptual connections.

 Class Management

If your students have had prior experience with arrays and area, go directly to the student page without an initial discussion.

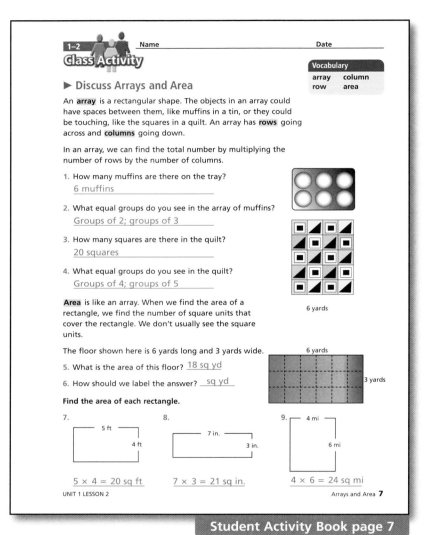

Student Activity Book page 7

▶ Discuss Arrays and Area WHOLE CLASS

Ask questions to establish the meaning of *array* and *area*.

● **What is an array?** objects arranged in rows and columns

● **What is the meaning of area?** the total number of square units that would cover a region, such as a rectangle.

● **How is a rectangle different from an array?** You can see the small square units of an array, but you can't see them on a rectangle.

Have students read and discuss the information on page 7 of the Student Activity Book. Students should understand that the answer to an array problem is found by multiplying the number of rows by the number of columns and is the total number of objects such as 12 cupcakes, but the answer to an area problem is given in square units, 12 square feet. Be sure they can identify the abbreviation *sq.*

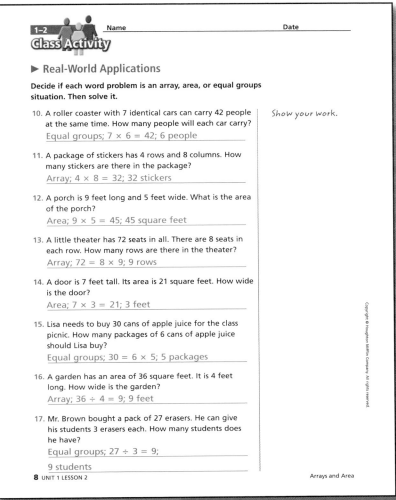

Student Activity Book page 8

The content of Student Activity Book page 8:

▶ **Real-World Applications**

Decide if each word problem is an array, area, or equal groups situation. Then solve it.

Show your work.

10. A roller coaster with 7 identical cars can carry 42 people at the same time. How many people will each car carry?
Equal groups; $7 \times 6 = 42$; 6 people

11. A package of stickers has 4 rows and 8 columns. How many stickers are there in the package?
Array; $4 \times 8 = 32$; 32 stickers

12. A porch is 9 feet long and 5 feet wide. What is the area of the porch?
Area; $9 \times 5 = 45$; 45 square feet

13. A little theater has 72 seats in all. There are 8 seats in each row. How many rows are there in the theater?
Array; $72 = 8 \times 9$; 9 rows

14. A door is 7 feet tall. Its area is 21 square feet. How wide is the door?
Area; $7 \times 3 = 21$; 3 feet

15. Lisa needs to buy 30 cans of apple juice for the class picnic. How many packages of 6 cans of apple juice should Lisa buy?
Equal groups; $30 = 6 \times 5$; 5 packages

16. A garden has an area of 36 square feet. It is 4 feet long. How wide is the garden?
Array; $36 \div 4 = 9$; 9 feet

17. Mr. Brown bought a pack of 27 erasers. He can give his students 3 erasers each. How many students does he have?
Equal groups; $27 \div 3 = 9$;
9 students

8 UNIT 1 LESSON 2 — Arrays and Area

The Learning Classroom

Building Concepts To emphasize that area involves square units, have students fold square pieces of paper and then unfold the paper to see the length, width, and square units.

▶ Real-World Applications INDIVIDUALS

Ask students to solve problems 10–17 on page 8. They also need to identify the type of situation (equal groups, array, or area). If there is confusion, remind the class that equal groups are not connected to each other in rows and columns. They are separate groups. For example, 3 plates that each holds 4 cookies would be equal groups. A cookie sheet with 3 rows of 4 cookies would be an array. Make a drawing on the board, if necessary. Area does not involve objects at all, only measurements. It is the number of square units that cover a shape. For example, the area of the cookie sheet is 4 square feet.

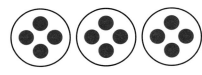

Equal Groups of Cookies

Array of Cookies

Arrays and Area **11**

Teaching the Lesson (continued)

Letter Notation for Area Problems

 25 MINUTES

Goal: Use simple algebraic notation and apply it to area problems.

Materials: Student Activity Book page 9

✓ **NCTM Standards:**
  Algebra
  Measurement
  Representation

✓ **Ongoing Assessment**

Have students show 3 × 2 as equal groups, as an array, and as area.

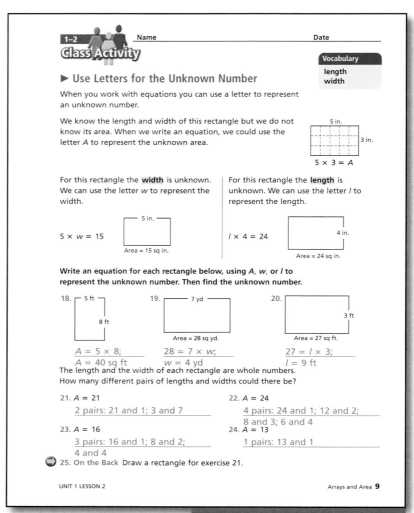

Student Activity Book page 9

▶ Use Letters for the Unknown Number INDIVIDUALS

Discuss exercises 18–20 on page 9 of the Student Activity Book with the students. This is the introduction of simple algebraic expressions. Point out that every area problem has three parts: length, width, and area. If we know two of these parts, we can find the one that is unknown. The letters replace the answer rule that students saw on the first day. They function in exactly the same way.

Exercises 21–24 give only the area. Students are asked to provide all the possible pairs of lengths and widths (assuming they are whole numbers). If students have trouble, for exercise 21 ask them "What number times what number equals 21?" Many students will produce the dimensions 7 × 3, but they may overlook the other possibility: 21 × 1.

② Extending the Lesson

Intervention
for students having difficulty

PAIRS

Cover It

Materials: Inch-Grid Paper (Copymaster M1)

Students find a rectangle in the classroom. They cover it with inch squares. Then they write an equation that represents the length, the width, and the area.

On Level
for students having success

PAIRS or SMALL GROUPS

Draw and Compare

Materials: Centimeter-Grid Paper (Copymaster M19), crayons, Digit Cards (Copymaster M2)

Give each student two digit cards face down. Tell the students to turn over the cards and draw a rectangle on the grid paper that uses the numbers on the cards. Have students color the area of their rectangles. The student with the largest area wins the round. Repeat several times.

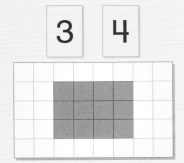

Challenge
for students seeking a challenge

INDIVIDUALS or PAIRS

Find Formulas

Materials: centimeter-grid paper

Ask students to use grid paper to draw the first 10 square numbers.

(1, 4, 9, 16, 25, 36, 49, 64, 81, 100)

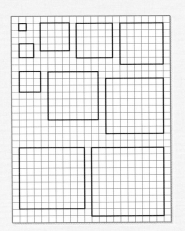

Then ask students to write a formula to determine the 100th square number.

($n \times n$ = any square number where n is the number of the term. $100 \times 100 = 10,000$)

 Math Writing Prompt

Intervention

Make a Drawing

Explain how 4×3 and 3×4 equal the same number. Draw equal groups, an array, or an area picture to support your answer.

 Math Writing Prompt

On Level

Write a Problem

Write a word problem about equal groups. Then write an equation to solve it.

 Math Writing Prompt

Challenge

Reasoning Skills

Write a word problem about a 10 x 10 array. Explain how you decided what situation to use and then write an equation to solve it.

③ Homework and Cumulative Review

 **1–2 Homework** **Goal:** Additional Practice

✔ Use this Homework page to provide students with more practice using equal groups, arrays, and areas to solve problems.

 **1–2 Remembering** **Goal:** Cumulative Review

This Remembering Activity would be appropriate any time after today's lesson.

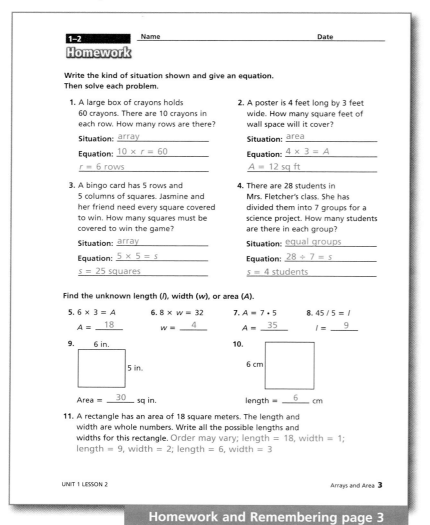

1–2 Homework Name _____ Date _____

Write the kind of situation shown and give an equation.
Then solve each problem.

1. A large box of crayons holds 60 crayons. There are 10 crayons in each row. How many rows are there?

Situation: _array_

Equation: _10 × r = 60_

r = 6 rows

2. A poster is 4 feet long by 3 feet wide. How many square feet of wall space will it cover?

Situation: _area_

Equation: _4 × 3 = A_

_A = 12 sq ft_

3. A bingo card has 5 rows and 5 columns of squares. Jasmine and her friend need every square covered to win. How many squares must be covered to win the game?

Situation: _array_

Equation: _5 × 5 = s_

s = 25 squares

4. There are 28 students in Mrs. Fletcher's class. She has divided them into 7 groups for a science project. How many students are there in each group?

Situation: _equal groups_

Equation: _28 ÷ 7 = s_

s = 4 students

Find the unknown length (l), width (w), or area (A).

5. 6 × 3 = A
A = _18_

6. 8 × w = 32
w = _4_

7. A = 7 • 5
A = _35_

8. 45 / 5 = l
l = _9_

9. 6 in. / 5 in.
Area = _30_ sq in.

10. 6 cm
length = _6_ cm

11. A rectangle has an area of 18 square meters. The length and width are whole numbers. Write all the possible lengths and widths for this rectangle. Order may vary; length = 18, width = 1; length = 9, width = 2; length = 6, width = 3

UNIT 1 LESSON 2   Arrays and Area **3**

Homework and Remembering page 3

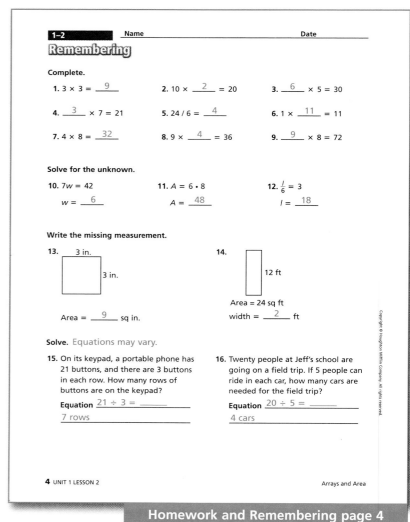

1–2 Remembering Name _____ Date _____

Complete.

1. 3 × 3 = _9_
2. 10 × _2_ = 20
3. _6_ × 5 = 30
4. _3_ × 7 = 21
5. 24 / 6 = _4_
6. 1 × _11_ = 11
7. 4 × 8 = _32_
8. 9 × _4_ = 36
9. _9_ × 8 = 72

Solve for the unknown.

10. 7w = 42
w = _6_

11. A = 6 • 8
A = _48_

12. $\frac{l}{6}$ = 3
l = _18_

Write the missing measurement.

13. 3 in. / 3 in.
Area = _9_ sq in.

14. 12 ft
Area = 24 sq ft
width = _2_ ft

Solve. Equations may vary.

15. On its keypad, a portable phone has 21 buttons, and there are 3 buttons in each row. How many rows of buttons are on the keypad?

Equation _21 ÷ 3 =_ _____
7 rows

16. Twenty people at Jeff's school are going on a field trip. If 5 people can ride in each car, how many cars are needed for the field trip?

Equation _20 ÷ 5 =_ _____
4 cars

4 UNIT 1 LESSON 2   Arrays and Area

Homework and Remembering page 4

Home or School Activity

 Sports Connection

Olympics The Olympics are held every four years. Athletes representing hundreds of countries from around the world compete in a wide variety of sporting events.

Have students research the official measurements for an Olympic pool. Then have them calculate the minimum area of a rectangular cover for an Olympic size pool.

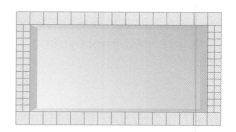

Explore the Multiplication Table

Vocabulary
column
row
Commutative Property
inverse operations
factor
product

Lesson Objectives

● Describe the patterns in the Multiplication Table.

● Understand that multiplication is commutative and that multiplication and division are inverse operations.

The Day at a Glance

Today's Goals	Materials	Math Talk
Quick Practice Practice basic multiplications using Easy Finger Factors. **❶ Teaching the Lesson** **A1:** Discuss the structure of the Multiplication Table and the patterns in it. **A2:** Learn to use the Target and observe commutativity and inverse operations in the Multiplication Table. **A3:** Complete a blank Multiplication Table to assess basic multiplication. **❷ Extending the Lesson** ▶ Differentiated Instruction **❸ Homework and Cumulative Review**	Student Activity Book pages 11–12 Class Multiplication Table Poster Targets Scissors Index cards Centimeter–grid paper (Copymaster M19) Calculators (optional) Homework and Remembering pages 5–6 Math Journals	In today's activities, the students are involved in discussion as they ▶ examine the multiplication table and discover patterns in the table ▶ solve multiplication problems using the Target square ▶ complete a multiplication table and record difficult products

Quick Practice

🕐 **5 MINUTES**   **Goal:** Practice basic multiplications using Easy Finger Factors.

Easy Finger Factors This is the same as yesterday's Quick Practice. Again, ask for 3 volunteers to be leaders. The first student leader gives a number from 0 to 5 by raising fingers on one hand and saying the number out loud. The second leader gives another number from 0 to 5 in the same way. The third leader gives a hand signal that the class will recognize as a go-signal. At that point, the seated students give the product of the two numbers. Repeat with other numbers.

Teaching Note

Watch for! Although these smaller factors are quite easy to multiply, some students get confused by the zero and the 1 factors. Watch to be sure the class doesn't say $5 \times 0 = 5$, for example.

Teaching the Lesson

Activity 1

Patterns in the Multiplication Table

 20 MINUTES

Goal: Discuss the structure of the Multiplication Table and the patterns in it.

Materials: Student Activity Book page 11, class Multiplication Table Poster, Targets

✔ **NCTM Standards:**
Number and Operations
Representation

The Learning Classroom

Math Talk One of the goals of this discussion, in addition to finding patterns, is to begin the process of establishing a classroom community where students talk, listen, and question each other. Concentrate today on creating an accepting atmosphere so that students will feel comfortable making contributions.

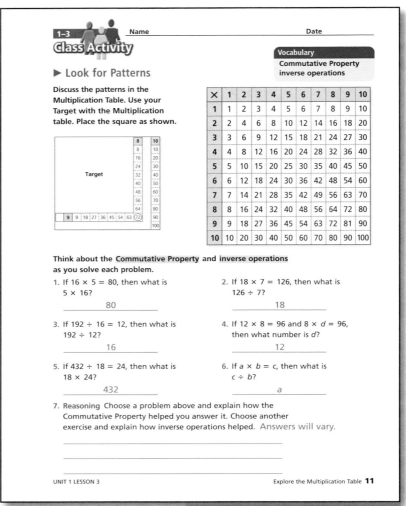

Student Activity Book page 11

▶ Look for Patterns WHOLE CLASS

Direct everyone's attention to the Multiplication Table on page 11 of the Student Activity Book. Have students describe the arrangement of the table and any interesting patterns they see.

There are many patterns in the Multiplication Table, ranging from obvious (all the numbers in the bottom row end in zero) to extremely intricate (numbers on the various diagonals increase in predictable ways). Validate any pattern that students observe.

As with arrays, encourage the class to use the word *row* for the numbers going across and *column* for the numbers going down.

► The Structure of the Multiplication Table WHOLE CLASS

After a few minutes of open discussion, begin drawing attention to the overall structure of the table. Below are the important structural features to elicit from the students. Some of these may already have been mentioned during the previous discussion. (For a sample of classroom dialogue, see Math Talk in Action in the side column.)

1. Each row and each column show a particular count-by such as 5, 10, 15. The first number is the number to count by. If students have not already mentioned this feature, pick several rows and columns and ask students what they see.

2. Since the rows and columns are both made the same way, the Multiplication Table has ten row and column "twins." If students have not already noticed this feature, demonstrate on the Class Multiplication Table Poster. Then ask students to find some twins on their own.

1	2	3	4	5	6	7	8	9	10
2	4	6	8	10	12	14	16	18	20
3	6	9	12	15	18	21	24	27	30
4	8	12	16	20	24	28	32	36	40
5	10	15	20	25	30	35	40	45	50
6	12	18	24	30	36	42	48	54	60
7	14	21	28	35	42	49	56	63	70
8	16	24	32	40	48	56	64	72	80
9	18	27	36	45	54	63	72	81	90
10	20	30	40	50	60	70	80	90	100

3. The answer to a multiplication problem is found by multiplying one number from the left column with another number from the top row. The answer is in the square that forms the intersection of a column and a row.

Elicit or explain that the smaller numbers that are multiplied together are called *factors*. The answer is called the *product*. (When we multiply, we are finding the unknown product. When we divide, we are finding an unknown factor.)

 Math Talk in Action

What do you see when you look down the 3-column?

Tara: Each number going down is 3 more than the previous number.

Sam: It looks like skip counting by 3.

What do you see when you look across the 3-row?

Jai: This row is the same as the 3-column.

What about the 5-column and the 5-row?

Sam: Each number going across and down is 5 more than the previous number.

Are all columns and rows built this way?

Collin: Yes because mulitplication means repeatedly adding the same group.

Teaching Note

Language and Vocabulary As words relating to multiplication are used throughout the lesson, write the words on the board and review their meaning. Words emphasized in this activity include:

column
row
factor
product

Activity 2

The Target

 20 MINUTES

Goal: Learn to use the Target and observe commutativity and inverse operations in the Multiplication Table.

Materials: Student Activity Book page 11, Targets

 NCTM Standards:
Number and Operations
Algebra
Reasoning and Proof

Differentiated Instruction

Extra Help Some students may have difficulty manipulating the Target. Pair those students with other students who can help them until they become comfortable handling the square.

► **Learn to Use the Target** WHOLE CLASS

Make sure each student has two Targets. (One will go home, and one will stay at school.) Have everyone experiment with the Target to see if they can explain how to practice multiplication with this device.

Multiplying: Position the Target on the Multiplication Table as shown, covering up the number in the circle with a finger. The transparent bars should be placed so that the factors are at each end. Students say the answer silently to themselves and then uncover the circle to see if they were right.

Now ask students if they can figure out how to practice division with the Target.

Dividing: Position the Target in the same way as before. Cover up the left end of the horizontal bar. Move the Target until the known factor appears at the top of the vertical bar and then move up or down until the product is in the circle. Solve the problem. Uncover the horizontal bar to see which number appears at the left end.

×	1	2	3	4	5	6	7	8	9	10
1	1	2	3	4	5	6	7	8	9	10
2	2	4	6	8	10	12	14	16	18	20
3	3	6	9	12	15	18	21	24	27	30
4	4	8	12	16	20	24	28	32	36	40
5	5	10	15	20	25	30	35	40	45	50
6	6	12	18	24	30	36	42	48	54	60
7	7	14	21	28	35	42	49	56	63	70
8	8	16	24	32	40	48	56	64	72	80
9	9	18	27	36	45	54	63	72	81	90
10	10	20	30	40	50	60	70	80	90	100

▶ Commutative and Inverse Relationships WHOLE CLASS

Ask everyone to multiply 8 × 7 and 7 × 8 using their Targets. Do they get the same answer? Yes If they know the answer to these two multiplication problems, what two division problems can they also solve? 56 ÷ 8 and 56 ÷ 7. Ask everyone to do these division problems with their Targets. Offer help as needed.

Now have the class contribute another multiplication problem. Students should do all four variations with the Targets. (Example: If they select 6 × 7, they should also do 7 × 6 and then 42 ÷ 7 and 42 ÷ 6.)

If students have trouble understanding the Commutative Property or inverse operations, encourage them to use arrays to visualize the numbers. Drawing arrays and then taking the arrays apart can help students to see how all of the numbers are related.

6 = 2 × 3
6 = 3 × 2

6 ÷ 2 = 3

6 ÷ 3 = 2

Activity continued ▶

The Learning Classroom

Math Talk How did your students explain their math thinking today? Students are often unfamiliar with this process; they are accustomed to providing math answers only. Encouraging students to talk more fully about their thinking will take repeated efforts on your part. Expect this to be a building process that lasts for several weeks.

Activity 2

Differentiated Instruction

Advanced Learners Some students may be ready to describe more details about their problem-solving strategies. You may want to encourage these students to do more explaining. Not only will they extend their own communication skills, they will model for other students how to talk about their thinking. The "child friendly language" may be more meaningful than your own way of talking about a concept.

► Use Critical Thinking INDIVIDUALS

Have everyone complete exercises 1–6 on page 11 of the Student Activity Book. The questions in this section all involve higher-order thinking skills as students consider the commutative property and inverse operations Students also receive some practice with easy algebraic expressions.

Some of these numbers may appear to be beyond the students' experience. That is done deliberately to ensure that they will apply the concepts of commutativity and inverse relationships and not just perform familiar computation.

If some students become intimidated when they encounter equations with large numbers, such as those in exercise 3, reassure them that they know how to solve these problems. They just need to think about the relationship between multiplication and division. Students will feel empowered when they realize that they can handle these exercises.

When students complete the page, have a whole-class discussion of the answers to problem 7.

Activity 3

Create a Multiplication Table

1–3 Class Activity

Name ______________________ Date ______________

Vocabulary
factor
product

► Complete a Multiplication Table

8. Look at the **factors** to complete the Multiplication Table. Leave blanks for the **products** you do not know.

1	**2**	**3**	**4**	**5**	**6**	**7**	**8**	**9**	**10**
2	4	6	8	10	12	14	16	18	20
3	6	9	12	15	18	21	24	27	30
4	8	12	16	20	24	28	32	36	40
5	10	15	20	25	30	35	40	45	50
6	12	18	24	30	36	42	48	54	60
7	14	21	28	35	42	49	56	63	70
8	16	24	32	40	48	56	64	72	80
9	18	27	36	45	54	63	72	81	90
10	20	30	40	50	60	70	80	90	100

9. Write the multiplications you need to practice.

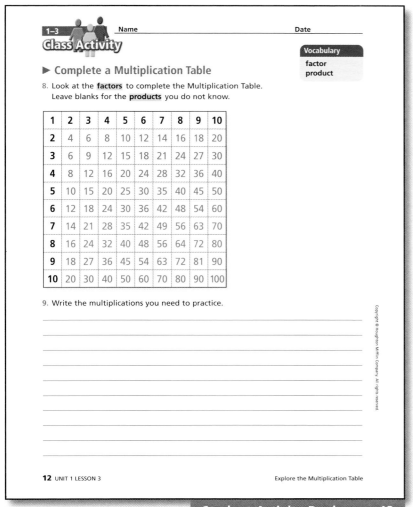

Student Activity Book page 12

► Complete a Multiplication Table INDIVIDUALS

The goal today is to discover which multiplications students know quickly and which ones they should work on during practice sessions. Emphasize that this is not a test.

Give the class about 6 minutes to fill in the blank table on page 12 of the Student Activity Book. Encourage students to leave a square blank when they do not immediately know the product. They should not take time to "figure it out." Tell students not to use count-bys because they are too slow. A faster strategy is needed for these problems.

When time is up, ask each student to write the multiplications that need practice. Ask volunteers to share the problems that are most difficult for them. Students may be surprised to learn that there is considerable agreement on which problems are difficult.

Activity continued ►

15 MINUTES

Goal: Complete a blank Multiplication Table to assess basic multiplication.

Materials: Student Activity Book page 12, class Multiplication Table Poster

NCTM Standards:
Number and Operations
Representation

The Learning Classroom

Helping Community You may find it valuable to train some students to help other students who are struggling. Many teachers find that after several days on an important topic, many of their students can work productively practicing problems (with other students helping). These student helpers can work at the board with a small group of students who are struggling.

Activity 3

The Learning Classroom

Math Talk By discussing answers, students become aware of other students' thinking. They may discover that they share opinions and difficulties with others in their class.

✓ Ongoing Assessment

Have students discuss

▶ how they can show that multiplication is commutative.

▶ examples of the Commutative Property of Multiplication.

▶ Strategies for Effective Practice ⟨WHOLE CLASS⟩

Divide the class Multiplication Table Poster into four sections and have the students do the same on the Multiplication Table they created. Ask the class which section contains most of their blank spaces. Probably most of the blanks will be in the last section, which contains the more difficult multiplications, or "toughies." The first section is the easy section; sections 2 and 3 contain more difficult multiplications. Discuss why sections 2 and 3 are harder than section 1 and why section 4 has the "toughies."

Tell the students that as part of today's homework they will practice the multiplication problems they missed. They can take one of the Targets home for the duration of this unit to use for further practice. Suggest that they focus on the section or sections that gave them the most trouble today.

✕	1	2	3	4	5	6	7	8	9	10
1	1	2	3	4	5	6	7	8	9	10
2	2		1	8	10	12	14		2	20
3	3			12	15	18	21			30
4	4	8	12	16	20	24	28	32	36	40
5	5	10	15	20	25	30	35	40	45	50
6	6	12	18	24	30	36	42	48	54	60
7	7	14	21	28	35	42	49	56	63	70
8	8		3	32	40	48	56		4	80
9	9	18	27	36	45	54	63	72	81	90
10	10	20	30	40	50	60	70	80	90	100

② Extending the Lesson

Differentiated Instruction
Activities for Individualizing

Intervention
for students having difficulty

PAIRS

Practice Triangles

Materials: scissors, Class Multiplication Table Poster, square sheets of paper

Students should make several triangles for all of the multiplications that they find difficult. They cut triangles by folding a square sheet of paper from corner to corner. Then they fold the large triangle in half. Unfolded, each sheet makes 4 triangles. Students can then cut out the triangles.

Have students write the products and factors on each of the three corners of the triangle.

One student should hold the triangle so that one corner is covered. Another student guesses the covered number.

On Level
for students having success

PAIRS

Find Facts

Materials: index cards

Give each student pair 21 index cards. Have students make 2 sets of cards, one set numbered 0–10 and the other numbered 0–9. Tell the students to mix the cards and place them in a pile number side down.

One student takes two cards from the top of the pile. If the student names the product of the two cards correctly, he or she scores that number of points. Then the student returns those cards, number side up, to the bottom of the pile. The next student takes a turn. The first student to earn 500 points wins.

Challenge
for students seeking a challenge

INDIVIDUALS

Extending Tables

Materials: Centimeter-Grid Paper (Copymaster M19), calculators (optional)

Give each student a sheet of grid paper. Tell students to create a multiplication table that uses the numbers 1–12 across the top and down the left side. Have students complete the table. Ask students to describe a vertical pattern, a horizontal pattern, and a diagonal pattern. Students may need to use calculators.

 Math Writing Prompt

Intervention

Draw and Explain
You know that 5 × 4 = 20. Explain why 20 ÷ 4 must equal 5. Draw equal groups or arrays if it will help.

 Math Writing Prompt

On Level

Reasoning Skills
Explain one of the patterns that appears in a multiplication table.

Math Writing Prompt

Challenge

9s Pattern
Explain a pattern for all products of 9.

③ Homework and Cumulative Review

Homework **Goal:** Additional Practice

✓ Use this Homework page to provide students with more practice with Multiplication Tables and Targets.

1–3

Remembering **Goal:** Cumulative Review

This Remembering Activity would be appropriate any time after today's lesson.

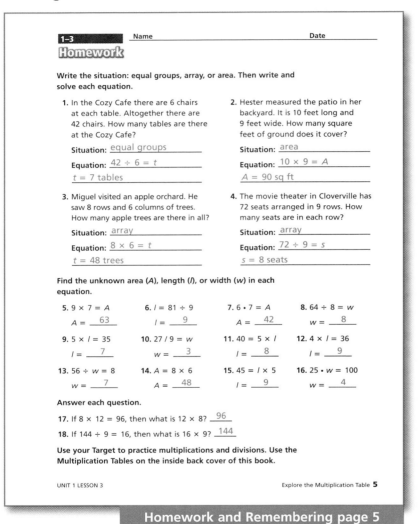

1–3 Name _____ Date _____
Homework

Write the situation: equal groups, array, or area. Then write and solve each equation.

1. In the Cozy Cafe there are 6 chairs at each table. Altogether there are 42 chairs. How many tables are there at the Cozy Cafe?

Situation: _equal groups_

Equation: _42 ÷ 6 = t_
t = 7 tables

2. Hester measured the patio in her backyard. It is 10 feet long and 9 feet wide. How many square feet of ground does it cover?

Situation: _area_

Equation: _10 × 9 = A_
_A = 90 sq ft_

3. Miguel visited an apple orchard. He saw 8 rows and 6 columns of trees. How many apple trees are there in all?

Situation: _array_

Equation: _8 × 6 = t_
t = 48 trees

4. The movie theater in Cloverville has 72 seats arranged in 9 rows. How many seats are in each row?

Situation: _array_

Equation: _72 ÷ 9 = s_
s = 8 seats

Find the unknown area (A), length (l), or width (w) in each equation.

5. 9 × 7 = A
A = _63_

6. l = 81 ÷ 9
l = _9_

7. 6 • 7 = A
A = _42_

8. 64 ÷ 8 = w
w = _8_

9. 5 × l = 35
l = _7_

10. 27 / 9 = w
w = _3_

11. 40 = 5 × l
l = _8_

12. 4 × l = 36
l = _9_

13. 56 ÷ w = 8
w = _7_

14. A = 8 × 6
A = _48_

15. 45 = l × 5
l = _9_

16. 25 • w = 100
w = _4_

Answer each question.

17. If 8 × 12 = 96, then what is 12 × 8? _96_
18. If 144 ÷ 9 = 16, then what is 16 × 9? _144_

Use your Target to practice multiplications and divisions. Use the Multiplication Tables on the inside back cover of this book.

UNIT 1 LESSON 3   Explore the Multiplication Table **5**

Homework and Remembering page 5

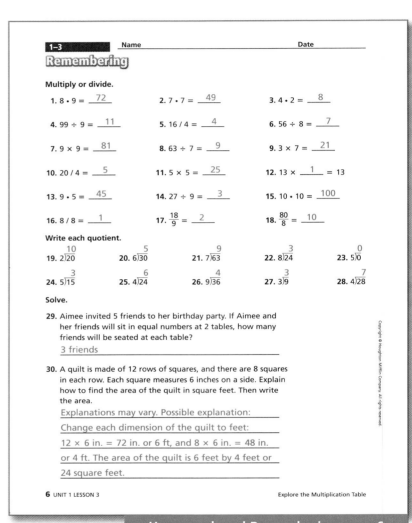

1–3 Name _____ Date _____
Remembering

Multiply or divide.

1. 8 • 9 = _72_
2. 7 • 7 = _49_
3. 4 • 2 = _8_
4. 99 ÷ 9 = _11_
5. 16 / 4 = _4_
6. 56 ÷ 8 = _7_
7. 9 × 9 = _81_
8. 63 ÷ 7 = _9_
9. 3 × 7 = _21_
10. 20 / 4 = _5_
11. 5 × 5 = _25_
12. 13 × _1_ = 13
13. 9 • 5 = _45_
14. 27 ÷ 9 = _3_
15. 10 • 10 = _100_
16. 8 / 8 = _1_
17. $\frac{18}{9}$ = _2_
18. $\frac{80}{8}$ = _10_

Write each quotient.

19. $2\overline{)20}$ _10_
20. $6\overline{)30}$ _5_
21. $7\overline{)63}$ _9_
22. $8\overline{)24}$ _3_
23. $5\overline{)0}$ _0_
24. $5\overline{)15}$ _3_
25. $4\overline{)24}$ _6_
26. $9\overline{)36}$ _4_
27. $3\overline{)9}$ _3_
28. $4\overline{)28}$ _7_

Solve.

29. Aimee invited 5 friends to her birthday party. If Aimee and her friends will sit in equal numbers at 2 tables, how many friends will be seated at each table?
3 friends

30. A quilt is made of 12 rows of squares, and there are 8 squares in each row. Each square measures 6 inches on a side. Explain how to find the area of the quilt in square feet. Then write the area.
Explanations may vary. Possible explanation:
Change each dimension of the quilt to feet:
12 × 6 in. = 72 in. or 6 ft, and 8 × 6 in. = 48 in.
or 4 ft. The area of the quilt is 6 feet by 4 feet or
24 square feet.

6 UNIT 1 LESSON 3   Explore the Multiplication Table

Homework and Remembering page 6

Home or School Activity

 Literature Connection

Read *Math Strategies that Multiply: The Best of Times* by Greg Tang and illustrated by Harry Briggs (Scholastic Press, 2002).

This book uses poems and pictures to help students learn their multiplications. Challenge students to write their own poems. Some students may write songs, too. Have the students share their poems or songs with each other.

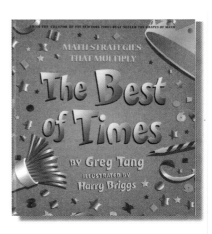

Make Combinations

Vocabulary

combination
factor
product
prime number
composite number

Lesson Objectives

• **Connect combinations to multiplication of equal groups.**

• **Write equations to solve word problems that involve multiplication.**

The Day at a Glance

Today's Goals	Materials	Math Talk
Quick Practice Practice basic multiplications using Medium Finger Factors.	Student Activity Book pages 13–16	In today's activities, the students are involved in discussion as they
1 Teaching the Lesson **A1:** Use multiplication to solve combination problems. **A2:** Write an equation using a letter to represent the unknown.	Tiles or counters Inch-Grid Paper (Copymaster M1) Colored blocks Number Cubes	▶ discover that combinations are multiplicative groups and can be used to solve word problems
2 Extending the Lesson ▶ Going Further: Primes and Composites ▶ Differentiated Instruction	Letter Cube Homework and Remembering pages 7–8	▶ use letters for unknown numbers in equations and then solve the equations
3 Homework and Cumulative Review	Math Journals	

Quick Practice

⏱ 5 minutes   **Goal:** Practice basic multiplications using Medium Finger Factors.

Medium Finger Factors Explain to the class that they did the easy section of the Multiplication Table earlier and will do the medium sections today. Again, send 3 student leaders to the front. This time the first leader gives a factor from 6 to 10 by raising fingers on *both* hands and saying the number out loud. The second leader gives a factor from 0 to 5 by using one hand. The third leader gives the hand signal, and the class responds with the product of the two factors. Repeat with other numbers.

1 Teaching the Lesson

Combinations as Multiplication

 25 MINUTES

Goal: Use multiplication to solve combination problems.

Materials: Student Activity Book page 13

 NCTM Standards:
Number and Operations
Problem Solving
Representation

Differentiated Instruction

English Language Leaners Lead a discussion about the word *combine*. When items are put together, they are combined. Ask the students to name items that they combine every day.

cereal and milk
bread and peanut butter
socks and shoes
reading and homework

Differentiated Instruction

Extra Help For students who have trouble understanding combinations, use visual aids to demonstrate the concept. Draw diagrams or pictures to show how things are combined. In some cases, it may be necessary for students to use physical models, such as blocks, tiles, or shapes in order to comprehend the concept.

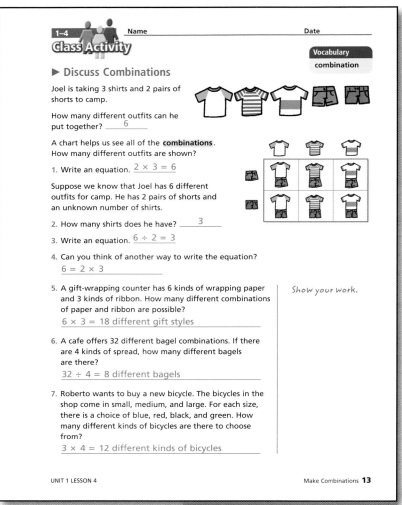

Student Activity Book page 13

▶ Discuss Combinations WHOLE CLASS

Have students look at the top of page 13. Have students list all the different outfits until they find all 6. Explain that the chart is similar to a multiplication table.

● There are 2 pairs of shorts on the side and 3 shirts at the top. What equation could we write that will show there are 6 outfits? $2 \times 3 = 6$

The combination table has rows and columns that are equal groups and multiplication means adding equal groups.

Complete exercises 1–4 with the students. Have students solve problems 5–7. For problem 7, ask the students how they can solve a word problem that has no numbers. Count the number of bicycle sizes and the number of colors given.

Equations With Letters

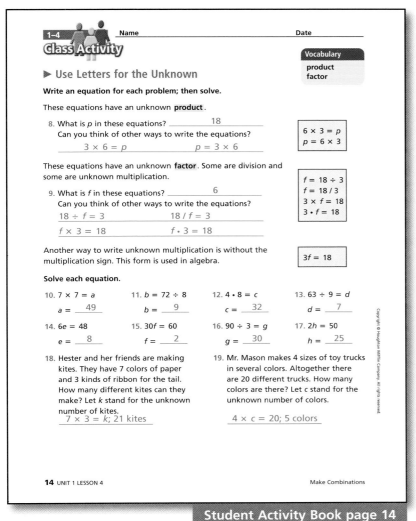

Student Activity Book page 14

▶ Use Letters for the Unknown WHOLE CLASS

Problems 8 and 9 on page 14 give students experience solving algebraic equations. Many students will be unfamiliar with expressions such as $3f$. Give several additional examples until they feel comfortable with this notation.

$4s = 12$ $49 = 7b$ $5w = 35$ $60 = 10d$ $7t = 56$

Have the class use mental math to complete exercises 10–17. Point out that any letter may be used to represent an unknown number.

Help students write and discuss equations for exercises 10–19. There will usually be two or more ways to write the equation. In problems 18 and 19, for example, students can either write division equations or equations with unknown multiplication to find the unknown factor.

---

 30 MINUTES

Goal: Write an equation using a letter to represent the unknown.

Materials: Student Activity Book page 14

 NCTM Standards:
Algebra
Problem Solving

Teaching Note

Math Symbols One reason we don't write the times sign ($\times$) in Algebra is that in equations we often use the letter x to represent the unknown. $4 \times x = 12$ can be confusing.

Students should become familiar with all forms of multiplication and division.

3×4	$3 \cdot n$	$3 * 4$	$3n$
$10 \div 2$	$2\overline{)10}$	$\frac{10}{2}$	$10/2$

The asterisk and slash are used on computers.

 Ongoing Assessment

Have students:

▶ show the different ways that 2 shapes could be 3 different colors. Use a table.

▶ give an example of an equation with an unknown number.

Extending the Lesson

Going Further: Primes and Composites

Goal: Classify numbers as prime or composite.

Materials: Student Activity Book page 15, tiles or counters (25 per student)

✔ **NCTM Standards:**
Number and Operations
Representation

▶ **Classify Numbers** │WHOLE CLASS│

Names for Numbers Write the number 10 on the board. Ask students to describe that number in as many ways as they can.

Tell students they will learn how to describe numbers in two new ways.

Identify Prime and Composite Numbers Have students read the text at the top of student page 15. Discuss the definitions of prime and composite numbers. Then study the examples together. Lead students to use their tiles to model the arrays shown for 5 and 6 to verify that those are the only possible arrays for each number.

Work through exercise 1 as a class. Lead students to make the following arrays to show 10.

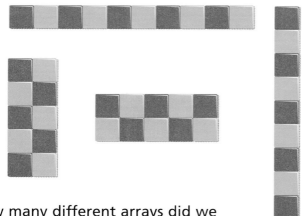

● How many different arrays did we make with 10 tiles? 4

● So, how many factors does 10 have? 4

● What are the factors of 10? 1, 2, 5, and 10

● So, is 10 a prime number or a composite number? composite number

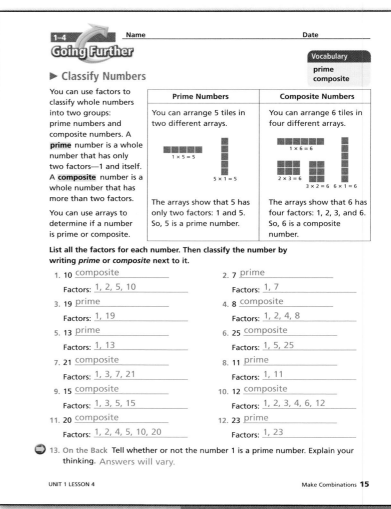

Have students complete exercises 2–12. Tell students to make arrays if they need to. Ask students how 25 (exercise 6) is different from all the other composite numbers in the exercises. It only has 3 factors (square number).

▶ **Critical Thinking** │WHOLE CLASS│

Ask students these questions after they complete all the exercises.

● The number 2 is the only even prime number. Why are all even numbers greater than 2 composite? All even numbers have 2 as a factor. So, every even number greater than 2 has at least 3 factors: 1, 2, and itself.

● The number 1 is the only number that is neither prime nor composite. Why do you think this is true? One is the only whole number that has only one factor, itself.

Intervention
for students having difficulty

PAIRS

Draw Combinations

Materials: Inch-Grid Paper (Copymaster M1), colored blocks (6 different colors)

Give each pair a set of 6 different colored blocks. Tell the students to start with two blocks and find how many combinations they can make using the remaining 4 blocks. They should record all of their findings by coloring squares on grid paper to represent their combinations. The students should repeat the activity and vary the number of blocks used. If additional colored blocks are available, students may use more than 6 blocks.

On Level
for students having success

SMALL GROUPS

Missing Numbers

Materials: 2 number cubes (labeled 1–6), 1 letter cube (labeled *a–f*)

Give each group 2 number cubes and 1 letter cube. When it is a student's turn, have the student roll all three cubes. Tell the student to make a multiplication or division equation using the two numbers and letter that are showing on the cubes. If the student correctly solves the equation, he or she earns 2 points. If not, other students may earn 1 point for a correct answer. All students take turns rolling the cubes. At the end of 8 rounds the student with the greatest number of points wins.

$$2 \times \boxed{c} = \boxed{6}$$
$$c = 3$$

$$4 \times \boxed{3} = \boxed{e}$$
$$e = 12$$

Challenge
for students seeking a challenge

PAIRS

Evaluate Expressions

Materials: 2 number cubes (labeled 1–6 and 7–12)

Give each pair of students 2 number cubes. One student rolls the 7–12 cube and writes an addition or multiplication expression that includes a letter and the number that was rolled. The other student rolls the 1–6 cube and uses that number to evaluate the expression. Correct answers score that number of points. Students take turns writing expressions and rolling the number cubes. High score at the end of 10 rounds wins.

Written: $12 - n$

Rolled: 5

Answer: $12 - 5 = 7$

 Math Writing Prompt

Intervention

Draw a Picture
Draw a table that shows how many different combinations there are for 3 kinds of shapes and 3 different colors. Explain your drawing.

 Math Writing Prompt

On Level

Write a Problem
Write a multiplication word problem in which one of the factors is unknown.

 Math Writing Prompt

Challenge

Reasoning Skills
Use the letters *a*, *b*, and *c* to write a related division equation for $a \times b = c$. Explain your thinking.

③ Homework and Cumulative Review

Homework **Goal:** Additional Practice

✔ Use this Homework page to provide students with more practice with making combinations and solving word problems.

Remembering **Goal:** Cumulative Review

This Remembering Activity would be appropriate any time after today's lesson.

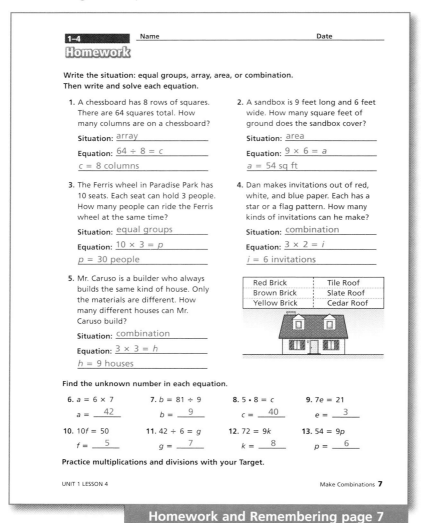

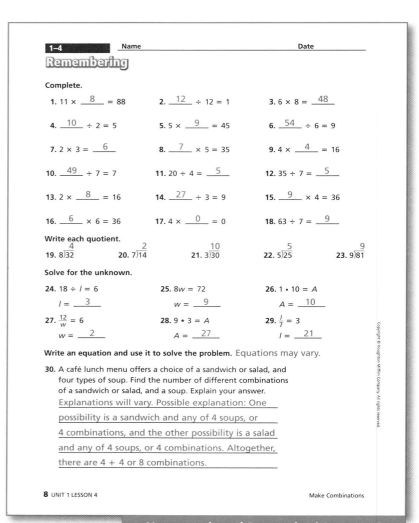

Home or School Activity

Literature Connection

Read *Math-terpieces: The Art of Problem-Solving* by Greg Tang and illustrated by Greg Paprocki (Scholastic Press 2003) to the class.

This is a book inspired by the artwork of twelve artists. The book focuses on improving problem-solving skills using problems based on combinations and permutations.

Ask students to write their own problem based on a piece of art.

UNIT 1
LESSON
5

Understand Comparisons

Lesson Objectives
- Understand multiplicative comparisons expressed two ways.
- Solve word problems and complete tables that involve comparisons.

Vocabulary
comparison

The Day at a Glance

Today's Goals	Materials	Math Talk
Quick Practice Practice basic multiplications using Medium Finger Factors.	Student Activity Book pages 17-20	In today's activities, the students are involved in discussion as they
1 Teaching the Lesson A1: Use multiplication to solve comparison problems. A2: Use tables and graphs to make comparisons.	Counters Number cubes Grid paper Markers	▶ learn how to express multiplication comparisons ▶ solve multiplication word problems using comparison bars
2 Extending the Lesson ▶ Differentiated Instruction	Index cards Venn diagram	▶ use data from tables and graphs to express multiplication comparisons
3 Homework and Cumulative Review	Homework and Remembering pages 9–10 Math Journals	

Quick Practice

🕐 5 MINUTES **Goal:** Practice basic multiplications using Medium Finger Factors.

Medium Finger Factors: Send 3 student leaders to the front. The first leader gives a factor from 6 to 10 by raising fingers on *both* hands and saying the number aloud. The second leader gives a factor from 0 to 5 by using one hand. The third leader gives the hand signal, and the class responds with the product of the two factors. Repeat with other numbers.

① Teaching the Lesson

Comparisons as Multiplication

35 MINUTES

Goal: Use multiplication to solve comparison problems.

Materials: Student Activity Book page 17–18

 NCTM Standards:
Number and Operations
Problem Solving
Representation

The Learning Classroom

Building Concepts When discussing how numbers compare, some students may give additive comparisons:

There are 4 more squares than circles; there are 4 fewer circles than squares. That is fine, but point out that we will be talking about comparisons that involve multiplication today.

▶ Express Comparisons Two Ways [WHOLE CLASS]

Draw 2 circles and 6 squares on the board. Ask your class to compare the number of circles to the number of squares.

Try to elicit from students that there are two ways to state the comparison in a multiplicative way:

1. There are 3 times as many squares as circles.
    $3 \times small\ number = large\ number$

2. There are $\frac{1}{3}$ as many circles as squares.
    $\frac{1}{3} \times large\ number = small\ number$

When making comparisons that show multiplication, it is crucial that student practice saying both kinds of comparing sentences. It is easier for students to solve problems using the first sentence. They can always switch from $\frac{1}{n} \times large\ number$ to $n \times small\ number$ when solving a problem.

1-5
Class Activity

Name _____ Date _____

Vocabulary
comparison

▶ Comparison With Unknown Numbers

You can use multiplication to solve **comparison** problems. All comparison problems involve a smaller amount and a larger amount.

1. There are 3 times as many deer as moose in the forest. If there are 5 moose, how many deer are there?
    (The larger amount is unknown.)
    ___15 deer___

    | Deer | | 3× |
    | Moose | 5 | |

2. There are $\frac{1}{3}$ as many moose as deer in the forest. If there are 15 deer, how many moose are there?
    (The smaller amount is unknown.)
    ___5 moose___

    | Deer | 15 |
    | Moose | |
    $\frac{1}{3}×$

3. There are 5 moose in the forest. There are 15 deer. How many times as many deer as moose are there?
    (The multiplier is unknown.)
    ___3 times___

    | Deer | —× 15 |
    | Moose | 5 |

4. Look at the scoreboard shown here. Write as many word problems as you can about the scoreboard that involve multiplication comparisons.

    | Red Team | Blue Team |
    | 6 | 24 |

    Word problems will vary.
    _____
    _____
    _____
    _____
    _____
    _____
    _____
    _____
    _____

UNIT 1 LESSON 5   Understand Comparisons **17**

Student Activity Book page 17

► Comparisons With Unknown Numbers WHOLE CLASS

Have everyone turn to page 17 in the Student Activity Book. Point out the boxes that show comparison bars. These are useful tools for visualizing comparisons. Discuss problems 1–4. Notice that problem 2 reveals that if you know that there are $\frac{1}{3}$ as many moose as deer, you also can say that there are 3 times as many deer as moose.

1–5
Class Activity

Name _____ Date _____

▶ Solve Comparison Problems

Draw comparison bars, write an equation, and solve each problem. Equations may vary.

Show your work.

5. Farmer Ruiz has 6 times as many cows as goats. He has 7 goats. How many cows does he have?
Let c = the number of cows
$c = 6 \times 7; \ c = 42$

Cows | 6 × | 7 | 7 | 7 | 7 | 7 | 7
Goats | 7

6. Nadia hiked 20 miles this weekend. Her sister Maria hiked only $\frac{1}{4}$ as many miles. How many miles did Maria hike?
Let m = the number of miles Maria hiked
$\frac{1}{4} \times 20 = m; \ m = 5$

Nadia | 4 × | 20
Maria | 5
$\frac{1}{4}$ ×

7. A baker made 35 apple pies today. He also made 7 peach pies. How many times as many apple pies as peach pies did he make?
Let t = how many times as many
$7t = 35; \ t = 5$

Apple | × | 35
Peach | 7

8. Nate practiced the trumpet for 10 hours last week. This week he practiced only $\frac{1}{5}$ as long. How long did Nate practice this week?
Let h = the number of hours Nate practiced this week
$\frac{1}{5} \times 10 = h; \ h = 2$

Last week | 5 × | 10
This week | 2
$\frac{1}{5}$ ×

9. How many times as many dark crayons are there as light crayons?
Let t = how many times as many
$3t = 9; \ t = 3$

18 UNIT 1 LESSON 5   Understand Comparisons

Student Activity Book page 18

► Solve Comparison Problems

In problems 5–9 on page 18, ask the class to draw comparison bars, write an equation using an appropriate letter to show the unknown number, and solve the word problems. Often several different equations will be possible.

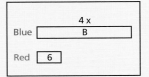
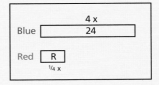
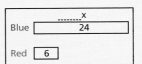

① Teaching the Lesson (continued)

Data That Shows Comparisons

 20 MINUTES

Goal: Use tables and graphs to make comparisons.

Materials: Student Activity Book page 19–20

 NCTM Standards:
Data Analysis and Probability
Problem Solving
Representation

Teaching Note

Math Background Multiplication means adding equal groups. In multiplication comparison situations the small amount is the equal group that is repeated *n* times to make the large amount.

 Ongoing Assessment

Ensure that students understand multiplication comparisons by having them:

▶ make a graph or table that shows "2 times as many."

▶ make a graph that shows "$\frac{1}{2}$ as many."

▶ explain the difference.

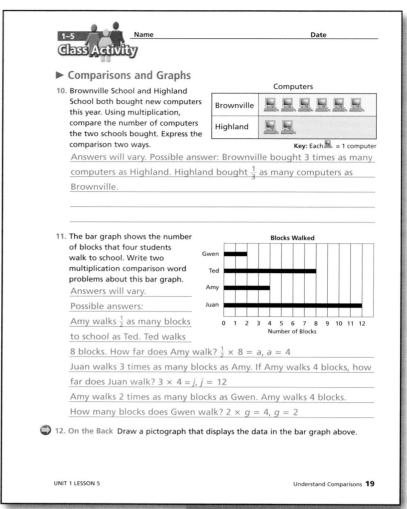

Student Activity Book page 19

▶ Comparisons and Graphs WHOLE CLASS

Have everyone discuss the table and graph problems 10 and 11. For problem 11, students should say their multiplication comparing sentences using two forms. Practice with students how to say a comparing sentence using a whole number if they are given a comparing sentence in fraction form.

If time permits, divide the students into groups and ask each group to put a picture graph on the chalkboard for the other students to discuss in comparative terms. The graph should use simple-to-draw icons, such as squares, circles, dollar signs, or stick figures. The multiplication must come out even. (For example, one row must be exactly 2, 3, 4, or 5 times as much as the other row.)

② Extending the Lesson

Intervention
for students having difficulty

`PAIRS`

Make Predictions

Materials: 2 number cubes (labeled 1–6)

Tell students they will be rolling two cubes to find sums. Ask them to predict which sums are more likely to be rolled. Students roll the cubes 50 times and record the sums.

Students write comparisons to check their predictions, for example, "We rolled twice as many fours as two threes." Ask students to give reasons why some sums happen more often than others.

Students should discover that the sum of 7 is most likely because there are more ways to make 7 than any other number. Sums of 2 and 12 are the least likely.

On Level
for students having success

`INDIVIDUALS`

Display Data

Materials: grid paper, markers, index cards (labeled $\frac{1}{4}$, $\frac{1}{2}$, $\frac{1}{3}$, 4, 2, 3)

Give each student a set of 6 index cards, graph paper, and markers. Write the numbers 4, 9, 10 and 12 on the board. Have the students select one index card and one number from the board. Tell the students to make two or more graphs that show a comparison using the numbers they have selected. Suggest that students use pictographs, bar graphs, and tables. Have students write a comparison problem to go along with their graphs.

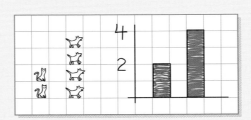

There were $\frac{1}{2}$ as many cats as dogs. There were 4 dogs.

Challenge
for students seeking a challenge

`SMALL GROUPS`

Venn Diagrams

Remind students that data can sometimes overlap and point out the overlapping circles. Tell students to find out which members of their group like vegetables, which like fruits, and which like both. They should write the student names in the appropriate places on a Venn Diagram. The overlapped area represents the students who like both fruits and vegetables. Have the groups find additional questions to poll and share the results with the class.

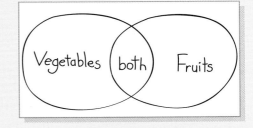

 Math Writing Prompt

Intervention

Write a Problem
Write a comparison problem using "times as many."

 Math Writing Prompt

On Level

Write a Problem
Write a comparison problem using "$\frac{1}{2}$ as many."

 Math Writing Prompt

Challenge

Reasoning Skills
Explain why the data in a Venn Diagram can't be shown on a bar graph.

1–5
Homework **Goal:** Additional Practice

✔ Use this Homework page to provide students with more practice with multiplicative comparisons.

1–5
Remembering **Goal:** Cumulative Review

This Remembering Activity would be appropriate any time after today's lesson.

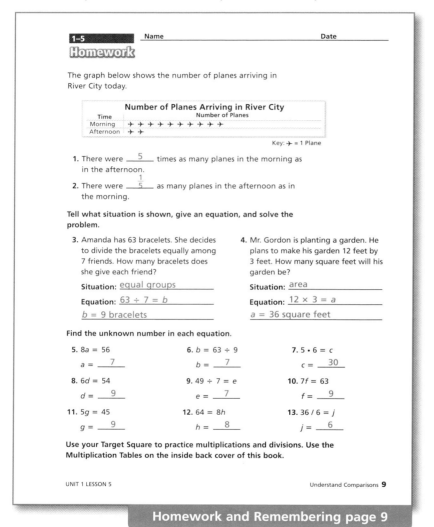

1–5 Name _____ Date _____
Homework

The graph below shows the number of planes arriving in River City today.

Number of Planes Arriving in River City

Time	Number of Planes
Morning	✈ ✈ ✈ ✈ ✈ ✈ ✈ ✈ ✈ ✈
Afternoon	✈ ✈

Key: ✈ = 1 Plane

1. There were __5__ times as many planes in the morning as in the afternoon.

2. There were __1/5__ as many planes in the afternoon as in the morning.

Tell what situation is shown, give an equation, and solve the problem.

3. Amanda has 63 bracelets. She decides to divide the bracelets equally among 7 friends. How many bracelets does she give each friend?

Situation: _equal groups_

Equation: _63 ÷ 7 = b_

b = 9 bracelets

4. Mr. Gordon is planting a garden. He plans to make his garden 12 feet by 3 feet. How many square feet will his garden be?

Situation: _area_

Equation: _12 × 3 = a_

a = 36 square feet

Find the unknown number in each equation.

5. $8a = 56$
a = __7__

6. $b = 63 ÷ 9$
b = __7__

7. $5 \cdot 6 = c$
c = __30__

8. $6d = 54$
d = __9__

9. $49 ÷ 7 = e$
e = __7__

10. $7f = 63$
f = __9__

11. $5g = 45$
g = __9__

12. $64 = 8h$
h = __8__

13. $36 / 6 = j$
j = __6__

Use your Target Square to practice multiplications and divisions. Use the Multiplication Tables on the inside back cover of this book.

UNIT 1 LESSON 5   Understand Comparisons **9**

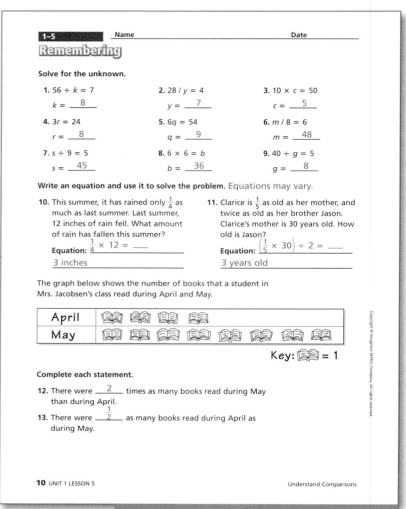

1–5 Name _____ Date _____
Remembering

Solve for the unknown.

1. $56 ÷ k = 7$
k = __8__

2. $28 / y = 4$
y = __7__

3. $10 × c = 50$
c = __5__

4. $3r = 24$
r = __8__

5. $6q = 54$
q = __9__

6. $m / 8 = 6$
m = __48__

7. $s ÷ 9 = 5$
s = __45__

8. $6 × 6 = b$
b = __36__

9. $40 ÷ g = 5$
g = __8__

Write an equation and use it to solve the problem. Equations may vary.

10. This summer, it has rained only $\frac{1}{4}$ as much as last summer. Last summer, 12 inches of rain fell. What amount of rain has fallen this summer?

Equation: $\frac{1}{4} × 12 = $ ___

3 inches

11. Clarice is $\frac{1}{5}$ as old as her mother, and twice as old as her brother Jason. Clarice's mother is 30 years old. How old is Jason?

Equation: $\left(\frac{1}{5} × 30\right) ÷ 2 = $ ___

3 years old

The graph below shows the number of books that a student in Mrs. Jacobsen's class read during April and May.

| April | 📖 📖 📖 📖 |
| May | 📖 📖 📖 📖 📖 📖 📖 📖 |

Key: 📖 = 1

Complete each statement.

12. There were __2__ times as many books read during May than during April.

13. There were __1/2__ as many books read during April as during May.

10 UNIT 1 LESSON 5   Understand Comparisons

Homework and Remembering page 9

Homework and Remembering page 10

Home or School Activity

Science Connection

Temperatures Every day the high and low temperatures are reported in the news.

Have students record the high and low temperatures for 5 consecutive days. Tell them to make two graphs, one that shows how the high temperatures compare and a second that shows how the low temperatures compare. Have them write some comparison problems using the information in the graphs.

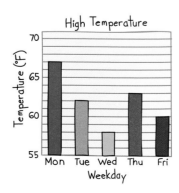

High Temperature

Practice With Multiplication Problems

Lesson Objectives

- Understand the everyday applications of multiplication and division.
- Generate and solve simple algebraic equations to represent multiplicative situations.

<table>
<tr><td colspan="2">Vocabulary</td></tr>
<tr><td>area</td><td>arrays</td></tr>
<tr><td>combination</td><td>comparison</td></tr>
<tr><td>equal groups</td><td></td></tr>
</table>

The Day at a Glance

Today's Goals	Materials	Math Talk
Quick Practice Practice basic multiplication. ❶ **Teaching the Lesson** **A1:** Recognize multiplication situations. ❷ **Extending the Lesson** ▶ Differentiated Instruction ❸ **Homework and Cumulative Review**	Student Activity Book pages 21–22 Quick Quiz 1 (Assessment Guide) Counters or blocks Index cards Square sheet of paper Ruler Paperclip Homework and Remembering pages 11–12 Math Journals	In today's activities, the students are involved in discussion as they ▶ review multiplication situations and write appropriate equations

Quick Practice

🕐 **5 MINUTES**   **Goal:** Practice basic multiplication.

Medium Finger Factors Once again, send three student leaders to the front. The first leader gives a factor from 6 to 10 by raising fingers on both hands and saying the number out loud. The second leader gives a factor from 0 to 5 by using one hand. The third leader gives the hand signal, and the class responds with the product of the two factors. Repeat with other numbers.

Teaching the Lesson

Recognize Multiplication Situations

 30 MINUTES

Goal: Recognize multiplication situations.

Materials: Student Activity Book pages 21–22

✓ **NCTM Standards:**
Number and Operations
Problem Solving
Representation
Communication

The Learning Classroom

Helping Community When students explaining at the board have difficulty, they usually welcome help from another student. Allowing other students to help instead of you will enable them to assume responsibility for one another's learning. Ask who they would like to help them. You can move on to another explainer while they redo their work. Of course, sometimes it is fine to go ahead and have the whole class help the student, with you leading with questions.

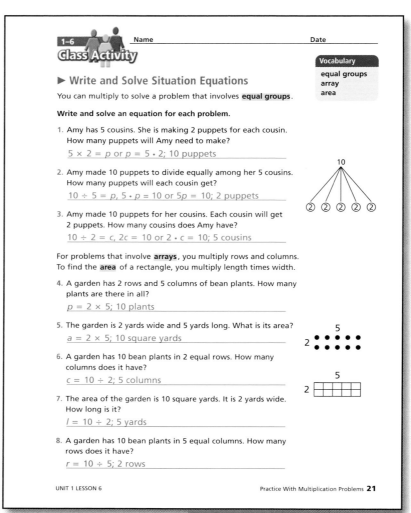

Student Activity Book page 21

▶ Introduce Situation Equations [WHOLE CLASS]

Present this problem to the class:

> "Three children each brought four books back to the library. How many books did they return?"

Invite three students to draw a picture on the board to represent this situation. Have each student explain their drawing to the class.

Ask one student to write an equation on the board to help solve the problem and explain their equation. Invite other students to write different forms of the equation on the board and explain them to the class.

▶ Write and Solve Situation Equations WHOLE CLASS

Equal Groups Direct students' attention to problems 1–3 on page 21. Invite several students to work at the board. Ask students to write and solve an equation for the first word problem, using the letter *p* for the unknown number of puppets. Discuss how the drawing shows 5 equal groups of 2, or 2 taken 5 times.

Have students do the same for the next word problem. Many students will write a division equation. If no one writes a multiplication equation, elicit one from the class.

Now have students write one division equation and one multiplication equation for the third problem, using *c* for the unknown number of cousins. You may point out that students can use any letter they want for an unknown, but that often the first letter of the unknown quantity is used, as *c* is used here to represent the unknown number of cousins.

Arrays and Area Review with the class how area is different from an array.

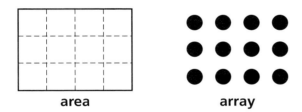

area   array

Have students generate equations and answers for problems 4–8 on page 21. The equations will be exactly the same in consecutive problems, but the label for the answer will be different. Students can use *a*, *b*, and *c* or any letter they choose for the unknowns.

The Learning Classroom

Helping Community It will be important to take some class time to discuss *good helping*. You may have students create a list that can be posted in the classroom. It is important that they understand that good helping does not mean telling answers, but taking other students through steps so that they come up with the answers themselves.

Activity continued ▶

1 Teaching the Lesson (continued)

Activity 1

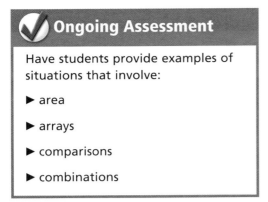

Ongoing Assessment

Have students provide examples of situations that involve:

► area

► arrays

► comparisons

► combinations

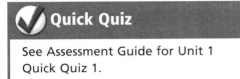

Quick Quiz

See Assessment Guide for Unit 1 Quick Quiz 1.

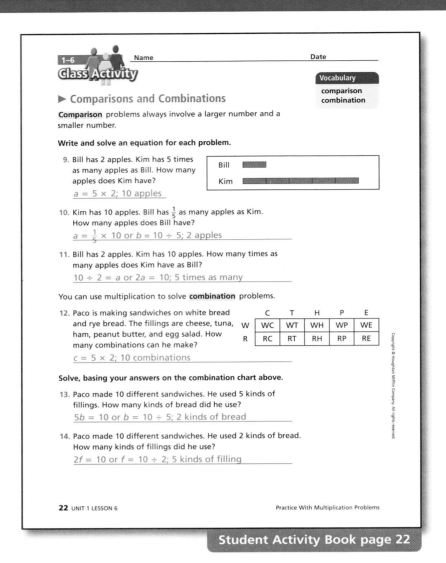

Student Activity Book page 22

► Comparisons and Combinations

Comparisons Work through problems 9–11 on page 22. The equation for problem 9 is the easiest to set up. The situation in problem 10 can be set up two ways. Students can either multiply by the fraction or divide by a whole number. The situation in problem 11 can also be set up with either a multiplication equation or a division equation.

Combinations Work through problems 12–14 on page 22. Students often are not given numbers for combination problems, but must count the items to find the numbers to be multiplied. In this case, there are 5 kinds of fillings and 2 kinds of bread. The chart shows that 10 combinations are possible if Paco makes sandwiches with just one filling. Ask your students to say all the combinations shown on the chart out loud (white bread with cheese, and so on). Then have everyone generate the various equations.

② Extending the Lesson

Activities for Individualizing

Intervention
for students having difficulty

PAIRS

Model Words

Materials: counters or blocks, index cards

Give counters or blocks and several index cards to each pair of students. Have students model equal groups, arrays, or comparisons with counters or blocks. After one student makes a model, the partner writes and solves a multiplication equation on an index card that the model could represent.

$2 \times 4 = a$
$a = 8$

$3c = 21$
$c = 7$

On Level
for students having success

SMALL GROUPS

Multiplication Challenge

Materials: square sheet of paper, ruler, paper clip

The group will need a paper clip, a pencil, and a square sheet of paper with diagonals drawn to form 4 equal sections. Have a student label the sections with the terms *array*, *area*, *combinations*, and *comparison*. The students will use the pencil point to hold the paper clip in the middle of the paper. Students take turns by spinning the paper clip "pointer." When the pointer lands on a section, the student tells a problem that involves that topic. The other students in the group solve the problem. Repeat until all students have had at least one turn.

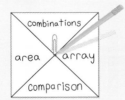

Challenge
for students seeking a challenge

PAIRS

Combinations

Have students show three methods to find the number of combinations for an ice cream dessert. The choices are:

- cone or dish
- vanilla, chocolate, or strawberry ice cream

Method 1: $2 \times 3 = 6$

Method 2: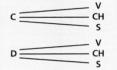

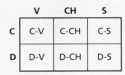

Method 3:

	V	CH	S
C	C-V	C-CH	C-S
D	D-V	D-CH	D-S

Now have each student write a problem about combinations that can be solved by the multiplication $3 \times 2 \times 4$. Students exchange and solve problems. Have them describe which method they prefer and why. (They should discover that when there are three factors, one table is not enough.)

 Math Writing Prompt

Intervention

Draw a Picture
Draw an array that shows 15 counters.

Tell how to write an equation for the array.

 Math Writing Prompt

On Level

Compare and Contrast
Explain how arrays and area are alike. Explain how they are different.

 Math Writing Prompt

Challenge

Reasoning Skills
Describe at least four different situations that 3×5 can represent.

3 Homework and Cumulative Review

Homework Goal: Additional Practice

✔ Use this Homework page to provide students with more practice with multiplication situations.

Remembering Goal: Cumulative Review

This Remembering Activity would be appropriate any time after today's lesson.

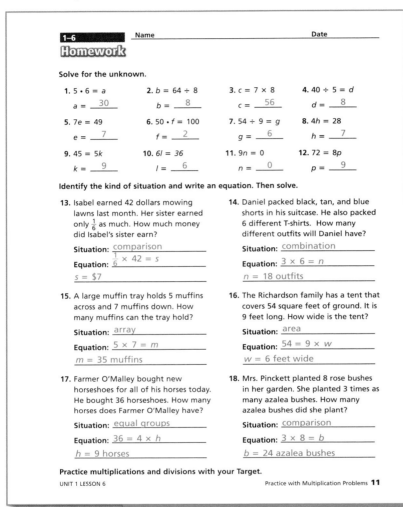

1–6
Homework

Name _____ Date _____

Solve for the unknown.

1. $5 \cdot 6 = a$
   $a = \underline{30}$

2. $b = 64 \div 8$
   $b = \underline{8}$

3. $c = 7 \times 8$
   $c = \underline{56}$

4. $40 \div 5 = d$
   $d = \underline{8}$

5. $7e = 49$
   $e = \underline{7}$

6. $50 \cdot f = 100$
   $f = \underline{2}$

7. $54 \div 9 = g$
   $g = \underline{6}$

8. $4h = 28$
   $h = \underline{7}$

9. $45 = 5k$
   $k = \underline{9}$

10. $6l = 36$
    $l = \underline{6}$

11. $9n = 0$
    $n = \underline{0}$

12. $72 = 8p$
    $p = \underline{9}$

Identify the kind of situation and write an equation. Then solve.

13. Isabel earned 42 dollars mowing lawns last month. Her sister earned only $\frac{1}{6}$ as much. How much money did Isabel's sister earn?
    Situation: comparison
    Equation: $\frac{1}{6} \times 42 = s$
    $s = \$7$

14. Daniel packed black, tan, and blue shorts in his suitcase. He also packed 6 different T-shirts. How many different outfits will Daniel have?
    Situation: combination
    Equation: $3 \times 6 = n$
    $n = 18$ outfits

15. A large muffin tray holds 5 muffins across and 7 muffins down. How many muffins can the tray hold?
    Situation: array
    Equation: $5 \times 7 = m$
    $m = 35$ muffins

16. The Richardson family has a tent that covers 54 square feet of ground. It is 9 feet long. How wide is the tent?
    Situation: area
    Equation: $54 = 9 \times w$
    $w = 6$ feet wide

17. Farmer O'Malley bought new horseshoes for all of his horses today. He bought 36 horseshoes. How many horses does Farmer O'Malley have?
    Situation: equal groups
    Equation: $36 = 4 \times h$
    $h = 9$ horses

18. Mrs. Pinckett planted 8 rose bushes in her garden. She planted 3 times as many azalea bushes. How many azalea bushes did she plant?
    Situation: comparison
    Equation: $3 \times 8 = b$
    $b = 24$ azalea bushes

Practice multiplications and divisions with your Target.

UNIT 1 LESSON 6   Practice with Multiplication Problems **11**

Homework and Remembering page 11

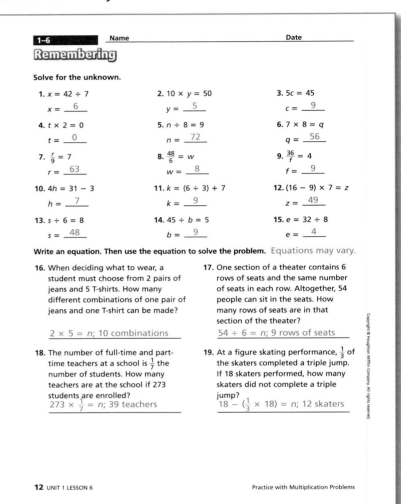

1–6
Remembering

Name _____ Date _____

Solve for the unknown.

1. $x = 42 \div 7$
   $x = \underline{6}$

2. $10 \times y = 50$
   $y = \underline{5}$

3. $5c = 45$
   $c = \underline{9}$

4. $t \times 2 = 0$
   $t = \underline{0}$

5. $n \div 8 = 9$
   $n = \underline{72}$

6. $7 \times 8 = q$
   $q = \underline{56}$

7. $\frac{r}{9} = 7$
   $r = \underline{63}$

8. $\frac{48}{6} = w$
   $w = \underline{8}$

9. $\frac{36}{f} = 4$
   $f = \underline{9}$

10. $4h = 31 - 3$
    $h = \underline{7}$

11. $k = (6 \div 3) + 7$
    $k = \underline{9}$

12. $(16 - 9) \times 7 = z$
    $z = \underline{49}$

13. $s \div 6 = 8$
    $s = \underline{48}$

14. $45 \div b = 5$
    $b = \underline{9}$

15. $e = 32 \div 8$
    $e = \underline{4}$

Write an equation. Then use the equation to solve the problem. Equations may vary.

16. When deciding what to wear, a student must choose from 2 pairs of jeans and 5 T-shirts. How many different combinations of one pair of jeans and one T-shirt can be made?
    $2 \times 5 = n$; 10 combinations

17. One section of a theater contains 6 rows of seats and the same number of seats in each row. Altogether, 54 people can sit in the seats. How many rows of seats are in that section of the theater?
    $54 \div 6 = n$; 9 rows of seats

18. The number of full-time and part-time teachers at a school is $\frac{1}{7}$ the number of students. How many teachers are at the school if 273 students are enrolled?
    $273 \times \frac{1}{7} = n$; 39 teachers

19. At a figure skating performance, $\frac{1}{3}$ of the skaters completed a triple jump. If 18 skaters performed, how many skaters did not complete a triple jump?
    $18 - (\frac{1}{3} \times 18) = n$; 12 skaters

12 UNIT 1 LESSON 6   Practice with Multiplication Problems

Homework and Remembering page 12

Home or School Activity

Art Connection

Arrays and Patterns Many patterns for tiles, bricks, and paving stones are made by using different colors and shadings in arrays.

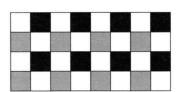

Have students find different designs that are made with arrays and use multiplication to find the number of tiles or bricks in those arrays. Then have students create their own designs on grid paper.

Discover Multiplication Patterns

Lesson Objectives

- Understand multiplicative relationships and patterns.
- Apply knowledge of patterns to problem-solving situations.

The Day at a Glance

Today's Goals	Materials	Math Talk
Quick Practice Practice basic multiplication.	Student Activity Book pages 23–26	In today's activities, the students are involved in discussion as they
1 Teaching the Lesson **A1:** Find and describe patterns in the count-bys. **A2:** Analyze and solve a problem.	Blocks or counters Hundred grid Crayons or markers	▶ find and describe patterns using hundred grids
2 Extending the Lesson ▶ Differentiated Instruction	Index cards	▶ explain how to use patterns to solve problems
3 Homework and Cumulative Review	Homework and Remembering pages 13–14 Math Journals	

Quick Practice

⏱ 5 MINUTES   **Goal:** Practice basic multiplication.

Difficult Finger Factors The class will practice with factors from the difficult section of the Multiplication Table today. Send 3 student leaders to the front. Two leaders will give factors from 6 to 10 by raising fingers on both hands and saying the number out loud. The third leader gives the hand signal, and the class responds with the product of the two factors. Repeat with other numbers.

Teaching the Lesson

Describe Patterns

 40 MINUTES

Goal: Find and describe patterns in the count-bys.

Materials: Student Activity Book pages 23–25

✔ **NCTM Standards:**
Reasoning and Proof
Problem Solving

The Learning Classroom

Building Concepts The pattern found in 9s count-bys is useful for problem solving because each count-by is equal to a multiple of 10 minus the number of the count-by in the pattern: 10 − 1, 20 − 2, 30 − 3, 40 − 4, and so on. For example, finding 8 × 9 is the same as finding the 8th count-by. Find the 8th multiple of 10 and then subtract 8:
8 × 10 = 80; 80 − 8 = 72

Check the answer by seeing if the digits add up to 9:
7 + 2 = 9

Teaching Note

Language and Vocabulary
Remind students that *products* and *count-bys* have the same meaning in this discussion. For example, in problem 4, *9 product* means *9s count-by*.

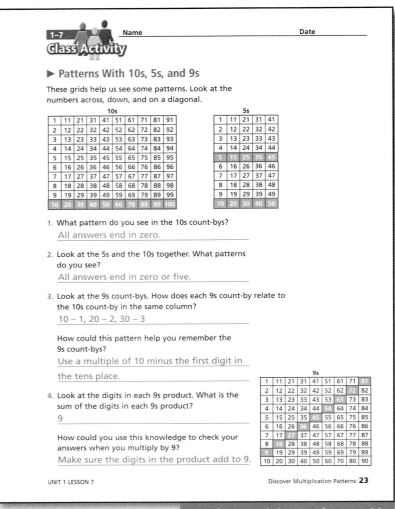

Student Activity Book page 23

▶ Patterns With 10s, 5s, 9s [WHOLE CLASS]

Explain that the diagram for tens on page 23 is a hundred grid (numbers in order from 1 to 100) and not a multiplication table. The other diagrams each show part of a hundred grid. Discuss the exercises together.

5s and 10s Count-Bys Have students compare the patterns that they see in the 5s and 10s count-bys. They should notice that the gaps between the 10s count-bys are twice the size. There are twice as many 5s in that part of the diagram. They might also point out that the 10s always end in 0, while the 5s end in either 5 or 0.

9s Count-Bys The central 9s pattern is that 9 is 1 less than 10, 18 is 2 less than 20, 27 is 3 less than 30, and so on. This pattern can be expressed in a number of ways. Some students might say that the ones digits in the 9s pattern decrease by 1 (9, 8, 7, 6, and so on), while the tens digits increase by 1 (0, 1, 2, 3, 4, and so on).

A Visual Activity for Multiplying by 9 You might want to show your class this interesting hand activity in which students use their fingers to see the "tens-minus-ones" pattern for 9s.

Students put both hands up with the palms facing them, as shown.

They each bend down a single finger to show the multiplier. The position of this finger changes, but only one multiplier finger is ever bent down. Starting at the left, the first finger bent down means they are multiplying by 1, the second finger means 2, and so on.

The answer is decoded by seeing all fingers to the left of the bent finger as tens and all fingers to the right of the bent finger as ones.

1 × 9 = 9
(0 tens, 9 ones)
The first finger is bent down and zero tens fingers are up.

2 × 9 = 18
(1 ten, 8 ones)
The second finger is bent down and 1 tens finger is up.

3 × 9 = 27
(2 tens, 7 ones)
The third finger is bent down and 2 tens fingers are up.

Activity continued ▶

Teaching Note

What to Expect From Students
In discussing the various count-bys, students may point out spatial relationships formed by some patterns as well as numeric relationships. For example, the 9s pattern forms a "diagonal" across the grid.

1	11	21	31	41	51	61	71	81	91
2	12	22	32	42	52	62	72	82	92
3	13	23	33	43	53	63	73	83	93
4	14	24	34	44	54	64	74	84	94
5	15	25	35	45	55	65	75	85	95
6	16	26	36	46	56	66	76	86	96
7	17	27	37	47	57	67	77	87	97
8	18	28	38	48	58	68	78	88	98
9	19	29	39	49	59	69	79	89	99
10	20	30	40	50	60	70	80	90	100

Teaching the Lesson (continued)

Activity 1

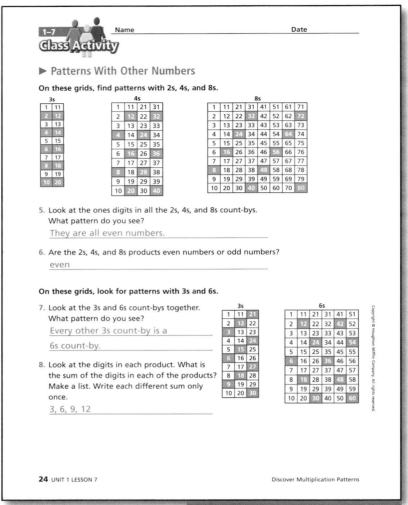

Student Activity Book page 24

▶ Patterns With Other Numbers WHOLE CLASS

Discuss exercises 5–8 as a class.

2s, 4s, and 8s Count-Bys On page 24, the class should notice that each pair of 2s makes a 4, and each pair of 4s makes an 8. Ask the students if they can explain why this pattern exists. Because 4 is twice as large as 2, we "skip" every other 2s product to get the 4s products (say 4, skip 6, say 8, skip 10, say 12, and so on). And because 8 is twice as large as 4, we skip every other product again (say 8, 16, 24, and so on). Also note that the products are all even numbers. If necessary, review odd and even numbers with the class.

3s and 6s Count-Bys Ask the students to find and compare as many patterns as they can in the 3s and 6s. Again, they should notice the "skip" pattern that was discussed with the 2s, 4s, and 8s. Ask them why this pattern exists. Because 6 is twice as large as 3, we skip every other 3s product to get the 6s products (say 6, 12, 18, and so on). Students should also discover that the digits in the products of the 3s and 6s always add up to 3, 6, or 9. (In the case of 48, the digits need to be added twice, $4 + 8 = 12$, and $1 + 2 = 3$.)

1–7 Class Activity

Name ______ Date ______

▶ Patterns in the Zeros and Ones

Solve.

9. $8 \times 0 =$ 0 10. 14×0 0 11. $0 \times 75 =$ 0

12. $0 \div 12 =$ 0 13. $0 \times 98 =$ 0 14. $1 \times$ 16 $= 16$

15. $68 \times 1 =$ 68 16. $85 \div 1 =$ 85 17. $500 \div 1 =$ 500

18. What pattern do you find in the zeros?
The product of zero and any number is zero, and zero divided by any other number is zero.

19. What pattern do you find in the ones?
The product of one and any number is that number, and any number divided by one is that number.

▶ Even-Odd Patterns

Solve.

20. If you multiply an odd number by an odd number, will the product be even or odd?
odd

21. If you multiply an even number by an even number, will the product be even or odd?
even

22. If you multiply an even number by an odd number, will the product be even or odd?
even

23. Which of these answers cannot be right? How do you know?

$23 \times 75 = 1{,}725$ $64 \times 18 = 1{,}152$ $47 \times 59 = 2{,}764$

$47 \times 59 = 2{,}764$ is wrong because an odd number times an odd number equals an odd number.

UNIT 1 LESSON 7 Discover Multiplication Patterns 25

Student Activity Book page 25

▶ Patterns in the Zeros and Ones WHOLE CLASS

Ask the class what they know about multiplication and division with 1 and 0.

- The product of one and any number is that number, and any number divided by one is that number. $n \times 1 = n$ and $n \div 1 = n$.
- The product of zero and any number is zero, and zero divided by any other number is zero. $n \times 0 = 0$ and $0 \div n = 0$.
- It is not possible to divide by zero.

Have students quickly complete exercises 9–19.

▶ Even-Odd Patterns WHOLE CLASS

Students can find the answers to exercises 20–23 by trying a few sample problems. Even × Even = Even; Even × Odd = Even; Odd × Odd = Odd

- Why is the product always an even number when one of the factors is even? If one factor is even, then the other factor is an addend that is used an even number of times. For example, $4 \times 3 = 3 + 3 + 3 + 3$.

Teaching Note

Math Background One way to understand that division by zero is impossible is to relate division and multiplication. For example, $12 \div 4 = 3$ because $3 \times 4 = 12$. To solve $12 \div 0 =$ what number, consider the related multiplication equation, what number $\times 0 = 12$. There is no number multiplied by zero that equals 12.

Teaching the Lesson (continued)

Activity 2

Applications

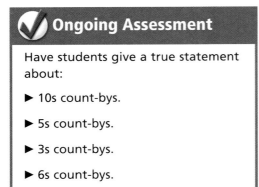

10 MINUTES

Goal: Analyze and solve a problem.

Materials: Student Activity Book page 26

✔ **NCTM Standards:**
Problem Solving
Reasoning and Proof
Connection

✔ Ongoing Assessment

Have students give a true statement about:

▶ 10s count-bys.

▶ 5s count-bys.

▶ 3s count-bys.

▶ 6s count-bys.

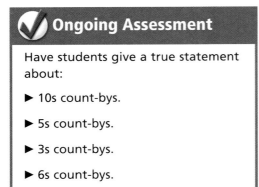

1–7
Class Activity

Name _____ Date _____

▶ The Puzzled Penguin

Dear Math Students,

Today my friend Lucy and I sold lemonade for 5 cents a glass. When we were done, my friend said, "There are 24 nickels here, so we made $1.20."

"How did you figure that out so fast?" I asked.

Lucy answered, "I started by multiplying 24 by 10, and then I . . ."

At that moment Lucy heard her mother calling and had to leave. I can't figure out what Lucy did. Why would anyone start by multiplying by 10 when a nickel is worth only 5 cents? Can you explain Lucy's thinking?

Thanks for your help.
The Puzzled Penguin

Answers will vary.

26 UNIT 1 LESSON 7   Discover Multiplication Patterns

Student Activity Book page 26

▶ The Puzzled Penguin WHOLE CLASS

Direct students' attention to page 26 in the Student Activity Book. Read the letter from the penguin together and ask the class to try to explain the multiplication strategy probably used by the penguin's friend, Lucy.

Your students already know that multiplying by 5 gives exactly half the result of multiplying by 10. This knowledge can be used as an aid in mental math. When dealing with multi-digit numbers, it is often simpler to multiply by 10 and then take half the answer than to try to multiply by 5 mentally.

For practice, ask your students to try multiplying the following numbers in their heads using this strategy: 18 × 5, 28 × 5, 800 × 5.

② Extending the Lesson

Activities for Individualizing

Intervention
for students having difficulty

INDIVIDUALS

Make Models

Materials: blocks or counters

Give each student counters or blocks. Have the students create a model that shows different count-bys. Then have them draw a picture of the model. Have students share their models by showing the pictures to others.

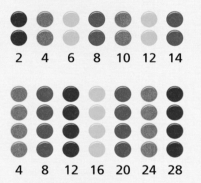

On Level
for students having success

PAIRS

Multiple Patterns

Materials: hundred grid, crayons or markers

Write this problem on the board:

There are 100 people in line at a movie theater. Every 6th person gets a free drink. Every 9th person gets free popcorn. Use a hundred grid to find which people get both a free drink and free popcorn.

1	11	21	31	41	51	61	71	81	91
2	12	22	32	42	52	62	72	82	92
3	13	23	33	43	53	63	73	83	93
4	14	24	34	44	54	64	74	84	94
5	15	25	35	45	55	65	75	85	95
6	16	26	36	46	56	66	76	86	96
7	17	27	37	47	57	67	77	87	97
8	18	28	38	48	58	68	78	88	98
9	19	29	39	49	59	69	79	89	99
10	20	30	40	50	60	70	80	90	100

Tell students to solve the problem and then compare solutions with their partner. Then have students make up their own problem, exchange, and solve.

Challenge
for students seeking a challenge

PAIRS

Use Substitution

Materials: index cards (21 per pair)

Have students use the index cards to make number cards labeled 0 to 10, letter cards labeled *a* to *f*, operation cards labeled $+$, $-$, $\times$, $\div$.

One student chooses a card of each kind and arranges the three cards to form an expression (such as $7 - c$ or $f \times 5$). The partner chooses a number card and substitutes that number for the variable in the expression. If the expression simplifies to a whole number and the partner correctly identifies that number, one point is earned.

The cards are shuffled and roles are reversed after each turn. The partner with the most points wins.

 Math Writing Prompt

Intervention
Explain Comparisons
Explain how the 2s count-by pattern and the 4s count-by pattern are alike and different.

 Math Writing Prompt

On Level
Make Comparisons
Explain how the patterns for 2s count-bys and 3s count-bys are alike and different.

 Math Writing Prompt

Challenge
Related Patterns
Explain how 3s count-bys, 6s count-bys, and 9s count-bys are related.

③ Homework and Cumulative Review

1–7
Homework **Goal:** Additional Practice

✔️ Use this Homework page to provide students with more practice with multiplication patterns.

1–7
Remembering **Goal:** Cumulative Review

This Remembering Activity would be appropriate any time after today's lesson.

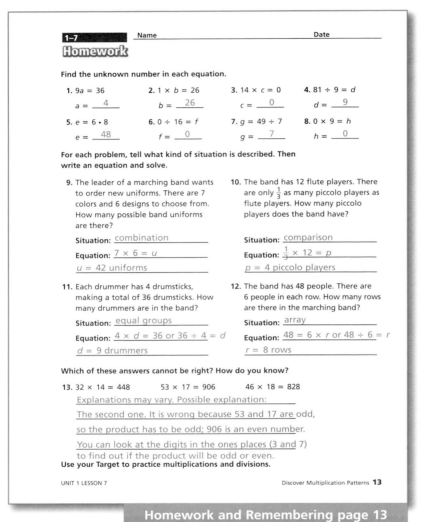

1–7
Homework   Name _____ Date _____

Find the unknown number in each equation.

1. $9a = 36$
   $a = \underline{4}$
2. $1 \times b = 26$
   $b = \underline{26}$
3. $14 \times c = 0$
   $c = \underline{0}$
4. $81 \div 9 = d$
   $d = \underline{9}$
5. $e = 6 \cdot 8$
   $e = \underline{48}$
6. $0 \div 16 = f$
   $f = \underline{0}$
7. $g = 49 \div 7$
   $g = \underline{7}$
8. $0 \times 9 = h$
   $h = \underline{0}$

For each problem, tell what kind of situation is described. Then write an equation and solve.

9. The leader of a marching band wants to order new uniforms. There are 7 colors and 6 designs to choose from. How many possible band uniforms are there?
   Situation: _combination_
   Equation: $7 \times 6 = u$
   $u = 42$ uniforms

10. The band has 12 flute players. There are only $\frac{1}{3}$ as many piccolo players as flute players. How many piccolo players does the band have?
    Situation: _comparison_
    Equation: $\frac{1}{3} \times 12 = p$
    $p = 4$ piccolo players

11. Each drummer has 4 drumsticks, making a total of 36 drumsticks. How many drummers are in the band?
    Situation: _equal groups_
    Equation: $4 \times d = 36$ or $36 \div 4 = d$
    $d = 9$ drummers

12. The band has 48 people. There are 6 people in each row. How many rows are there in the marching band?
    Situation: _array_
    Equation: $48 = 6 \times r$ or $48 \div 6 = r$
    $r = 8$ rows

Which of these answers cannot be right? How do you know?

13. $32 \times 14 = 448$ $53 \times 17 = 906$ $46 \times 18 = 828$
    Explanations may vary. Possible explanation:
    The second one. It is wrong because 53 and 17 are odd,
    so the product has to be odd; 906 is an even number.
    You can look at the digits in the ones places (3 and 7)
    to find out if the product will be odd or even.

Use your Target to practice multiplications and divisions.

UNIT 1 LESSON 7   Discover Multiplication Patterns **13**

Homework and Remembering page 13

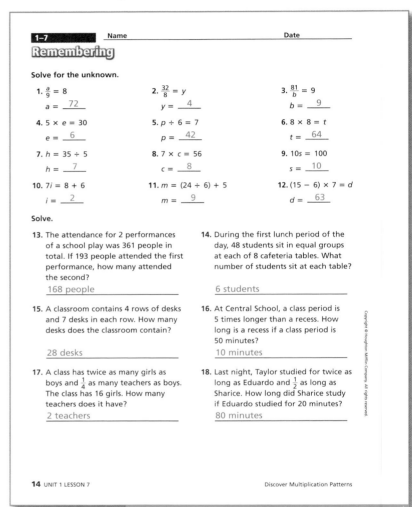

1–7
Remembering   Name _____ Date _____

Solve for the unknown.

1. $\frac{a}{9} = 8$
   $a = \underline{72}$
2. $\frac{32}{8} = y$
   $y = \underline{4}$
3. $\frac{81}{b} = 9$
   $b = \underline{9}$
4. $5 \times e = 30$
   $e = \underline{6}$
5. $p \div 6 = 7$
   $p = \underline{42}$
6. $8 \times 8 = t$
   $t = \underline{64}$
7. $h = 35 \div 5$
   $h = \underline{7}$
8. $7 \times c = 56$
   $c = \underline{8}$
9. $10s = 100$
   $s = \underline{10}$
10. $7i = 8 + 6$
    $i = \underline{2}$
11. $m = (24 \div 6) + 5$
    $m = \underline{9}$
12. $(15 - 6) \times 7 = d$
    $d = \underline{63}$

Solve.

13. The attendance for 2 performances of a school play was 361 people in total. If 193 people attended the first performance, how many attended the second?
    168 people

14. During the first lunch period of the day, 48 students sit in equal groups at each of 8 cafeteria tables. What number of students sit at each table?
    6 students

15. A classroom contains 4 rows of desks and 7 desks in each row. How many desks does the classroom contain?
    28 desks

16. At Central School, a class period is 5 times longer than a recess. How long is a recess if a class period is 50 minutes?
    10 minutes

17. A class has twice as many girls as boys and $\frac{1}{4}$ as many teachers as boys. The class has 16 girls. How many teachers does it have?
    2 teachers

18. Last night, Taylor studied for twice as long as Eduardo and $\frac{1}{2}$ as long as Sharice. How long did Sharice study if Eduardo studied for 20 minutes?
    80 minutes

14 UNIT 1 LESSON 7   Discover Multiplication Patterns

Homework and Remembering page 14

Home or School Activity

 Literature Connection

Read *One Grain of Rice: A Mathematical Folktale* by Demi (Scholastic, 1997) to the class. This is a cultural story about a girl in India. The mathematics involves doubling each day for 30 days.

After reading this folktale to your class, ask students to write doubling stories of their own.

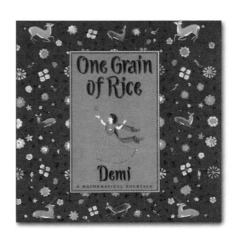

Functions

Lesson Objectives

- Describe a function and express it as an equation.
- Connect functions to real-life situations.

Vocabulary

function
variable

The Day at a Glance

Today's Goals	Materials	Math Talk
Quick Practice Practice basic multiplication.	Student Activity Book pages 27–28	In today's activities, the students are involved in discussion as they
① Teaching the Lesson **A1:** Identify and apply the rule of an input-output table. **A2:** Write an equation to express a function that models a real-life situation.	Homework and Remembering pages 15–16 Math Journals	▶ examine input-output relationships to determine function rules
② Extending the Lesson ▶ Differentiated Instruction		▶ write and apply function rules to solve real-life problems
③ Homework and Cumulative Review		

Quick Practice

🕐 **5 MINUTES**   **Goal:** Practice basic multiplication.

Difficult Finger Factors The class will continue to practice with factors from the difficult section of the Multiplication Table. Send three student leaders to the front. Two leaders will give factors from 6 to 10 by raising fingers on both hands and saying the number out loud. The third leader gives the hand signal, and the class responds with the product of the two factors. Repeat using other numbers.

1 Teaching the Lesson

Activity 1

Function Tables

25 MINUTES

Goal: Identify and apply the rule of an input-output table.

Materials: Student Activity Book page 27

NCTM Standards:
Algebra
Connection
Representation

Teaching Note

Language and Vocabulary Review with the students the meaning of the word *function*. A *function* can be thought of as a *rule* (which is often mathematical). If the input of the function is a number, the rule is applied to the input and exactly one number is output. In this lesson, each function consists of an operation and a number.

Differentiated Instruction

Extra Help For students who have trouble with the concept of input and output, suggest that they create a drawing like this one:

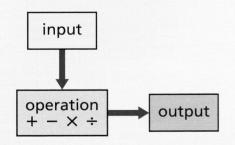

A visual representation of something going into a box in which an operation is performed to create a number going out may help to make the concept more easily understood.

1–8 Class Activity

Name Date

Vocabulary
function

▶ Input-Output Tables

A **function** is a rule that pairs each input with only one output. Functions can be shown in different ways. The table of input and output values at the right is one way to show a function.

The rule for the function table is *add 3* because every output is 3 more than its input.

Rule: Add 3	
Input	Output
0	3
1	4
2	5
5	8
9	12

Complete each table.

1.

Rule: Add 8	
Input	Output
1	9
2	10
3	11
4	12
5	13

2.

Rule: Multiply by 5	
Input	Output
0	0
6	30
8	40
9	45
4	20

For each table, write the rule and then complete the table.

3.

Rule: Multiply by 4	
Input	Output
0	0
2	8
3	12
4	16
6	24

4.

Rule: Add 7	
Input	Output
7	14
2	9
15	22
3	10
11	18

UNIT 1 LESSON 8 Functions 27

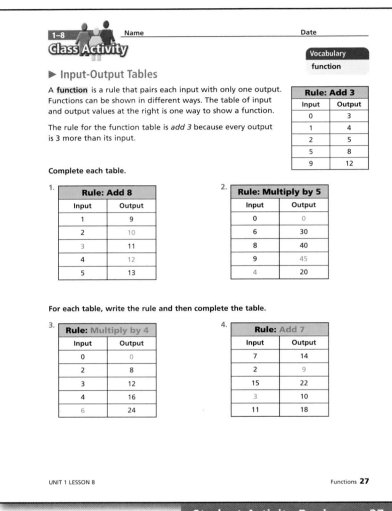

Student Activity Book page 27

▶ Input-Output Tables WHOLE CLASS

Identify the Rule Read the introduction at the top of page 27 in the Student Activity Book aloud or read them together. Invite students to look at the first input-output table and consider the following:

- Which numbers are shown as inputs for this function? 0, 1, 2, 5, 9
- For the first input-output pair, the input is 0. Why is the output 3? The rule is to add 3.
- What output is missing in the last row of the table? 12 Write the output.

Have the students complete exercises 1–4. To complete exercises 3 and 4, the students must first identify the rule. Use Solve and Discuss for exercises 3 and 4.

Real-World Applications

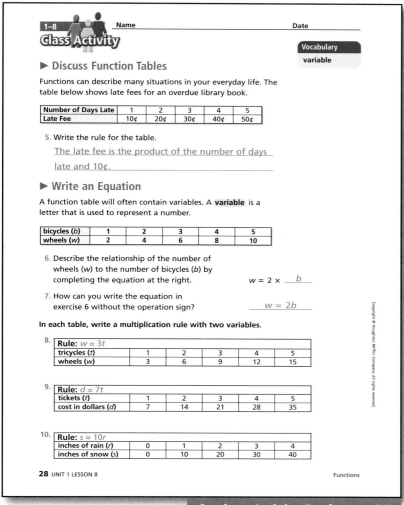

Student Activity Book page 28

▶ Discuss Function Tables [INDIVIDUALS]

Read the top of page 28 aloud or read it together. Have students look at the table that shows number of days late and late fees. Invite students to compare each pair of numbers in the table, then decide the rule that describes their relationship.

After a rule has been agreed upon, ask the students to decide if the rule is true for *each* pair of numbers in the table, and then have students complete exercise 5 by writing the rule.

 25 MINUTES

Goal: Write an equation to express a function that models a real-world situation.

Materials: Student Activity Book page 28

 NCTM Standards:
Algebra
Problem Solving
Connection
Representation

 Math Talk

Give students the opportunity to share their descriptions of the rule. Possible descriptions might include:

Each day is 10 cents more.

You add 10 cents every day.

The late fee is 10 times the day number.

Activity continued ▶

① Teaching the Lesson (continued)

Activity 2

▶ Write An Equation WHOLE CLASS

The next part of the activity involves writing an equation. To help students become more proficient with writing equations, write the following equation and table on the board:

$$output = input + 1$$

input	1	2	3	4	5
output	2	3	4	5	6

$$output = input + 1$$

● Is the rule *output = input + 1* true for each number pair in the table? yes

Then erase letters from the words input and output so the equation and table look like this:

$$o = i + 1$$

i	1	2	3	4	5
o	2	3	4	5	6

$$o = i + 1$$

Point out that the variable i represents the input of the function, and the variable o represents the output.

● Is the rule $o = i + 1$ true for each number pair in the table? yes
   Emphasize that both equations (output = input + 1 and $o = i + 1$) represent the same function.

Now have students study the bicycles and wheels function table and then complete the equation in the space provided (exercise 6). They should then complete exercise 7, working cooperatively if necessary to recognize that $w = 2 \times b$ can be written in a simpler way as $w = 2b$.

Use Solve and Discuss for exercises 8–10. You might choose to have students work in pairs or in small groups.

② Extending the Lesson

Differentiated Instruction

Activities for Individualizing

Intervention
for students having difficulty

PAIRS

Chart Functions

Have students fold a sheet of paper into thirds. Tell the students to write *input* in the first column, *rule* in the second column, and *output* in the third column.

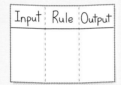

Write these rules on the board:

add 5
subtract 1
multiply by 2

Invite the students to work in pairs. One student randomly selects a number to be the input and then chooses a rule from the list on the board. The partner solves for the output. The first student checks the partner's work. Roles are reversed and the activity is repeated several times.

 Math Writing Prompt

Intervention

Define Terms
Explain what *input* and *output* mean. Use an example.

On Level
for students having success

PAIRS

Generate a Pattern

Write the relationship 1 yard = 3 feet on the board. Working in pairs, ask each student to write a multiplication rule for the relationship, using *y* to represent the number of yards and *f* to represent the number of feet.

If students include a multiplication symbol (such as × or •) in their rule, ask them to rewrite the rule in a simpler way. ($f = 3y$)

Have students create and complete a function table for the relationship, then describe the relationship using words.

$f = 3y$	
y	f
1	3
2	6
3	9
4	12
5	15

The values representing *f* are 3s count-bys.

 Math Writing Prompt

On Level

Reasoning
Explain how a multiplication rule can give count-bys as outputs.

Challenge
for students seeking a challenge

INDIVIDUALS

Growth Over Time

Tell students that in proper conditions, some bamboo plants may grow at a rate of 8 inches or more per day.

Write on the board:

Growth rate: 8 inches per day
Beginning height: 5 feet
Target height: 10 feet

Ask students to construct and complete a table to determine the number of days it will take the plant to reach its target height. (8 days)

Start Height = 60 in.		
Day Number	Daily Growth	Total Height
1	60 + 8	68
2	68 + 8	76
3	76 + 8	84
4	84 + 8	92
5	92 + 8	100
6	100 + 8	108
7	108 + 8	116
8	116 + 8	124
Target Height: 120 in.		

Then have students write an equation that can be used to find the height for any day.

(8 in. × day number) + 60

 Math Writing Prompt

Challenge

Problem Solving
Explain how to find how many days it will take a bamboo plant to reach its mature height of 45 feet, if it grow 8 inches each day.

③ Homework and Cumulative Review

Homework **Goal:** Additional Practice

✓ Use this Homework page to provide students with more practice with functions.

Remembering **Goal:** Cumulative Review

This Remembering Activity would be appropriate any time after today's lesson.

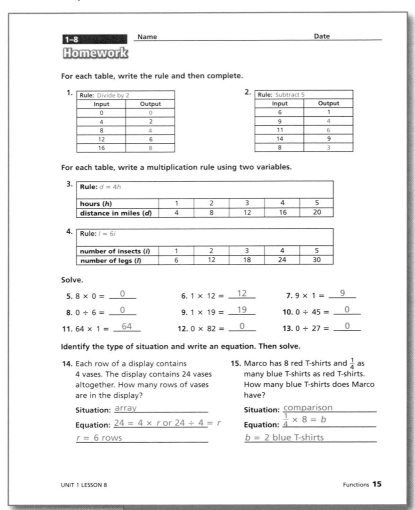

1-8
Name _____ Date _____
Homework

For each table, write the rule and then complete.

1. **Rule:** Divide by 2

Input	Output
0	0
4	2
8	4
12	6
16	8

2. **Rule:** Subtract 5

Input	Output
6	1
9	4
11	6
14	9
8	3

For each table, write a multiplication rule using two variables.

3. **Rule:** $d = 4h$

hours (h)	1	2	3	4	5
distance in miles (d)	4	8	12	16	20

4. **Rule:** $l = 6i$

number of insects (i)	1	2	3	4	5
number of legs (l)	6	12	18	24	30

Solve.

5. $8 \times 0 = \underline{0}$ 6. $1 \times 12 = \underline{12}$ 7. $9 \times 1 = \underline{9}$

8. $0 \div 6 = \underline{0}$ 9. $1 \times 19 = \underline{19}$ 10. $0 \div 45 = \underline{0}$

11. $64 \times 1 = \underline{64}$ 12. $0 \times 82 = \underline{0}$ 13. $0 \div 27 = \underline{0}$

Identify the type of situation and write an equation. Then solve.

14. Each row of a display contains 4 vases. The display contains 24 vases altogether. How many rows of vases are in the display?

Situation: array
Equation: $24 = 4 \times r$ or $24 \div 4 = r$
$r = 6$ rows

15. Marco has 8 red T-shirts and $\frac{1}{4}$ as many blue T-shirts as red T-shirts. How many blue T-shirts does Marco have?

Situation: comparison
Equation: $\frac{1}{4} \times 8 = b$
$b = 2$ blue T-shirts

UNIT 1 LESSON 8   Functions **15**

Homework and Remembering page 15

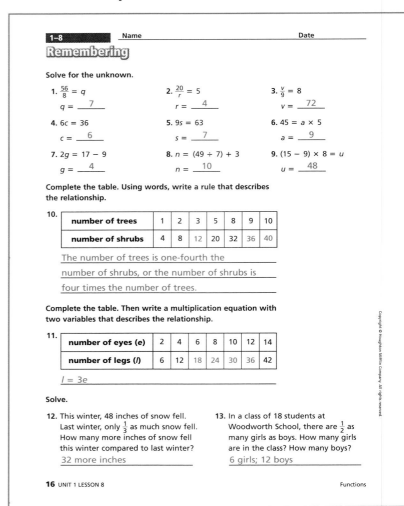

1-8
Name _____ Date _____
Remembering

Solve for the unknown.

1. $\frac{56}{8} = q$
$q = \underline{7}$

2. $\frac{20}{r} = 5$
$r = \underline{4}$

3. $\frac{v}{9} = 8$
$v = \underline{72}$

4. $6c = 36$
$c = \underline{6}$

5. $9s = 63$
$s = \underline{7}$

6. $45 = a \times 5$
$a = \underline{9}$

7. $2g = 17 - 9$
$g = \underline{4}$

8. $n = (49 \div 7) + 3$
$n = \underline{10}$

9. $(15 - 9) \times 8 = u$
$u = \underline{48}$

Complete the table. Using words, write a rule that describes the relationship.

10.

number of trees	1	2	3	5	8	9	10
number of shrubs	4	8	12	20	32	36	40

The number of trees is one-fourth the number of shrubs, or the number of shrubs is four times the number of trees.

Complete the table. Then write a multiplication equation with two variables that describes the relationship.

11.

number of eyes (e)	2	4	6	8	10	12	14
number of legs (l)	6	12	18	24	30	36	42

$l = 3e$

Solve.

12. This winter, 48 inches of snow fell. Last winter, only $\frac{1}{3}$ as much snow fell. How many more inches of snow fell this winter compared to last winter?

32 more inches

13. In a class of 18 students at Woodworth School, there are $\frac{1}{2}$ as many girls as boys. How many girls are in the class? How many boys?

6 girls; 12 boys

16 UNIT 1 LESSON 8   Functions

Homework and Remembering page 16

Home or School Activity

Language Arts Connection

The Math Machine Imagine a math machine that produces an output number for every number that is input.

If a machine uses the rule $4 + x$, then four is added to each input number to produce an output number. For example, if the input number is 5, then the output number is $4 + 5$, or 9.

Write a story about a math machine, including what it looks like and how it works.

Multiplication Strategies

Lesson Objectives

- Understand how multiplication factors can be regrouped to solve problems.
- Apply knowledge of patterns, sequences, and multiplication properties to problem-solving situations.

The Day at a Glance

Today's Goals	Materials	Math Talk
Quick Practice Practice basic multiplication.	Student Activity Book pages 29–32	In today's activities, the students are involved in discussion as they
1 **Teaching the Lesson** A1: Discuss strategies that involve adding or subtracting from a known product to find an unknown product. A2: Discuss strategies that involve regrouping factors to find a product and apply various strategies to specific multiplication situations.	Homework and Remembering pages 17–18 Math Journals	► generate strategies for finding an unknown product by working with known products ► explain how to decide whether a given multiplication is correct
2 **Extending the Lesson** ► Going Further: Guess and Check ► Differentiated Instruction		
3 **Homework and Cumulative Review**		

Quick Practice

🕐 **5 MINUTES** **Goal:** Practice basic multiplication.

Difficult Finger Factors The class will practice with factors from the difficult section of the Multiplication Table today and tomorrow. Send three student leaders to the front. For each turn, two leaders give factors from 6 to 10 by showing the number with fingers on both hands and saying the number aloud and the third leader signals the class to respond with the product of the two factors. Your class should be able to practice 15–20 multiplications during the Quick Practice.

Teaching the Lesson

Work With Known Products

 25 MINUTES

Goal: Discuss strategies that involve adding or subtracting from a known product to find an unknown product.

Materials: Student Activity Book page 29

✔ **NCTM Standards:**
Number and Operations
Communication

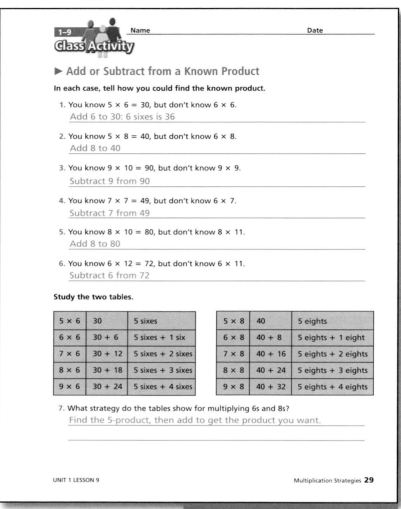

Student Activity Book page 29

▶ Add or Subtract From a Known Product WHOLE CLASS

Direct everyone's attention to problems 1–6. All of these questions focus on strategies that involve starting with a known product and then adding or subtracting a factor to arrive at an unknown product. Elicit the answers to these questions from the students rather than explaining the strategy yourself. Ask leading questions, such as "How many more than 5 × 6 is 6 × 6?" In some situations, such as those presented in problems 5 and 6, students can easily figure out products that are not part of the traditional multiplication table. This set of problems helps students realize that they often know more than they think they do.

Give students time to study the tables before beginning discussion of problem 7. These tables present an adding-on strategy based on 5-groups that works well for multiplying 6s and 8s. These two groups tend to be among the more difficult multiplications and divisions. Be sure that students see and understand the patterns in the tables.

More Work With Factors

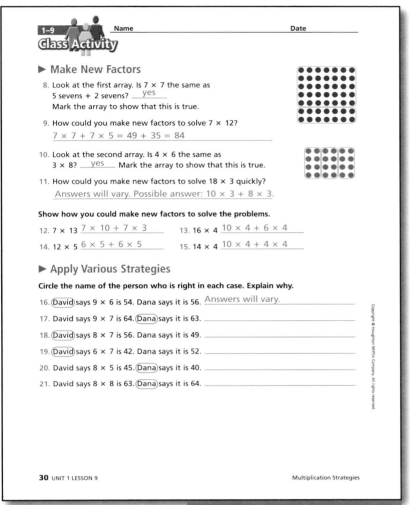

Student Activity Book page 30

The facsimile page shows:

1–9
Class Activity

Name _____ Date _____

▶ **Make New Factors**

8. Look at the first array. Is 7 × 7 the same as 5 sevens + 2 sevens? __yes__
Mark the array to show that this is true.

9. How could you make new factors to solve 7 × 12?
7 × 7 + 7 × 5 = 49 + 35 = 84

10. Look at the second array. Is 4 × 6 the same as 3 × 8? __yes__ Mark the array to show that this is true.

11. How could you make new factors to solve 18 × 3 quickly?
Answers will vary. Possible answer: 10 × 3 + 8 × 3.

Show how you could make new factors to solve the problems.

12. 7 × 13   7 × 10 + 7 × 3   13. 16 × 4   10 × 4 + 6 × 4
14. 12 × 5   6 × 5 + 6 × 5   15. 14 × 4   10 × 4 + 4 × 4

▶ **Apply Various Strategies**

Circle the name of the person who is right in each case. Explain why.

16. (David) says 9 × 6 is 54. Dana says it is 56. Answers will vary.
17. David says 9 × 7 is 64. (Dana) says it is 63. _____
18. (David) says 8 × 7 is 56. Dana says it is 49. _____
19. (David) says 6 × 7 is 42. Dana says it is 52. _____
20. David says 8 × 5 is 45. (Dana) says it is 40. _____
21. David says 8 × 8 is 63. (Dana) says it is 64. _____

30 UNIT 1 LESSON 9   Multiplication Strategies

Student Activity Book page 30

▶ Make New Factors [WHOLE CLASS]

This activity builds on the previous activity. Once students realize that they can add or subtract one more factor to a known product, the door opens for making new factors in other ways. As the class discusses the work on these problems, be aware that there are other ways of making new factors than those shown on the student page facsimile. For example, 7 × 7 can be seen as 6 × 7 + 1 × 7 or 3 × 7 + 4 × 7. Some students may make new factors based on products they are familiar with.

▶ Apply Various Strategies [WHOLE CLASS]

Students have a wide variety of strategies to use as they discuss problems 16–21 on page 30. They can mention various ways of making new factors in order to build from the known to the unknown. Other special strategies are also shown in the answers on the student page. Let this be a relatively free discussion in which students share their own strategies for dealing with these more difficult problems.

🕐 **25 MINUTES**

Goal: Discuss strategies that involve regrouping factors to find a product and apply various strategies to specific multiplication situations.

Materials: Student Activity Book, page 30

 NCTM Standards:
Number and Operations
Communication

Teaching Note

Properties of Multiplication The Distributive property of multiplication will be taught formally later in this unit, along with the Commutative and Associative properties. Students encounter all of these properties in various contexts throughout the unit before being introduced to them by name. Right now the essential thing is for students to see that making new factors (distributivity) is a potential solution strategy.

✔ Ongoing Assessment

During the discussion of problems 8–15, you can informally assess students' ability to ungroup and regroup factors as they work toward finding unknown products. Be sure that students understand that they should only break apart one factor and then multiply both parts by the other factor.

② Extending the Lesson

Going Further: The Guess and Check Strategy

Goal: Discuss and use the Guess and Check problem-solving strategy.

Materials: Student Activity Book pages 31–32

✓ **NCTM Standard:**
Problem Solving

▶ Guess and Check [PAIRS]

Lead the whole class through the top of page 31. Then students work in pairs to fill out the table and discuss the way Samuel solved the problem. Help students to see that the result of each guess should help to make the next guess better. Samuel's first guess had the correct sum, but not the correct product. He got the correct product with his next guess, but had the wrong sum. His last guess had both the correct product and the correct sum.

Have students continue working in pairs on problems 1–3. When everyone is done, use the Math Talk Solve and Discuss method (see page xix) to go over these problems.

After students write their own problems for exercise 4, they can exchange with a partner and solve each other's problems.

1–9 Going Further

Name _____ **Date** _____

▶ Guess and Check

When you don't know how to think about solving a problem, you may want to guess an answer and check whether it is correct. You may have to guess more than once.

Samuel wanted to solve this problem: The product of two numbers is 24. Their sum is 11. What are the numbers?

Samuel decided to guess and check. He made this table to keep track of his guesses. When the answer to both "Check" questions is *yes*, Samuel will know he has found the answer. Complete the table to see how Samuel's guesses led to the answer.

First Guess: 6 and 5	Second Guess: 6 and 4	Third Guess: 8 and 3
Product: ___30___	Product: ___24___	Product: ___24___
Sum: ___11___	Sum: ___10___	Sum: ___11___
Check:	Check:	Check:
Is the product 24? __no__	Is the product 24? __yes__	Is the product 24? __yes__
Is the sum 11? __yes__	Is the sum 11? __no__	Is the sum 11? __yes__

Use Guess and Check to solve each problem.   *Show your work.*

1. Together, Joan and Paul have 17 model cars. Joan has 5 more than Paul. How many cars does Paul have?
   <u>6 cars</u>

2. Beth and Ned have 24 trading cards altogether. Beth has twice as many as Ned. How many cards does Ned have?
   <u>8 cards</u>

3. The sum of 3 numbers is 10. Their product is 30. What are the numbers? <u>2, 3, and 5</u>

4. **On the Back** Write a problem that can be solved using Guess and Check. Show how to solve it.
   Answers will vary.

UNIT 1 LESSON 9   Multiplication Strategies **31**

Student Activity Book page 31

The Learning Classroom

Helping Community When stronger math students finish their work early, let them help others who may be struggling. Students like to take on this role and enjoy helping each other. This helps these students who may otherwise become bored as they wait to challenge themselves by explaining math content.

Intervention

for students having difficulty

PAIRS

Two Ways to See Multiplication

Provide practice with understanding multiplication as repeated addition. Have students make tables that show a product and how it can be expressed as a sum of one of its factors. Choose products that are easy to represent at first. Then move students towards the more difficult products.

4 x 2	
4 + 4	
4 x 3	
4 + 4 + 4	
4 x 4	
4 + 4 + 4 + 4	

 Math Writing Prompt

Intervention

Explain Your Thinking
Tell why 5 × 3 is the same as 3 + 3 + 3 + 3 + 3. Use words, numbers, or drawings.

On Level

for students having success

PAIRS

3 Different Ways

One partner will choose the factors for an unknown product. The other partner will name a known product with one of its factors. Then they will work together to show at least 2 ways to find the unknown product using the known product.

> Unknown Product:
> 8 x 8
> Known Product:
> 8 x 5 = 40
>
> Way 1:
> 8 x 8 = 40 + 8 + 8 + 8 = 64
>
> Way 2:
> 8 x 5 + 8 x 5 – 8 – 8 = 64

 Math Writing Prompt

On Level

Why Different Ways Are Important
Tell why it is important to know different ways to use a product you know to find a product that you don't know. Give an example that shows your thinking.

Challenge

for students seeking a challenge

PAIRS

How Many Different Ways?

Students choose a known product and its factors, and make 5 other products from the known product. Suggest that they try to do each one a different way. For each one, they tell how they made the new product from the known product.

> Known Product: 3 x 7 = 21
>
> New Product 1: 6 x 7 = 42
> 6 is 2 x 3, so I added 21 + 21.
>
> New Product 2: 9 x 7 = 63
> 9 is 3 more than 6, so I added the results of 3 x 7 = 21 and 6 x 7 = 42 to get 63.
>
> New Product 3: 3 x 8 = 24
> 3 x 8 will be 3 more than 3 x 7, so I added 3 to 21.

 Math Writing Prompt

Challenge

Use a Known Product
Show how you can use 3 × 3 = 9 to find 9 × 9 = 81. Explain your thinking for each step you take.

 **Homework and Cumulative Review**

Homework and Cumulative Review

1-9
Homework **Goal:** Additional Practice

✓ You can quickly review this homework to assess how well the class understands how to regroup factors to find new products.

1-9
Remembering **Goal:** Cumulative Review

This Remembering activity would be appropriate anytime after this lesson.

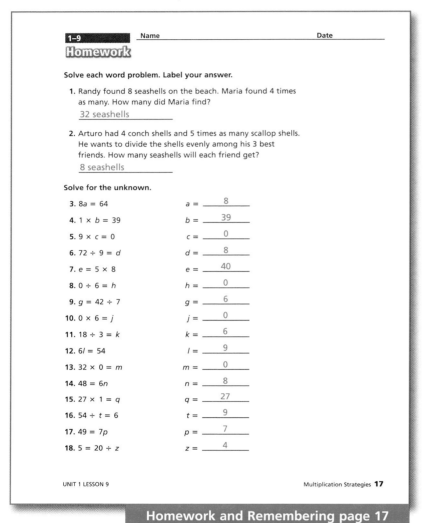

1-9   Name   Date
Homework

Solve each word problem. Label your answer.

1. Randy found 8 seashells on the beach. Maria found 4 times as many. How many did Maria find?
   <u>32 seashells</u>

2. Arturo had 4 conch shells and 5 times as many scallop shells. He wants to divide the shells evenly among his 3 best friends. How many seashells will each friend get?
   <u>8 seashells</u>

Solve for the unknown.

3. $8a = 64$ $a = \underline{8}$
4. $1 \times b = 39$ $b = \underline{39}$
5. $9 \times c = 0$ $c = \underline{0}$
6. $72 \div 9 = d$ $d = \underline{8}$
7. $e = 5 \times 8$ $e = \underline{40}$
8. $0 \div 6 = h$ $h = \underline{0}$
9. $g = 42 \div 7$ $g = \underline{6}$
10. $0 \times 6 = j$ $j = \underline{0}$
11. $18 \div 3 = k$ $k = \underline{6}$
12. $6l = 54$ $l = \underline{9}$
13. $32 \times 0 = m$ $m = \underline{0}$
14. $48 = 6n$ $n = \underline{8}$
15. $27 \times 1 = q$ $q = \underline{27}$
16. $54 \div t = 6$ $t = \underline{9}$
17. $49 = 7p$ $p = \underline{7}$
18. $5 = 20 \div z$ $z = \underline{4}$

UNIT 1 LESSON 9   Multiplication Strategies **17**

Homework and Remembering page 17

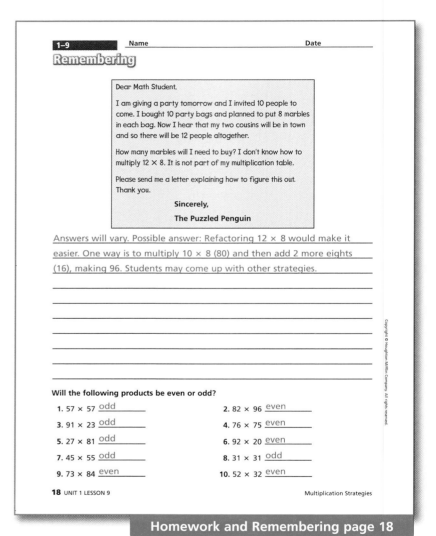

1-9   Name   Date
Remembering

Dear Math Student,

I am giving a party tomorrow and I invited 10 people to come. I bought 10 party bags and planned to put 8 marbles in each bag. Now I hear that my two cousins will be in town and so there will be 12 people altogether.

How many marbles will I need to buy? I don't know how to multiply 12×8. It is not part of my multiplication table.

Please send me a letter explaining how to figure this out. Thank you.

     Sincerely,

     The Puzzled Penguin

<u>Answers will vary. Possible answer: Refactoring 12×8 would make it</u>
<u>easier. One way is to multiply 10×8 (80) and then add 2 more eights</u>
<u>(16), making 96. Students may come up with other strategies.</u>

Will the following products be even or odd?

1. 57×57 <u>odd</u>   2. 82×96 <u>even</u>
3. 91×23 <u>odd</u>   4. 76×75 <u>even</u>
5. 27×81 <u>odd</u>   6. 92×20 <u>even</u>
7. 45×55 <u>odd</u>   8. 31×31 <u>odd</u>
9. 73×84 <u>even</u>   10. 52×32 <u>even</u>

18 UNIT 1 LESSON 9   Multiplication Strategies

Homework and Remembering page 18

Home or School Activity

 Math-to-Math Connection

Greatest Product Game This game can be played with two or more players. Use index cards to make two sets of number cards, each with a digit from 0–9. The first player shuffles the cards and deals 3 cards to each person in the group. Players must try to find the greatest product that is the sum of two cards multiplied by the third card. The player with the highest product keeps his or her cards.

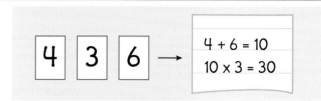

The other players put their cards back into the deck. Repeat the game until there are not enough cards to deal to everyone. The player with the most cards is the winner.

A variation of the game would be to find the least product: find the difference of two cards and multiply the difference by the third card.

Multiplication and Division Practice

Lesson Objectives

- Increase the speed and accuracy of division.
- Assess multiplication and division skills.

The Day at a Glance

Today's Goals	Materials	Math Talk
Quick Practice Practice basic multiplication.	Student Activity Book pages 33–46	In today's activities, the students are involved in discussion as they
① Teaching the Lesson A1: Use special materials to practice division. A2: Take multiplication and division quizzes and correct mistakes.	Division Cards Targets Crayons or markers	▶ share strategies for division problems
② Extending the Lesson ▶ Differentiated Instruction	Scissors Factor Field	▶ take multiplication and division quizzes to find out what they need to practice
③ Homework and Cumulative Review	Homework and Remembering pages 19–20 Math Journals	

Quick Practice

🕐 **5 MINUTES**   **Goal:** Practice basic multiplication.

Difficult Finger Factors Send three student leaders to the front. Two leaders will give factors from 6 to 10 by raising fingers on both hands and saying the number out loud. The third leader gives the hand signal, and the class responds with the product of the two factors. Repeat with other numbers.

Teaching the Lesson

Division Practice

 30 MINUTES

Goal: Use special materials to practice division.

Materials: Division Cards, Student Activity Book page 33

✔ **NCTM Standard:**
Number and Operations

Differentiated Instruction

Special Needs Some students may have a great number of division cards to practice. Have these students work with a helper. Have them focus on learning the easier problems first.

Have students share strategies for finding or remembering their more difficult divisions. Discuss how to use multiplication to do division.

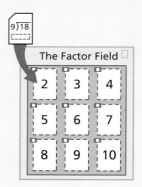

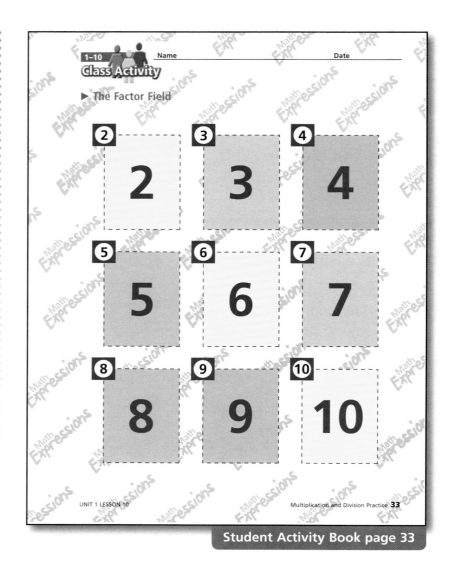

> **Student Activity Book page 33**

▶ The Factor Field INDIVIDUALS

Every student should have a set of Division Cards on pages 35–44 and a copy of the *Factor Field* on page 33. Have everyone mix up the cards and place them so the sides without the answers are face up. (The slanted corners of the cards will line up.)

Students read each problem and then place the card on the Factor Field in the section that corresponds to the answer. If students do not know an answer quickly, they should put the card aside.

When all the cards have been placed, students should confirm correct placement by picking up the cards in each section and turning them over to reveal the answers are all the same.

If any cards were misplaced, they should be added to the pile to study later. Students should study these cards and then put the cards on the Factor Field again.

Diagnostic Quizzes

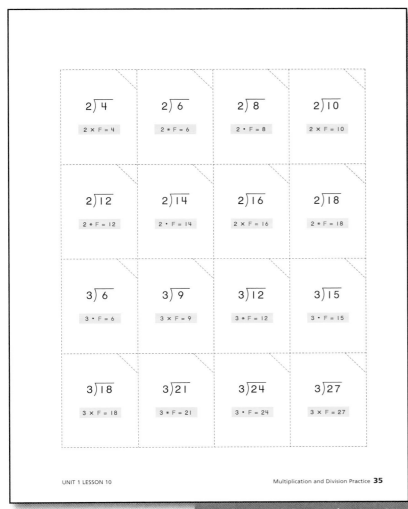

▶ Multiplication Quiz [INDIVIDUALS]

Tell the class that they will take a multiplication and a division quiz today to help them find out what they need to practice. The quizzes will not be graded. The multiplication quiz is on page 45 of the Student Activity Book. Tell students to wait until you give a signal to start and then to work quickly. If they do not immediately know the answer to a problem, they should move on. They will not have much time to stop and "figure out" answers. This is a quiz to see what they know automatically. If there is time at the end, they can go back to any unfinished problems and try to work them out.

Allow only *3 minutes* for this quiz.

Read the answers out loud and have students circle their own mistakes.

Activity continued ▶

 25 MINUTES

Goal: Take multiplication and division quizzes and correct mistakes.

Materials: Student Activity Book pages 35–36, Targets

 NCTM Standard:
Number and Operations

Multiplication and Division Practice **65**

① Teaching the Lesson (continued)

Activity 2

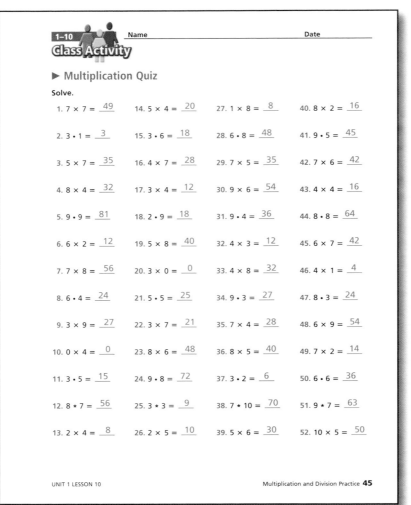

Student Activity Book page 45

Student Activity Book page 46

The page 45 worksheet shows:

1–10 Class Activity

▶ **Multiplication Quiz**

Solve.

1. 7 × 7 = 49
2. 3 • 1 = 3
3. 5 × 7 = 35
4. 8 × 4 = 32
5. 9 • 9 = 81
6. 6 × 2 = 12
7. 7 × 8 = 56
8. 6 • 4 = 24
9. 3 × 9 = 27
10. 0 × 4 = 0
11. 3 • 5 = 15
12. 8 * 7 = 56
13. 2 × 4 = 8
14. 5 × 4 = 20
15. 3 • 6 = 18
16. 4 × 7 = 28
17. 3 × 4 = 12
18. 2 • 9 = 18
19. 5 × 8 = 40
20. 3 × 0 = 0
21. 5 • 5 = 25
22. 3 × 7 = 21
23. 8 × 6 = 48
24. 9 • 8 = 72
25. 3 * 3 = 9
26. 2 × 5 = 10
27. 1 × 8 = 8
28. 6 • 8 = 48
29. 7 × 5 = 35
30. 9 × 6 = 54
31. 9 • 4 = 36
32. 4 × 3 = 12
33. 4 × 8 = 32
34. 9 • 3 = 27
35. 7 × 4 = 28
36. 8 × 5 = 40
37. 3 • 2 = 6
38. 7 * 10 = 70
39. 5 × 6 = 30
40. 8 × 2 = 16
41. 9 • 5 = 45
42. 7 × 6 = 42
43. 4 × 4 = 16
44. 8 • 8 = 64
45. 6 × 7 = 42
46. 4 × 1 = 4
47. 8 • 3 = 24
48. 6 × 9 = 54
49. 7 × 2 = 14
50. 6 • 6 = 36
51. 9 * 7 = 63
52. 10 × 5 = 50

UNIT 1 LESSON 10   Multiplication and Division Practice **45**

The page 46 worksheet shows:

1–10 Class Activity

▶ **Division Quiz**

Solve.

1. 24 ÷ 8 = 3
2. 56 / 7 = 8
3. 35 ÷ 5 = 7
4. $\frac{32}{4}$ = 8
5. 81 ÷ 9 = 9
6. 64 / 8 = 8
7. 30 ÷ 6 = 5
8. $\frac{72}{9}$ = 8
9. 0 ÷ 4 = 0
10. 27 / 3 = 9
11. 15 ÷ 5 = 3
12. $\frac{12}{4}$ = 3
13. 49 ÷ 7 = 7
14. 18 ÷ 3 = 6
15. $\frac{12}{3}$ = 4
16. 18 ÷ 9 = 2
17. 40 / 5 = 8
18. 42 ÷ 6 = 7
19. $\frac{25}{5}$ = 5
20. 21 ÷ 3 = 7
21. 24 / 4 = 6
22. 35 ÷ 7 = 5
23. $\frac{2}{2}$ = 1
24. 28 ÷ 4 = 7
25. 9 / 3 = 3
26. 80 ÷ 8 = 10
27. 6 ÷ 1 = 6
28. 27 / 9 = 3
29. 63 ÷ 7 = 9
30. $\frac{8}{2}$ = 4
31. 6 ÷ 6 = 1
32. 42 / 7 = 6
33. 36 ÷ 4 = 9
34. $\frac{28}{7}$ = 4
35. 20 ÷ 4 = 5
36. 36 / 9 = 4
37. 21 ÷ 7 = 3
38. $\frac{15}{3}$ = 5
39. 54 ÷ 6 = 9
40. 45 ÷ 9 = 5
41. $\frac{0}{2}$ = 0
42. 16 ÷ 4 = 4
43. 36 / 6 = 6
44. 32 ÷ 8 = 4
45. $\frac{72}{8}$ = 9
46. 24 ÷ 3 = 8
47. 54 / 9 = 6
48. 10 ÷ 5 = 2
49. $\frac{18}{6}$ = 3
50. 56 ÷ 8 = 7
51. 63 / 9 = 7
52. 48 ÷ 6 = 8

46 UNIT 1 LESSON 10   Multiplication and Division Practice

 Ongoing Assessment

Have students:

▶ explain how 54 ÷ 6, 45 ÷ 5, and 72 ÷ 8 are alike.

▶ find 32 ÷ 4 and check it by multiplying.

 Class Management

Looking Ahead In tonight's homework students will be writing multiplication or division word problems that may be used for practice at a later date.

▶ Division Quiz [INDIVIDUALS]

The division quiz is found on page 46 of the Student Activity Book. Again, tell the class to wait until you give a signal to start and then to work quickly. Allow *3 minutes* for this quiz. Again, read the answers out loud and ask students to circle their mistakes.

When students have finished correcting the division quiz, ask them to compare the answers they missed on the multiplication quiz with the ones they missed on the division quiz. Do they see any relationship? Often students who miss a problem such as 9 × 6 will also miss 54 ÷ 9 and 54 ÷ 6.

Give the students a few minutes to practice the problems they missed with their Target. Students who did not make any mistakes can begin their homework or practice to get faster.

② Extending the Lesson

Intervention
for students having difficulty

INDIVIDUALS

Division Arrays

Materials: crayons or markers

Give each student some crayons or markers. Write these numbers on the board:

54, 48, 42, 64, and 56

Tell the students to:

- Choose one of the numbers and draw an array for that number.
- Circle equal groups in the array.
- Write a division for their drawing.

$$48 \div 8 = 6 \text{ or } 48 \div 6 = 8$$

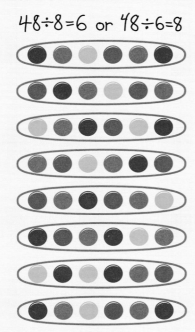

On Level
for students having success

PAIRS

Cover the Field

Materials: Division Cards (one set), Factor Field (1 per student)

The Division Cards should be mixed up and placed in a stack. The side without the answer should be facing up (the slanted corners will line up).

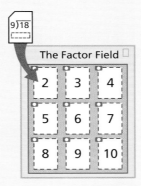

Players take turns drawing a card, reading the problem out loud, giving the answer, and then checking it. If the answer is correct, that player places the card on the Factor Field in the section that corresponds to the answer. Multiple cards can be stacked in any section. If a student gives a wrong answer, the card goes to the bottom of the stack and is not placed on the Factor Field. The first student to "cover the field" wins the game.

Challenge
for students seeking a challenge

PAIRS

Finding Prime Factors

Write these facts about prime numbers on the board:

A prime number is a counting number greater than 1 whose only factors are 1 and itself. Some prime numbers are:

2, 3, 5, 7, 11, 13, 17, 19, 23

Show students how to use a factor tree to factor a number into its prime factors:

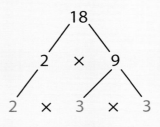

$$18 = 2 \times 3 \times 3$$

Ask students to factor these numbers into their prime factors:

10, 26, 33, 40, and 42

 Math Writing Prompt

Intervention

Explain Your Thinking

Explain how you can use equal groups to solve basic division. Draw a picture if needed.

 Math Writing Prompt

On Level

Work Backward

Explain how basic multiplications can be used to find answers to basic divisions. Give an example.

 Math Writing Prompt

Challenge

Think Beyond

If a number is not prime, and it has 17 as a prime factor, can that number be less than 34? Explain.

③ Homework and Cumulative Review

Homework **Goal:** Additional Practice

✓ Use this Homework page to provide students with more practice with multiplication and division.

Remembering **Goal:** Cumulative Review

This Remembering Activity would be appropriate any time after today's lesson.

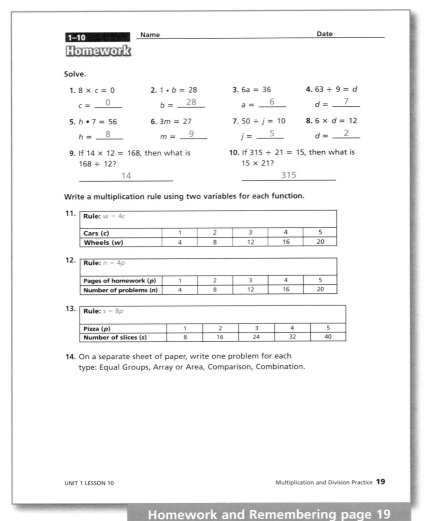

1–10
Homework Name ____ Date ____

Solve.

1. $8 \times c = 0$
$c = \underline{0}$

2. $1 \cdot b = 28$
$b = \underline{28}$

3. $6a = 36$
$a = \underline{6}$

4. $63 \div 9 = d$
$d = \underline{7}$

5. $h \cdot 7 = 56$
$h = \underline{8}$

6. $3m = 27$
$m = \underline{9}$

7. $50 \div j = 10$
$j = \underline{5}$

8. $6 \times d = 12$
$d = \underline{2}$

9. If $14 \times 12 = 168$, then what is $168 \div 12$?
_____ 14 _____

10. If $315 \div 21 = 15$, then what is 15×21?
_____ 315 _____

Write a multiplication rule using two variables for each function.

11. **Rule:** $w = 4c$

Cars (c)	1	2	3	4	5
Wheels (w)	4	8	12	16	20

12. **Rule:** $n = 4p$

Pages of homework (p)	1	2	3	4	5
Number of problems (n)	4	8	12	16	20

13. **Rule:** $s = 8p$

Pizza (p)	1	2	3	4	5
Number of slices (s)	8	16	24	32	40

14. On a separate sheet of paper, write one problem for each type: Equal Groups, Array or Area, Comparison, Combination.

UNIT 1 LESSON 10
Multiplication and Division Practice **19**

Homework and Remembering page 19

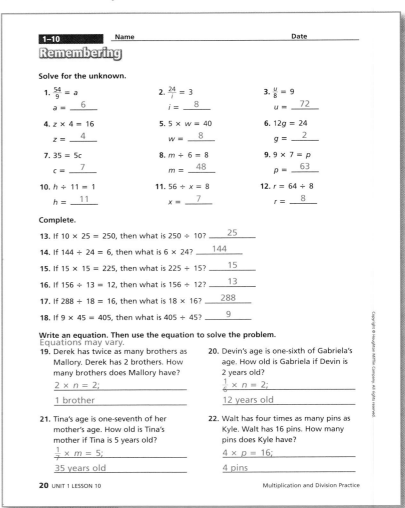

1–10
Remembering Name ____ Date ____

Solve for the unknown.

1. $\frac{54}{9} = a$
$a = \underline{6}$

2. $\frac{24}{i} = 3$
$i = \underline{8}$

3. $\frac{u}{8} = 9$
$u = \underline{72}$

4. $z \times 4 = 16$
$z = \underline{4}$

5. $5 \times w = 40$
$w = \underline{8}$

6. $12g = 24$
$g = \underline{2}$

7. $35 = 5c$
$c = \underline{7}$

8. $m \div 6 = 8$
$m = \underline{48}$

9. $9 \times 7 = p$
$p = \underline{63}$

10. $h \div 11 = 1$
$h = \underline{11}$

11. $56 \div x = 8$
$x = \underline{7}$

12. $r = 64 \div 8$
$r = \underline{8}$

Complete.

13. If $10 \times 25 = 250$, then what is $250 \div 10$? ___25___

14. If $144 \div 24 = 6$, then what is 6×24? ___144___

15. If $15 \times 15 = 225$, then what is $225 \div 15$? ___15___

16. If $156 \div 13 = 12$, then what is $156 \div 12$? ___13___

17. If $288 \div 18 = 16$, then what is 18×16? ___288___

18. If $9 \times 45 = 405$, then what is $405 \div 45$? ___9___

Write an equation. Then use the equation to solve the problem.
Equations may vary.

19. Derek has twice as many brothers as Mallory. Derek has 2 brothers. How many brothers does Mallory have?
$2 \times n = 2;$
1 brother

20. Devin's age is one-sixth of Gabriela's age. How old is Gabriela if Devin is 2 years old?
$\frac{1}{6} \times n = 2;$
12 years old

21. Tina's age is one-seventh of her mother's age. How old is Tina's mother if Tina is 5 years old?
$\frac{1}{7} \times m = 5;$
35 years old

22. Walt has four times as many pins as Kyle. Walt has 16 pins. How many pins does Kyle have?
$4 \times p = 16;$
4 pins

20 UNIT 1 LESSON 10
Multiplication and Division Practice

Homework and Remembering page 20

Home or School Activity

 Science Connection

Drinking Water Many health experts recommend that we drink a certain amount of water every day. One easy-to-remember recommendation is 8 eight-ounce glasses a day.

Suppose a person drinks 64 ounces of water in one day. Have students find out how many cups, pints, and quarts are equivalent to 64 ounces. Suggest that students use the library or Internet to find other recommendations. How much would that be in a week? a year?

LIQUID MEASURE		
8 oz	=	1 cup
16 oz	=	1 pint
32 oz	=	1 qt

Write Word Problems

Lesson Objectives

- Write and share solutions to multiplication and division word problems.
- Consolidate single-digit multiplications and corresponding divisions in a variety of contexts.

Vocabulary
factor
product

The Day at a Glance

Today's Goals	Materials	Math Talk
Quick Practice Practice basic multiplication.	Quick Practice materials	In today's activities, the students are involved in discussion as they

❶ **Teaching the Lesson**
A1: Share and solve word problems written for homework.
A2: Practice multiplication by solving Scrambled Multiplication Tables.
	Student Activity Book
	  pages 47–48
	Quick Quiz (Assessment
	  Guide)
	Scissors
		▶ review types of multiplication and division word problems
		▶ determine missing factors and products using Scrambled Multiplication Tables

❷ **Extending the Lesson** ▶ Differentiated Instruction	Number cubes Timer or watch with second hand	
❸ **Homework and Cumulative Review**	Grid paper Crayons or markers Homework and Remembering pages 21–22 Math Journals	

Quick Practice

🕐 **5 MINUTES**   **Goal:** Practice basic multiplication.
Materials: Multiplication Poster

Multiplication in Motion Tell students that they need to remember their numbers. The students quickly count off from 2 to 10, repeating the sequence until every student in the class has a number. Then the student leader points to a product on the Multiplication Poster. Every student who has a number that is a factor of this product stands. Then, going in order, the standing students announce the factors. (Many numbers, such as 24, will have more than 2 possible factors.) Repeat with other products.

Teaching the Lesson

Word Problem Festival

 20 MINUTES

Goal: Share and solve word problems written for homework.

Materials: Student Activity Book page 47

✔ **NCTM Standards:**
Number and Operations
Problem Solving

 Class Management

Advance Preparation Try to discuss all four types of word problems in this activity. It will probably be necessary to prepare ahead of time by getting one problem of each type written on the board or an overhead transparency. Circulate around the room and try to enlist your volunteers ahead of time, looking at the word problems your students wrote, and identifying one of each type. When all four problems are written on the board or transparency, be sure to focus students' attention on one problem at a time.

1–11
Class Activity

Name _____ Date _____

▶ Share Solutions

Write 4 multiplication or division word problems for the class to solve. Write one problem for each of the 4 types shown below.

Equal Groups	Array or Area

Comparison	Combination

UNIT 1 LESSON 11   Write Word Problems **47**

Student Activity Book page 47

▶ **Share Solutions** WHOLE CLASS

Write Problems If you assigned the homework for lesson 10, students should use those problems for this lesson. They can write their solutions in the corresponding spaces on page 47.

If you did not assign the homework for Lesson 10, give students time to write a problem of each type on page 47.

Math Talk Ask a student volunteer to share a word problem. Invite several students to solve it at the board while the others work at their seats. Ask students to explain their solutions. All students should have written an appropriate equation and a labeled answer. After solving, have the students discuss what problem type they just solved (equal groups, array, area, comparison, or combinations).

Now ask someone to contribute a different kind of word problem, and repeat the same process. Eventually, examples of all four types should be included. (Include either an array or area; both types are not necessary.)

For some problems, either division or unknown multiplication (such as $7a = 35$) can be used. Try to elicit both methods.

Scrambled Tables

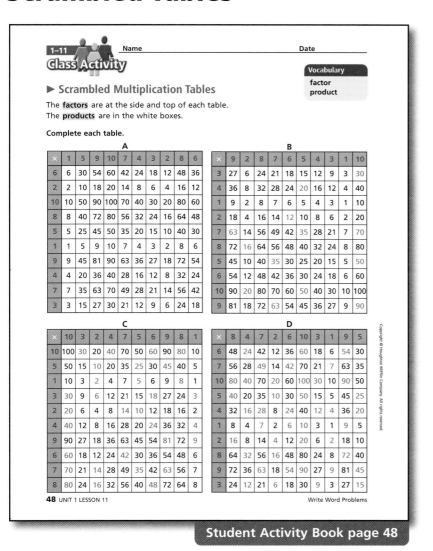

Student Activity Book page 48

 35 MINUTES

Goal: Practice multiplication by solving Scrambled Multiplication Tables.

Materials: Student Activity Book page 48

 NCTM Standards:
Number and Operations
Reasoning and Proof

Differentiated Instruction

Extra Help If students have trouble getting started on Table A, suggest the following strategy:

Locate the product 1 in the table. Its factors can only be 1 and 1, so write the factor 1 in the shaded portion for that column and that row.

Now look at this row of products:

1, 5, 9, 10, 7, 4, 3, 2, 8, 6

The missing factors in the shaded row at the top of the table must be the same:

1, 5, 9, 10, 7, 4, 3, 2, 8, 6

A similar strategy can be used to find the missing factors in the shaded column on the left.

Activity continued ▶

1 Teaching the Lesson (continued)

Activity 2

The Learning Classroom

Helping Community Continue to create a classroom where students are not competing, but desire to collaborate and help one another. Communicate often that your goal as a class is for everyone to understand the math you are studying. Tell students that this will require everyone to work together to help each other. Assign helping partners to students as needed.

Quick Quiz

See Assessment Guide for Unit 1 Quick Quiz 2.

Ongoing Assessment

Have students write a multiplication problem for:

► equal groups.

► array.

► area.

► comparison.

► combination.

► Scrambled Multiplication Tables INDIVIDUALS

Have everyone look at Table A on page 48 of the Student Activity Book. Review the terms *factor* and *product*. Explain that in a *scrambled* multiplication table, the rows and the columns have been moved around, but that each row and column still shows all the products for some factors. Ask the class to label each column and row with the correct factor. Allow the students to work alone for a minute and then go over the missing factors.

Table B has a few missing products along with the missing factors. Allow students to work alone for a minute. Then, ask the class to share some strategies for figuring out the factors. Many students will start by locating some of the easy multiplications, such as the 10s row and column and the 1s row and column. Make sure everyone has caught on to the basic process. Then, allow the class to finish Table B.

As students finish Table B, have them check to see that their table is correct by multiplying some factors together, just as they would with a regular Multiplication Table. (The intersection of a row and column gives the product of those two factors.)

Now have everyone work alone to finish Tables C and D. If any students are confused, either work with them or give them each a helping partner.

② Extending the Lesson

Activities for Individualizing

Intervention
for students having difficulty
PAIRS

Mixed-Up Multiplication

Materials: scissors

Tell each student to write a different set of multiplications on the same sheet of paper (such as 7s by one student and 9s by the partner). When all multiplications are recorded, each student cuts the paper between multiplications to make strips. One student takes a strip, covers up either the product or one of the factors, and the partner gives the missing number.

Students take turns, choosing strips and posing missing number problems to the partner.

1	x	7	=	7
2	x	7	=	14
3	x	7	=	21
4	x	7	=	28
5	x	7	=	35
6	x	7	=	42
7	x	7	=	49
8	x	7	=	56
9	x	7	=	63
10	x	7	=	70

On Level
for students having success
SMALL GROUPS

Fast Multiplication

Materials: 2 number cubes labeled 1–6, timer or watch with a second hand

Divide students into groups of three or more. One student is the timer. A second student tosses the number cubes. These are tossed one at a time to determine a two-digit product. For example, if a 3 and then a 6 are tossed, the product is 36. The students have 20 seconds to write as many multiplications as they can for the product. At the end of 20 seconds, the multiplications are checked for correctness. Students take turns timing and tossing cubes.

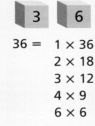

$$36 = \begin{array}{l} 1 \times 36 \\ 2 \times 18 \\ 3 \times 12 \\ 4 \times 9 \\ 6 \times 6 \end{array}$$

Challenge
for students seeking a challenge
INDIVIDUALS

Multiplication Patterns

Materials: grid paper, crayons or markers

Give each student a sheet of grid paper and several markers or crayons. Tell the students to color one square on the grid paper. Next, use a different color for all of the surrounding squares. Continue this step several times, using a different color on each repetition. Write a multiplication to show the number of squares for each color. Find a pattern for your multiplications.

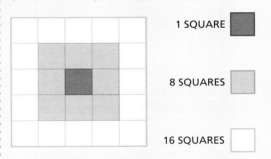

1 SQUARE

8 SQUARES

16 SQUARES

The pattern after the first square is 8, 16, 24, 32, 40, 48...
1×8=8, 2×8=16, 3×8=24, 4×8=32,...

Students may repeat the activity using a row of two squares or some other configuration to start.

 Math Writing Prompt

Intervention

Define Terms
Write a sentence using the words *multiply*, *factor*, and *product*.

 Math Writing Prompt

On Level

Word Problems
Write an equal groups problem. Then, solve the problem.

 Math Writing Prompt

Challenge

Use Patterns
Describe how you could create your own scrambled multiplication table.

③ Homework and Cumulative Review

 **Homework** **Goal:** Additional Practice

✓ Use this Homework page to provide students with more practice with multiplication and division.

 **Remembering** **Goal:** Cumulative Review

This Remembering Activity would be appropriate anytime after today's lesson.

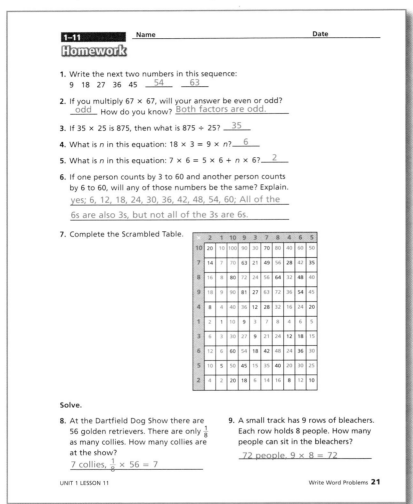

1-11 Homework Name ____ Date ____

1. Write the next two numbers in this sequence:
9 18 27 36 45 __54__ __63__

2. If you multiply 67 × 67, will your answer be even or odd? __odd__ How do you know? __Both factors are odd.__

3. If 35 × 25 is 875, then what is 875 ÷ 25? __35__

4. What is n in this equation: $18 \times 3 = 9 \times n$? __6__

5. What is n in this equation: $7 \times 6 = 5 \times 6 + n \times 6$? __2__

6. If one person counts by 3 to 60 and another person counts by 6 to 60, will any of those numbers be the same? Explain.
__yes; 6, 12, 18, 24, 30, 36, 42, 48, 54, 60; All of the__
__6s are also 3s, but not all of the 3s are 6s.__

7. Complete the Scrambled Table.

Solve.

8. At the Dartfield Dog Show there are 56 golden retrievers. There are only $\frac{1}{8}$ as many collies. How many collies are at the show?
__7 collies, $\frac{1}{8} \times 56 = 7$__

9. A small track has 9 rows of bleachers. Each row holds 8 people. How many people can sit in the bleachers?
__72 people, $9 \times 8 = 72$__

UNIT 1 LESSON 11 — Write Word Problems **21**

Homework and Remembering page 21

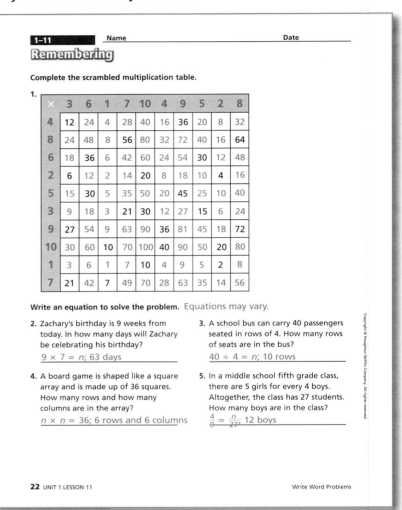

1-11 Remembering Name ____ Date ____

Complete the scrambled multiplication table.

1.

×	3	6	1	7	10	4	9	5	2	8
4	12	24	4	28	40	16	36	20	8	32
8	24	48	8	56	80	32	72	40	16	64
6	18	36	6	42	60	24	54	30	12	48
2	6	12	2	14	20	8	18	10	4	16
5	15	30	5	35	50	20	45	25	10	40
3	9	18	3	21	30	12	27	15	6	24
9	27	54	9	63	90	36	81	45	18	72
10	30	60	10	70	100	40	90	50	20	80
1	3	6	1	7	10	4	9	5	2	8
7	21	42	7	49	70	28	63	35	14	56

Write an equation to solve the problem. Equations may vary.

2. Zachary's birthday is 9 weeks from today. In how many days will Zachary be celebrating his birthday?
__$9 \times 7 = n$; 63 days__

3. A school bus can carry 40 passengers seated in rows of 4. How many rows of seats are in the bus?
__$40 \div 4 = n$; 10 rows__

4. A board game is shaped like a square array and is made up of 36 squares. How many rows and how many columns are in the array?
__$n \times n = 36$; 6 rows and 6 columns__

5. In a middle school fifth grade class, there are 5 girls for every 4 boys. Altogether, the class has 27 students. How many boys are in the class?
__$\frac{4}{9} = \frac{n}{27}$; 12 boys__

22 UNIT 1 LESSON 11 — Write Word Problems

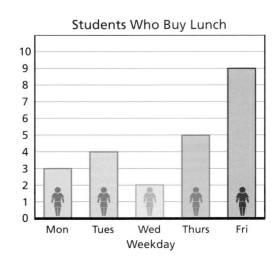

Homework and Remembering page 22

Home or School Activity

 Math-to-Math Connection

Class Data Have students collect data about their class, such as buying lunch or traveling to school. Then have students choose a way to display the data. They might choose a table, graph, or other graphic representation. Next, tell students to write 2 conclusions about the data. Challenge them to use multiplication or division in their comparisons.

Students Who Buy Lunch

Equations With Parentheses

Lesson Objectives

- Understand everyday applications of multiplication and division.
- Generate and solve algebraic equations that involve grouping with parentheses.

Vocabulary

equation
parentheses

The Day at a Glance

Today's Goals	Materials	Math Talk
Quick Practice Practice basic multiplication. **1 Teaching the Lesson** A1: Use parentheses to group numbers in an equation. A2: Solve word problems with mixed operations by writing the corresponding equations. **2 Extending the Lesson** ▶ Going Further ▶ Differentiated Instruction **3 Homework and Cumulative Review**	Quick Practice Materials Class Multiplication Table Poster Student Activity Book pages 49–50 Markers Homework and Remembering pages 23–24 Math Journals	In today's activities, students are involved in discussion as they: ▶ explain the use of parentheses ▶ describe various strategies for solving problems

Quick Practice

5 MINUTES   **Goal:** Practice basic multiplication.
Materials: pointer, Class Multiplication Table Poster

Multiplication in Motion The students quickly count off from 2 to 10, repeating the sequence until every student in the class has a number. Then the student leader points to a product on the Class Multiplication Table Poster in the medium or difficult sections of the table. Every student who has a number that is a factor of this product stands. Then, going in order, the standing students announce the factors. Repeat with the other products.

Teaching the Lesson

Introduce Parentheses

 20 MINUTES

Goal: Use parentheses to group numbers in an equation.

Materials: Student Activity Book page 49

✔ **NCTM Standards:**
Algebra
Communication

The Learning Classroom

Math Talk Aspire to make your classroom a place where all students listen to understand one another. Explain to students that this is different than just being quiet when someone else is talking. This involves thinking about what a person is saying so that you could explain it yourself or help them explain it more clearly. Also, students need to listen so that they can ask a question or help the explainer. Listening can also help them learn more about a concept.

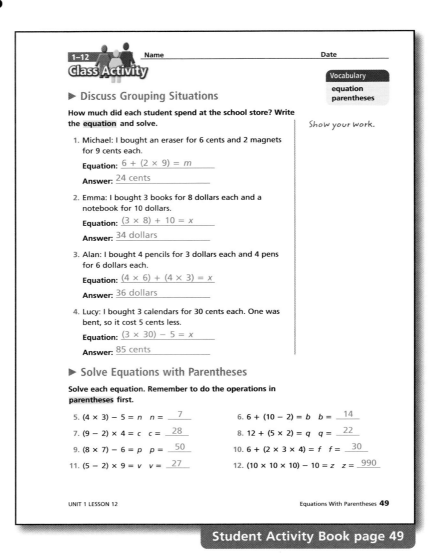

Student Activity Book page 49

▶ **Discuss Grouping Situations** WHOLE CLASS

Ask students to look at problem 1 on page 49. Have them discuss Michael's purchases and write the equation that corresponds with this situation. Invite one or two students to work at the board. They will likely write: $m = 6 + (2 \times 9)$.

Let students solve the equation and compare results. They should discover that there could be two different answers, depending on which operation they do first. (If they add $6 + 2 = 8$ and then multiply that result by 9, they will get 72. If they multiply $2 \times 9 = 18$ and add that result to 6, they will get 24.) Which one is right? If they read the word problem again, it should be clear that the answer is 24 cents.

Use Parentheses Explain that parentheses can be used to group the numbers in an equation. The parentheses tell us which operations to do first. They are removed after the operation inside them is performed. The equation is written and solved this way:

$$6 + (2 \times 9) = m$$
$$6 + 18 = 24$$

Repeat this procedure for Emma's purchases. Ask students to write an equation that uses parentheses for grouping. Again, invite several students to work at the chalkboard. During the discussion be sure to explain that the second equation is the simplified version.

$$(3 \times 8) + 10 = e$$
$$24 + 10 = 34 \text{ cents}$$

Then have students write equations for Alan's and Lucy's purchases and solve them. Note that the equation for Alan's purchases requires two sets of parentheses and that Lucy's situation involves subtraction rather than addition.

Alan: $(4 \times 3) + (4 \times 6) = a$
 $12 + 24 = 36 \text{ cents}$

Lucy: $(3 \times 30) - 5 = l$
 $90 - 5 = 85 \text{ cents}$

▶ Solve Equations With Parentheses WHOLE CLASS

Most of the equations in exercises 5–12 can be solved quickly. Ask students to give the simplified version of the equation orally, and then you can write it on the board. After that they can give the answer orally. For example, in the first problem, students would call out "12 minus 5 equals *n*." After you write that simplified equation on the board, they would call out "*n* = 7." This procedure reinforces the two-step process: simplifying (by doing the step inside the parentheses) and then solving.

Teaching Note

Math Background It may be helpful to understand the difference between an expression and an equation. An expression can be a number, a variable or unknown represented by a letter, or any combination of numbers, variables, operation signs, and grouping symbols. An equation is a number sentence with an equals sign, showing that two expressions are equal. Knowing how to use parentheses as a grouping symbol is a key skill in algebra, so it is important that your students get a good start on this topic.

Activity 2

Multi-Step Word Problems

 25 MINUTES

Goal: Solve word problems with mixed operations by writing the corresponding equations.

Materials: Student Activity Book page 50

 NCTM Standards:
Problem Solving
Algebra

Ongoing Assessment

Check student understanding of the use of parentheses to set up problems by observing students at work on the problems on Student Activity Book page 50. Be sure that they choose the right numbers to group as they analyze the problems.

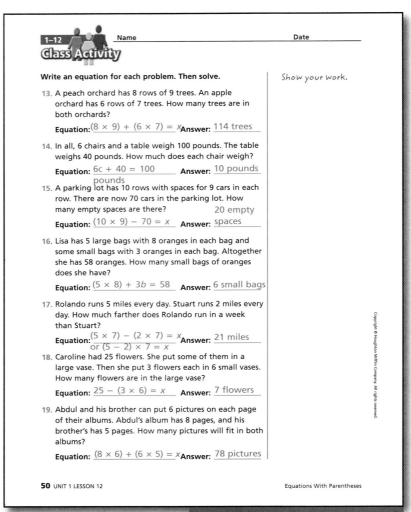

Student Activity Book page 50

►Use Parentheses to Solve Complex Word Problems INDIVIDUALS

Ask students to write an equation for each word problem before solving it on page 50. In most cases the equation will need to be simplified before it can be solved. Learning how to write these equations is just as important as finding the answer.

Be sure students write an algebraic equation with a letter for the unknown quantity, not just an expression. Afterwards, discuss each problem. There may be more than one way to approach some problems. Ask volunteers to show and explain their work.

② Extending the Lesson

Intervention
for students having difficulty

`PAIRS`

Two Ways With Parentheses

Provide students with pairs of expressions with the same numbers and operations, but different positions for the parentheses. Have students work in pairs to evaluate the pairs of expressions and see how their values differ. This will help students focus on why it is important to carry out the operations inside the parentheses first.

$$(4 + 3) \times 2 \qquad (10 - 3) \times 2$$
$$4 + (3 \times 2) \qquad 10 - (3 \times 2)$$

$$(6 \times 5) - 4 \qquad (8 \times 4) - 3$$
$$6 \times (5 - 4) \qquad 8 \times (4 - 3)$$

On Level
for students having success

`SMALL GROUPS`

Shopping Spree

Materials: large sheets of paper, markers

The group decides whether to run a bake sale, a farmers' market, or a garage sale. Then students work together to make a chart of the items that will be sold along with their prices in dollars. Each student has $25 to spend and writes an equation to show the total cost of his or her purchases. The goal is to spend exactly $25.

Farmers' Market	
Bunch of Carrots	$2
Bag of Spinach	$3
Basket of Apples	$4
Watermelon	$5
Basket of Pears	$6
Bunch of Radishes	$1
Pound of Potatoes	$2
Pound of Tomatoes	$4
Quart of Raspberries	$7

$$(2 \times 5) + (3 \times 6) + 7 = 25$$

Challenge
for students seeking a challenge

`INDIVIDUALS`

Is the Answer the Same?

Ask students to write an equation with five numbers without parentheses. Next, solve it using the order of operations rules and then rewrite and solve it four times using a set of parentheses in a different place each time. Have students check whether any of the answers are the same and explain why this is so.

$$a = 10 + 4 \times 5 - 3 \times 6$$
$$a = 12$$

$$a = (10 + 4) \times 5 - 3 \times 6$$
$$a = 52$$

$$a = 10 + (4 \times 5) - 3 \times 6$$
$$a = 12$$

$$a = 10 + 4 \times (5 - 3) \times 6$$
$$a = 58$$

$$a = 10 + 4 \times 5 - (3 \times 6)$$
$$a = 12$$

(You get the same answers when the parentheses go around numbers you work with first using order of operations.)

 Math Writing Prompt

Intervention

Explain Your Thinking

Write an equation for this situation: Add three to the product of four and five. Explain why you wrote it as you did.

 Math Writing Prompt

On Level

Reasoning Skills

Tell why it is important to use parentheses when you solve problems that have more than one step. Give an example that shows your reasoning.

 Math Writing Prompt

Challenge

The Same Answer

Think of an equation with three numbers that would have the same answer no matter where you put parentheses. Explain why it works.

③ Homework and Cumulative Review

1–12

Homework **Goal:** Additional Practice

✓ You can quickly review this homework to assess how well the class understands the use of parentheses.

1–12

Remembering **Goal:** Cumulative Review

This Remembering activity would be appropriate anytime after this lesson.

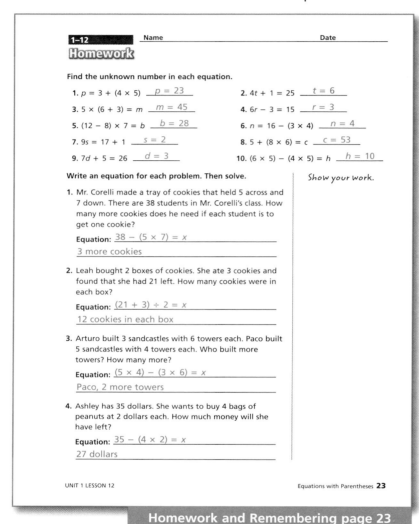

1–12 Name _____ Date _____

Homework

Find the unknown number in each equation.

1. $p = 3 + (4 \times 5)$ ___$p = 23$___   2. $4t + 1 = 25$ ___$t = 6$___

3. $5 \times (6 + 3) = m$ ___$m = 45$___   4. $6r - 3 = 15$ ___$r = 3$___

5. $(12 - 8) \times 7 = b$ ___$b = 28$___   6. $n = 16 - (3 \times 4)$ ___$n = 4$___

7. $9s = 17 + 1$ ___$s = 2$___   8. $5 + (8 \times 6) = c$ ___$c = 53$___

9. $7d + 5 = 26$ ___$d = 3$___   10. $(6 \times 5) - (4 \times 5) = h$ ___$h = 10$___

Write an equation for each problem. Then solve. *Show your work.*

1. Mr. Corelli made a tray of cookies that held 5 across and 7 down. There are 38 students in Mr. Corelli's class. How many more cookies does he need if each student is to get one cookie?

   Equation: $38 - (5 \times 7) = x$
   3 more cookies

2. Leah bought 2 boxes of cookies. She ate 3 cookies and found that she had 21 left. How many cookies were in each box?

   Equation: $(21 + 3) \div 2 = x$
   12 cookies in each box

3. Arturo built 3 sandcastles with 6 towers each. Paco built 5 sandcastles with 4 towers each. Who built more towers? How many more?

   Equation: $(5 \times 4) - (3 \times 6) = x$
   Paco, 2 more towers

4. Ashley has 35 dollars. She wants to buy 4 bags of peanuts at 2 dollars each. How much money will she have left?

   Equation: $35 - (4 \times 2) = x$
   27 dollars

UNIT 1 LESSON 12   Equations with Parentheses **23**

Homework and Remembering page 23

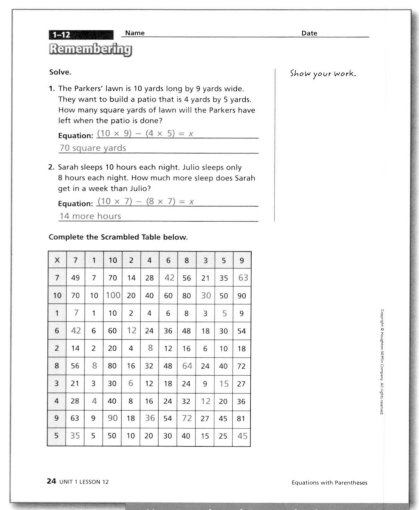

1–12 Name _____ Date _____

Remembering

Solve. *Show your work.*

1. The Parkers' lawn is 10 yards long by 9 yards wide. They want to build a patio that is 4 yards by 5 yards. How many square yards of lawn will the Parkers have left when the patio is done?

   Equation: $(10 \times 9) - (4 \times 5) = x$
   70 square yards

2. Sarah sleeps 10 hours each night. Julio sleeps only 8 hours each night. How much more sleep does Sarah get in a week than Julio?

   Equation: $(10 \times 7) - (8 \times 7) = x$
   14 more hours

Complete the Scrambled Table below.

X	7	1	10	2	4	6	8	3	5	9
7	49	7	70	14	28	42	56	21	35	63
10	70	10	100	20	40	60	80	30	50	90
1	7	1	10	2	4	6	8	3	5	9
6	42	6	60	12	24	36	48	18	30	54
2	14	2	20	4	8	12	16	6	10	18
8	56	8	80	16	32	48	64	24	40	72
3	21	3	30	6	12	18	24	9	15	27
4	28	4	40	8	16	24	32	12	20	36
9	63	9	90	18	36	54	72	27	45	81
5	35	5	50	10	20	30	40	15	25	45

24 UNIT 1 LESSON 12   Equations with Parentheses

Homework and Remembering page 24

Home or School Activity

Language Arts Connection

Parentheses and Punctuation Just as parentheses tell what order to do operations in an equation, punctuation helps to make the meaning of a sentence clear. Quotation marks and commas let the reader know who said or did something. Write the following sentence on the board.

> Jacob said Caleb likes to play soccer.

Ask students to decide whether Jacob or Caleb likes to play soccer and then add punctuation that makes the meaning clear. Ask students to write more sentences that can be punctuated in different ways to mean different things. Challenge students to write a sentence that needs parentheses to make its meaning clear.

"Jacob," said Caleb, "likes to play soccer."

Jacob said, "Caleb likes to play soccer."

Combinations and Comparisons

Vocabulary

combination
Associative
   Property
Commutative
   Property

Lesson Objective

● Solve multiple combination and comparison problems.

The Day at a Glance

Today's Goals	Materials	123 Math Talk
Quick Practice Practice basic multiplication.	Quick Practice materials	In today's activities, the students are involved in discussion as they
❶ **Teaching the Lesson** **A1:** Represent and solve combination problems that have more than two factors. **A2:** Solve comparison word problems that have misleading language.	Student Activity Book pages 51–52 index cards (optional) Counters Number cubes	► solve problems with combinations ► solve problems with comparisons
❷ **Extending the Lesson** ► Differentiated Instruction	Grid paper MathBoard materials	
❸ **Homework and Cumulative Review**	Homework and Remembering pages 25–26 Math Journals	

Quick Practice

 5 MINUTES   **Goal:** Practice basic multiplication.
   Material: Multiplication Poster

Multiplication in Motion The students count off from 2 to 10, repeating the sequence until every student has a number. Then the student leader points to a product on the Multiplication Poster. Again, the leader points only to products that are in the difficult section. Every student who has a number that is a factor of this product stands. Then, going in order, the standing students announce the factors. Repeat with other products.

Teaching the Lesson

Problems With Multiple Combinations

 25 MINUTES

Goal: Represent and solve combination problems that have more than two factors.

Materials: Student Activity Book page 51

✔ **NCTM Standards:**
Number and Operations
Algebra
Problem Solving
Data Analysis and Probability

The Learning Classroom

Math Talk Always start by eliciting student ideas about a new topic. Students will increase their engagement in classes if they believe that their contributions will be heard. This may involve allowing for interruptions from students during teacher explanations of content. The teacher continues to decide what is important to continue exploring, but allows students to "own" new ideas or strategies. Often students come up with and explain strategies that the teacher was about to teach.

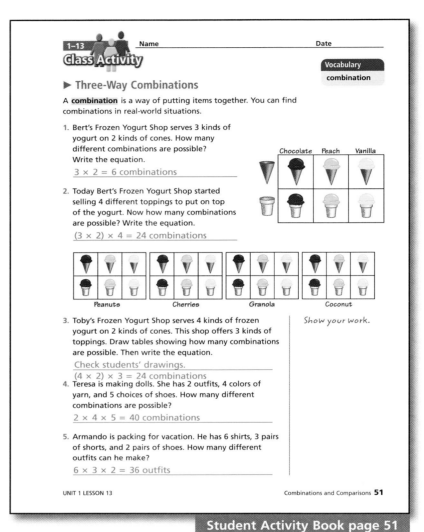

Student Activity Book page 51

▶ Three-Way Combinations WHOLE CLASS

Have students solve the problems on page 51. For the first problem, you can find the number of combinations by using two factors: $3 \times 2 = 6$. The second problem adds another element—different toppings. Because each of the 6 different cones can now have 4 different toppings, the expression from problem 1 gets multiplied by 4. Write the equation on the board: $(3 \times 2) \times 4 = 24$. Check to be sure that students understand.

Students can draw tables like the ones they just discussed to find the answer to problems. Have them draw *empty* tables (no pictures). They should discover that Toby's Frozen Yogurt Shop also offers 24 possible combinations.

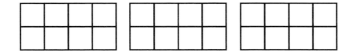

Write the equation that corresponds with this situation: $(4 \times 2) \times 3 = 24$.

Ask students if they notice anything interesting about the equations in problems 2 and 3. Help students see that the answer is the same even though the numbers are grouped differently: $(3 \times 2) \times 4$ has the same value as $(4 \times 2) \times 3$.

Remind students that the yogurt shops in problems 2 and 3 had the same number of total choices because the same three numbers were involved. The expressions $(3 \times 2) \times 4$ and $(4 \times 2) \times 3$ have the same value. Here the *Associative* and *Commutative Properties* were used.

▶ Practice With Combinations WHOLE CLASS

For problems 4–5 on page 51 of the Student Activity Book, students can multiply the numbers together to find the total number of combinations. They now know that parentheses are not necessary because the numbers can be multiplied in any order.

Sometimes a strategic choice can make the multiplication easier. The numbers in Problem 4, for example, are not given in the best order for multiplying. Discuss with students how these numbers could be reordered to make computation easier.

The Learning Classroom

Math Talk You can create math conversations by eliciting multiple strategies for solving problems. When you ask, "Did anyone solve this problem differently?" your students will pay greater attention to the work on the board because they will be comparing and contrasting it with their own math strategies. The comparisons and contrasts that result can naturally prompt significant math talk.

Teaching the Lesson (continued)

Comparison Problems With Misleading Language

 25 MINUTES

Goal: Solve comparison word problems that have misleading language.

Materials: Student Activity Book page 52, index cards (optional)

✔ **NCTM Standards:**
Number and Operations
Algebra

Differentiated Instruction

English Learners Review with students the meaning of the words *combination* and *comparison*.

► *Combination* refers to how items are put together or *combined*.

► *Comparison* refers to how items relate to one another or *compare*.

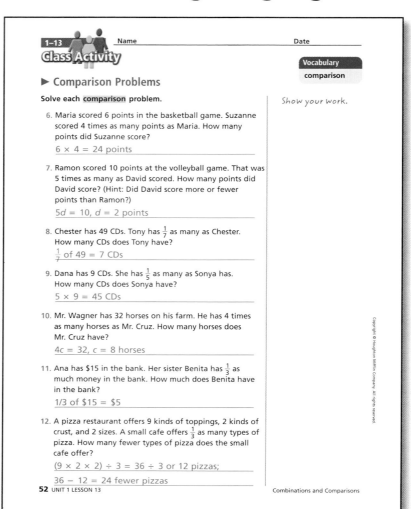

Student Activity Book page 52

► Comparison Problems WHOLE CLASS

Direct students' attention to problems 6 and 7 on page 52 of the Student Activity Book. These two problems look similar, but they are totally different. Problem 6 is a traditional multiplication comparison problem that students can probably solve easily. Problem 7 is likely to confuse many students if they do not read very carefully. Point out the hint given for problem 7.

● Ramon made 5 times as many points as David, so David made fewer points. If *d* represents David's points, then $5d = 10$ points and $d = 2$ points.

Use Comparison Bars The most difficult part of solving problems that have misleading comparisons is keeping track of who has more and who has less. Show students how to draw and label quick comparison bars to help them see Ramon's and David's points in Problem 7. They should not try to make the proportions accurate, but just make a quick sketch.

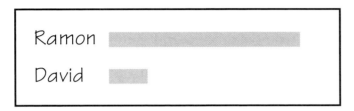

Now ask students to draw comparison bars to help them solve Problems 8 and 9.

8.

Chester

Tony

$\frac{1}{7}$ of 49 = 7 CDs

Tony has 7 CDs.

9.

Dana

Sonya

9 × 5 = 45 CDs

Sonya has 45 CDs.

Activity continued ▶

① Teaching the Lesson (continued)

Activity 2

Ask students to solve the remaining problems in this section. Invite several students to work at the board. Students may decide for themselves whether they want to use the comparison bars or not. In any case, they should explain how they decide who has the larger amount.

Some students may have difficulty with problem 12 because it is a combination *and* comparison problem. Tell students to find the number of combinations for the types of pizzas the restaurant offers, and then use that information in solving the comparison problem.

Writing Problems One way to know if students understand a problem type is to ask them to write a problem using a similar structure.

Have students write their own comparison and combination problems. They could write them on index cards with the answer on the back.

You could use these problems today or save them for another day. Ask a student to choose an index card and work the solution at the board. Then the student shares how he or she found the answer with the class. The class could ask questions about the method for solving or offer other ways to solve the problem. Then another student chooses a different problem.

This activity could also be done by students working in small groups or pairs. One student chooses a problem and shares the solution with the other students. Then another student in the group chooses a different problem.

These problems could also be done as a home activity. Students choose a problem that is not their own. Then they take it home and share their method of solving with a family member. When they return the next day, they could also share their method with the class.

② Extending the Lesson

Intervention
for students having difficulty
SMALL GROUPS

Many Times

Materials: counters, number cube

Have students take turns being the "caller" for their group. The caller forms a group of counters (less than 10) and the other students count the total. The caller then rolls a number cube, and uses that number to call out, "_____ times as many!" The rest of the students work together to make a model of that many counters.

For example, if the caller forms a group of 7 counters and rolls a 4, then he or she would call out, "4 times as many!" The rest of the students would then make 4 groups of 7 counters to get a total of 28 counters.

On Level
for students having success
PAIRS

Grid Combinations

Materials: grid paper

Show students how to outline congruent rectangles on grid paper to model this product: $3 \times 2 \times 4 = 24$

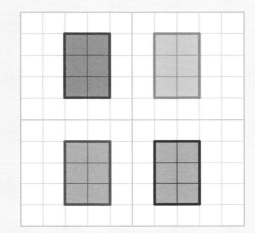

Have students verify that a total of 24 grid squares are outlined.

Then challenge students to use the same method to model that same product in two other ways.

Challenge
for students seeking a challenge
INDIVIDUALS

Tree Diagrams

Materials: MathBoard materials

On their MathBoards, have students show all of the ways that the digits 1, 2, and 3 can be combined to form a three-digit number. Tell students they can use each digit more than once.

A diagram with 1 in the hundreds place is shown below.

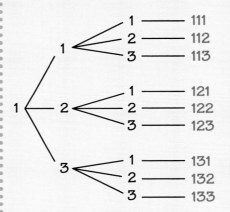

Challenge students to verify that a total of 27 three-digit numbers can be formed.

 Math Writing Prompt

Intervention

Explain Your Thinking
Why are parentheses not necessary in this multiplication?
$4 \times (5 \times 2)$

 Math Writing Prompt

On Level

Make a List
Create a menu with 2 drinks, 4 dinners, and 3 desserts. Then list all of the different ways for 1 drink, 1 dinner, and 1 dessert.

 Math Writing Prompt

Challenge

Create a Problem
Write a three-way combination problem.

**3** Homework and Cumulative Review

1–13
Homework **Goal:** Additional Practice

✓ Use this Homework page to provide students with more practice with combinations and comparisons.

1–13
Remembering **Goal:** Cumulative Review

This Remembering Activity would be appropriate anytime after today's lesson.

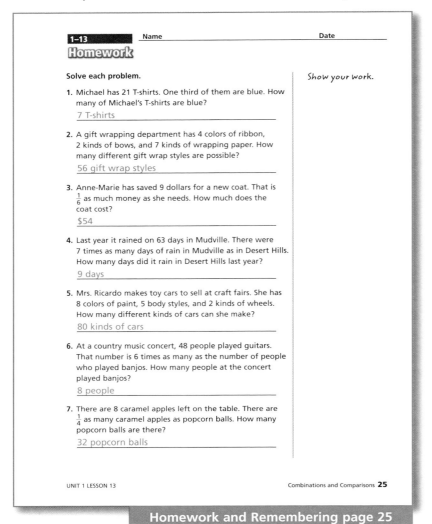

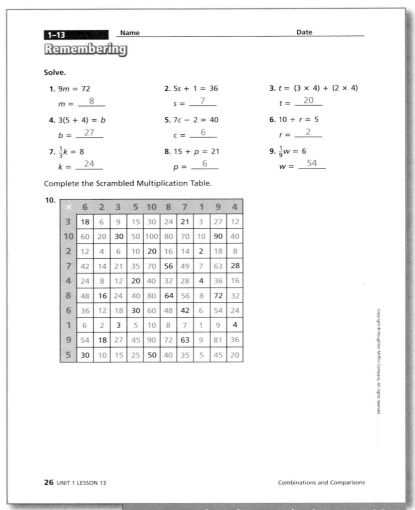

Homework and Remembering page 25

Homework and Remembering page 26

Home or School Activity

Language Arts Connection

Letters and Words Have your students look at an English dictionary. Ask, "Did you ever think that combining just 26 letters could make so many words?" Point out that some letters are used in more words than others. According to experts, E, T, and A are the most frequently used letters in the English language.

Tell your students to list all of the ways that the letters E, T, and A can be combined, using each letter once. They should try to identify which combinations are actual words and then use a dictionary to check.

Can you guess what English word is used **THE** most?

Practice With Factors

Lesson Objective

- **Find factors to solve puzzles that involve proportional relationships.**

The Day at a Glance

Today's Goals	Materials	Math Talk
Quick Practice Practice division.	Quick Practice Materials	In today's activities, the students are involved in discussion as they
① **Teaching the Lesson** **A1:** Find factors to solve puzzles that involve proportional relationships. **A2:** Practice finding factors.	Student Activity Book pages 53–58 Class Multiplication Table Poster Multiplication Tables	► review combinations and comparisons ► use proportional relationships to solve puzzles
② **Extending the Lesson** ► Differentiated Instruction	Small game token Index Cards	
③ **Homework and Cumulative Review**	Grid paper Scissors MathBoard materials Homework and Remembering pages 27–28 Math Journals	

Quick Practice

⏱ **5 MINUTES**   **Goal:** Practice division.
Materials: Set of Division Cards

Division in Motion The students count off from 2 to 10, repeating the sequence until every student in the class has a number. Then two student leaders take turns reading a division problem from the Division Cards. Every student whose assigned number is the answer stands. One student leader gives a hand signal and the standing students all say the answer in unison.

① Teaching the Lesson

Activity 1

Factor Puzzles

 30 MINUTES

Goal: Find factors to solve puzzles that involve proportional relationships.

Materials: Student Activity Book pages 53–54

 NCTM Standards:
Number and Operations
Algebra

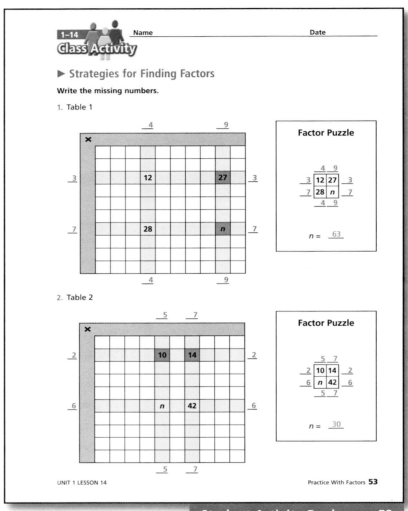

Student Activity Book page 53

▶ Strategies for Finding Factors WHOLE CLASS

Ask the class to look at Table 1 on page 53 of the Student Activity Book. This shows a part of the Multiplication Table. Work with the class to determine the row and column numbers and then fill in the eight blanks provided around the table. You may want to use the discussion points that follow.

Students can use count-bys to find the factors.

1. What count-by has 12 and 27? The 3s.
   Tell the students to write 3 in the pair of blanks to the left and right of that row.

2. What count-by has 12 and 28? The 4s.
   Tell the students to write 4 above and below that column.

3. What row are the 28 and *n* in? How do you know? We know that 28 is in the 4s column, so we can ask, "4 times what is 28?" The answer is 7. So, 28 and *n* must be in the 7s row.
   Tell the students to write 7 to the left and right of this row.

4. What column are the 27 and *n* in? How do you know? We know that 27 is in the 3s row, so we can ask, "3 times what is 27?" The answer is 9. So, 27 and *n* must be in the 9s column.
   Tell the students to write 9 above and below this column.

5. What number is *n*? How can we find out? Look at the numbers written on the outside of the table. *n* is in the 7s row and the 9s column. Multiply 7 × 9. So, *n* = 63.

6. On the Class Multiplication Table, circle the four numbers that make up this puzzle: 12 and 27 from Row 3; 28 and 63 from Row 7. Do they form a rectangle? yes What column are 12 and 28 in? column 4 What column are 27 and 63 in? column 9

7. Ask students to look at the Factor Puzzle next to Table 1. Have students solve this puzzle, using the same strategy they used when these numbers were in a larger table.

As students complete the puzzle, it doesn't matter if they work with the rows or columns first.

Give your students a few minutes to find the row and column numbers for Table 2. Then have them solve the Factor Puzzle next to it. Ask students to describe their strategies.

Activity continued ▶

Teaching Note

Math Background The Factor Puzzles not only enable students to practice multiplication and division, but also help them develop the ability to do proportional thinking. Proportional thinking will be emphasized when students learn about ratio and proportions in Unit 6. They will apply proportional thinking in Unit F when they explore similarity and scale drawings.

Activity 1

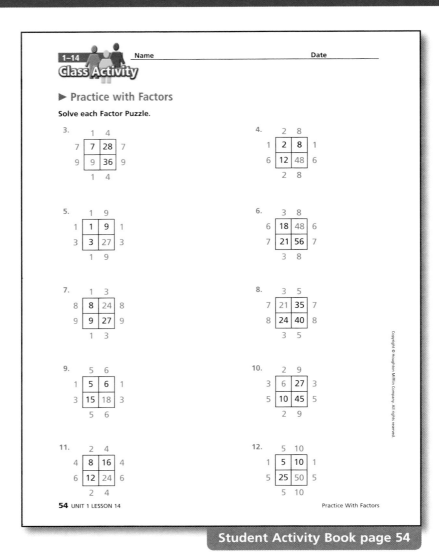

Student Activity Book page 54

▶ **Practice With Factors** INDIVIDUALS

Have the class turn to page 54 in the Student Activity Book. This page has more Factor Puzzles for the students to solve. Students can verify their work by finding the four cells on a Multiplication Table. Their answer is correct if the cells form a rectangle.

Students can use any factors they know to complete any puzzle. Write this puzzle on the board.

12	18
20	

- Name two factor pairs for 12 that are different from 1 and 12. 2 and 6, or 3 and 4. Choose one of those pairs. Write the factors outside one row and in one column.

```
        4
    ┌───────┬───────┐
  3 │  12   │  18   │ 3
    ├───────┼───────┤
    │  20   │       │
    └───────┴───────┘
        4
```

- 4 times what number = 20? 5 Write 5s outside the remaining row.

```
        4
    ┌───────┬───────┐
  3 │  12   │  18   │ 3
    ├───────┼───────┤
  5 │  20   │       │ 5
    └───────┴───────┘
        4
```

- 3 times what number = 18? 6 Write 6s outside the remaining column.

```
        4       6
    ┌───────┬───────┐
  3 │  12   │  18   │ 3
    ├───────┼───────┤
  5 │  20   │       │ 5
    └───────┴───────┘
        4       6
```

- The missing number is the product of which two numbers? 5 and 6 What is the missing number? 30 Write 30 in the box.

```
        4       6
    ┌───────┬───────┐
  3 │  12   │  18   │ 3
    ├───────┼───────┤
  5 │  20   │  30   │ 5
    └───────┴───────┘
        4       6
```

You could repeat these steps using 2 and 6. The missing number will always be 30.

Activity 2

Factor the Footprints

 30 MINUTES

Goal: Practice finding factors.

Materials: *Factor the Footprints* game board (Student Activity Book pages 55–58), small game token for each student

✔ **NCTM Standard:**
Number and Operations

Ongoing Assessment

Have students:

► determine what factors these numbers have in common: 12, 58, 72.

► explain how they found the common factors.

► Factor the Footprints PAIRS

Setting Up Divide the class into pairs. Each pair will need the *Factor the Footprints* game board. Each person will need a token of some kind. The students tape pages 55 and 57 together to make a game board as shown:

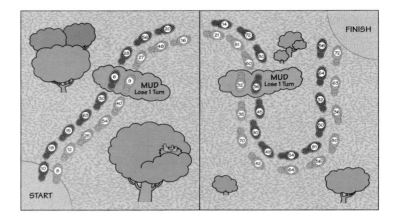

Game Rules One player will follow the trail of dark footprints, and the other will follow the trail of light footprints. Placing the marker on the first footprint, the first player names all the possible factor pairs for the number shown. The factor 1 is not permitted. The factors should be given in equation form, as in 3 × 6 = 18. The player moves forward one space for each correct equation named. The second player does the same, following a different trail. The first player to reach the Finish wins the game.

Playing the Game Player 1 has landed on a footprint marked 12. He says, "6 × 2 is 12 and 4 × 3 is 12." He has given 2 equations, so he moves ahead 2 spaces. (Reversing the order of the factors to produce another equation is not permitted.) It is now Player 2's turn. She has landed on a footprint marked 24. She says, "8 × 3 is 24 and 6 × 4 is 24." She also says, "12 × 2 is 24." Generating factors that are not part of the regular Multiplication Table is allowed, so she moves ahead 3 spaces.

Disputed Equations and Lost Turns If one player gives an equation that the other player believes to be incorrect, they can consult the Multiplication Table or check by using other strategies. A player who gives an incorrect equation loses that turn. Players who land in one of the two mud puddles on the board also lose a turn.

Have the pairs switch trails and play a second game if time permits.

② Extending the Lesson

Intervention
for students having difficulty
SMALL GROUPS

Factor Mix

Materials: index cards (9 per group)

Have students write the numbers 2, 3, 4, 6, 8, 12, and 24 on their index cards (one number per card). Of the two remaining cards, write a multiplication sign on one and an equals sign on the other. Students should then arrange their index cards to make as many multiplication equations as they can.

2	×	3	=	6
8	×	3	=	24

On Level
for students having success
PAIRS

Factor Grids

Materials: grid paper

Have pairs of students work together to outline rectangles on grid paper that model the factors of 6, 12, 15, and 16. For example, to model the factors of 6, students should draw different rectangles that cover exactly 6 grid squares. Have students write a multiplication equation for each rectangle model.

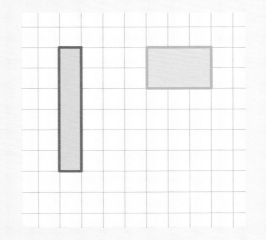

Challenge
for students seeking a challenge
INDIVIDUALS

Common Factors

Materials: MathBoard materials

Write the following pairs of numbers on the board.

24 and 32   12 and 20

30 and 18   36 and 42

Tell the students to list all the factors of each pair of numbers on their MathBoards. Then circle all the common factors for each pair. Challenge students to identify the two factors that are common to all eight numbers. (1 and 2)

24:	①	②	3	4	6	8	12	24
32:	①	②	4	8	16	32		

 Math Writing Prompt

Intervention
Write a Definition

Use the words *multiply* and *product* to explain what *factors* are.

 Math Writing Prompt

On Level
Explain Your Thinking

What number is a factor of every whole number? Why?

 Math Writing Prompt

Challenge
Write Number Clues

Choose any two-digit number. Then write three clues to describe that number. At least one of your clues should use the word *factor*. Challenge a partner to use the clues to name the number.

③ Homework and Cumulative Review

1-14
Homework **Goal:** Additional Practice

✔ Use this Homework page to provide students with more practice with basic proportional relationships.

1-14
Remembering **Goal:** Cumulative Review

This Remembering Activity would be appropriate any time after today's lesson.

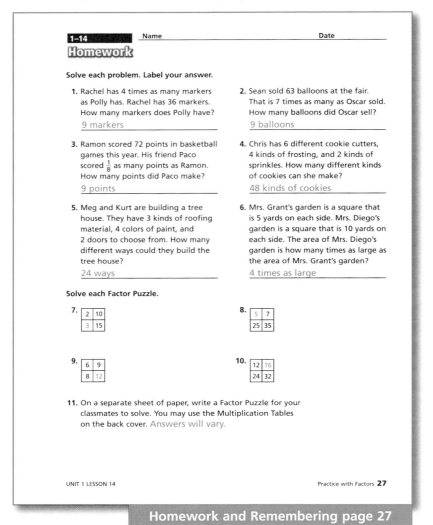

Homework and Remembering page 27

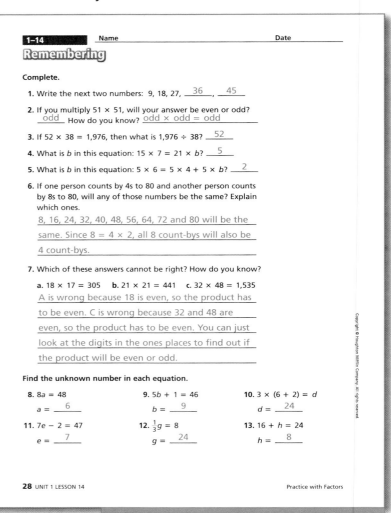

Homework and Remembering page 28

Home or School Activity

Science Connection

Herbivores and Carnivores In general, herbivores, animals that eat only plants, sleep less than carnivores, animals that eat only meat. Ask students to do research to find the names of some carnivores and herbivores and to see how long they sleep each day (on average).

Then ask students to calculate how many days it takes for each of their animals to sleep for a total of 24 hours.

DAILY SLEEPING HABITS	
Animal	**Number of Hours**
Cow	4 hours
Giraffe	2 hours
Horse	3 hours
Seal	6 hours
Tiger	16 hours

Multiple-Step Problems

Lesson Objectives

- Solve multiple-step problems involving equations with multiplication chains.
- Solve equations with several unknowns.

The Day at a Glance

Today's Goals	Materials	Math Talk
Quick Practice Practice division skills.	Quick Practice materials	In today's activities, the students are involved in discussion as they
1 Teaching the Lesson **A1:** Solve and discuss word problems with multiplication chains. **A2:** Solve equations that include algebraic expressions.	Student Activity Book pages 59–60 Counters Homework and Remembering pages 29–30 Math Journals	▶ explore comparison and multiplication chains ▶ solve equations with algebraic expressions at the class board
2 Extending the Lesson ▶ Differentiated Instruction		
3 Homework and Cumulative Review		

Quick Practice

🕐 **5 MINUTES**   **Goal:** Practice division skills.
Materials: Division Cards

Division in Motion The students count off from 2 to 10, repeating the sequence until everyone has a number. Then two student leaders take turns reading a division problem from the Division Cards. Every student whose number is the answer stands. One student leader gives a hand signal and the standing students all say the answer in unison.

Teaching the Lesson

Comparison Chains

 30 MINUTES

Goal: Solve and discuss word problems with multiplication chains.

Materials: Student Activity Book pages 59–60

✔ **NCTM Standards:**
Number and Operations
Algebra

Teaching Note

What to Expect From Students

Most students will not use parentheses and will instead write and solve the second equation shown at the right, 4 + 12 + 16 = 32 days. That is fine.

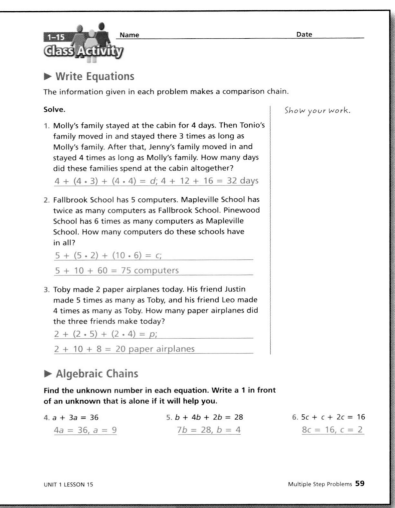

Student Activity Book page 59

▶ Write Equations WHOLE CLASS

Discuss the first two problems on page 59 of the Student Activity Book with the class. In each of these problems, students need to read carefully to determine which numbers are multiplied.

Problem 1 The original number (4 days) is multiplied each time.

4 + (4 × 3) + (4 × 4)
4 + 12 + 16 = 32 days

Problem 2 The comparison chain develops differently. The original number is multiplied to make the second number, and then the second number (*not* the original number) is multiplied to make the third number. Again, most students will not bother with the parentheses and will simply multiply as they go.

$5 + (5 \times 2) + (10 \times 6)$
$5 + 10 + 60 = 75$ computers

Problem 3 This problem is similar to problem 1, with the original number being multiplied each time.

$2 + 10 + 8 = 20$ paper airplanes

▶ Algebraic Chains WHOLE CLASS

Ask students to look at the equation in exercise 4 on page 59 of the Student Activity Book. How many times is the variable *a* being added altogether? 4 If your class has difficulty with this, give them another equation type that is familiar to them, such as $a + 4 = 12$. When *a* is by itself, it always means 1*a* (or $1 \times a$). Therefore, the first equation really means $1a + 3a$.

These equation chains can be solved in two steps. First, add all of the unknowns together. Then solve.

Problem 4 $a + 3a = 36$
or $1a + 3a = 36$
$4a = 36$, so $a = 9$

Problem 5 $b + 4b + 2b = 28$
or $1b + 4b + 2b = 28$
$7b = 28$, so $b = 4$

Problem 6 $5c + c + 2c = 16$
or $5c + 1c + 2c = 16$
$8c = 16$, so $c = 2$

Activity continued ▶

The Learning Classroom

Helping Community One reason that students are uncomfortable doing math work and thinking in public is that they may not be correct. You can help students change their perspective on errors. For example, you can respond to errors as opportunities for learning. You can model this for students as you make your own errors, by saying, "Oh, that's OK, I see what I did." Fixing your errors models a healthy approach for students.

Activity 1

Teaching Note

Watch for! Students may be inexperienced in creating algebraic equations to solve word problems. You may need to remind students that a variable w in isolation really means $1w$. So $w + 3w = 4w$.

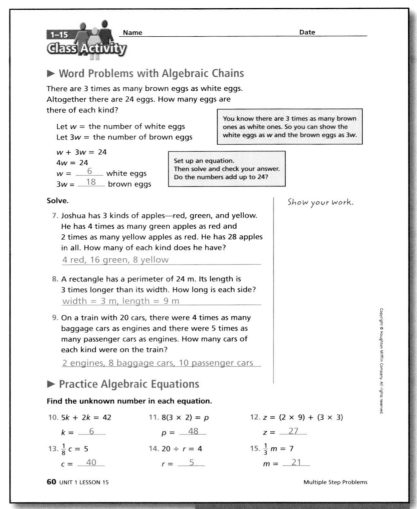

Student Activity Book page 60

▶ Word Problems With Algebraic Chains WHOLE CLASS

Have students look at the problem at the top of page 60. Work through the problem together. It will serve as a model for the other problems on this page.

These problems give the totals and the multipliers. To find each answer, students need to set up an algebraic equation with a variable for the first unknown quantity. Once they have found the first unknown quantity, they can find the others.

 **Math Talk**

Use Share and Discuss for exercises 7, 8, and 9. Give students an opportunity to share their ideas for using variables to represent the problem.

Remind them that finding the first unknown is not enough. They also need to go back and find the other answers.

Problem 7 $r + 4r + 2r = 28$
$7r = 28$
$r = 4$, so 4 red, 16 green, and 8 yellow apples

Problem 8 $w + 3w + w + 3w = 24$
$8w = 24$
$w = 3$, so the rectangle is 3 meters by 9 meters.
This equation could also be set up with parentheses:
$2(w + 3w) = 24$

Problem 9 $e + 4e + 5e = 20$
$10e = 20$
$e = 2$, so 2 engines, 8 baggage cars, and 10 passenger cars

Check Answers Remind students to add the separate answers in each problem to decide if they get the correct total. In the last problem, for example, they should add $2 + 8 + 10$ to see if they get 20, the total number of cars on the train. This is a good self-check.

Activity 2

Consolidation of Equations

▶ Practice Algebraic Equations [WHOLE CLASS]

Ask students to solve for the unknown quantity in each equation in Exercises 10–15 on page 60 of the Student Activity Book.

Invite some students to work at the classroom board.

Some students may have trouble with exercise 11: $8(3 \times 2) = p$. If so, remind them that $8(3 \times 2)$ is just like $8n$. It means the quantity in parentheses is taken 8 times, so it can be simplified to 8×6 or 48.

 20 MINUTES

Goal: Solve equations that include algebraic expressions.

Materials: Student Activity Book page 60

 NCTM Standards:
Number and Operations
Algebra

 Ongoing Assessment

Have students discuss:

▶ how to determine which number is multiplied to solve comparison chains.

▶ how to set up equations to solve word chains.

▶ how to self-check results from algebraic equations.

① Extending the Lesson

Going Further: Order of Operations

Write the two sentences shown below on the board. Be sure to include the quotation marks in each sentence you write.

> Jill said, "Amy is first in line."

> "Jill," said Amy, "is first in line."

Ask the students to compare the sentences.

- In the first sentence, who is speaking? Jill Who is first in line? Amy

- In the second sentence, who is speaking? Amy Who is first in line? Jill

Have students note that although the words in each sentence are identical, punctuation changes the meaning of the sentences.

Write the expression shown below on the board.

$$8 + 4 \div 2$$

Have students note that the expression contains two different operations, then ask:

- If you add first, then divide, what number does the expression simplify to? 6

- If you divide first, then add, what number does the expression simplify to? 10

Point out that only one answer is correct, and ask students to describe what additional information they might need to help decide which answer is correct. Lead their discussion to suggest when more than one operation is present, a set of rules is needed to help decide which operation is completed first.

Write the following rules on the board. As you write, ask the students to write the rules in their Math Journals.

Order of Operations

- Work inside parentheses.

- Multiply and divide, from left to right.

- Add and subtract, from left to right.

Have students look again at the expression $8 + 4 \div 2$ on the board. Ask:

- We said the expression could be simplified to 6 or to 10. Which is correct? 10 Why? The Order of Operations states that multiplication and division must be completed before addition and subtraction.

Write the expression $13 - 3 \cdot 2 + 5 = n$ on the board and have students apply the Order of Operations to simplify the expression and find the value of n.

$$13 - 3 \cdot 2 + 5 = n$$
$$13 - 6 + 5 = n$$
$$7 + 5 = n$$
$$12 = n$$

Encourage students to write a variety of numerical expressions such as those used in this activity, or lengthier expressions. Each expression should include at least one addition or subtraction and at least one multiplication or division. The students should simplify each expression they write, then exchange expressions and compare their answers with those of their classmates.

② Extending the Lesson

Intervention
for students having difficulty
SMALL GROUPS

Counter Chains

Materials: counters

Have students use counters to model the first three word problems on page 59.

4 counters for Molly's family

3 groups of 4 counters for Tonio's family

4 groups of 4 counters for Jenny's family

Then ask students to count the total number of counters to find the total number of days.

 Math Writing Prompt

Intervention

Write Comparison Sentences
Use the phrase "times as many" to write a sentence about your ears and toes.

On Level
for students having success
PAIRS

Guess and Check

Have students solve this problem using any method they choose.

Tyler is twice as old as Megan. Brandon is half as old as Tyler.

How old are Tyler and Brandon if Megan is 8 years old?

Equation:
m = 8
t = 2*m*
b = 2*m* ÷ 2

t = 2 • 8
Since Tyler is twice as old as Megan and Megan is 8, Tyler is 16.

b = 2 • 8 ÷ 2
Since Brandon is half as old as Tyler and Tyler is twice Megan's age, Brandon is 8.

 Math Writing Prompt

On Level

Write Your Own
Write a word problem for this equation:

$$n + 4n = 25$$

Challenge
for students seeking a challenge
INDIVIDUALS

Inverse Equations

Write this equation on the board:
$$5n + 7 = 22$$

Have students copy the equation and then use inverse operations to write two more equations that have the same solution. They should solve all three equations to verify that they all have the same solution.

$$5n + 7 = 22$$
$$5n = 22 - 7$$
$$7 = 22 - 5n$$

Students can repeat the activity, using these equations:

$$36 = 9f + 1$$
$$18 - 4p = 10$$

Math Writing Prompt

Challenge

Explain Your Thinking
Is the following true? How do you know?

$$4n + 3n + n = 6n + 2n$$

 # **3** **Homework and Cumulative Review**

Homework **Goal:** Additional Practice

✓ Include students' work for page 29 as part of their portfolios.

Remembering **Goal:** Cumulative Review

This Remembering Activity would be appropriate any time after today's lesson.

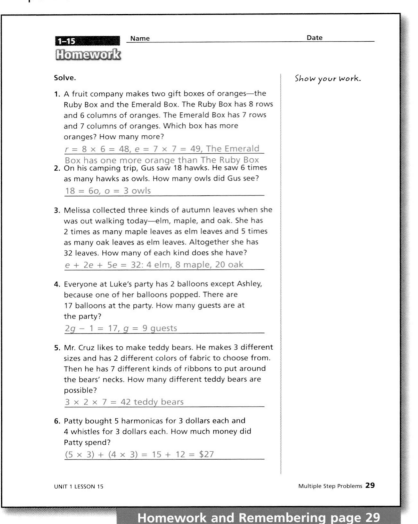

1–15 Name _____ Date _____
Homework

Solve. Show your work.

1. A fruit company makes two gift boxes of oranges—the Ruby Box and the Emerald Box. The Ruby Box has 8 rows and 6 columns of oranges. The Emerald Box has 7 rows and 7 columns of oranges. Which box has more oranges? How many more?
   $r = 8 \times 6 = 48$, $e = 7 \times 7 = 49$, The Emerald Box has one more orange than The Ruby Box

2. On his camping trip, Gus saw 18 hawks. He saw 6 times as many hawks as owls. How many owls did Gus see?
   $18 = 6o$, $o = 3$ owls

3. Melissa collected three kinds of autumn leaves when she was out walking today—elm, maple, and oak. She has 2 times as many maple leaves as elm leaves and 5 times as many oak leaves as elm leaves. Altogether she has 32 leaves. How many of each kind does she have?
   $e + 2e + 5e = 32$: 4 elm, 8 maple, 20 oak

4. Everyone at Luke's party has 2 balloons except Ashley, because one of her balloons popped. There are 17 balloons at the party. How many guests are at the party?
   $2g - 1 = 17$, $g = 9$ guests

5. Mr. Cruz likes to make teddy bears. He makes 3 different sizes and has 2 different colors of fabric to choose from. Then he has 7 different kinds of ribbons to put around the bears' necks. How many different teddy bears are possible?
   $3 \times 2 \times 7 = 42$ teddy bears

6. Patty bought 5 harmonicas for 3 dollars each and 4 whistles for 3 dollars each. How much money did Patty spend?
   $(5 \times 3) + (4 \times 3) = 15 + 12 = \$27$

UNIT 1 LESSON 15 Multiple Step Problems **29**

Homework and Remembering page 29

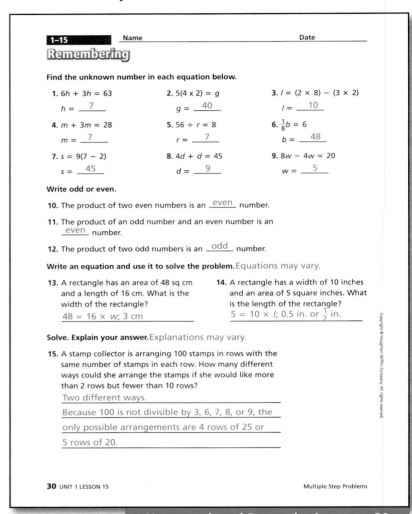

1–15 Name _____ Date _____
Remembering

Find the unknown number in each equation below.

1. $6h + 3h = 63$
   $h = \underline{7}$

2. $5(4 \times 2) = g$
   $g = \underline{40}$

3. $l = (2 \times 8) - (3 \times 2)$
   $l = \underline{10}$

4. $m + 3m = 28$
   $m = \underline{7}$

5. $56 \div r = 8$
   $r = \underline{7}$

6. $\frac{1}{8}b = 6$
   $b = \underline{48}$

7. $s = 9(7 - 2)$
   $s = \underline{45}$

8. $4d + d = 45$
   $d = \underline{9}$

9. $8w - 4w = 20$
   $w = \underline{5}$

Write odd or even.

10. The product of two even numbers is an <u>even</u> number.

11. The product of an odd number and an even number is an <u>even</u> number.

12. The product of two odd numbers is an <u>odd</u> number.

Write an equation and use it to solve the problem. Equations may vary.

13. A rectangle has an area of 48 sq cm and a length of 16 cm. What is the width of the rectangle?
    $48 = 16 \times w$; 3 cm

14. A rectangle has a width of 10 inches and an area of 5 square inches. What is the length of the rectangle?
    $5 = 10 \times l$; 0.5 in. or $\frac{1}{2}$ in.

Solve. Explain your answer. Explanations may vary.

15. A stamp collector is arranging 100 stamps in rows with the same number of stamps in each row. How many different ways could she arrange the stamps if she would like more than 2 rows but fewer than 10 rows?
    Two different ways.
    Because 100 is not divisible by 3, 6, 7, 8, or 9, the only possible arrangements are 4 rows of 25 or 5 rows of 20.

30 UNIT 1 LESSON 15 Multiple Step Problems

Homework and Remembering page 30

Home or School Activity

 ### Social Studies Connection

Number Systems As people worked with numbers and learned to count and do operations, they also invented math symbols.

Copy this table on the board.

Symbol	First Use
+, −	1498
=	1557
×	1637
÷	1659

Have your students copy it, make a time line, and write two equations that people in 1600 could write and two equations that they could not write.

History of Math Symbols

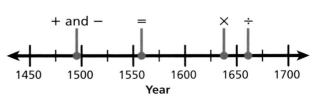

Properties of Multiplication

Vocabulary
Commutative Property
Associative Property
Distributive Property
expression
example
counterexample

Lesson Objective
- Analyze and apply the Commutative, Associative, and Distributive properties.

The Day at a Glance

Today's Goals	Materials	Math Talk
Quick Practice Practice division skills.	Quick Practice Materials	In today's activities, the students are involved in discussion as they
① **Teaching the Lesson** **A1:** Define and apply the Commutative, Associative, and Distributive Properties. **A2:** Prove or disprove whether the Commutative, Associative, and Distributive Properties apply to all operations.	Student Activity Book pages 61–64 Quick Quiz 3 (Assessment Guide Unit 1) Grid paper	▶ define the various properties of multiplication
② **Extending the Lesson** ▶ Differentiated Instruction	Homework and Remembering pages 31–32 Math Journals	▶ determine which properties apply to other operations
③ **Homework and Cumulative Review**		

Quick Practice

 5 MINUTES **Goal:** Practice division skills.
Materials: Division Cards

Division in Motion The students count off from 2 to 10, repeating the sequence until everyone has a number. Then two student leaders take turns reading a division problem from the Division Cards. Every student who has the number that is the answer stands. One student leader gives a hand signal and the standing students all say the answer in unison.

Teaching the Lesson

Explore Multiplication Properties

 30 MINUTES

Goal: Define and apply the Commutative, Associative, and Distributive Properties.

Materials: Student Activity Book pages 61–62

✔ **NCTM Standards:**
Number and Operations
Algebra

 Class Management

Are your students still directing their explanations to you rather than the other students? Remember to move to the side or the back of the room and direct the class from there. Also, you should not do all the talking. Pause after posing a question and wait for students to answer. Ask, "Why do you think this is so?" rather than giving all the explanations. Soon the students will learn to start questioning themselves. Many teachers find that this is their most difficult challenge, but that it really pays off when they succeed.

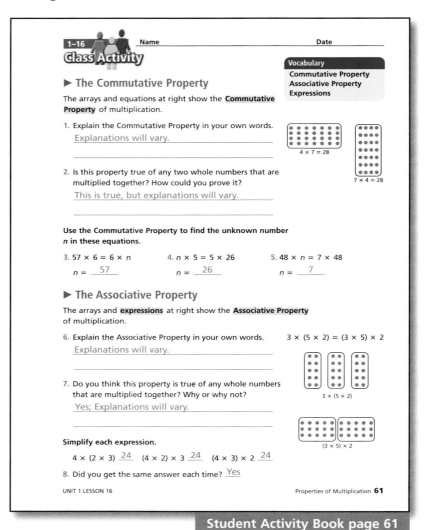

Student Activity Book page 61

▶ The Commutative Property WHOLE CLASS

The three properties discussed in this lesson have already been introduced in various problem-solving situations, but they have not been identified by name. Since your students have already encountered them before in other contexts, they will probably catch on rather quickly.

Direct students' attention to problems 1–2 on page 61 in the Student Activity Book. Explain that multiplication has three properties that often make problems easier to solve. Have everyone read and answer the questions in this section. Elicit several explanations of the Commutative Property from various students so that everyone is clear about the term. The factors can be put in a different order. The factors can be flipped without changing the product.

If your students know the word *commuter* or *commute*, you might want to make that connection: a commuter moves from one place to another. Similarly, the factors of a multiplication problem can be moved from one place to another without changing the product. Have students complete exercises 3–5.

▶ The Associative Property | WHOLE CLASS |

Students encountered this property when they did combination problems with three or more numbers. After looking over the arrays on page 61 of the Student Activity Book, elicit several explanations of the Associative Property from the class.

● The factors can be grouped together in different ways without changing the product.

If your students know the word *associate*, you might want to make that connection: the factors can associate with each other in any way. It should be clear from the arrays that any grouping can take place without changing the product.

Explain that being able to multiply different factors first can sometimes make multiplication much easier. Give students the problem $(9 \times 4) \times 2$. It simplifies to 36×2. Now ask students if they can use the Associative Property to make the problem easier: $9 \times (4 \times 2)$ simplifies to 9×8. It is easier to multiply 9×8 than to multiply 36×2.

Teaching Note

Math Background We have defined multiplication as putting together equal groups. We are using arrays to demonstrate and justify the properties because arrays support general "proofs" that can extend to any number (for example, you can rotate the array to see commutativity). Given our definitions of multiplication, there is an extra step in these "proofs" that could be discussed with advanced students. This would ask students to use the definition of multiplication as equal groups in the array "proofs". One explanation of these extra steps in the argument is given below:

Commutativity: The array shows 7 groups of 4 put together to make the total array. When the array is rotated, the groups of 4 go across instead of down but there are still 7 of them. No numbers changed, so the total is still the same. (The same argument can be made generally by using *a* and *b* instead of specific numbers.)

Associativity: The array shows 3 groups of 5 x 2, or 10, put together to make the total array of 30 dots. When the array is reorganized, there are 2 groups of 5×3, or 15, but there are still 30 dots in total. The factors remained the same, so the total is still the same. (The same argument can be made generally by using *a*, *b*, and *c* instead of specific numbers.)

Distributivity: The array shows 4 groups of 3 and 4 groups of 2 put together to make the total array. When the array is looked at as a whole instead of as 2 separate groups, it shows 4 groups of 5. The sum of the factors (2 + 3) is not changed, so the total is still the same. (The same argument can be made generally by using *a*, *b*, and *c* instead of specific numbers.)

Activity continued ▶

Activity 1

Teaching Note

What to Expect From Students

Exercise 11 presents examples that are designed to help students discover the advantage of multiplying the total. The first example, (6 × 3) + (6 × 4), yields 18 + 24, which some students may not be able add in their heads. But removing one pair of parentheses gives us 6 × (3 + 4) or 6 × 7, which students are likely to know automatically.

 **Quick Quiz**

See Assessment Guide for Unit 1 Quick Quiz 3.

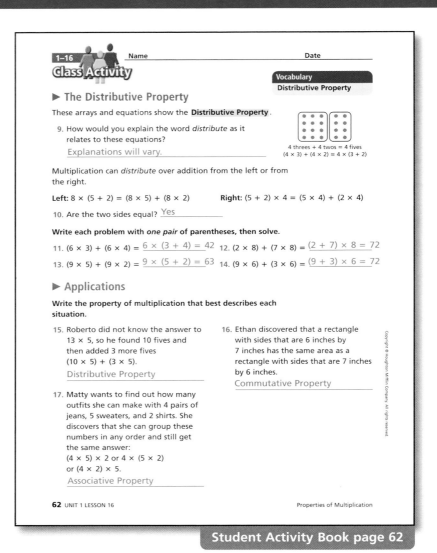

Student Activity Book page 62

► The Distributive Property WHOLE CLASS

Students encountered this property as one possible strategy for solving multiplication problems they did not know. (7 × 8 = 5 eights + 2 eights = 40 + 16 = 56.) After discussing the array in exercise 9 on page 62, elicit several explanations of the Distributive Property. This property is more difficult to state, and so students may need your help.

- If two numbers are added together and multiplied by the same factor, the multiplication can be done to the total $a \times (b + c)$ or to one number at a time $(a \times b) + (a \times c)$. In other words, the multiplication can be "spread out" or distributed.

There is often an advantage in doing the multiplication to the total or, stated another way, first simplifying the problem so that it has only one pair of parentheses.

► Applications WHOLE CLASS

Direct students' attention to Problems 15–17 on page 62. Read the problems together and have the students discuss which properties were applied in each situation described.

Teaching the Lesson

Reasoning and Properties

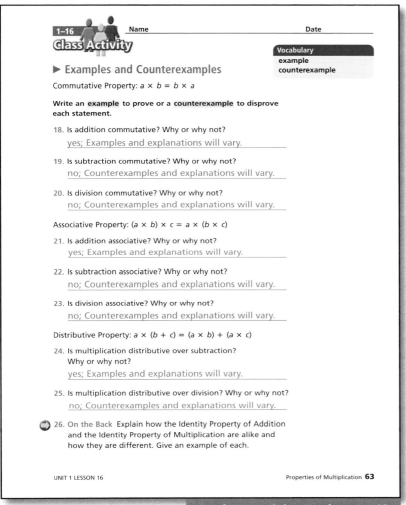

Student Activity Book page 63

► Examples and Counterexamples [WHOLE CLASS]

In problems 17–19 on page 63 of the Student Activity Book, students are asked to try some experiments to decide which properties are unique to multiplication and which ones are true of other operations as well. Students should use examples and counterexamples to help them decide. The process of testing and discovery is the important part of this activity. The class should make the following discoveries:

Commutative Property: Addition and multiplication are commutative, but subtraction and division are not.

Associative Property: Addition and multiplication are associative, but subtraction and division are not.

Distributive Property: Students already know that multiplication is distributive over addition. They should discover that it is also distributive over subtraction but not over division.

 20 MINUTES

Goal: Prove or disprove whether the Commutative, Associative, and Distributive Properties apply to all operations.

Materials: Student Activity Book page 63

 NCTM Standards:
Number and Operations
Algebra

Teaching Note

Language and Vocabulary
Students use examples to prove a property or argument. Introduce the word *counterexample*. When students use examples to disprove a property or argument they are called counterexamples.

 Ongoing Assessment

Have students give an example of:

► the Commutative Property.

► the Associative Property.

► the Distributive Property.

② Extending the Lesson

Going Further: Algebra Game

An important algebraic skill is the ability to evaluate an expression. To evaluate an expression means to substitute a known value (or values) for an unknown value (or values).

In previous lessons, students have evaluated expressions when, for example, they were given the values of l and w and used the formula $A = lw$ to find the area of a rectangle.

A variation of the idea of evaluating involves assigning a number to each letter of the alphabet, then finding the sum of the values of the letters in a variety of words.

Write the following list on the board, and as you write, ask the students to record the list in their Math Journals.

a = 1	n = 14
b = 2	o = 15
c = 3	p = 16
d = 4	q = 17
e = 5	r = 18
f = 6	s = 19
g = 7	t = 20
h = 8	u = 21
i = 9	v = 22
j = 10	w = 23
k = 11	x = 24
l = 12	y = 25
m = 13	z = 26

For this activity, invite students to work in pairs. Write a word such as *jar* on the board, and ask each pair of students to find the sum of the letters.

$$j + a + r = 10 + 1 + 18$$

$$j + a + r = 29$$

Ask each pair of students to find the sum of another short word such as *book*.

$$b + o + o + k = 2 + 15 + 15 + 11$$

$$b + o + o + k = 43$$

Then have the students find the sum of the letters of their first and last names. Which student has the greatest sum? The least? Which students have the same sum, or nearly the same sum?

You can extend the activity in many ways. For example, challenge each group to name the greatest possible sum and the least possible sum for a two letter word, a three letter word, and/or a four letter word.

Conclude the activity by inviting the student pairs to share their work. Which pair named a two letter word with the greatest sum? The least sum?

Intervention
for students having difficulty

SMALL GROUPS

Grid Models

Materials: grid paper

Have students draw rectangles on grid paper to illustrate these multiplication properties.

Commutative Property

$3 \times 4 = 4 \times 3$

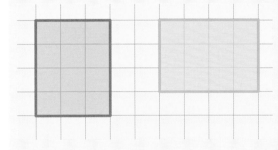

Associative Property

$(3 \times 4) \times 2 = 3 \times (4 \times 2)$

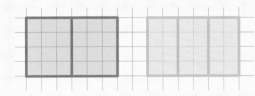

On Level
for students having success

PAIRS

Mental Math

Tell students that they can use multiplication properties to make computations easier so that they can be completed mentally.

Ask students to identify the property used in the following example: Distributive Property

$5 \times 26 =$ _____

$5 \times (20 + 6) =$ _____

$(5 \times 20) + (5 \times 6) =$ _____

$100 + 30 =$ _____

130

Have pairs solve the following problems. One student should solve with paper and pencil. The other student should solve with mental math.

$9 \times 31 =$ _____

$6 \times 107 =$ _____

$7 \times 52 =$ _____

$8 \times 105 =$ _____

Challenge
for students seeking a challenge

INDIVIDUALS

Use Substitution

Have students prove that addition is commutative by writing an algebraic example using variables instead of numbers.

$a + b = b + a$

Then have students choose values for the variables and prove by substitution that the addition is commutative.

When $a = 1$ and $b = 2$, both sides of the equation equal 3.

$1 + 2 = 2 + 1$
        $3 = 3$

Repeat this activity using the Associative and Distributive Properties.

 Math Writing Prompt

Intervention

Explain a Property
Explain the Commutative Property. Be sure to use the word *order* in your explanation.

 Math Writing Prompt

On Level

Explain Your Thinking
Explain the Associative Property. Try to use the word *associate* in your description.

 Math Writing Prompt

Challenge

True or False
For all whole numbers *a*, *b*, and *c*, if *a* is greater than *b*, then $a - c$ is greater than $b - c$. Give an example or counterexample.

 **Homework and Cumulative Review**

Homework **Goal:** Additional Practice

✓ Use this Homework page to provide students with more practice with multiplication properties.

Remembering **Goal:** Cumulative Review

This Remembering Activity would be appropriate any time after today's lesson.

1–16 Name _____ Date _____
Homework

Use the Commutative Property to solve for *n* in these equations.

1. $45 \times 7 = 7 \times n$ 2. $n \times 8 = 8 \times 29$ 3. $36 \times n = 9 \times 36$
   $n =$ __45__ $n =$ __29__ $n =$ __9__

Use the Associative Property to solve each problem.

4. $(9 \times 3) \times 3 =$ __$9 \times 9 = 81$__
5. $2 \times (5 \times 7) =$ __$10 \times 7 = 70$__
6. $(8 \times 4) \times 2 =$ __$8 \times 8 = 64$__

Use the Distributive Property to write each problem with only two factors. Then solve the problems.

7. $(7 \times 3) + (7 \times 5) =$ __$7 \times 8 = 56$__   8. $(3 \times 9) + (4 \times 9) =$ __$7 \times 9 = 63$__
9. $(8 \times 5) + (8 \times 4) =$ __$8 \times 9 = 72$__   10. $(2 \times 6) + (8 \times 6) =$ __$10 \times 6 = 60$__

Solve.

11. For Fall Festival, Mrs. Marco bought 6 bags of Golden Delicious apples. She handed out 43 apples and had 5 left over. How many apples were in each bag?
    __$6b = 43 + 5$, $b = 8$ apples__

12. Juice boxes are sold in packs of 6. Tony brought 5 packs of juice boxes to a party, and Victor brought 4 packs. How many juice boxes are there at the party altogether?
    __$(5 \times 6) + (4 \times 6) = 54$ juice boxes__

13. Everyone in Mrs. Bowman's art class has 8 jars of paint except Jerome, who has 10. There are 74 jars of paint in the room. How many students are there in Mrs. Bowman's art class?
    __$8s + 10 = 74$, $s = 8$, 9 students__
    __total including Jerome__

14. Lisa needs to make 2 times as many tuna as cheese sandwiches and 4 times as many ham as cheese sandwiches. If Lisa makes 56 sandwiches, how many of each of the 3 kinds will she make?
    __$c + 2c + 4c = 56$: 8 cheese,__
    __16 tuna, 32 ham__

UNIT 1 LESSON 16   Properties of Multiplication **31**

Homework and Remembering page 31

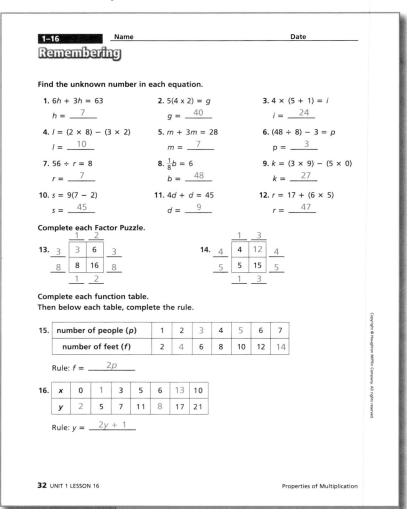

1–16 Name _____ Date _____
Remembering

Find the unknown number in each equation.

1. $6h + 3h = 63$ 2. $5(4 \times 2) = g$ 3. $4 \times (5 + 1) = i$
   $h =$ __7__ $g =$ __40__ $i =$ __24__

4. $l = (2 \times 8) - (3 \times 2)$ 5. $m + 3m = 28$ 6. $(48 \div 8) - 3 = p$
   $l =$ __10__ $m =$ __7__ $p =$ __3__

7. $56 \div r = 8$ 8. $\frac{1}{8}b = 6$ 9. $k = (3 \times 9) - (5 \times 0)$
   $r =$ __7__ $b =$ __48__ $k =$ __27__

10. $s = 9(7 - 2)$ 11. $4d + d = 45$ 12. $r = 17 + (6 \times 5)$
    $s =$ __45__ $d =$ __9__ $r =$ __47__

Complete each Factor Puzzle.

13.

	1	2	
3	3	6	3
8	8	16	8
	1	2	

14.

	1	3	
4	4	12	4
5	5	15	5
	1	3	

Complete each function table. Then below each table, complete the rule.

15.

number of people (*p*)	1	2	3	4	5	6	7
number of feet (*f*)	2	4	6	8	10	12	14

Rule: $f =$ __$2p$__

16.

x	0	1	3	5	6	13	10
y	2	5	7	11	8	17	21

Rule: $y =$ __$2y + 1$__

32 UNIT 1 LESSON 16   Properties of Multiplication

Homework and Remembering page 32

Home or School Activity

 Language Arts Connection

Suffixes in Math Explain that a suffix is something added to the end of a root word that changes its meaning. For example, the suffix *-itive* can change a verb to an adjective. The suffix *-itive* means "having the ability or quality of." Sometimes the spelling of the root word changes a little when the suffix is added.

Verb:	create
Definition:	to make something new
Adjective:	creative
Definition:	having the ability to make something new

Ask students to use a dictionary to find the definitions of the verbs *add*, and *multiply*. Then use the meanings of those verbs and the suffix *-itive* to write their own definitions for the adjectives *additive* and *multiplicative*.

Unit Review and Test

Lesson Objectives

● **Assess student progress on unit objectives.**

The Day at a Glance

Today's Goals	Materials
1 Assessing the Unit ▶ Assess student progress on unit objectives. ▶ Use activities from unit lessons to reteach content. **2 Extending the Assessment** ▶ Use remediation for common errors. There is no homework assignment on a test day.	Unit 1 Test, Student Activity Book pages 65–66 Unit 1 Test, Form A or B, Assessment Guide (optional) Unit 1 Performance Assessment, Assessment Guide (optional)

Quick Practice

 5 MINUTES   **Goal:** Review any skills you choose to meet the needs of your students.

Choose any Quick Practice activities that provide support for your students. The following may be helpful:

Easy Finger Factors, Unit 1, Lessons 2–3

Medium Finger Factors, Unit 1, Lessons 4–6

Difficult Finger Factors, Unit 1, Lessons 7–10

Multiplication in Motion, Unit 1, Lessons 11–13

Division in Motion, Unit 1, Lessons 14–16

 Class Management

Review and Test Day You may want to choose a quiet game or other activity (reading a book or working on homework for another subject) for students who finish early.

① Assessing the Unit

Assess Unit Objectives

 45 MINUTES (more if schedule permits)

Goal: Assess student progress on unit objectives.

Materials: Student Activity Book pages 65–66; Assessment masters A4–13 (optional)

▶ Review and Assessment

If your students are ready for assessment on the unit objectives, you may use either the test on the Student Activity Book pages or one of the forms of the Unit 1 Test in the Assessment Guide to assess student progress.

If you feel that students need some review first, you may use the test on the Student Activity Book pages as a review of unit content, and then use one of the forms of the Unit 1 Test in the Assessment Guide to assess student progress.

To assign a numerical score for all of these test forms, use 4 points for each question.

You may also choose to use the Unit 1 Performance Assessment. Scoring for that assessment can be found in its rubric in the Assessment Guide.

▶ Reteaching Resources

The chart at the right lists the test items, the unit objectives they cover, and the lesson activities in which the objective is covered in this unit. You may revisit these activities with students who do not show mastery of the objectives.

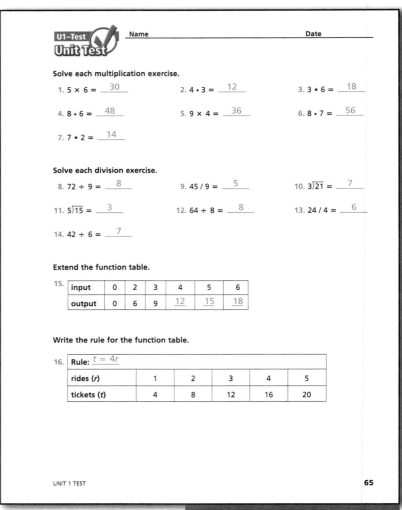

Student Activity Book page 65

Unit Test Items	Unit Objectives Tested	Activities to Use for Reteaching
1–14	**1.1** Recall basic multiplication and division.	Lesson 1, Activity 1 Lesson 2, Activity 1 Lesson 3, Activities 1–2 Lesson 3, Activity 2 Lesson 4, Activity 1 Lesson 5, Activity 1 Lesson 6, Activity 1 Lesson 7, Activity 1 Lesson 9, Activity 1 Lesson 10, Activities 1–2 Lesson 14, Activities 1–2
15–16	**1.2** Identify and write rules for a function table.	Lesson 8, Activity 1 Lesson 8, Activity 2

Student Activity Book page 66

U1–Test
Unit Test

Name _____ Date _____

Solve each equation.

17. $3j = 24$
    $j = \underline{\ 8\ }$

18. $90 = 10k$
    $k = \underline{\ 9\ }$

19. $80 \cdot 0 = s$
    $s = \underline{\ 0\ }$

20. $n = 24 - (7 \times 2)$
    $n = \underline{\ 10\ }$

Use the Properties of Multiplication to solve for n.

21. $659 \times 1,357 = 1,357 \times n$
    $n = \underline{\ 659\ }$

22. $(201 \times 340) \times 980 = n \times (340 \times 980)$
    $n = \underline{\ 201\ }$

Solve.   *Show your work.*

23. Ashley and Maria collect stamps. Maria has 15 stamps. Ashley has 3 times as many stamps as Maria. How many stamps does Ashley have?
    $15 \times 3 = 45$ stamps

24. At baseball practice, Juan and Michael practiced catching fly balls. Michael caught 21 fly balls. That is three times as many as Juan caught. How many fly balls did Juan catch?
    $21 \div 3 = 7$ fly balls

25. **Extended Response** Ella has a jar with pennies, nickels, and dimes. She has one third as many dimes as pennies. She has four times as many nickels as dimes. Altogether she has 32 coins. How many of each coin does she have? Explain how you solved the problem.
    $d + 3d + 4d = 32$; $8d = 32$; $d = 4$; She has
    4 dimes, 12 pennies, and 16 nickels. I let d
    represent dimes, then I wrote an equation
    using the information from the problem.

66 UNIT 1 TEST

Unit Test Items	Unit Objectives Tested	Activities to Use for Reteaching
17–20	**1.3** Solve algebraic equations involving multiplication and division.	Lesson 4, Activity 2 Lesson 12, Activity 1
21–22	**1.4** Identify and use the properties of multiplication.	Lesson 18, Activity 1
23–25	**1.5** Solve one- and two-step problems involving multiplication and division.	Lesson 11, Activity 1 Lesson 13, Activities 1–2 Lesson 15, Activity 1

▶ Assessment Resources

Free Response Tests
Unit 1 Test, Student Activity Book pages 65–66
Unit 1 Test, Form A, Assessment Guide, pages A4–A5

Extended Response Item
The last item in the Student Activity Book test and in the Form A test will require an extended response as an answer.

Multiple Choice Test
Unit 1 Test, Form B, Assessment Guide, pages A6–A9

Performance Assessment
Unit 1 Performance Assessment, Assessment Guide, page A10
Unit 1 Performance Assessment Rubric, Assessment Guide, page A13

▶ Portfolio Assessment

Teacher-selected Items for Student Portfolios:

- Homework, Lesson 15
- Class Activity work, Lessons 6, 8, and 13

Student-selected Items for Student Portfolios:

- Favorite Home or School Activity
- Best Writing Prompt

② Extending the Assessment

Unit Objective 1.1

Recall basic multiplication and division.

Common Error: Does Not Know Basic Multiplications and Divisions

Remediation The rhythmic recitation of count-bys can help students memorize their multiplications and divisions.

Give students practice reciting count-bys orally. Then follow with oral practice using the corresponding multiplications.

Unit Objective 1.2

Identify and write rules for a function table.

Common Error: Has Difficulty Identifying a Pattern Rule

Remediation Try creating a table with 3 rows. Then work with students to recognize the pattern by asking questions. For example:

Stars	1	2	3
Rule	x 5	x 5	x 5
Points	5	10	15

What must you do to the 1 to get 5? What must you do to the 2 to get 10? And so on.

Then ask, "What do you think you must do to get the 10th number in the pattern?" Extend the table to show that the answer will be 50.

Unit Objective 1.3

Solve algebraic equations involving multiplication and division.

Common Error: Confuses Sums and Products of Zero

Remediation Remind students that the product of any factor and zero is zero.

Unit Objective 1.4

Identify and use the properties of multiplication.

Common Error: Uses Properties Incorrectly

Remediation Explain that although both properties involve a change in order, the Commutative Property involves two numbers and the Associative Property involves three or more numbers.

- The Commutative Property lets students memorize only one-half of basic facts.

- The Associative Property lets students rearrange addends or factors in any order to make a computation easier.

Unit Objective 1.5

Solve one- and two-step problems involving multiplication and division.

Common Error: Can't Distinguish Between Multiplication and a Division Problem

Remediation Have students work in pairs to analyze a variety of multiplication and division problems. Have them list the similarities and differences of each problem. For example:

- Both problems involve equal groups.

- When you need to find the total, you use multiplication.

- When you are separating the total, you use division.

Perimeter and Area

THIS UNIT EXPLORES perimeter and area of rectangles, triangles, and parallelograms.

Activities in this unit help students to understand how perimeter and area are measured and how they can be determined. A Big Idea for the unit is that perimeter and area are two different measurements of the same shape and that each has its own kind of unit of measurement: linear units for perimeter and square units for area.

Students will use what they learn about area in this unit again in Unit 4, where area is used as a graphic model for multi-digit multiplication.

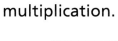

Planning Unit A Unit Pacing: 9–13 days

Lesson Title	Lesson Resources	Materials and Manipulatives	
		Math Expressions	**Other**
1 Square Units and Area	Family Letter Student Activity Book pages 67–70 Homework and Remembering pages 33–34	Grid Paper (Copymaster M18)	Scissors, tacks, board that will accept tacks, string, ruler, Math Journals
2 Perimeter and Area of Rectangles	Student Activity Book pages 71–74 Homework and Remembering pages 35–36	Centimeter-Grid Paper (Copymaster M19)	Centimeter rulers, Math Journals
3 Area of Right Triangles and Parallelograms	Student Activity Book pages 75–80 Homework and Remembering pages 37–38	Acute and Obtuse Triangles (Copymaster M20), Centimeter-Grid Paper (Copymaster M19), Geoboards (Copymaster M21)	Scissors, Geoboards and rubber bands, two straws, Math Journals
4 The Area of Any Triangle	Student Activity Book pages 81–86 Homework and Remembering pages 39–40	Centimeter rulers, Centimeter-Grid Paper (Copymaster M19)	Scissors, Math Journals
5 Consolidate Perimeter and Area	Student Activity Book pages 87–90 Homework and Remembering pages 41–42	Centimeter-Grid Paper (Copymaster M19)	Centimeter rules, Math Journals
6 Customary Units of Length (optional)	Student Activity Book pages 91–92, Homework and Remembering pages 43–44	Inch-Grid Paper (Copymaster M2)	Tape measures, one-foot rulers, or yardsticks, scissors, colored paper at least 12 in. on each side, Math Journals
☑ Unit Review and Test	Student Activity Book pages 93–94 Assessment Guide		

Unit A Assessment

✓ Unit Objectives Tested	Unit Test Items	Lessons
A.1 Find perimeter and area of polygons.	1–4	2, 3
A.2 Use customary and metric measurements to solve problems involving perimeter and area.	5, 6, 9, 10	1, 6
A.3 Find perimeter and area of complex figures.	7, 8	5

Formal Assessment

Open or Free Response Tests

- Unit Review and Test (Student Activity Book pages 93–94, Teacher's Guide pages 159–162)
- Unit A Test Form A (Assessment Guide)
- Unit A Open Response Test (Test Generator)
- Test Bank Items for Unit A (Test Generator)

Multiple Choice Tests

- Unit A Test Form B (Assessment Guide)
- Unit A Multiple Choice Test (Test Generator)
- Test Bank Items for Unit A (Test Generator)

Performance Tasks

- Unit A Performance Assessment (Assessment Guide)
- Unit A Performance Assessment (Test Generator)

Informal Assessment

Ongoing Assessment

In every Teacher's Guide lesson

Performance Assessment

- Class discussions
- Small-group work
- Individual work on teacher-selected tasks

Portfolios

- See Unit A Review and Test for suggestions for selecting items for portfolios.
- Some Homework pages are noted as suitable for portfolio inclusion.

Review Opportunities

Homework and Remembering

- Homework pages provide review of recently taught topics.
- Remembering pages provide cumulative review.

Teacher's Guide

- Unit Review and Test (pages 159–162)

Teacher's Resource Book

- Problem Bank

Test Generator CD-ROM

- Test Bank Items can be used to create custom review sheets.

Unit A Teaching Resources

Reaching All Learners

Advanced Learners

Lesson 3, page 134

Lesson 5, page 147

Individualizing Instruction

Activities
- Intervention (in every lesson)
- On Level (in every lesson)
- Challenge (in every lesson)

Math Writing Prompts
- Intervention (in every lesson)
- On Level (in every lesson)
- Challenge (in every lesson)

Cross-Curricular Links • Home or School Activities

 Language Arts Connection
Measure a Room (Lesson 2, page 128)

 Science Connection
Traction Action (Lesson 3, page 136)

 Math-to-Math Connection
Triangular Numbers (Lesson 4, page 142)

 Social Studies Connections
Quilts (Lesson 5, page 150)
Customary Measurement
(Lesson 6, page 158)

Teaching Unit A

Putting Research into Practice for Unit A

From Current Research:

Measurement estimation is the process of using mental and visual information to measure or make comparisons without the use of measuring instruments. It is a practical skill. Almost every day, we make estimates of measures. Do I have enough sugar to make the cookies? Will the car fit in that space? Can you throw the ball 50 feet? Is this suitcase over the weight limit? About how long is the fence? Will this paper cover the box? Each of these involves estimation.

Besides its value outside the classroom, estimation in measurement activities helps students focus on the attribute being measured, adds intrinsic motivation, and helps develop familiarity with standard units. Therefore, measurement estimation both improves measurement instruction and develops a valuable life skill.

Techniques of Measurement Estimation

Just as for computational estimation, specific strategies exist for estimating measures. Four strategies can be taught specifically:

1. *Develop and use benchmarks or referents for important units.* (This strategy was also mentioned as a way to develop familiarity with units.) Students should have a good referent for single units and also useful multiples of standard units. Referents or benchmarks for 1, 5, 10, and perhaps 100 pounds might be useful. A referent for 500 milliliters is very useful. These benchmarks can then be compared mentally to objects being estimated: "That tree is about as tall as four doorways, or between 8 and 9 meters tall."

2. *Use "chunking" when appropriate.* It may be easier to estimate the shorter chunks along the wall than to estimate the whole length as one. The weight of a stack of books is easier if some estimate is given to an "average" book.

3. *Use subdivisions.* This is a similar strategy to chunking, with the chunks imposed on the object by the estimator. For example, if the wall length to be estimated has no useful chunks, it can be mentally divided in half and then in fourths or even eighths by repeated halving until a more manageable length is arrived at. Length, volume, and area measurements all lend themselves to this technique.

4. *Iterate a unit mentally or physically.* For length, area, and volume, it is sometimes easy to mark off single units visually. You might use your hands or make marks or folds to keep track as you go. For length, it is especially useful to use a body measure as a unit and iterate with that. If you know, for example, that your stride is about $\frac{3}{4}$ meter, you can walk off a length and then multiply to get an estimate. Hand and finger widths are useful for shorter measures.

Van de Walle, John A. *Elementary and Middle School Mathematics: Teaching Developmentally.* 4th ed. New York: Addison, 2001. 294.

Other Useful References: Perimeter and Area

Ferrer, Bellasanta B., Bobbie Hunter, Kathryn C. Irwin, Maureen J. Sheldon, Charles S. Thompson, and Catherine P. Vistro-Yu. "By the Unit or Square Unit?" *Mathematics Teaching in the Middle School* 7.3 (Nov. 2001).

Learning Math: Geometry. Annenberg/CPB Learner.org. 1997–2004. <www.learner.org/resources/series167.html>.

Learning Math: Measurement. Annenberg/CPB Learner.org. 1997–2004. <www.learner.org/resources/series184.html>.

National Council of Teachers of Mathematics. *Learning and Teaching Measurement* (NCTM 2003 Yearbook). Ed. Douglas H. Clements. Reston: NCTM, 2003.

National Council of Teachers of Mathematics. *Mathematics Teaching in the Middle School* (Focus Issue: Measurement) 9.8 (Apr. 2004).

National Council of Teachers of Mathematics. *Principles and Standards for School Mathematics.* Reston: NCTM, 2000.

Math Background

In *Math Expressions,* a Geometry and Measurement mini-unit follows each regular unit. This facilitates connections and enables review problems to extend throughout the year. In this unit, students use the multiplication and division skills they have learned in Unit 1 to find and understand areas of triangles and other shapes. In turn, they will use area models to visualize work with fractions and decimals later this year.

Measurement and Geometry are interconnected and support each other in many ways. In order to understand area and perimeter for triangles and parallelograms, students must be able to think spatially about these shapes.

In lesson 3, students manipulate right triangles to see that two congruent right triangles can always form a rectangle. This allows them to generalize from the formula for finding the area of a rectangle that they have already worked with, to a strategy to find the area of a right triangle.

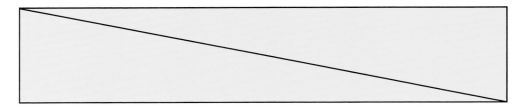

Then, students cut apart parallelograms to show that any parallelogram can be reconstructed into a rectangle. From this, students are able to develop a strategy to find the area of any parallelogram.

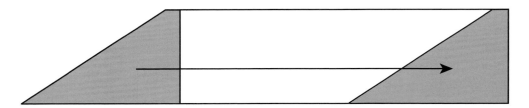

And, once students are comfortable with their strategy to find the area of parallelograms, they can show that any triangle is really half of a parallelogram, leading to a strategy for finding the area of any triangle.

Developing formulas to find the area of parallelograms and triangles ensures that students understand what the formulas mean, and helps students to apply and generalize the formulas later, when presented with more complex shapes.

In Unit B, students will return to the concept of perimeter to develop a strategy to find the circumference of a circle.

Square Units and Area

Lesson Objectives

- Define and relate common metric units of area.
- Select the appropriate metric unit for measuring a particular object.

Vocabulary
meter
decimeter
centimeter
millimeter

The Day at a Glance

Today's Goals	Materials	123 Math Talk
1 Teaching the Lesson A1: Visualize square metric units and build a square meter from smaller units. A2: Measure classroom objects and calculate the area. **2 Extending the Lesson** ▶ Differentiated Instruction **3 Homework and Cumulative Review**	Student Activity Book pages 67–70 Scissors Grid Paper (Copymaster M18) Tacks Board that will accept tacks String Ruler Homework and Remembering pages 33–34 Math Journals Family Letter	In today's activities, the students are involved in discussion as they ▶ share what they know about area ▶ brainstorm ways to make a square meter from cut-out grids ▶ talk about the square meter they made

① Teaching the Lesson

Relate Metric Area Measures

 25 MINUTES

Goal: Visualize square metric units and build a square meter from smaller units.

Materials: Student Activity Book page 67, scissors (1 per student), Grid Paper (Copymaster M18)

 NCTM Standard:
Measurement

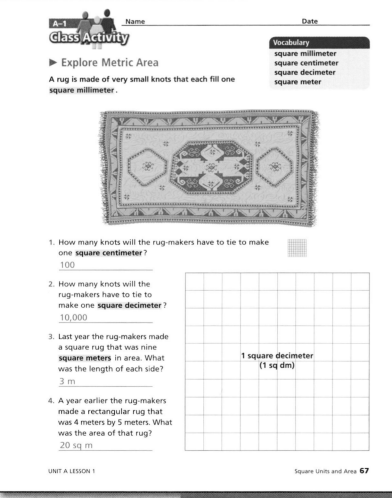

Student Activity Book page 67

▶ Explore Metric Area [WHOLE CLASS]

Write the symbols for common metric lengths on the board (meter: m, decimeter: dm, centimeter: cm, and millimeter: mm). Point to them randomly, and have the students respond by saying the name of the unit and then showing the approximate length with their hands.

Ask students to share what they know about the area of a rectangle or square.

● **Define area.** Area is the number of square units that cover a region.

● **How do you find the area of a rectangle or square?** by multiplying the length times the width

As a class, discuss questions 1–4. Direct students' attention to the drawings of the square centimeter and square decimeter on this page.

● **What does each small square inside the square centimeter represent?** 1 sq mm

● **What does each square inside the square decimeter represent?** 1 sq cm

As you work through the questions with the class, discuss the patterns involved in multiplying numbers with zeros. The product will always have the same number of zeros as the two factors:

● 10 × 10 = 100 (2 zeros)

● 100 × 10 = 1,000 (3 zeros)

● 100 × 100 = 10,000 (4 zeros)

▶ Construct a Square Meter WHOLE CLASS

Give each student scissors and Copymaster M18. Have students cut out the grid along the heavy outside line. Explain that students are going to create a rug with an area of one square meter, using the grids. Encourage them to brainstorm methods for making the square meter.

- How many square decimeters are in the grid? 4

- How many decimeters are in one meter? 10

- Then how many square decimeters are in one square meter? 10 rows of 10 decimeters; 10 × 10 = 100

- If we have 4 square decimeters and we need 100, how many pages do we need to put together to make the rug? 25

- How should we place the pages to make a square? 5 across and 5 down

Have students carry out the plan by making a square meter on the floor. If you have fewer than 25 students, you will need to cut out a few extra masters. When students are finished, discuss the results. A sample dialogue appears in the side column.

 Math Talk in Action

This is one square meter. Suppose that a family will sit around this rug and drink tea. How many people can comfortably sit around the rug?

Mara: Probably four. It is the size of a small kitchen table.

That's a good way to think of it. Now, how many centimeters are there along each side of a square meter?

Hamid: 100

So how many square centimeters do we have in this square meter?

Hamid: 100 × 100 or 10,000

Good. Now look at all the little square millimeters. Each represents a knot in the rug. How many knots did it take to make this rug? How can we figure it out?

Jamyce: We just found out that there are 10,000 square centimeters in this square meter. Each square centimeter contains 100 square millimeters, or 100 knots. So 10,000 × 100 = 1,000,000.

That's right. Now we can see what 1 million looks like.

 Class Management

Looking Ahead Have students save their grids for Activity 2. For Lesson 4 you will need the items listed below. You may want to start gathering them now.

- ▶ An empty half-gallon milk or juice carton with a square bottom

- ▶ A one-liter container filled with water or other liquid

- ▶ Packages of food marked in liters and grams

- ▶ A milliliter dropper, if available

Calculate Metric Area

 20 MINUTES

Goal: Measure classroom objects and calculate the area.

Materials: Student Activity Book page 68

 NCTM Standard:
Measurement

A–1
Class Activity

Name _____ Date _____

▶ Identify the Appropriate Unit

What metric unit is the most sensible unit for measuring each of the following?

5. the area of a postage stamp
   sq mm

6. the length of a noodle
   cm

7. the area of a tabletop
   sq dm

8. the length of a ladybug
   mm

9. the area of an envelope
   sq cm

10. the length of a sidewalk
    m

Name an object you can measure using each of these units. Possible answers are given.

11. millimeter
    length of a paperclip

12. centimeter
    length of a textbook

13. decimeter
    length of a car

14. square millimeters
    area of a baseball card

15. square meters
    area of a driveway

68 UNIT A LESSON 1   Square Units and Area

Student Activity Book page 68

▶ Identify the Appropriate Unit

WHOLE CLASS

Ask students to read Student Activity Book page 68.

● What unit of measure is appropriate for exercise 6?
  length units

● What unit of measure is appropriate for exercise 7?
  square units, for area

Explain that sometimes the unit selected is a matter of how precise the measurements need to be. In exercise 7 for example, measuring the tabletop in centimeters will give a more accurate answer than decimeters, but it will be harder to calculate mentally (for example, 3 × 5 dm is easier to multiply than 31 × 52 cm).

Have students work together in pairs or small groups to complete exercises 5–15.

▶ Calculate the Area of Real-World Objects   SMALL GROUPS

Divide the class into four or five teams. On the board, list four or five rectangular objects in the classroom, such as a notebook page, a sticky note, a desktop. (Try to include one object that is best measured in square centimeters, one in square decimeters, and one in square millimeters.)

Teams circulate and measure each item to the nearest whole square unit with their metric grid. They should then figure out and record the approximate area.

When most teams are finished, discuss and compare the results. Invite students to tell which measuring unit they chose and the approximate area of each object.

 Ongoing Assessment

Observe the students as they measure the objects and estimate area. Use questioning to assess understanding.

▶ Why did you choose that unit?

▶ What is the smallest unit that you know?

▶ What is the greatest unit that you know?

② Extending the Lesson

Activities for Individualizing

Intervention
for students having difficulty

PAIRS

String Rectangles

Materials: Grid Paper (Copymaster M18), tacks, board that will accept tacks, string

Students make rectangles on Copymaster M18 using tacks and string.

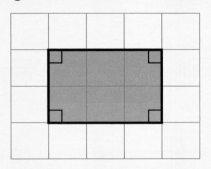

Both partners calculate the area in square centimeters and compare. They can check their work by counting squares, if necessary.

On Level
for students having success

PAIRS

The Predict and Verify Game

Materials: Grid Paper (Copymaster M18) or ruler

Player A draws a rectangle. Player B predicts the area of the rectangle in square millimeters, then measures with Copymaster M18 or a ruler, and calculates the area.

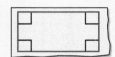

If the prediction is within 25 square millimeters, Player B scores a point. If not, Player A scores a point. Take turns until someone has ten points.

Challenge
for students seeking a challenge

INDIVIDUALS

Calculate Area

Students draw two figures on a sheet of paper. Rectangle A has one side of length 3 dm and one side of length 450 mm. Square B has one side of length 4 m. Students find the area of each figure in square centimeters and in square millimeters.

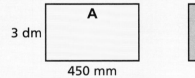

Rectangle A: 450 mm = 45 cm, 3 dm = 30 cm; area = 45 × 30 = 1,350 sq cm = 135,000 sq mm

Square B: 4 m = 400 cm; area = 400 × 400 = 160,000 sq cm = 16,000,000 sq mm

---

 Math Writing Prompt

Intervention

Explain Your Thinking
Explain how to multiply 20 × 10.

 Math Writing Prompt

On Level

Summarize
In your own words, describe how millimeters, centimeters, decimeters, and meters are related and how square millimeters, square centimeters, square decimeters, and square meters are related.

 Math Writing Prompt

Challenge

Problem Solving
A garden is a 10-meter square. Each side of the garden has 6 fence posts. How many fence posts enclose the garden? 20

③ Homework and Cumulative Review

Homework Goal: Additional Practice

✓ For homework, students practice what they know about how metric measurements relate to one another, and calculate area and perimeter.

Remembering Goal: Cumulative Review

This Remembering activity is appropriate any time after today's lesson.

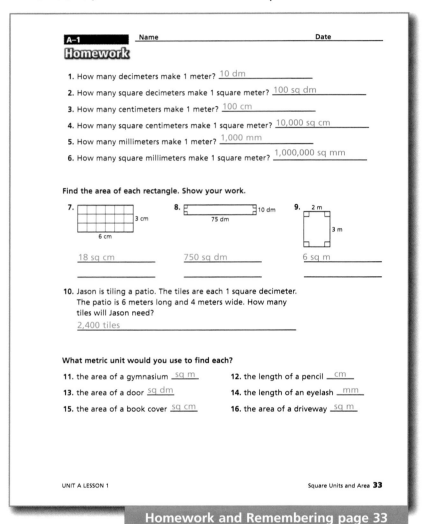

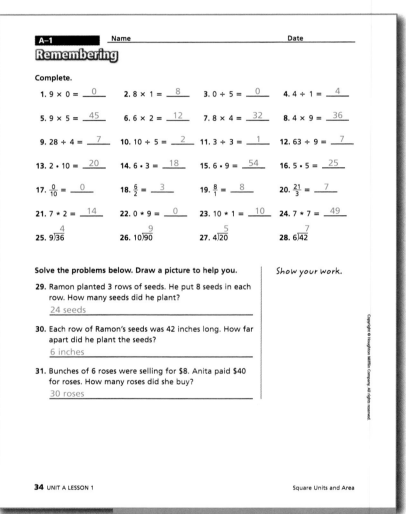

Homework and Remembering page 33

Homework and Remembering page 34

Home or School Connection

Have children take home the Family Letter on Student Activity Book pages 69-70. This letter explains how the concepts of measuring perimeter and area are developed in *Math Expressions*. It gives parents and guardians a better understanding of the learning that goes on in math class and creates a bridge between school and home. A Spanish translation of this letter is on the following page in the Student Activity Book.

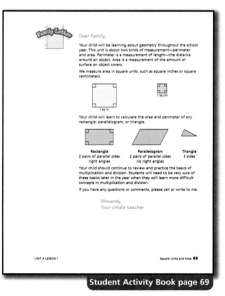

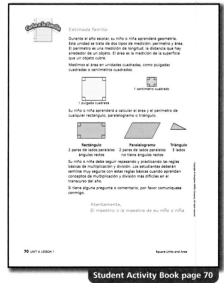

Student Activity Book page 69

Student Activity Book page 70

Perimeter and Area of Rectangles

Vocabulary

perimeter
area
rectangle
square unit
centimeter
square centimeter

Lesson Objectives

- Construct rectangles of given widths and lengths.
- Distinguish between the area and the perimeter of a rectangle.

The Day at a Glance

Today's Goals	Materials	123 Math Talk
1 Teaching the Lesson A1: Construct rectangles and visualize perimeter and area. Derive general formulas for calculating perimeter and area. A2: Measure to find perimeter and area. **2 Extending the Lesson** ▶ Going Further: Make Estimates ▶ Differentiated Instruction **3 Homework and Cumulative Review**	Student Activity Book pages 71–74 Centimeter ruler Centimeter-Grid Paper (Copymaster M19) Homework and Remembering pages 35–36 Math Journals	In today's activities, the students are involved in discussion as they ▶ describe what they know about perimeter and area ▶ derive formulas for calculating perimeter and area ▶ solve problems involving perimeter and area

Teaching the Lesson

Activity 1

Visualize Perimeter and Area

🕐 **20 MINUTES**

Goal: Construct rectangles and visualize perimeter and area. Derive general formulas for calculating perimeter and area.

Materials: Student Activity Book page 71, centimeter ruler (1 per student)

 NCTM Standards:
Measurement
Communication

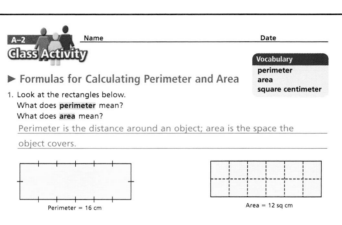

Student Activity Book page 71

▶ Formulas for Calculating Perimeter and Area WHOLE CLASS

Direct students' attention to exercise 1 and ask them what they already know about perimeter and area. Be sure they understand that the perimeter of a rectangle is the distance around, expressed in length units. The area of a rectangle is the number of square units the rectangle covers. Elicit from students that the opposite sides of a rectangle are always of equal length.

For exercises 2–6, students draw rectangles with their centimeter rulers. They mark each centimeter as they work, which helps them visualize the perimeter. Students then connect the marks to make square centimeters to help them to visualize the area.

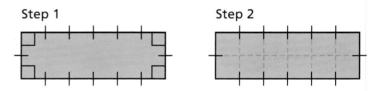

The final row in the table will show the general formula for finding the area and the perimeter:

$A = l \times w$
$P = l + w + l + w$
$\quad = 2 \times l + 2 \times w$

Activity 2

Real-World Applications

 20 MINUTES

Goal: Measure to find perimeter and area.

Materials: Student Activity Book page 72

 NCTM Standard:
Measurement

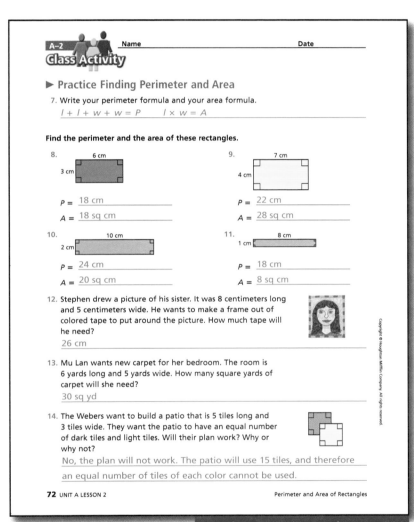

A–2
Class Activity

Name   Date

▶ **Practice Finding Perimeter and Area**

7. Write your perimeter formula and your area formula.
   $l + l + w + w = P$ $l \times w = A$

Find the perimeter and the area of these rectangles.

8. 6 cm
    3 cm

    $P =$ 18 cm
    $A =$ 18 sq cm

9. 7 cm
    4 cm

    $P =$ 22 cm
    $A =$ 28 sq cm

10. 10 cm
    2 cm

    $P =$ 24 cm
    $A =$ 20 sq cm

11. 8 cm
    1 cm

    $P =$ 18 cm
    $A =$ 8 sq cm

12. Stephen drew a picture of his sister. It was 8 centimeters long and 5 centimeters wide. He wants to make a frame out of colored tape to put around the picture. How much tape will he need?
    26 cm

13. Mu Lan wants new carpet for her bedroom. The room is 6 yards long and 5 yards wide. How many square yards of carpet will she need?
    30 sq yd

14. The Webers want to build a patio that is 5 tiles long and 3 tiles wide. They want the patio to have an equal number of dark tiles and light tiles. Will their plan work? Why or why not?
    No, the plan will not work. The patio will use 15 tiles, and therefore an equal number of tiles of each color cannot be used.

72 UNIT A LESSON 2   Perimeter and Area of Rectangles

Student Activity Book page 72

▶ Practice Finding Perimeter and Area

WHOLE CLASS

As a class, discuss exercises 7–11. Ask students to use the general formulas to find the perimeter and area for each exercise.

 Math Talk in Action

Let's consider problem 14. What answer did you get?

Marco: I said their plan won't work because 5 tiles by 3 tiles means they want 5 × 3 = 15 tiles. You can't have half of the tiles light and half of the tiles dark when it's an odd number.

Good. Did anyone use a different method to come up with an answer?

Linh: I drew the patio and shaded every other tile darker. There was one extra darker one when I was done.

That's a good method, too.

Create a Patio Design Challenge pairs of students to create a new design for a rectangular patio with an equal number of light and dark tiles. Ask them to draw the rectangular patio square tile by square tile. Then ask them to shade half the tiles to see if their design works. Possible answers: 4 tiles × 5 tiles; 4 tiles × 3 tiles

Students who are finished quickly can investigate other patio designs that will work.

 Ongoing Assessment

As students create their patio designs, ask questions about how to find the area and perimeter of their designs. Make sure they understand that perimeter is measured in length units and area is measured in square units.

Extending the Lesson

Going Further: Make Estimates

Goal: Estimate the area and perimeter of an irregular figure on a grid.

Materials: Student Activity Book page 73

✓ **NCTM Standards:**
Geometry
Measurement
Problem Solving
Reasoning and Proof

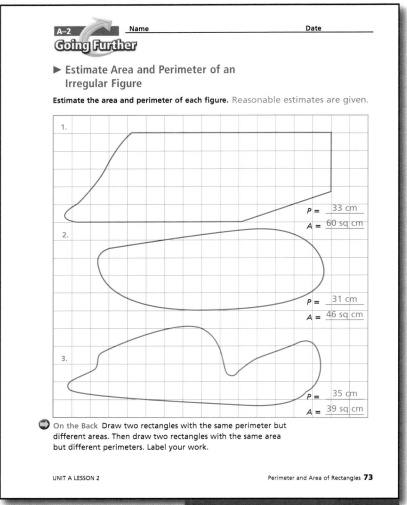

Student Activity Book page 73

▶ Estimate Area and Perimeter of an Irregular Figure

Ask students to describe different strategies that could be used to make a reasonable estimate of the perimeter of the figure.

To demonstrate one way to estimate the area, ask students to draw, inside the figure, a rectangle that is as large as possible. A sample drawing might look like this:

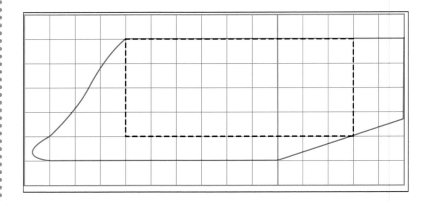

- What is the area of your rectangle? 36 sq cm

- How many whole unit squares are still outside your rectangle? 18

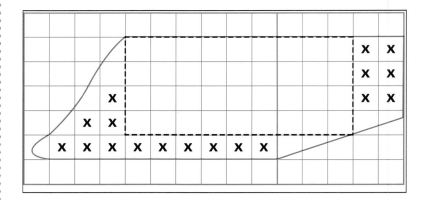

- What is the total area so far? 54 sq cm

- How many partial squares are along the edges? 11

- About how much area do they cover? 5 or 6 sq cm

- What do you estimate is the area of the irregular figure? 60 sq cm

Invite students to solve and discuss the other exercises in a similar manner.

Intervention
for students having difficulty

`PAIRS`

Birthday Rectangles

Materials: Centimeter-Grid Paper (Copymaster M19)

Each partner draws a rectangle on grid paper. They use their birth month for the width and the day for the length. The rectangle below represents a birthdate of April 10.

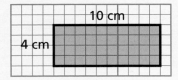

Partners work together to calculate the area and perimeter of the rectangles.

 Math Writing Prompt

Intervention

Summarize
Write the formulas for finding the perimeter and area of a rectangle. Explain the meaning of perimeter and area.

On Level
for students having success

`PAIRS`

Which One Is It?

Each student draws and labels the dimensions of a rectangle on paper. The student records one measurement correctly—the perimeter or the area—and records the other measurement incorrectly. The partner then must decide which measurement is correct.

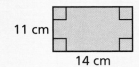

 Math Writing Prompt

On Level

Odd and Even
Vernon thinks that area can be an odd number or an even number, but perimeter is always an even number. Do you agree with him? Explain.

Challenge
for students seeking a challenge

`INDIVIDUALS`

Make Rectangles

Students draw and label as many different rectangles as they can that have an area of 24 square units. They repeat the challenge for rectangles with a perimeter of 24 units.

Rectangle dimensions (area):
1×24, 2×12, 3×8, 4×6

Rectangle dimensions (perimeter):
1×11, 2×10, 3×9, 4×8, 5×7, 6×6

 Math Writing Prompt

Challenge

Problem Solving
A room is 11 ft by 12 ft, and 8 ft high. The door is 7 ft by 3 ft and the window is 4 ft by 3 ft. Johanna is painting the walls but not the window or door. Can she use just one can of paint, which covers about 500 sq ft? Explain.

 **Homework and Cumulative Review**

A–2

Homework **Goal:** Additional Practice

✓ Include students' work for page 35 as part of their portfolios.

A–2

Remembering **Goal:** Cumulative Review

This Remembering activity is appropriate any time after today's lesson.

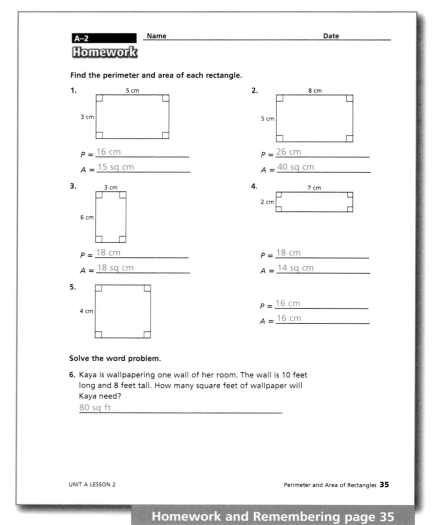

A–2
Homework

Name _____ Date _____

Find the perimeter and area of each rectangle.

1. 5 cm / 3 cm
    P = 16 cm
    A = 15 sq cm

2. 8 cm / 5 cm
    P = 26 cm
    A = 40 sq cm

3. 3 cm / 6 cm
    P = 18 cm
    A = 18 sq cm

4. 7 cm / 2 cm
    P = 18 cm
    A = 14 sq cm

5. 4 cm
    P = 16 cm
    A = 16 cm

Solve the word problem.

6. Kaya is wallpapering one wall of her room. The wall is 10 feet long and 8 feet tall. How many square feet of wallpaper will Kaya need?
   80 sq ft

UNIT A LESSON 2   Perimeter and Area of Rectangles **35**

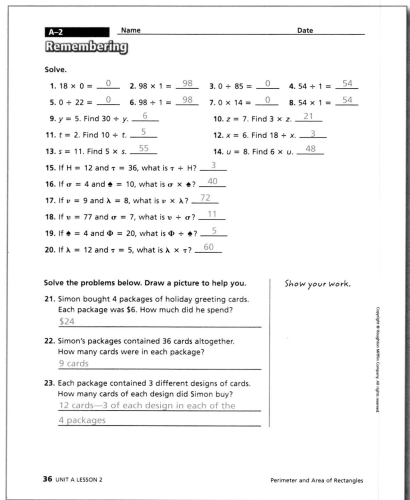

A–2
Remembering

Name _____ Date _____

Solve.

1. $18 \times 0 =$ 0
2. $98 \times 1 =$ 98
3. $0 \div 85 =$ 0
4. $54 \div 1 =$ 54
5. $0 \div 22 =$ 0
6. $98 \div 1 =$ 98
7. $0 \times 14 =$ 0
8. $54 \times 1 =$ 54
9. $y = 5$. Find $30 \div y$. 6
10. $z = 7$. Find $3 \times z$. 21
11. $t = 2$. Find $10 \div t$. 5
12. $x = 6$. Find $18 \div x$. 3
13. $s = 11$. Find $5 \times s$. 55
14. $u = 8$. Find $6 \times u$. 48
15. If $H = 12$ and $\tau = 36$, what is $\tau \div H$? 3
16. If $\sigma = 4$ and $\spadesuit = 10$, what is $\sigma \times \spadesuit$? 40
17. If $\nu = 9$ and $\lambda = 8$, what is $\nu \times \lambda$? 72
18. If $\upsilon = 77$ and $\sigma = 7$, what is $\upsilon \div \sigma$? 11
19. If $\spadesuit = 4$ and $\Phi = 20$, what is $\Phi \div \spadesuit$? 5
20. If $\lambda = 12$ and $\tau = 5$, what is $\lambda \times \tau$? 60

Solve the problems below. Draw a picture to help you.

Show your work.

21. Simon bought 4 packages of holiday greeting cards. Each package was $6. How much did he spend?
    $24

22. Simon's packages contained 36 cards altogether. How many cards were in each package?
    9 cards

23. Each package contained 3 different designs of cards. How many cards of each design did Simon buy?
    12 cards—3 of each design in each of the 4 packages

36 UNIT A LESSON 2   Perimeter and Area of Rectangles

Homework and Remembering page 35

Homework and Remembering page 36

Home or School Activity

 Language Arts Connection

Measure a Room Have students write instructions for someone to follow to measure the perimeter of a room. Then they explain what it means to measure the area of a room. Explain how measuring perimeter is different from measuring area.

Measure the lengths of two adjacent walls of the room. To find perimeter, add the lengths. Multiply by 2. To find area, just multiply one length by the other.

Area of Right Triangles and Parallelograms

Lesson Objectives

● Classify angles by size, and classify triangles by the size of their angles.

● Derive formulas for areas of parallelograms and right triangles.

The Day at a Glance

Today's Goals	Materials	123 Math Talk
1 Teaching the Lesson **A1:** Recognize different kinds of angles and triangles. **A2:** Derive the formula for perimeter and area of a right triangle using a rectangle. **A3:** Identify the height of a parallelogram. Derive the formula for perimeter and area of a parallelogram using a rectangle. **2 Extending the Lesson** ▶ Going Further: Simpler Problems ▶ Differentiated Instruction **3 Homework and Cumulative Review**	Student Activity Book pages 75–80 Acute and Obtuse Triangles (Copymaster M20) Scissors Centimeter-Grid Paper (Copymaster M19) Geoboards and rubber bands or Geoboard (Copymaster M4) Two straws Homework and Remembering pages 37–38 Math Journals	In today's activities, the students are involved in discussion as they ▶ describe and identify triangles by their angle measures ▶ generate a formula for finding the perimeter and area of a right triangle ▶ compare the area of rectangles with that of right triangles and parallelograms of the same height

Teaching the Lesson

Angles and Triangles

 15 MINUTES

Goal: Recognize different kinds of angles and triangles.

Materials: Student Activity Book page 75, Acute and Obtuse Triangles (Copymaster M20), scissors

✔ **NCTM Standards:**
Geometry
Measurement
Reasoning

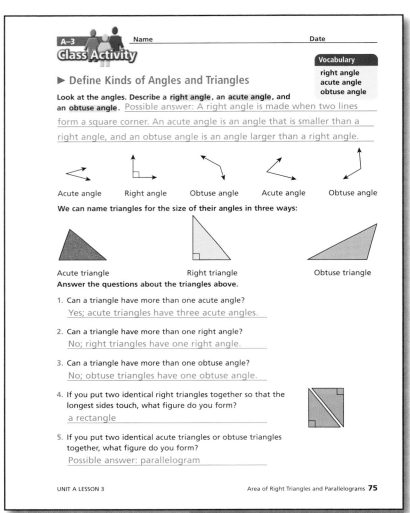

Student Activity Book page 75

▶ Define Kinds of Angles and Triangles

WHOLE CLASS

Direct students' attention to the angles at the top of Student Activity Book page 75. Ask students to explain

the difference between an acute angle, a right angle, and an obtuse angle. If students need more practice, they can use two pencils to make angles.

Have students look at the three kinds of triangles shown in the illustrations. Use the following questions to help students define kinds of triangles.

● Can a triangle have more than one acute angle? Yes; a triangle can have as many as three acute angles.

Help students see that the other two triangles have two acute angles. Therefore, the definition of an acute triangle is one that has three acute angles or one in which all of the angles are acute.

● Can a triangle have more than one right angle? no

Students can try to draw such a triangle; they won't be able to close the figure. Therefore, the definition of a right triangle is a triangle that has one right angle.

● Can a triangle have more than one obtuse angle? no

Again, students will not be able to close the figure if they try to draw it. Therefore, the definition of an obtuse triangle is a triangle with one obtuse angle.

● If you put two identical right triangles together so that the longest sides touch, what figure is formed? a rectangle

Emphasize that a right triangle is half of a rectangle. Since a rectangle is a kind of parallelogram, a right triangle is also half of a parallelogram. If necessary, review the definition of a parallelogram (opposite sides are parallel).

For question 5, students can visualize the answer or experiment with the cutouts on Copymaster M20.

Explore Right Triangles

 15 MINUTES

Goal: Derive the formula for perimeter and area of a right triangle using a rectangle.

Materials: Student Activity Book page 76, Centimeter-Grid Paper (Copymaster M19)

 NCTM Standards:
Geometry
Measurement

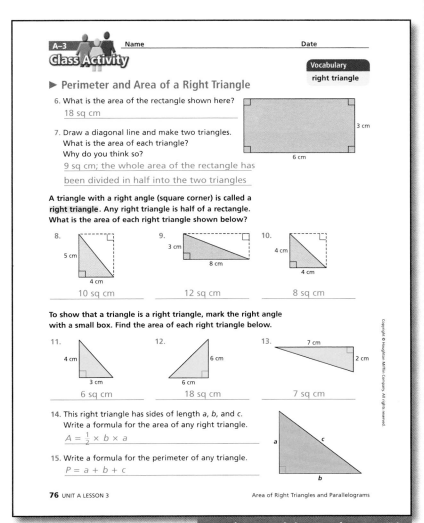

Student Activity Book page 76

► Perimeter and Area of a Right Triangle WHOLE CLASS

Ask students to discuss exercises 6 and 7. Help students see that a right triangle is always exactly half of a rectangle. Assign exercises 8–13. Finally, ask students to complete exercises 14 and 15, generating a formula for calculating the area, and then the perimeter, of a right triangle:

$$Area = \frac{1}{2} \ base \times height \qquad Perimeter = a + b + c$$

Teaching Note

What to Expect from Students When finding the area of a triangle, students may approach the multiplication in several ways. They may multiply the base by the height and then divide the result by 2. They may take $\frac{1}{2}$ of the base and then multiply that number by the height. The answer will be the same.

Example: base = 6, height = 4

Option 1: $6 \times 4 = 24$, $24 \div 2 = 12$. The area is 12 square units.

Option 2: $\frac{1}{2}$ of $6 = 3$ and $3 \times 4 = 12$. The area is 12 square units.

✔ Ongoing Assessment

Have students complete the following activity:

On centimeter-grid paper draw a line 6 cm long. Draw a perpendicular line from one end, 8 cm long. Complete the triangle. What is the area of the triangle? Measure the longest side. What is the perimeter of the triangle?

Activity 3

Area of a Parallelogram

 30 MINUTES

Goal: Identify the height of a parallelogram. Derive the formula for perimeter and area of a parallelogram using a rectangle.

Materials: Student Activity Book pages 77–79, scissors, geoboards and rubber bands or Geoboard (Copymaster M4)

 NCTM Standards:
Geometry
Measurement

▶ Experiment With Parallelograms

WHOLE CLASS

Have students look at the vertical dotted line inside each parallelogram. Explain that this line shows the height of the parallelogram. Elicit from students a definition of height, and discuss it. Students should understand why the line can be drawn from anywhere along the base. (The parallel lines stay the same distance apart.)

● Each dotted line segment shows the height of the parallelogram. How can we define height? a line segment that is perpendicular to the base

● Can we draw a height in more than one place along the base? yes

Have students cut out each pair of parallelograms. Then have them cut out the identical parallelograms 16 and 17 and switch the pieces to align them along the dotted line. Tell them that these two parallelograms have a base of 6 centimeters and a height of 3 centimeters.

Help students to find the area of the new parallelograms they have made. See the sample discussion below:

● What figure was formed when you switched the pieces around? a rectangle

● If the length is 6 cm and the width is 3 cm, what is the area of this rectangle? 18 sq cm

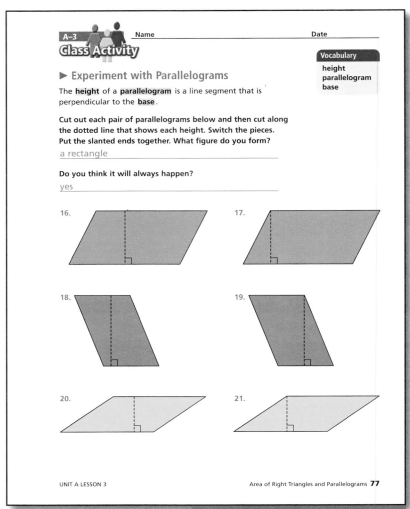

Student Activity Book page 77

● Now think about the parallelogram you cut to make the rectangle. Did it have the same area as this rectangle? Yes, it is made of the same two pieces.

● Put the two pieces back the way they were. How can you find the area of this parallelogram? Multiply the base times the height. That is the same as multiplying the length times the width of the rectangle.

● What about the other parallelogram you cut? Does it matter where you draw the line of height? No, we can still make the same-size rectangle, and so the area is the same.

Ask the class to experiment with the other two pairs of parallelograms to see if the results are always the same. Can they always make a rectangle by switching the pieces? If so, then the formula for finding the area of a parallelogram must be generally true:

$$A = base \times height$$

▶ Find the Area of a Parallelogram

INDIVIDUALS

Have students complete exercises 22–25 and discuss why *h* is used in one formula and *s* in the other. Invite students to complete the exercises on the page.

Teaching Note

Watch For! In writing the formulas, make sure students use *h*, and not *s* for the height. When measuring perimeter, students need to understand that they are measuring the distance around the whole parallelogram so they need to use *s* rather than *h*. Students can measure *s* and *h* to prove that the two measurements are different in parallelograms, and using the wrong measurement will result in errors.

 Alternate Approach

Geoboards Students can use different colors of rubber bands to make rectangles and parallelograms on geoboards. Note that when the bases are the same length (same number of dots) and the heights are the same length, the triangles on each end are congruent. So, the sum of the common area and the area of one triangle must be the same as the area of the rectangle.

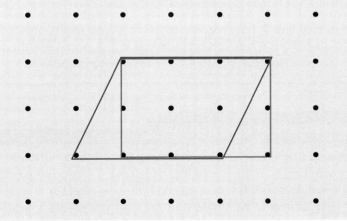

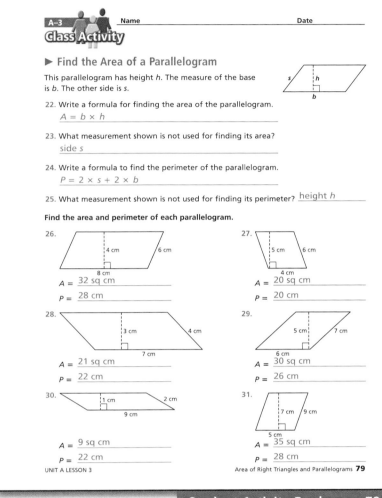

Student Activity Book page 79

② Extending the Lesson

Going Further: Simpler Problems

Goal: Use a simpler problem to solve a problem.

Materials: Student Activity Book page 80

✓ **NCTM Standard:**
Problem Solving

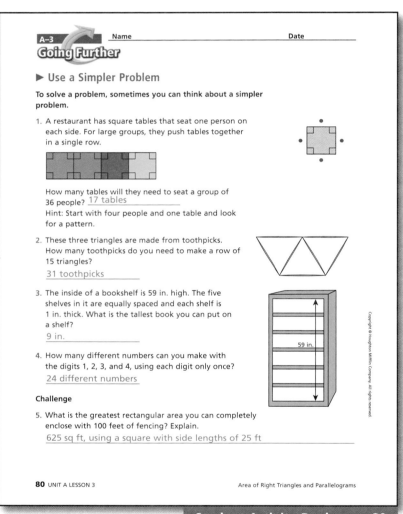

Student Activity Book page 80

▶ Use a Simpler Problem PAIRS

Discuss problem 1.

● How many people can sit around one table? 4

● When you put two tables together, how many people can sit around them? Draw a picture to help you decide. 6

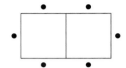

● When you put three tables together, how many people can sit around them? 8

● What number pattern is starting to happen? 4, 6, 8 even numbers

● How is the number pattern related to the number of tables? Subtract 2 from the number of people and divide by 2 to get the number of tables.

● How can you use the pattern to solve the problem? 36 − 2 = 34; 34 ÷ 2 = 17; they need 17 tables

Have the pairs continue with the other problems.

📁 Class Management

Walk around the room and observe the pairs as they solve the problems. Make sure students remember to solve the original problem after modeling it in a simpler way.

▶ In problem 2, you started with 3 toothpicks and found that you had to add 2 toothpicks for each new triangle. How many toothpicks do you add to 3 to get 14 more triangles? 2 × 14 = 28; 28 + 3 = 31 toothpicks

▶ In problem 3, one shelf would take up 1 in. of inside space. How much space do five shelves take? 5 in. How much space is left for books? 59 in. − 5 in. = 54 in. How much space is there for books on each shelf? 54 ÷ 6 = 9 in.

▶ In problem 4, how many numbers can you make with 2, 3, and 4 if 1 is the first digit? 6 What if 2, 3, and 4 are the first digits? 6 So how many can you make altogether? 24

Differentiated Instruction

Advanced Learners: Students can use a string or a ribbon of known length to form a variety of shapes. Then using a ruler and various formulas, students will discover that for any length, a circle is the shape that encloses the greatest area.

Intervention
for students having difficulty

PAIRS

Make a Parallelogram

Materials: grid or dot paper, scissors

Students trace a rectangle or draw one on grid paper or dot paper. They cut out the rectangle and then cut it along a diagonal to make two right triangles.

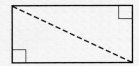

Students show how to put the two triangles together to make a parallelogram that is not a rectangle.

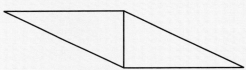

Ask students to tell what they know about the areas of the original rectangle and the parallelogram.

They are the same.

On Level
for students having success

INDIVIDUALS

Investigate Math

Materials: Centimeter-Grid Paper (Copymaster M19)

On centimeter-grid paper, students draw a line 3 cm long. They draw a perpendicular line from one end, 4 cm long. They complete the triangle and measure the third side.

Next, students draw a square on each side of the triangle and calculate the area of each square.

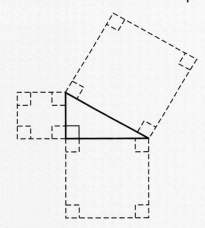

Students add the areas of the two smaller squares and describe what they notice. The total area of the two smaller squares is the same as the area of the big square.

Challenge
for students seeking a challenge

INDIVIDUALS

Straw Quadrilaterals

Materials: two straws cut at the same place to make two pairs of congruent line segments

Students make a rectangle with the straws. They measure the rectangle and estimate its area.

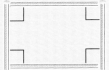

They push the straws to change the rectangle into different parallelograms, measuring the parallelograms each time.

How does the area change? gets smaller and smaller

What doesn't turn? perimeter

 Math Writing Prompt

Intervention
Draw a Picture
Show how to find the height of a parallelogram with a base measuring 8 cm and area of 24 sq cm.

 Math Writing Prompt

On Level
Use Reasoning
A right triangle has sides of 5 cm, 12 cm, and 13 cm. How can you tell which sides are perpendicular? What is the area of the triangle?

 Math Writing Prompt

Challenge
Investigate Math
What is the smallest possible perimeter of a parallelogram with a base of 6 cm and a height of 3 cm? Explain your answer.

 # Homework and Cumulative Review

Homework **Goal:** Additional Practice

✔ Include students' work for page 37 as part of their portfolios.

Remembering **Goal:** Cumulative Review

This Remembering activity is appropriate any time after today's lesson.

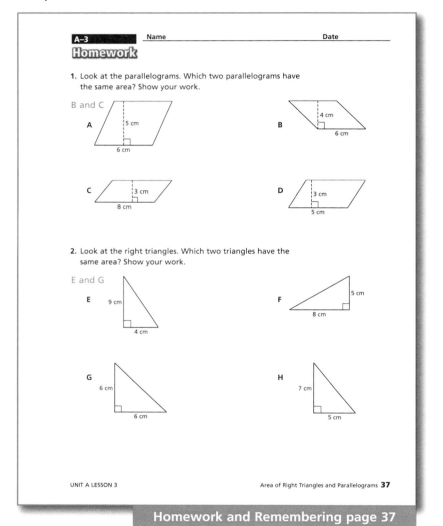

A–3   Name   Date

Homework

1. Look at the parallelograms. Which two parallelograms have the same area? Show your work.

   B and C

   A   5 cm   6 cm

   B   4 cm   6 cm

   C   3 cm   8 cm

   D   3 cm   5 cm

2. Look at the right triangles. Which two triangles have the same area? Show your work.

   E and G

   E   9 cm   4 cm

   F   5 cm   8 cm

   G   6 cm   6 cm

   H   7 cm   5 cm

UNIT A LESSON 3   Area of Right Triangles and Parallelograms **37**

Homework and Remembering page 37

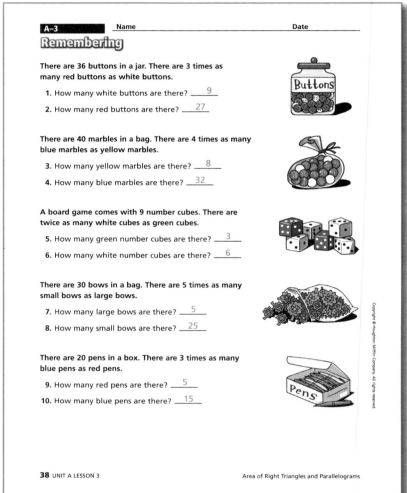

A–3   Name   Date

Remembering

There are 36 buttons in a jar. There are 3 times as many red buttons as white buttons.

1. How many white buttons are there? _9_

2. How many red buttons are there? _27_

There are 40 marbles in a bag. There are 4 times as many blue marbles as yellow marbles.

3. How many yellow marbles are there? _8_

4. How many blue marbles are there? _32_

A board game comes with 9 number cubes. There are twice as many white cubes as green cubes.

5. How many green number cubes are there? _3_

6. How many white number cubes are there? _6_

There are 30 bows in a bag. There are 5 times as many small bows as large bows.

7. How many large bows are there? _5_

8. How many small bows are there? _25_

There are 20 pens in a box. There are 3 times as many blue pens as red pens.

9. How many red pens are there? _5_

10. How many blue pens are there? _15_

38 UNIT A LESSON 3   Area of Right Triangles and Parallelograms

Homework and Remembering page 38

Home or School Activity

 ### Science Connection

Traction Action The parallelogram is used in the design of tires to give better traction on the road. Look for and list other examples of products or designs that use the parallelogram.

The Area of Any Triangle

Lesson Objectives

- Find the area of any triangle.
- Identify the height of any triangle.
- Recognize that the area of a triangle is always one half the area of a parallelogram with the same height and base.

Vocabulary

triangle
parallelogram
area
base
height

The Day at a Glance

Today's Goals	Materials	123 Math Talk
1 Teaching the Lesson **A1:** Cut out identical triangles to construct parallelograms, and discover the formula for the area of a triangle. **A2:** Draw and measure triangles and parallelograms.	Scissors Student Activity Book pages 81–86 Centimeter rulers Centimeter-Grid Paper (Copymaster M19) Homework and Remembering pages 39–40 Math Journals	In today's activities, the students are involved in discussion as they ▶ discover that they can create a parallelogram by combining two congruent triangles ▶ find out how to identify the height of different kinds of triangles
2 Extending the Lesson ▶ Differentiated Instruction		
3 Homework and Cumulative Review		

1 Teaching the Lesson

Area of Triangles

 30 MINUTES

Goal: Cut out identical triangles to construct parallelograms, and discover the formula for the area of a triangle.

Materials: scissors, Student Activity Book pages 81–84

 NCTM Standards:
Geometry
Measurement

▶ Experiment With Triangles WHOLE CLASS

Have students cut out the two acute triangles on Student Activity Book page 81 and follow the directions. No matter which sides students place together (*a*, *b*, or *c*), students will discover that the result is a parallelogram. Students can repeat the exercise using the obtuse triangles. The results will be the same. Students have already discovered that two right triangles make a rectangle (which is a special kind of parallelogram). They can conclude that every triangle is half of a parallelogram.

▶ Calculate the Area of a Triangle

WHOLE CLASS

Invite students to answer questions 1 and 2. Then have them use *A* to represent area, *b* to represent base, and *h* to represent height as they complete exercise 3. The following formula will allow them to find the area of any kind of triangle: $A = \frac{1}{2}b \times h$ or $A = b \times h \div 2$. Students can use the formula to answer questions 4 and 5.

Discuss questions 6 to 8. The height of an acute triangle is easy to find because it is inside the triangle. The height of a right triangle is the same as one of its sides, and the height of an obtuse triangle is outside the triangle.

Teaching Note

Math Background Remind students that line segment *AE* can also be written as $\overline{AE}$.

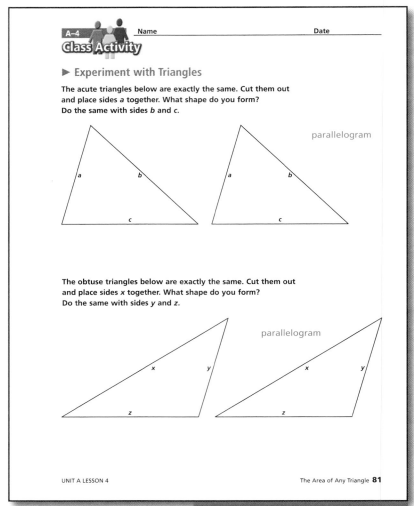

Student Activity Book page 81

In question 6, line segment *AE* shows the height of the obtuse triangle. The line must start at the very top of the triangle and be perpendicular to the base. Students can think of the base as being extended to meet the line. You may want to draw this on the board.

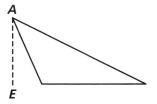

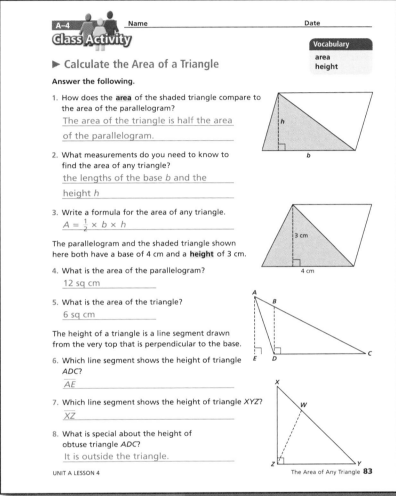

A-4 Class Activity

Name _____ **Date** _____

▶ Calculate the Area of a Triangle

Vocabulary
area
height

Answer the following.

1. How does the **area** of the shaded triangle compare to the area of the parallelogram?

   The area of the triangle is half the area of the parallelogram.

2. What measurements do you need to know to find the area of any triangle?

   the lengths of the base b and the height h

3. Write a formula for the area of any triangle.

   $A = \frac{1}{2} \times b \times h$

The parallelogram and the shaded triangle shown here both have a base of 4 cm and a **height** of 3 cm.

4. What is the area of the parallelogram?

   12 sq cm

5. What is the area of the triangle?

   6 sq cm

The height of a triangle is a line segment drawn from the very top that is perpendicular to the base.

6. Which line segment shows the height of triangle *ADC*?

   $\overline{AE}$

7. Which line segment shows the height of triangle *XYZ*?

   $\overline{XZ}$

8. What is special about the height of obtuse triangle *ADC*?

   It is outside the triangle.

UNIT A LESSON 4   The Area of Any Triangle **83**

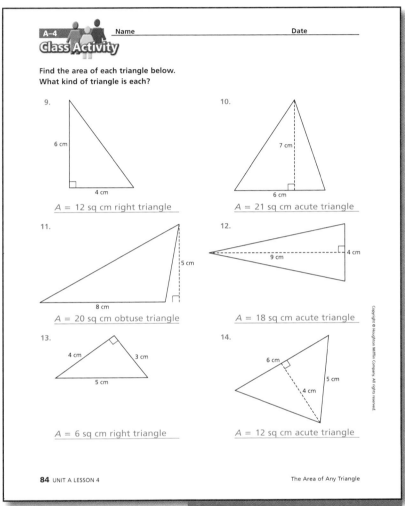

A-4 Class Activity

Name _____ **Date** _____

Find the area of each triangle below. What kind of triangle is each?

9. 6 cm, 4 cm

   A = 12 sq cm right triangle

10. 7 cm, 6 cm

    A = 21 sq cm acute triangle

11. 5 cm, 8 cm

    A = 20 sq cm obtuse triangle

12. 9 cm, 4 cm

    A = 18 sq cm acute triangle

13. 4 cm, 3 cm, 5 cm

    A = 6 sq cm right triangle

14. 6 cm, 5 cm, 4 cm

    A = 12 sq cm acute triangle

84 UNIT A LESSON 4   The Area of Any Triangle

In question 7, line segment *XZ* shows the height of the right triangle. The side is already perpendicular to the base, so no special lines need to be drawn.

The height of a right triangle is the same as one of the sides.

Teaching Note

What to Expect from Students The order of operations does not matter here. If a triangle has a base of 8 and a height of 3, students can take $\frac{1}{2}$ of the base (4) and multiply it by the height (4 × 3 = 12). Or they can multiply the base times the height (24) and take half of that entire quantity (12). The results will be the same.

● Does it matter if side *XZ* or side *ZY* is called the height? No; *XZ* is perpendicular to *ZY*. If you turn the triangle so that *XZ* is the base, then *ZY* will be the height.

For question 8, emphasize that the height of an obtuse triangle is a line segment outside the triangle. The base must be extended to see that it is perpendicular.

Have students calculate the area of the triangles in exercises 9–14.

Teaching the Lesson (continued)

Activity 2

Triangles and Parallelograms

 15 MINUTES

Goal: Draw and measure triangles and parallelograms.

Materials: rulers, Student Activity Book pages 85–86

✓ **NCTM Standards:**
Geometry
Measurement

▶ Draw Parallelograms and Triangles

INDIVIDUALS

Have students complete exercises 15–21.

Then have them complete exercises 22–30. Point out that any non-rectangular parallelogram with two unequal sides can be divided into triangles in two different ways to create either two acute triangles or two obtuse triangles.

 Class Management

Walk around the room and observe as pairs draw parallel lines to create parallelograms. Watch for students who are drawing lines that do not look parallel. Ask questions to help them make better drawings.

▶ Does your line look the same distance everywhere from *AC*?

▶ How can you line up an edge of your ruler with *AC* and make a parallel line through *B*?

 Ongoing Assessment

Ask students to draw a parallelogram on grid paper and to measure the base and height. Have them divide their parallelogram into triangles and calculate the area of each triangle.

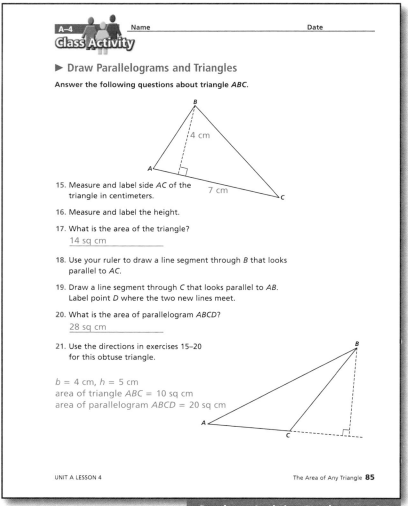

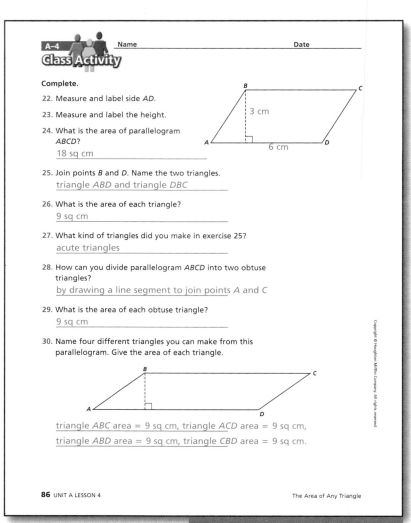

Student Activity Book page 85

Student Activity Book page 86

Extending the Lesson

Intervention
for students having difficulty
PAIRS

Right Triangles

Materials: Centimeter rulers

Students draw any right triangle.

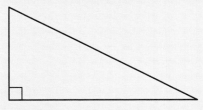

They measure and label the sides to the nearest centimeter and tell what they know about the two shorter sides. They are perpendicular.

Students make a rectangle with a copy of their triangle.

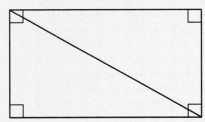

Have them tell how to find the area of the rectangle (multiply the measures of the two short sides of the triangle) and the area of one of the triangles (multiply the measures of the two short sides and divide by 2).

On Level
for students having success
PAIRS

Divide Rectangles

Materials: Centimeter-Grid Paper (Copymaster M19), scissors

Students draw a rectangle on grid paper. They measure the sides to the nearest centimeter and estimate the area and perimeter.

Next, students cut their rectangle into two triangles and estimate the area of each triangle.

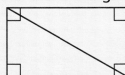

Students use the triangles to make a new parallelogram that is not a rectangle, measure the sides, and estimate the perimeter of the new parallelogram.

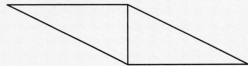

Students explain which of the two quadrilaterals has the greater perimeter, and whether their answer is always true.

The parallelogram has a greater perimeter. The slanted lines are longer than the vertical sides of the rectangle.

Challenge
for students seeking a challenge
INDIVIDUALS

Draw Triangles

Materials: centimeter rulers

Students draw a triangle with a base of 12 cm and a height of 4 cm.

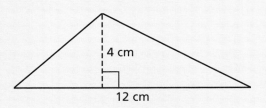

They calculate the area of the triangle. They then measure the sides to the nearest centimeter, label the sides with the measurements, and estimate the perimeter.

Answers will vary. Many triangles are possible.

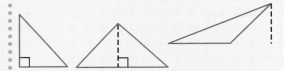

 Math Writing Prompt

Intervention

Draw a Picture
What kind of triangle do you make when you cut a square in half along a diagonal? Draw an example and explain how to find the area of the triangle.

 Math Writing Prompt

On Level

Explain Your Thinking
Explain how you know the area of a triangle is one half the area of a parallelogram with the same base and height.

 Math Writing Prompt

Challenge

Investigate Math
Can you put two copies of the same triangle together to make a quadrilateral that is not a parallelogram? Explain how.

③ Homework and Cumulative Review

Homework **Goal:** Additional Practice

✓ For homework, students find the perimeter and area of various regular polygons.

Remembering **Goal:** Cumulative Review

This Remembering activity is appropriate any time after today's lesson.

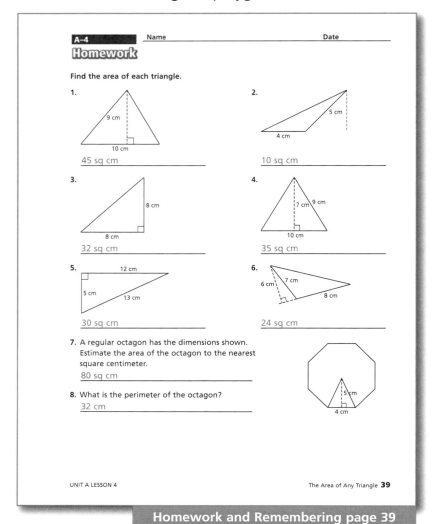

A–4   Name   Date

Homework

Find the area of each triangle.

1.
9 cm
10 cm
45 sq cm

2.
5 cm
4 cm
10 sq cm

3.
8 cm
8 cm
32 sq cm

4.
7 cm   9 cm
10 cm
35 sq cm

5.
12 cm
5 cm
13 cm
30 sq cm

6.
6 cm   7 cm
8 cm
24 sq cm

7. A regular octagon has the dimensions shown. Estimate the area of the octagon to the nearest square centimeter.
80 sq cm

8. What is the perimeter of the octagon?
32 cm

5 cm
4 cm

UNIT A LESSON 4   The Area of Any Triangle **39**

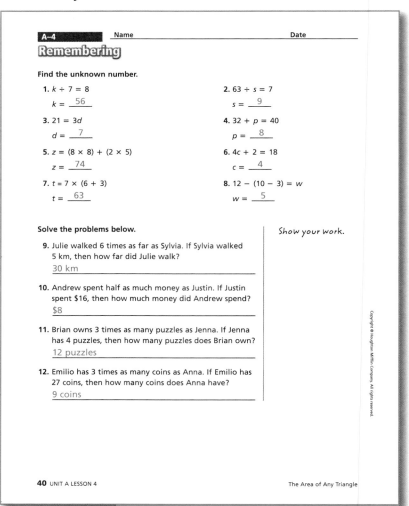

A–4   Name   Date

Remembering

Find the unknown number.

1. $k \div 7 = 8$
$k = \underline{56}$

2. $63 \div s = 7$
$s = \underline{9}$

3. $21 = 3d$
$d = \underline{7}$

4. $32 + p = 40$
$p = \underline{8}$

5. $z = (8 \times 8) + (2 \times 5)$
$z = \underline{74}$

6. $4c + 2 = 18$
$c = \underline{4}$

7. $t = 7 \times (6 + 3)$
$t = \underline{63}$

8. $12 - (10 - 3) = w$
$w = \underline{5}$

Solve the problems below.   *Show your work.*

9. Julie walked 6 times as far as Sylvia. If Sylvia walked 5 km, then how far did Julie walk?
30 km

10. Andrew spent half as much money as Justin. If Justin spent $16, then how much money did Andrew spend?
$8

11. Brian owns 3 times as many puzzles as Jenna. If Jenna has 4 puzzles, then how many puzzles does Brian own?
12 puzzles

12. Emilio has 3 times as many coins as Anna. If Emilio has 27 coins, then how many coins does Anna have?
9 coins

40 UNIT A LESSON 4   The Area of Any Triangle

Homework and Remembering page 39   Homework and Remembering page 40

Home or School Activity

 Math-to-Math Connection

Triangular Numbers Students build triangles by starting with one dot and adding new rows with one more dot each time. Invite them to investigate the number of dots. The total number of dots in each triangle is called a triangular number. Have students find the next three triangular numbers.

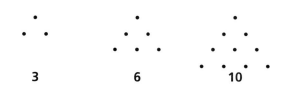

1   3   6   10

Consolidate Perimeter and Area

Lesson Objectives

● Select or infer the dimensions needed to find the area and perimeter of triangles and parallelograms.

● Recognize smaller figures embedded in larger figures.

● Find the perimeter and area of complex geometric figures composed of multiple smaller shapes.

The Day at a Glance

Today's Goals	Materials	123 Math Talk
1 Teaching the Lesson **A1:** Identify necessary dimensions for calculating area and perimeter. **A2:** Find the area and perimeter of various triangles and parallelograms. **A3:** Visualize and discuss strategies for finding the area and perimeter of complex geometric shapes. **A4:** (optional) Estimate the area of regular polygons. **2 Extending the Lesson** ▶ Differentiated Instruction **3 Homework and Cumulative Review**	Student Activity Book pages 87–90 Centimeter rulers Centimeter-Grid Paper (Copymaster M19) Homework and Remembering pages 41–42 Math Journals	In today's activities, the students are involved in discussion as they ▶ identify necessary dimensions for calculating perimeter and area of figures ▶ identify smaller figures embedded in larger figures ▶ describe how to find area and perimeter of complex figures ▶ estimate the area of regular polygons

Teaching the Lesson

Appropriate Measurements

 20 MINUTES

Goal: Identify necessary dimensions for calculating area and perimeter.

Materials: Student Activity Book page 87

✔ **NCTM Standards:**
Geometry
Measurement
Problem Solving

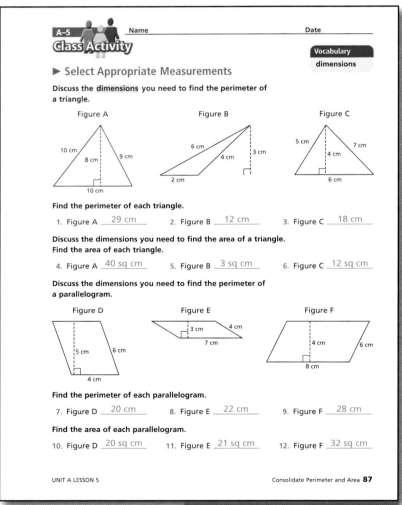

Student Activity Book page 87

► **Select Appropriate Measurements**

WHOLE CLASS

Have the class discuss exercises 1–6.

When calculating the perimeter or area of a geometric figure, students will often be presented with dimensions that they do not need. The exercises on this page will help them make the appropriate discriminations.

● Why don't you need the height of each triangle to find the perimeter? The perimeter is the distance around the triangle. The height isn't a side of the triangles.

● For what kind of triangle might the height be part of the perimeter? Why? A right triangle, because one of the perpendicular sides can be the height.

Before beginning exercises 7–12, be sure your students understand that opposite sides of a parallelogram, like opposite sides of a rectangle, are equal in length.

● Why don't you need the height of each parallelogram to find the perimeter? The perimeter is the distance around the parallelogram. The height isn't a side of the parallelogram.

● For what kind of parallelogram might the height be part of the perimeter? Why? A rectangle or a square, because one of the perpendicular sides can be the height.

Applications

 15 MINUTES

Goal: Find the area and perimeter of various triangles and parallelograms.

Materials: Student Activity Book page 88

✔ **NCTM Standards:**
Geometry
Measurement

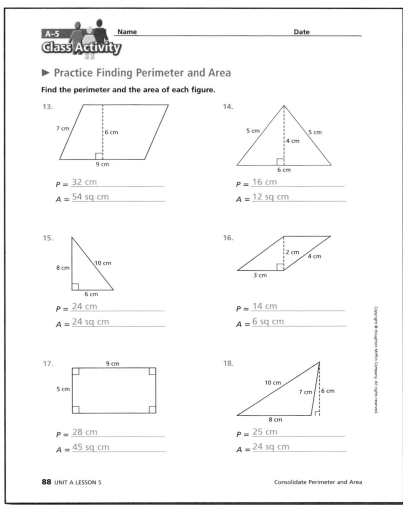

Student Activity Book page 88

▶ Practice Finding Perimeter and Area

WHOLE CLASS

Have students complete exercises 13–18, determining which dimensions they need to use each time. Students will need to supply the missing dimensions of parallelograms to find the perimeter, using their knowledge that opposite sides are equal. Alternatively, they can add the two sides that are given and then multiply by 2. They can use the same process for the rectangle in exercise 17 since rectangles are special kinds of parallelograms.

Students will need to ignore all sides except the base when finding the area of both triangles and parallelograms.

 Ongoing Assessment

Tell students that the formula $A = b \times h$ can be used to find the area of any parallelogram. Ask them to use a diagram to explain the formula. Then ask, How can you change this formula and use it to find the area of any triangle?

Activity 3

Area and Perimeter of Complex Figures

 25 MINUTES

Goal: Visualize and discuss strategies for finding the area and perimeter of complex geometric figures.

Materials: Student Activity Book page 89

✔ **NCTM Standards:**
Geometry
Measurement

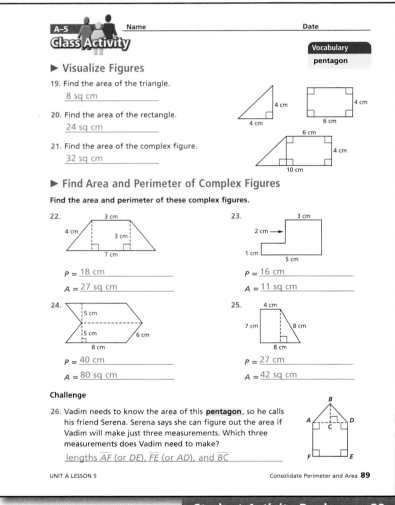

Student Activity Book page 89

▶ **Visualize Figures** WHOLE CLASS

Have students complete exercises 19 and 20. The figure in exercise 21 is a combination of the first two. Be sure that students do not assume that the bottom shape is a combination of the triangle and the rectangle just because it looks that way. Ask probing questions to be sure that they can identify all the unknown dimensions.

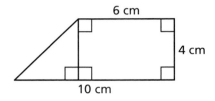

● **How do you know that this is the same rectangle?** We know that opposite sides are equal, so the bottom side must be 6 cm and the left side must be 4 cm.

● **How do you know the height of the triangle in exercise 19?** The height is 4 cm because the height of this triangle is also one side of the rectangle. Because it is opposite the side that is 4 cm, it must also be 4 cm.

● **How do you know the length of the base of the triangle?** Subtract 6 cm from the long, 10-cm side of the figure. We get 4 cm as the length of the base.

● **How do you know the area of the triangle in the complex figure is the same as the area of the triangle in exercise 19?** The triangles have congruent bases and congruent heights.

● **How can you find the area of the figure in exercise 21?** Add the areas of the figures from exercises 18 and 19: 8 sq cm + 24 sq cm = 32 sq cm.

▶ Find Area and Perimeter of Complex Figures PAIRS

Help students find the area and perimeter of the complex figures in exercises 22–25. Remind students that they can find unknown lengths by using what they know about triangles and parallelograms.

Exercise 22: The right side of this figure is identical to the left side, so students can conclude that the right side is 4 cm long. They can now find the perimeter. They can find the length of the base of each right triangle by subtracting the top length (3 cm) from the bottom length (7 cm), which gives 4 cm. Because there are two triangles, the base of each is half of that measurement, or 2 cm. Students can now find the area of the square (9 sq cm) and the two right triangles (3 sq cm + 3 sq cm) and add them together.

Exercise 23: Students can find the length of the right side by adding the two lengths on the opposite side: 2 cm + 1 cm. They can find the length of the top of the small projecting rectangle by subtracting 3 cm from 5 cm. Students can now find the perimeter. They can find the area by adding the areas of the two embedded rectangles together: 2 sq cm + 9 sq cm.

Exercise 24: The figure is made up of two identical parallelograms. By applying their knowledge that opposite sides are equal, students can supply all the outside dimensions and find the perimeter. To find the area of the whole figure, students can find the area of one parallelogram and then multiply by 2.

Exercise 25: The perimeter is the sum of the lengths. The dotted line that is the height of the embedded right triangle is 7 cm because it is directly opposite the other 7-cm side of the rectangle. To find the base of the triangle, students subtract 4 cm from 8 cm. Once they know these dimensions, students can find the area of the two figures separately and add them together.

Differentiated Instruction

Advanced Learners: Discuss strategies for solving exercise 26. To solve this problem, students need to see the embedded rectangle and triangle. The first measurement they need is the base of the triangle (AD), which is also one side of the rectangle. The other necessary measurements are the height of the triangle (BC) and the other side of the rectangle (either AF or DE, which are the same length).

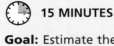

❶ Teaching the Lesson (continued)

Activity 4

Area of Regular Polygons (optional)

 15 MINUTES

Goal: Estimate the area of regular polygons.

Materials: centimeter rulers, Student Activity Book page 90

✔ **NCTM Standards:**
Geometry
Measurement

▶ Area of a Regular Pentagon

WHOLE CLASS

Ask students to make a rough sketch of a regular pentagon. Have them mark a point as close to the center of the pentagon as possible, and then join the point by line segments to each vertex of the pentagon.

● How many triangles did you make? 5

● Are they all congruent? Yes; the pentagon is regular so their bases are all the same. The distances to the center are all the same.

● If the area of the whole pentagon is 10 sq cm, what is the area of each triangle? 2 sq cm

● How can you find the area of the whole pentagon by measuring? Measure the base and height of one triangle and find its area. Then multiply by 5.

Have the students complete exercises 27 and 28 on Student Activity Book page 120. Before completing exercises 29 and 30, ask the students to estimate the area of the regular pentagon, and after the remaining exercises have been completed, compare their estimates with their answers to exercise 30.

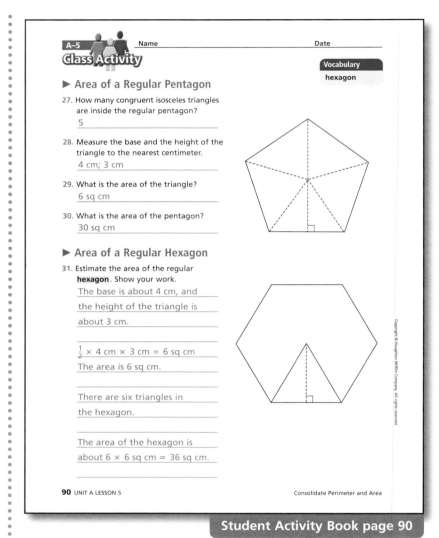

Student Activity Book page 90

▶ Area of a Regular Hexagon

INDIVIDUALS

Students apply what they've learned to estimate the area of the hexagon in exercise 31.

② Extending the Lesson

Intervention
for students having difficulty

INDIVIDUALS

Make a Figure

Materials: Centimeter-Grid Paper (Copymaster M19)

Students draw on grid paper two different parallelograms that have the same base and height. Students explain why the two parallelograms must have the same area.

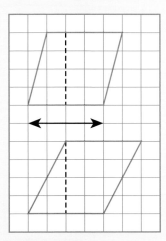

You can cut both parallelograms and rearrange them to make the same rectangle.

On Level
for students having success

PAIRS

Use Reasoning

A rectangle and a non-rectangular parallelogram have the same base and height.

Which has the greater perimeter? Explain your answer.

The non-rectangular parallelogram has a greater perimeter. The top and bottom are the same length but the slanted sides are longer than those of the rectangle.

Challenge
for students seeking a challenge

INDIVIDUALS

Estimate Area

Materials: Centimeter-Grid Paper (Copymaster M19)

Students draw a picture on grid paper. They estimate the area of the figure by counting squares. Students should begin by counting the whole centimeter squares inside the figure, and then count the partial squares along the edges of the figure. Students decide whether to count each partial square as a whole, a half, or nothing.

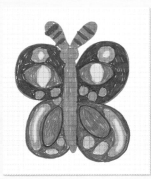

 Math Writing Prompt

Intervention

Draw a Picture
Draw two complex figures with the same area and different perimeters. Explain why their perimeters are different.

 Math Writing Prompt

On Level

Right Triangles
The sides of a right triangle measure 5 cm, 12 cm, and 13 cm. Explain how to find the area of the triangle.

 Math Writing Prompt

Challenge

Area of a Trapezoid
Sketch a trapezoid. Use what you know about triangles and parallelograms to explain what measurements you need to find the area of the trapezoid.

③ Homework and Cumulative Review

A–5
Homework **Goal:** Additional Practice

✓ Include students' work for page 41 as part of their portfolios.

A–5
Remembering **Goal:** Cumulative Review

This Remembering activity is appropriate any time after today's lesson.

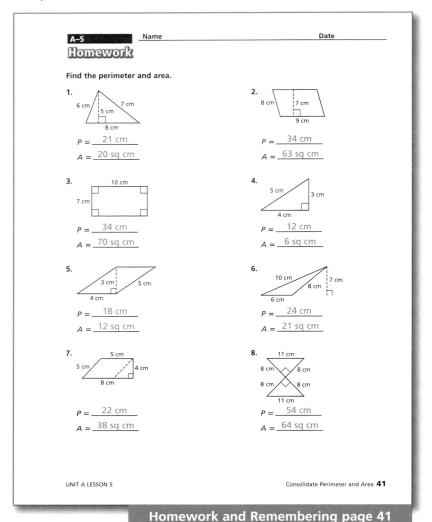

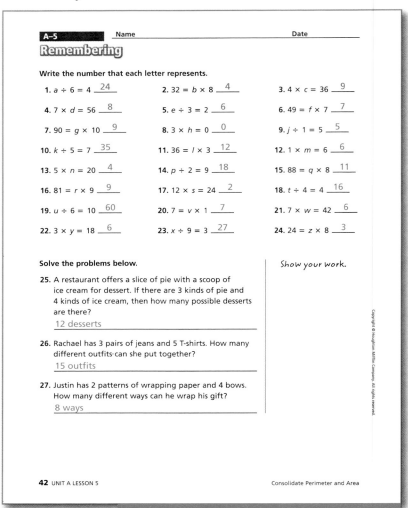

Home or School Activity

Social Studies Connection

Quilts Quilts are made up of complex figures sewn together to make a pattern. Have students research online or in books such as Mary Cobb's *The Quilt-Block History of Pioneer Days with Projects Kids Can Make* (The Millbrook Press, 1995). Have them find and draw at least three different examples of quilt patterns and describe each one using the language of geometry.

Customary Units of Length

Lesson Objectives

- Calculate perimeter and area in customary units.
- Estimate and measure perimeter and area in customary units.

Vocabulary

inch	square inch
foot	square foot
yard	square yard

The Day at a Glance

Today's Goals	Materials	123 Math Talk
1 Teaching the Lesson **A1:** Calculate the perimeter and area of various figures. **A2:** Estimate and measure area and perimeter. **2 Extending the Lesson** ▶ Differentiated Instruction **3 Homework and Cumulative Review**	Student Activity Book pages 91–92 Tape measures, one-foot rulers, or yardsticks Scissors Colored paper at least 12 in. on each side Inch-Grid Paper (Copymaster M2) Homework and Remembering pages 43–44 Math Journals	In today's activities, the students are involved in discussion as they ▶ talk about the relationship among customary measurements and among some metric and customary measurements ▶ describe how to estimate and measure the perimeter and area of the classroom

① Teaching the Lesson

Inches, Feet, and Yards

 20 MINUTES

Goal: Calculate the perimeter and area of various figures.

Materials: Student Activity Book pages 91–92

 NCTM Standards:
Measurement
Reasoning and Proof

▶ Convert Units [WHOLE CLASS]

Review the customary units of length and ask questions about equivalent units.

- What units do you usually use to measure the length of things at home? Possible answers: inches, feet, and yards

- Name some things that are about one inch long or wide. Possible answers: width of a thumb, quarter, thickness of a textbook

- Name some things that are about one foot long or wide. Possible answers: a person's foot, a box of tissue (or cereal), length of a book

- Name some things that are about one yard long or wide. Possible answers: my desk, a window, a picture on the wall

- How many inches are equal to one foot? 12

- How many feet are equal to one yard? 3

- So, how many inches are equal to one yard? $3 \times 12 = 36$

Review the abbreviations for inch, yard, and foot. Write *in.*, *ft*, and *yd* on the board. Explain that we write *in.* with a period so we don't confuse it with the word *in.* The other abbreviations do not need periods.

Now lead a discussion on how to convert among units. On the board, write:

48 in. = _____ ft

_____ ft = 15 yards

- If you know a stick is 48 in. long, how can you find its length in feet? There are 12 in. in a foot, so divide by 12; $48 \div 12 = 4$ ft.

- If you know a lawn is 15 yd long, how can you find its length in feet? There are 3 ft in every one of the 15 yards, so multiply $3 \times 15 = 45$ ft.

- When you convert from a small unit to a larger unit, what operation do you use? Why? Division; the number of units will decrease.

- When you convert from a large unit to a smaller unit, what operation do you use? Why? Multiplication; you need more of the smaller units to measure the same length.

A-6
Class Activity

Name _____   Date _____

Vocabulary
inch
foot
yard

► Convert Units

The **inch** (in.) **foot** (ft) and **yard** (yd) are commonly used units of measure in the Customary System of Measurement.

Complete.

1. 24 in. = __2__ ft
2. 24 ft = __8__ yd
3. 72 in. = __2__ yd
4. __60__ in. = 5 ft
5. __18__ ft = 6 yd
6. __108__ in. = 3 yd
7. 12 ft = __144__ in.
8. 12 yd = __36__ ft
9. 10 yd = __360__ in.

► Calculate Perimeter

Calculate the perimeter of each figure in feet.

10.
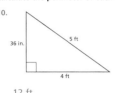
36 in.   5 ft   4 ft

____12 ft____

11.
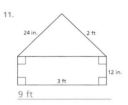
24 in.   2 ft   3 ft   12 in.

____9 ft____

Calculate the perimeter of each figure in yards.

12.
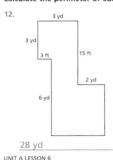
3 yd   3 yd   3 ft   15 ft   2 yd   6 yd

____28 yd____

13.
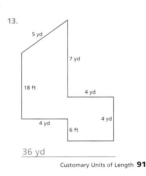
5 yd   7 yd   18 ft   4 yd   4 yd   4 yd   6 ft

____36 yd____

UNIT A LESSON 6   Customary Units of Length **91**

Student Activity Book page 91

Compare a Meter and a Yard Discuss the relative sizes of meters and yards.

● Which metric unit looks about the same length as a yard? a meter

Have students measure a meter in inches.

● About how long is a meter in inches? 39 in.

● Which is longer, a meter or a yard? A meter; a yard is only 36 in.

Invite students to complete exercises 1–9.

► Calculate Perimeter INDIVIDUALS

Have students complete exercises 10–13. Remind students that they cannot add two numbers unless they are expressed in the same units. For example, when you add two nickels and three dimes, you need to convert the units to find the total amount in cents.

Teaching Note

Watch For! Be aware of students who simply add the measurements shown. Remind them that there are some dimensions left unmarked that need to be included in the perimeter. Students can find these dimensions by looking at the total lengths of the opposite sides.

Activity continued ▶

Customary Units of Length   **153**

① Teaching the Lesson (continued)

▶ Calculate Area WHOLE CLASS

As a class, discuss the customary units used to measure area.

- A square that is 1 cm on each side has an area of 1 sq cm. Draw a square that is one inch on each side. What is the area of your square? 1 sq in.

- Draw a square that is one foot on each side. What is the area of your square? 1 sq ft

- What is the area of a square that is one yard on each side? 1 sq yd

Compare Square Meters and Square Yards Students constructed a square meter in Lesson 1 of this unit. Ask them to use 3 one-foot lengths to show an area of one square yard.

- What unit of area looks about the same size as one square yard? 1 sq m

Discuss the relative sizes of one square meter and one square yard.

- Which is greater, one square meter or one square yard? 1 sq m because each side of a meter square is greater than a yard

Assign exercises 14–19. Remind students that they need to convert dimensions into the same units before they can multiply them, and that some dimensions may be missing. Students can find missing dimensions by looking at the opposite sides.

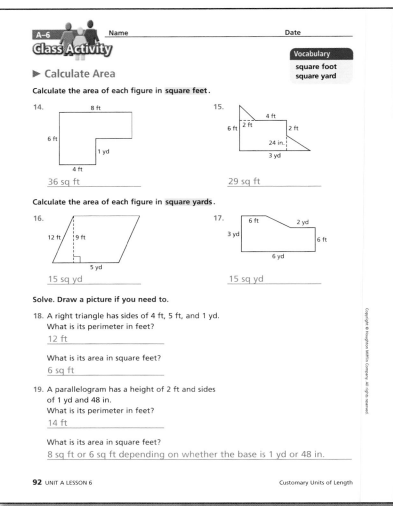

Real-World Applications

 40 MINUTES

Goal: Estimate and measure area and perimeter.

Materials: tape measures, one-foot rulers, or yardsticks

 NCTM Standard:
Measurement

▶ Estimate Baseboard for the Classroom PAIRS

Explain that students are going to estimate the perimeter of the classroom in order to replace the classroom baseboard. Have students pace off the length and width of the classroom with a partner. They count the number of paces in the width and the number in the length. Students measure the length of their pace by walking a few steps and stopping in stride. A partner measures the length from the heel of one foot to the heel of another.

Discuss the methods the students used.

● What unit did you use to measure your pace?

● How did you use the number of paces to calculate the length and width of the classroom? Multiply the number of paces by the measurement of one pace.

Most students will use feet for the size of the pace. Encourage discussion of alternative methods of estimation. You might discuss adjusting the pace to reach a whole number of feet (two or three feet). Some students may experiment with measuring from heel to toe as one foot, and estimate the number of feet more directly. Some students may use inches to estimate more accurately with a calculator if available.

On the board, create a table in which each pair of students can record their results.

Pair		Length of a Pace	Number of Paces	Measurement of Classroom
1	Width:			
	Length:			
2	Width:			
	Length:			
3	Width:			
	Length:			

Discuss the collected data.

● Who had the greatest length and width?

● Who had the least?

● Within what range do most of the results fall?

● What length should we use for our estimate? What width?

Use the numbers that students choose for the estimate to calculate the perimeter of the classroom.

● How much baseboard do we need for the whole classroom?

✓ Ongoing Assessment

Encourage students to explain their thinking by asking such questions as

▶ What customary unit of measurement is best for measuring the area of a book cover?

▶ What customary unit of measurement is best for measuring the area of the school yard?

▶ What customary unit of measurement is best for measuring the area of a classroom?

Activity continued ▶

▶ Carpet the Classroom SMALL GROUPS

Use the length and width measurements estimated in the baseboard activity. Draw a rectangle on the board, about the same shape as the classroom. Label the dimensions.

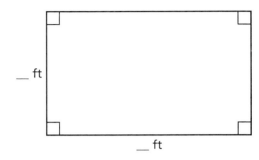

Explain to students that they are going to make a plan to use carpet tiles to cover the classroom floor. The carpet tiles come in two sizes: one-foot squares and two-foot squares. Students will estimate the number of tiles they need.

Divide the class into two groups. The pairs in one group will estimate the number of one-foot squares; the pairs in the other group, two-foot squares. Students need to be sure they have enough tiles to cover the whole floor — they can't have too few.

When the students have made their estimates, bring them together and discuss the results.

● How many one-foot squares do you need?

● How do you know you'll have enough to cover the whole floor? We added an extra foot to each length estimate before we multiplied to find the area.

● How many two-foot squares do you need?

● How did you find the total? We divided each length by 2 to find the number of tiles that fit along each wall. Then we multiplied to find the number of tiles to cover the area.

● How do you know you'll have enough to cover the whole floor? We made sure to add an extra tile along each wall.

Discuss the relationship among the two results.

● What is the area of a two-foot tile? 4 sq ft

● How many one-foot tiles do you need to cover the same area as a two-foot tile covers? 4

● How can you use the number of one-foot tiles to find the number of two-foot tiles? divide by 4

● How can you use the number of two-foot tiles to find the number of one-foot tiles? multiply by 4

Invite students to check their results.

● Multiply the number of two-foot tiles by 4. Is it about the same as the estimate for one-foot tiles? Yes, it's close.

● Why might it be a bit different? The two-foot tiles are much bigger. They are a less accurate unit of measure. With two-foot tiles you might have more leftover tiles after you cut them down along the edges.

② Extending the Lesson

Intervention
for students having difficulty
PAIRS

Make a Square Yard

Materials: scissors, colored paper at least 12 in. on each side

Students measure a one-foot square on paper and cut out nine copies of the square. They arrange the squares to make one square yard and determine the perimeter of the square yard.

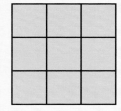

Next, students rearrange the squares to make other shapes and tell the area (1 sq yd or 9 sq ft) and perimeter of the new shapes (answers will vary).

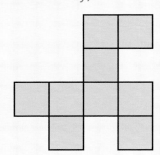

On Level
for students having success
PAIRS

Investigate Math

Materials: Inch-Grid Paper (Copymaster M2)

On their grid paper students draw a complex figure with an area of 60 sq in. They label its dimensions in inches and then suggest possible dimensions for a rectangle with the same area.

Possible answers: 5 × 12 or 6 × 10 or 3 × 20 or 2 × 30

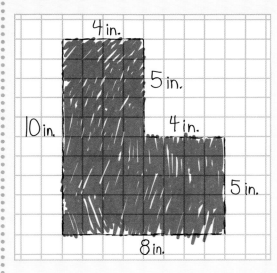

Challenge
for students seeking a challenge
INDIVIDUALS

Use Reasoning

Students draw an L-shaped figure made of two rectangles. They label the dimensions in yards and show how to use subtraction to find the area.

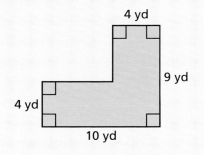

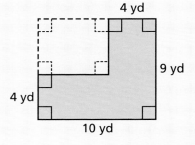

Possible answer: The big rectangle is 90 sq yd.

The dotted rectangle is 30 sq yd.

The area of the figure is 90 − 30 = 60 sq yd.

Students draw another figure whose area they can find using subtraction.

 Math Writing Prompt

Intervention
Change Units
If a rectangle is 24 in. x 36 in., what is its perimeter in feet? What is its area in square feet?

 Math Writing Prompt

On Level
Explain Your Thinking
Will cutting up and rearranging a figure change its perimeter or area? Explain your answer.

 Math Writing Prompt

Challenge
Investigate Math
How many square inches are in a square foot? Use your answer to estimate how many square inches are in a square meter.

③ Homework and Cumulative Review

 **Homework** **Goal:** Additional Practice

✔ For homework, students calculate the perimeter and area of various figures in customary units.

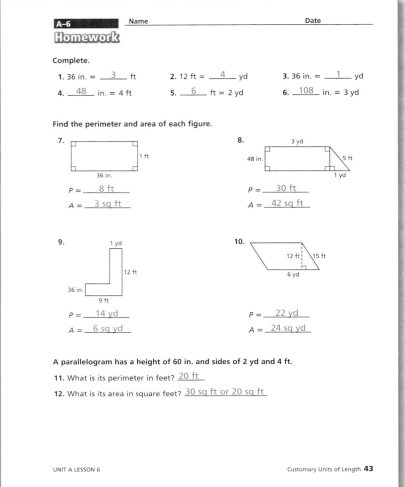

Homework and Remembering page 43

 **Remembering** **Goal:** Cumulative Review

This Remembering activity is appropriate any time after today's lesson.

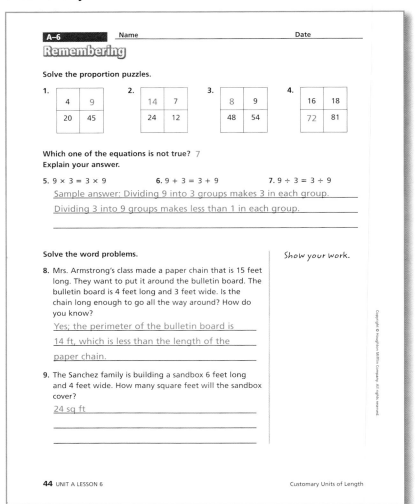

Homework and Remembering page 44

Home or School Activity

 Social Studies Connection

Customary Measurement Ask students why it is important to measure in units that are a consistent size. What measurement system is used in most of the world? Ask students why they think units such as inches, feet, and yards are called *customary units*.

Unit Review and Test

Lesson Objective

● **Assess student progress on unit objectives.**

The Day at a Glance

Today's Goals	Materials
1 Teaching the Lesson ▶ Assess student progress on unit objectives. ▶ Use activities from unit lessons to reteach content. **2 Extending the Lesson** ▶ Use remediation for common errors. There is no homework assignment on a test day.	Unit A Test, Student Activity Book pages 93–94 Unit A Test, Form A or B, Assessment Guide (optional) Unit A Performance Assessment, Assessment Guide (optional)

Teaching the Lesson

Assess Unit Objectives

45 MINUTES (more if schedule permits)

Goal: Assess student progress on unit objectives

Materials: Student Activity Book pages 93–94; Assessment masters A14–A23 (optional)

▶ Review and Assessment

If your students are ready for assessment on the unit objectives, you may use either the test on the Student Activity Book pages or one of the forms of the Unit A Test in the Assessment Guide to assess student progress.

If you feel that students need some review first, you may use the test on the Student Activity Book pages as a review of unit content, and then use one of the forms of the Unit A Test in the Assessment Guide to assess student progress.

To assign a numerical score for all of these test forms, use 10 points for each question.

You may also choose to use the Unit A Performance Assessment. Scoring for that assessment can be found in its rubric in the Assessment Guide.

▶ Reteaching Resources

The chart lists the test items, the unit objectives they cover, and the lesson activities in which the objective is covered in this unit. You may revisit these activities with students who do not show mastery of the objectives.

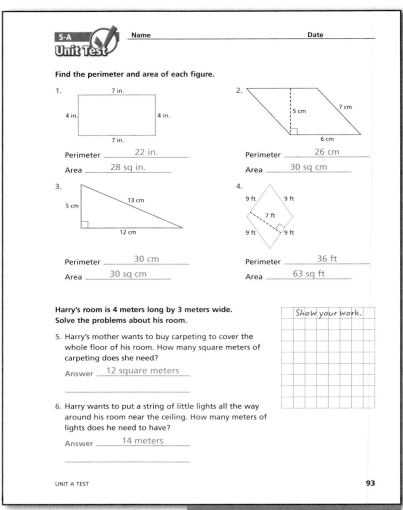

Student Activity Book page 93

Unit Test Items	Unit Objectives Tested	Activities to Use for Reteaching
1–4	**A.1** Find perimeter and area of polygons.	Lesson 2, Activity 2 Lesson 3, Activity 2 Lesson 3, Activity 3
5, 6, 9, 10	**A.2** Use customary and metric measurements to solve problems involving perimeter and area.	Lesson 1, Activity 2 Lesson 6, Activity 1
7, 8	**A.3** Find perimeter and area of complex figures.	Lesson 5, Activity 3

5–A
Unit Test

Name _____ Date _____

Find the perimeter and area of each figure.

7.

```
        7 cm
   ┌──────────┐
4 cm│          │╲ 5 cm
   │          │ ╲
   └──────────┘──╲
      10 cm
```

Perimeter _____ 26 cm _____
Area _____ 34 sq cm _____

8.

```
      ╲     5 ft
       ╲_____
7 ft    │   3 ft
        │   2 ft ┌─ 2 ft
        │        │  ┌─ 2 ft
        └────────┴──┘
            9 ft
```

Perimeter _____ 30 ft _____
Area _____ 38 sq ft _____

Solve the word problems.

9. A parallelogram has a height of 36 in. and sides of 2 ft and 4 ft. What is its area in square feet?

   6 sq ft

   Show your work.

10. **Extended Response** Gina is framing a picture that is 9 in. wide and 10 in. high. She has 3 ft of framing material. Does she have enough material to frame the picture? Explain your answer.

    No. The perimeter of the picture is 38 in.

    She would need more than that to frame the

    picture. She has 3 ft of frame. That is only

    36 in.

94 UNIT A TEST

Student Activity Book page 94

▶ Assessment Resources

Free Response Tests
Unit A Test, Student Activity Book pages 93–94
Unit A Test, Form A, Assessment Guide

Extended Response Item
The last item in the Student Activity Book test and in the Form A test will require an extended response as an answer.

Multiple Choice Test
Unit A Test, Form B, Assessment Guide

Performance Assessment
Unit A Performance Assessment, Assessment Guide, page A21
Unit A Performance Assessment Rubric, Assessment Guide

▶ Portfolio Assessment

Teacher-selected Items for Student Portfolios:

- Homework, Lessons 2, 3, 5

- Class Activity work, Lessons 4, 6

Student-selected Items for Student Portfolios

- Favorite Home or School Activity

- Best Writing Prompt

② Extending the Assessment

Unit Objective A.1

Find perimeter and area of polygons.

Common Error: Doesn't Use All Measurements

In finding perimeter, students may fail to use the lengths of all sides of a polygon.

Remediation Remind students that the number of addends used to find the perimeter must equal the number of sides of the polygon. Suggest that it may help to count the sides and the addends as a check that all sides have been included.

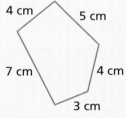

5 sides √
4 cm
5 cm
4 cm
3 cm
+ 7 cm
23 cm

Unit Objective A.2

Use customary and metric measurements to solve problems involving perimeter and area.

Common Error: Doesn't Label the Answer

In writing answers to problems, students may not include a unit of measure with their numerical answers.

Remediation Point out that a measurement problem usually requires a unit of measure with the answer. Emphasize that it is important to look back at the problem to see what unit of measure is needed for the label.

Common Error: Forgets to Convert Units

In setting up the computation needed to find an answer, students may not be using the same unit for all dimensions.

Remediation Remind students that they need to compute with the same unit of measure. Suggest that they check to see that all units of measure are the same and that they stop to convert any measurements that are not the same before doing any computation.

Unit Objective A.2

Find perimeter and area of complex figures.

Common Error: Includes the Same Length More Than Once

In finding the perimeter of a complex figure, students may lose track of how the lengths of the sides relate to the whole figure and may include a length more than once.

Remediation Remind students that they need to use only the lengths of the line segments that are around the edges of the figure to find the perimeter. Suggest that they mark each side as they include it in the addends they are using to find the perimeter.

Common Error: Includes Part of the Area More Than Once

When decomposing a complex figure, students may include part of the area more than once.

Remediation Remind students that they first separate the figure into smaller parts for which they can find the area. Suggest that they shade each part of the complex figure as they find its area to prevent including it in another part. They might even write in the area for each part of the figure.

Addition and Subtraction With Whole Numbers and Decimals

UNIT 2 BUILDS upon the concepts of number combinations and comparisons. The activities in this unit help students gain a practical understanding of addition and subtraction of whole numbers and decimals, and the relationship between the two operations. Students are expected to apply their understanding of addition and subtraction to numeric calculations and real-world problem-solving situations. This includes the use of graphing, situation and solution equations, and metric measurement to understand addition and subtraction relationships.

UNIT 2 CONTENTS

Unit 2 Assessment

✓ Unit Objectives Tested	Unit Test Items	Lessons
2.1 Read, write, and identify the place value of decimals and whole numbers.	1–4	1, 4, 5
2.2 Compare, order, and round numbers and estimate sums and differences.	5–8	2, 12, 15
2.3 Add and subtract whole numbers and decimals.	9–12	3, 6, 7, 8, 10
2.4 Interpret and make pictographs, bar graphs, and line graphs.	13–18	11–15
2.5 Solve a variety of problems involving addition and subtraction of whole numbers and decimals.	19–20	9, 16–19

Formal Assessment

Open or Free Response Tests

- Quick Quizzes (Assessment Guide)
- Unit Review and Test (Student Activity Book pages 153–154, Teacher's Guide pages 293–296)
- Unit 2 Test Form A (Assessment Guide)
- Unit 2 Open Response Test (Test Generator)
- Test Bank Items for Unit 2 (Test Generator)

Multiple Choice Tests

- Unit 2 Test Form B (Assessment Guide)
- Unit 2 Multiple Choice Test (Test Generator)
- Test Bank Items for Unit 2 (Test Generator)

Performance Tasks

- Unit 2 Performance Assessment (Assessment Guide)
- Unit 2 Performance Assessment (Test Generator)

Informal Assessment

Ongoing Assessment

- In every Teacher's Guide lesson

Performance Assessment

- Class discussions
- Small-group work
- Quick Practice (in every lesson)
- Individual work on teacher-selected tasks

Portfolios

- See Unit 2 Review and Test for suggestions for selecting items for portfolios.
- Some Homework pages are noted as suitable for portfolio inclusion.

Review Opportunities

Homework and Remembering

- Homework pages provide review of recently taught topics.
- Remembering pages provide cumulative review.

Teacher's Guide

- Unit Review and Test (page 293–296)
- Finger Factors (multiple pages)
- Division Cards (multiple pages)
- MathBoards (multiple pages)
- Write-On and Check sheets (multiple pages)

Teacher's Resource Book

- Problem Bank

Test Generator CD-ROM

- Test Bank Items can be used to create custom review sheets.

Planning Unit 2 Unit Pacing: 26–30 days

Lesson Title	Lesson Resources	Materials and Manipulatives	
		Math Expressions	**Other**
1 Thousand to Thousandths	Student Activity Book pages 95–98 Homework and Remembering pages 45–46 Family Letter	Product Cards	number cubes, tokens or counters, ruler, Math Journals
2 Equate and Compare	Homework and Remembering pages 47–48	MathBoard materials	grid paper, crayons, Math Journals
3 Use Decimal Numbers	Homework and Remembering pages 49–50	MathBoard materials, Place Value Parade poster	meter stick, Meter Stick (Copymaster M21), colored string or yarn, scissors, transparent tape, centimeter rulers, centimeter grid paper (Copymaster M19), Math Journals
4 Billions to Billionths	Student Activity Book pages 103–110 Homework and Remembering pages 51–52	MathBoard materials, Place Value Parade poster	Patterns from Billions to Billionths (Copymaster M22), Secret Code Cards (Copymaster M23) scissors, index cards, paper clips, Math Journals
5 Use Place Value	Student Activity Book pages 111–112 Homework and Remembering pages 53–54 Quick Quiz 1		calculators, number cubes, Math Journals
6 Add Whole Numbers and Decimals	Student Activity Book pages 113–114 Homework and Remembering pages 55–56	MathBoard materials	centimeter rulers, play or real money—dollars, dimes and pennies, Math Journals
7 Add to Millions	Student Activity Book pages 115–116 Homework and Remembering pages 57–58	MathBoard materials	place value charts, calculators, Math Journals
8 Subtract Whole Numbers and Decimals	Student Activity Book pages 117–118 Homework and Remembering pages 59–60	MathBoard materials	Play money, calculators, Math Journals
9 Place Value Word Problems	Student Activity Book pages 119–122 Homework and Remembering pages 61–62	MathBoard materials	Index cards, Math Journals
10 Properties and Strategies	Student Activity Book pages 123–124 Homework and Remembering pages 63–64 Quick Quiz 2		index cards, grid paper, Math Journals
11 Pictographs With Large Numbers	Student Activity Book pages 125–126 Homework and Remembering pages 65–66		counters, grid paper, Math Journals
12 Round Numbers on Graphs	Student Activity Book pages 127–130 Homework and Remembering pages 67–68		Secret Code Cards (Copymaster M23), Math Journals
13 Bar Graphs and Rounding	Student Activity Book pages 131–132 Homework and Remembering pages 69–70		connecting cubes, grid paper, Math Journals
14 Introduce Line Graphs	Student Activity Book pages 133–136 Homework and Remembering pages 71–72	MathBoard materials	grid paper, Math Journals

Lesson Title	Lesson Resources	Materials and Manipulatives	
		Math Expressions	**Other**
15 Graphs With Decimal Numbers	Student Activity Book pages 137–140 Homework and Remembering pages 73–74 **Quick Quiz 3**		Grid paper, meter sticks, Math Journals
16 Classify Word Problems	Student Activity Book pages 141–144 Homework and Remembering pages 75–76		counters, Math Journals
17 Situation and Solution Equations	Student Activity Book pages 145–148 Homework and Remembering pages 77–78		index cards, centimeter rulers, grid paper (optional), Math Journals
18 Comparison Problems	Student Activity Book pages 149–150 Homework and Remembering pages 79-80		counters, Math Journals
19 Two-Step Word Problems	Student Activity Book pages 151–152 Homework and Remembering pages 81–82 **Quick Quiz 4**		grid paper, play money (optional), Math Journals
✓ **Unit 2 Review and Test**	Student Activity Book pages 153–154 Assessment Guide		

Unit 2 Teaching Resources

Differentiated Instruction

Reaching All Learners

English Learners

Lesson 13, page 246

Lesson 16, page 264

Lesson 17, page 275

Extra Help

Lesson 8, page 213   Lesson 12, page 238, 239

Lesson 13, page 246   Lesson 15, page 259

Lesson 17, page 274

Special Needs

Lesson 5, page 192

Lesson 7, page 206

Lesson 12, page 239

Individualizing Instruction

Activities
- Intervention (in every lesson)
- On Level (in every lesson)
- Challenge (in every lesson)

Math Writing Prompts
- Intervention (in every lesson)
- On Level (in every lesson)
- Challenge (in every lesson)

Cross-Curricular Links • Home or School Activities

 Social Studies Connections

Commas or Dots? (Lesson 4, page 190)

Lots of Time (Lesson 6, page 202)

Millions of People (Lesson 7, page 208)

Morse Code (Lesson 17, page 278)

Great Lakes (Lesson 18, page 286)

 Science Connections

Millions and Billions of Miles (Lesson 5, page 196)

Seeing Colors (Lesson 8, page 216)

Animal Facts (Lesson 9, page 222)

Your Weather (Lesson 15, page 262)

 Art Connection

Stone Age Art (Lesson 11, page 236)

 Music Connection

Orchestra Arrangements (Lesson 10, page 228)

 Language Arts Connection

Metric Prefixes (Lesson 3, page 182)

Comparison Suffixes (Lesson 16, page 270)

 Multicultural Connection

Melting Pot (Lesson 13, page 250)

 Technology Connections

Calculator Zeros (Lesson 2, page 174)

Computer Graphing (Lesson 14, page 256)

 Real-World Connections

Shopping Trip (Lesson 12, page 244)

Perimeter and Area (Lesson 19, page 292)

Teaching Unit 2

Putting Research into Practice for Unit 2

From Our Curriculum Research Project

High-level goals are achieved by enabling all children to enter the mathematical activity at their own level. Teachers accomplish this by using rich and varied language about a given problem so that all children come to understand the problem situation, by mathematizing (focusing on the mathematical features of) a situation to which all children can relate (and that may be generated by a child) , and by having children draw models of the problem situation. Cumulative experiencing and practicing of important knowledge skills helps children move through developmental trajectories to more advanced methods. Peer helping provides targeted assistance when necessary. The knowledge of the helper also increases. Assessment provides feedback to all and permits realistic adjustments of proximal learning goals by children and by the teacher.

Fuson, Karen C., et al. "Blending the Best of the Twentieth Century to Achieve a Mathematics Equity Pedagogy in the Twenty-First Century." *Learning Mathematics for a New Century, 2000 Yearbook.* Reston: NCTM, 2000. 197–212.

From Current Research: Promoting Meaningful Mastery of Addition and Subtraction

The development of number sense and computational fluency should be part of the mathematics curriculum. Providing activities that develop conceptual understanding of number operations, rather than focusing on memorization and rules, gives students an opportunity to use strategies that are natural for them. Students may then develop their own problem solving techniques.

Postlewait, Kristian, Michelle Adams, and Jeffrey Shih. "Promoting Meaningful Mastery of Addition and Subtraction." *Teaching Children Mathematics*, February, 2003, Vol. 9, Issue 6, pages 354–357.

Other Useful References: Addition and Subtraction of Whole Numbers and Decimals

Van de Walle, John A. "Decimal and Percent Concepts and Decimal Computation." *Elementary and Middle School Mathematics: Teaching Developmentally* (Third Edition). New York: Longman, 2001, pages 274–291.

Math Background

Concept Building Activities

Place Value for Addition and Subtraction

Students should now have experience working with the place values of large and small numbers. They may have been asked to estimate to the largest place value or even a specific place value.

Estimate to the Largest Place Value:	Estimate to a Specific Place Value:
279 to the largest place is 300	279 to the nearest 10 is 280

Students who have experience with place value have a better understanding of the base ten system. They can then use this information to help them group numbers and ungroup numbers as needed when adding and subtracting.

Place Value and Decimals

When students understand how base ten place values work for whole numbers, it is a fairly easy transition to base ten values for decimals. The places still represent multiples of ten and the naming convention is very similar. Addition and subtraction follow the same grouping and ungrouping rules over the place values.

Whole Number Addition:

$$\begin{array}{r} \overset{1}{4}16 \\ +\ 128 \\ \hline 544 \end{array}$$

Decimal Addition:

$$\begin{array}{r} \overset{1}{4}1.6 \\ +\ 12.8 \\ \hline 54.4 \end{array}$$

Problem Solving

Real-World Problem-Solving

Throughout the unit, real-world situations are used as the context for problem-solving situations. Students use Solve and Discuss methods to apply strategies for solving addition and subtraction of large numbers and decimals.

Fluency Days

Fluency days provide students with in-class opportunities to assess themselves on basic multiplications and divisions. Students will monitor their own learning through the use of hands-on materials and quick activities that were first introduced in Grade 5 Unit 1. A lesson reference is included for a more detailed description of each activity. If your students need more practice to build fluency, include a Fluency Day in your teaching plan for this unit or use one or more of these activities throughout the school year.

Diagnostic Quizzes (See Unit 1 Lesson 10)

These diagnostic quizzes are designed to help students determine which multiplications and divisions they "automatically" know and which they still need to study. Distribute copies of the multiplication quiz, division quiz, or both to the whole class. You can also divide the class and distribute a different version to each group depending on students' needs. Give a signal to start and then allow only 3 minutes for students to complete each. Then read the answers aloud and have students circle their own mistakes. Allow some time for students to work out any unfinished or missed problems in class. Encourage students to take home their quizzes for further practice.

Division Cards (See Unit 1 Lesson 10)

Students may practice with these cards individually or with a partner. Students first make sure their cards are stacked correctly so that the side without the answers is face up in their stack (the slanted corners on the right should line up). Then, one student reads the problem, solves the problem mentally, and turns the card over to check his or her answer. Students then sort their Division Cards into *Fast*, *Slow*, and *Don't Know* piles. They practice the *Slow* and *Don't Know* piles. Product cards are also used with the *Factor Field* game introduced in Unit 1.

Games

The Factor Field (Unit 1 Lesson 10)—Students practice their divisions by reading each division problem on their Division Cards and then placing the card on the *Factor Field* game board section that corresponds to the answer.

Factor the Footprints (Unit 1 Lesson 14)—Students practice finding factors with a partner by naming all the possible factor pairs they can find for each number they follow along the *Factor the Footprints* game board path.

Teaching Unit 2 (Continued)

Target Practice (See Unit 1 Lesson 3)

The Target is used together with students' multiplication tables. It may be used either independently or with an in-class practice partner. The Target circle shows a product. The shaded overlay with the transparent L-shape and Target circle can be moved to any product. The ends of the L show the factors, and the Target shows the product. Covering the product provides multiplication practice while covering one end of the L provides division practice.

Scrambled Multiplication Tables (See Unit 1 Lesson 11)

These scrambled tables are multiplication tables with the rows and columns moved around. Students practice their multiplications by completing the missing factors or products in each table.

Factor Puzzles (See Unit 1 Lesson 14)

Students use their knowledge of count-bys and multiplications to fill in the unknown section of the Factor Puzzle. Students verify their work by finding the corresponding four cells on the Multiplication Table. Their answer is correct if the cells form a rectangle. Have students solve these individually or with a partner. You may also challenge students to create their own Factor Puzzles and exchange papers with a partner. Factor Puzzles not only enable students to practice multiplication and division, but also help them develop the ability to do proportional thinking.

12	18
20	

Thousands to Thousandths

Lesson Objectives

- Use fractions and decimals to describe relationships among different place values.
- Represent real-life situations with decimal numbers.

The Day at a Glance

Today's Goals	Materials	123 Math Talk
1 Teaching the Lesson A1: Discuss patterns in a place-value chart. A2: Identify and write decimal amounts for real-world situations. **2 Extending the Lesson** ▶ Differentiated Instruction **3 Homework and Cumulative Review**	Student Activity Book pages 95–98 Number cubes Tokens or counters Ruler Homework and Remembering pages 45–46 Math Journals Family Letter	In today's activities, the students are involved in discussion as they ▶ identify, read, and write decimal numbers ▶ use decimals in real-world situations

Quick Practice

This section provides repetitive, short activities that either help students become faster and more accurate at a skill or help to prepare ground for new concepts.

Quick Practice for this unit will start with Lesson 2.

① Teaching the Lesson

Explore Decimal Numbers

 30 MINUTES

Goal: Discuss patterns in a place-value chart.

Materials: Student Activity Book page 95

 NCTM Standards:
Number and Operations
Communication

Teaching Note

Language and Vocabulary
Emphasize to students the importance of careful reading. Write these words on the board:

Tens	Ten**ths**
Hundreds	Hundred**ths**
Thousands	Thousand**ths**

Explain that the words with "th" represent parts of a whole—fractions less than 1.

Teaching Note

Math Background Students should understand these main points before continuing with the activity:

• The decimal point separates whole numbers from parts of a whole.

• The numbers after the decimal point represent fractions less than 1.

• 33.3 means $33\frac{3}{10}$.

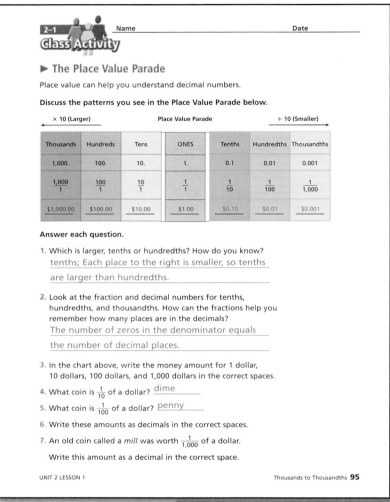

Student Activity Book page 95

▶ The Decimal Point WHOLE CLASS

Write the number 33 on the board. Ask the class to tell the value of each 3. 3 tens, 3 ones Now write a decimal point and another 3 to the right of the decimal to show the number 33.3. Ask,

● What is the name of the dot? decimal point

● What do the numbers in front of the decimal point represent? whole numbers

● What do the numbers after the decimal point represent? parts of a whole

● What does the decimal point do? It separates whole numbers from parts of a whole.

● What is the value of the last 3? 3 tenths

▶ The Place Value Parade WHOLE CLASS

Direct students' attention to page 95. Ask students to study the chart and then describe any patterns. (Several are described at the right.)

Now have the class discuss the questions below the Place Value Parade:

1. Some students may be confused by the fact that the decimal numbers become smaller as we move to the right, while the words sound as if they are getting larger (tenths, hundredths, thousandths). If this is an issue, remind students of what they already know about fractions. Tenths are larger than hundredths because the whole is split into fewer pieces. It may be helpful for students to imagine a fraction bar divided into tenths and hundredths.

2. Students should know that the number of decimal places equals the number of zeros in the denominator of the fraction. Tenths have one decimal place, just as 10 has one zero. Hundredths have two decimal places, just as 100 has two zeros, and so on.

3. Students are already familiar with decimal numbers in money and can probably write the missing dollar amounts in the chart.

4–6. The penny amount is one-hundredth (0.01), but the dime amount appears as 10 hundredths (0.10) instead of 1 tenth (0.1). Ask students how we know that 10 hundredths is the same as 1 tenth. If we write these amounts as fractions, we see that $\frac{10}{100}$ can be simplified to $\frac{1}{10}$.

▶ Name the Decimal Places WHOLE CLASS

Write these decimal numbers on the board:

0.5	0.05	0.005
0.7	0.07	0.007

Ask students to say the numbers as you point to them in order, left to right. Then have students practice as you point to the numbers out of order.

If students have difficulty, remind them of the place value names for whole numbers—tens, hundreds, thousands. Tell them to use the "th" to get the place value names for places after the decimal point—tenths, hundredths, thousandths. Have students say "tenths, hundredths, thousandths" as you point to the decimal places, moving to the right from the decimal point. Have them repeat this pattern until it becomes automatic.

To reinforce students' understanding, ask:

● What are the place values that are greater than one? tens, hundreds, thousands

● What are the place values that are less than one? tenths, hundredths, thousandths

Teaching Note

Math Background Looking at the row of place names or the row of fractions, the place-value chart is symmetrical, with the line of symmetry going through the ones place. On either side of the ones, the other place values match up: tens with tenths, hundreds with hundredths, and thousands with thousandths.

Places in the place-value chart get larger to the left and smaller to the right. Each place to the left is 10 times as large, and each place to the right is $\frac{1}{10}$ as large. Stated another way, moving one place to the left multiplies a number by 10, and moving one place to the right divides a number by 10.

Teaching Note

Watch for Students may not clearly describe the relationships in the place-value chart. Ask the students to help each other when someone has trouble. At times your students may describe only a partial pattern, for example, "The tenths are 10 times greater than the hundredths." Help them to extend their description to the whole system, such as "Each place is 10 times greater as we move to the left."

Activity 2

Practice With Decimals

 15 MINUTES

Goal: Identify and write decimal amounts for real-world situations.

Materials: Student Activity Book page 96

✔ **NCTM Standards:**
Number and Operations
Communication
Problem Solving

Teaching Note

Language and Vocabulary Remind students to say *and* when they see a decimal point. For exercise 14, encourage students to emphasize the word as they say "two *and* four hundredths." Have several volunteers say it individually, and then have the class say it in unison.

 Ongoing Assessment

Ask students to say and write amounts such as:

▶ 0.05

▶ 9.52

▶ 8.001

▶ 24 cents

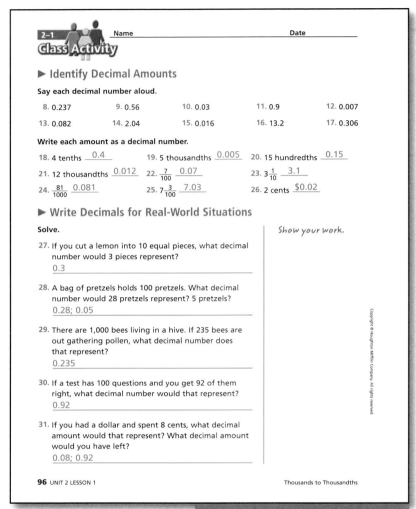

Student Activity Book page 96

The activity book page shows:

2–1 Class Activity — Name / Date

▶ **Identify Decimal Amounts**

Say each decimal number aloud.

8. 0.237   9. 0.56   10. 0.03   11. 0.9   12. 0.007

13. 0.082   14. 2.04   15. 0.016   16. 13.2   17. 0.306

Write each amount as a decimal number.

18. 4 tenths _0.4_   19. 5 thousandths _0.005_   20. 15 hundredths _0.15_

21. 12 thousandths _0.012_   22. $\frac{7}{100}$ _0.07_   23. $3\frac{1}{10}$ _3.1_

24. $\frac{81}{1000}$ _0.081_   25. $7\frac{3}{100}$ _7.03_   26. 2 cents _$0.02_

▶ **Write Decimals for Real-World Situations**

Solve.   *Show your work.*

27. If you cut a lemon into 10 equal pieces, what decimal number would 3 pieces represent?
0.3

28. A bag of pretzels holds 100 pretzels. What decimal number would 28 pretzels represent? 5 pretzels?
0.28; 0.05

29. There are 1,000 bees living in a hive. If 235 bees are out gathering pollen, what decimal number does that represent?
0.235

30. If a test has 100 questions and you get 92 of them right, what decimal number would that represent?
0.92

31. If you had a dollar and spent 8 cents, what decimal amount would that represent? What decimal amount would you have left?
0.08; 0.92

96 UNIT 2 LESSON 1   Thousands to Thousandths

▶ Identify Decimal Amounts [WHOLE CLASS]

On page 96 of the Student Activity Book, students must identify decimal numbers. One strategy is to first read the number, ignoring the decimal point and leftmost zeros, and then decide whether it is tenths, hundredths, or thousandths. For exercise 8, guide the class with these instructions and questions:

● Look at exercise 8. Cover the zero and the decimal point with your finger. Now say the number that you see. 237

● There are 3 places after the decimal. Is the third decimal place tenths, hundredths, or thousandths? thousandths

● Now say the decimal number. 237 thousandths

Have students complete exercises 9–17 by saying the decimal numbers aloud, and then exercises 18–26 by writing the decimal numbers.

Have the class solve problems 27–31. Offer help as needed.

② Extending the Lesson

Intervention
for students having difficulty

PAIRS

Line Up Wholes!

Materials: number cubes labeled 1–6, tokens or counters, ruler

Give each pair of students 2 number cubes, 2 tokens, and 1 ruler. Each pair of students uses the ruler to draw a number line 12 units long. Taking turns, students roll both number cubes, add the numbers, and place their tokens at the correct place on the number line. The student closest to 12 wins that round.

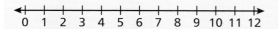

On Level
for students having success

PAIRS

Line Up Decimals!

Materials: ruler

Give each student a ruler. Have students draw a number line from 0 to 1 with tick marks for every tenth. Write these numbers on the board: 0.2, 1.0, 0.65 Have students plot the numbers on their number line.

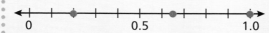

Next, tell students to draw another number line and plot 0.4, 0.9, and 0.25. Have them compare their drawings with their partners'. Then they can give each other decimal numbers to plot.

Challenge
for students seeking a challenge

PAIRS

Estimate!

Materials: ruler

Have students draw a number line from 0 to 4 with tick marks at whole numbers and halves. Ask students to use estimation to place these numbers on the number line: 3.16, 2.75, 1.8, 3.55

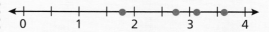

Challenge students to create other number lines and plot higher numbers. For example: 74.75, 152.1, and 173.27

 Math Writing Prompt

Intervention

Explain Your Thinking
Explain how *tens* and *tenths* are different.

 Math Writing Prompt

On Level

Explain Your Thinking
Explain how these numbers are different:
one hundred two thousandths
one hundred *and* two thousandths

 Math Writing Prompt

Challenge

Describe Relationships
Describe the relationships among a one-dollar bill, a penny, and a dime.

③ Homework and Cumulative Review

2-1
Homework **Goal:** Additional Practice

✔ Use this Homework page to provide students with more practice with writing decimals.

2-1
Remembering **Goal:** Cumulative Review

This Remembering Activity would be appropriate any time after today's lesson.

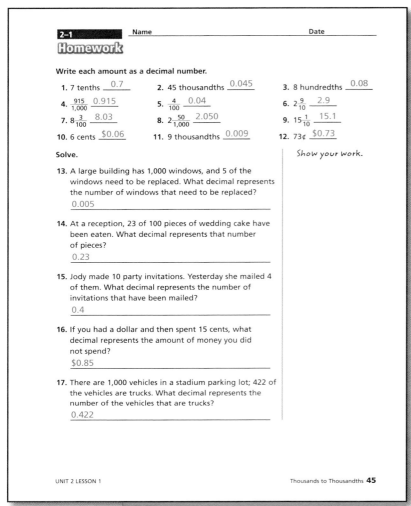

2-1 Name _____ Date _____
Homework

Write each amount as a decimal number.

1. 7 tenths __0.7__ 2. 45 thousandths __0.045__ 3. 8 hundredths __0.08__

4. $\frac{915}{1,000}$ __0.915__ 5. $\frac{4}{100}$ __0.04__ 6. $2\frac{9}{10}$ __2.9__

7. $8\frac{3}{100}$ __8.03__ 8. $2\frac{50}{1,000}$ __2.050__ 9. $15\frac{1}{10}$ __15.1__

10. 6 cents __$0.06__ 11. 9 thousandths __0.009__ 12. 73¢ __$0.73__

Solve.   *Show your work.*

13. A large building has 1,000 windows, and 5 of the windows need to be replaced. What decimal represents the number of windows that need to be replaced?
0.005

14. At a reception, 23 of 100 pieces of wedding cake have been eaten. What decimal represents that number of pieces?
0.23

15. Jody made 10 party invitations. Yesterday she mailed 4 of them. What decimal represents the number of invitations that have been mailed?
0.4

16. If you had a dollar and then spent 15 cents, what decimal represents the amount of money you did not spend?
$0.85

17. There are 1,000 vehicles in a stadium parking lot; 422 of the vehicles are trucks. What decimal represents the number of the vehicles that are trucks?
0.422

UNIT 2 LESSON 1   Thousands to Thousandths **45**

Homework and Remembering page 45

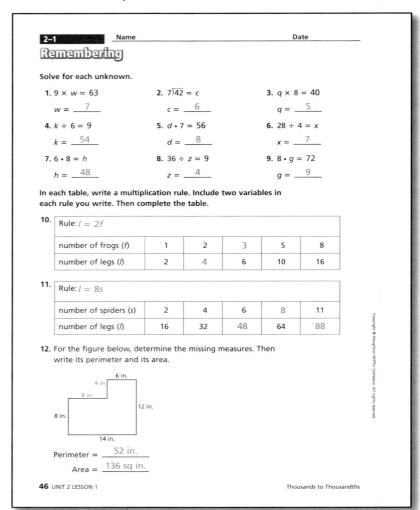

2-1 Name _____ Date _____
Remembering

Solve for each unknown.

1. $9 \times w = 63$ 2. $7\overline{)42} = c$ 3. $q \times 8 = 40$
  $w = $ __7__ $c = $ __6__ $q = $ __5__

4. $k \div 6 = 9$ 5. $d \cdot 7 = 56$ 6. $28 \div 4 = x$
  $k = $ __54__ $d = $ __8__ $x = $ __7__

7. $6 \cdot 8 = h$ 8. $36 \div z = 9$ 9. $8 \cdot g = 72$
  $h = $ __48__ $z = $ __4__ $g = $ __9__

In each table, write a multiplication rule. Include two variables in each rule you write. Then complete the table.

10. Rule: $l = 2f$

number of frogs (f)	1	2	3	5	8
number of legs (l)	2	4	6	10	16

11. Rule: $l = 8s$

number of spiders (s)	2	4	6	8	11
number of legs (l)	16	32	48	64	88

12. For the figure below, determine the missing measures. Then write its perimeter and its area.

Perimeter = __52 in.__
Area = __136 sq in.__

46 UNIT 2 LESSON 1   Thousands to Thousandths

Homework and Remembering page 46

Home and School Connection Math Letter

Family Letter Have children take home the Family Letter on Student Activity Book page 97. This letter explains how the concept of addition and subtraction with whole numbers and decimals is developed. A Spanish translation of this letter is on page 98.

The information in the letter gives parents and guardians a better understanding of the learning that goes on in math class and creates a bridge between school and home.

168 UNIT 2 LESSON 1

Student Activity Book Page 97

Student Activity Book Page 98

UNIT 2
LESSON 2

Equate and Compare

Lesson Objectives

- **Understand equivalent decimal numbers.**
- **Understand that the placement of zeros can affect the value of a decimal number.**
- **Compare decimal numbers.**

The Day at a Glance

Today's Goals	Materials	Math Talk
Quick Practice Practice saying decimal numbers aloud.	MathBoard materials Grid paper Homework and Remembering pages 47–48 Math Journals	In today's activities, the students are involved in discussion as they ▶ recognize tenths and hundredths using a decimal bar ▶ insert zeros in whole numbers and decimals ▶ compare decimals using an inequality sign
1 Teaching the Lesson **A1:** Find equivalent decimals using tenths, hundredths, and thousandths. **A2:** Discover how the placement of zeros can affect the value of a number. **A3:** Compare decimal numbers.		
2 Extending the Lesson ▶ Differentiated Instruction		
3 Homework and Cumulative Review		

Quick Practice

🕐 **5 MINUTES**   **Goal:** Practice saying decimal numbers aloud.

Read Decimal Numbers Send two student leaders to the board and have them each write four different decimal numbers. Then each leader points to the numbers in order and says them out loud, omitting the place value name. The class responds with the place value name, emphasizing the –*ths* sound. (No number should be smaller than thousandths.)

> Example:
> Leader writes 0.23.
> Leader says:
> "twenty-three."
> Class says:
> "hundred*ths*."

① Teaching the Lesson

Decimal Equivalents

 25 MINUTES

Goal: Find equivalent decimals using tenths, hundredths, and thousandths.

Materials: MathBoard materials

 NCTM Standards:
Number and Operations
Communication
Representation

Teaching Note

Math Symbols The bar used here is similar to a fraction bar. Remind students that every decimal represents a fraction. For example, 0.1 represents $\frac{1}{10}$. This reminder may be helpful when you ask them how to show that 0.5 and 0.50 are equal.

▶ Represent Decimals [WHOLE CLASS]

Visualize Tenths Have each student position the MathBoard so the long bar divided into 100 parts is at the top. Remind the class that the bar shows one whole. Ask them to:

● Label one end 0 and the other end 1.0.

● Label every other heavy mark with tenths.

| 0 | 0.1 | 0.2 | 0.3 | 0.4 | 0.5 | 0.6 | 0.7 | 0.8 | 0.9 | 1.0 |

Visualize Hundredths Ask the class:

● How many small sections are there on the bar? 100

● What does each small section represent? one hundredth

Have students write the number of hundredths under each number of tenths.

| 0 | 0.1 | 0.2 | 0.3 | 0.4 | 0.5 | 0.6 | 0.7 | 0.8 | 0.9 | 1.0 |
| 0 | 0.10 | 0.20 | 0.30 | 0.40 | 0.50 | 0.60 | 0.70 | 0.80 | 0.90 | 1.00 |

Select a pair of labels, such as 0.5 and 0.50. Tell the students that we need to prove that these two amounts are equal, using our knowledge of equivalent fractions. Have a student write $0.50 = \frac{50}{100}$ on the board and then show that it equals 0.5. Divide the numerator and denominator by 10; $0.50 = \frac{50}{100} = \frac{50 \div 10}{100 \div 10} = 0.5$

Extend to Thousandths Now ask the class to imagine that the bar is divided into thousandths, which means each small section would be divided into 10 very tiny sections. Ask how many thousandths there are from zero to the one tenth mark. $10 \times 10 = 100$ Have students write the number of thousandths under each number of hundredths.

0	0.1	0.2	0.3	0.4	0.5	0.6	0.7	0.8	0.9	1.0
0	0.10	0.20	0.30	0.40	0.50	0.60	0.70	0.80	0.90	1.00
0	0.100	0.200	0.300	0.400	0.500	0.600	0.700	0.800	0.900	1.000

Again, select two decimal numbers, such as 0.6 and 0.600, and ask the class to prove that they are equal. $0.600 = \frac{600}{1000} = \frac{600 \div 100}{1000 \div 100} = \frac{6}{10} = 0.6$ Ask the class if the zeros at the *end* of a decimal number change the value. no

Insert Zeros

▶ Zeros in Different Numbers [WHOLE CLASS]

Zeros in Whole Numbers Write 42 on the board. Then write the same two digits with zeros inserted in various places:

| 42 | 420 | 4200 | 042 | 4002 | 0042 |

Tell pairs or small groups to discuss the numbers. Ask:

- Which numbers are equal to 42? 042 and 0042

- Where can you write zeros without changing the value of a whole number? before the whole number

- Why does writing a zero at the end or in the middle change the number? at least one other digit moves to a new place

Demonstrate the last point with an example, such as changing 42 to 402. Explain that the 4 in the tens place is moved to the hundreds place.

Zeros in Decimal Numbers Write 0.67 on the board. Then say the number. Write the same two digits with zeros inserted in various places:

| 0.67 | 0.607 | 0.670 | 0.067 | 0.6700 |

Have the groups decide which numbers are equal to 0.67. Then ask:

- Can you write zeros after a decimal number without changing its value? yes

- Which numbers are *not* equal to 0.67? 0.607 and 0.067

- Where does writing a zero *change* the value? after the decimal point and before the last nonzero digit

- Why does writing a zero after the decimal point and before the last nonzero digit change the number? At least one other digit moves to a new place.

Zeros in Decimals Greater Than One Now write 6.7 on the board. Tell the class that 6 is the whole number part and 7 is the decimal part. Then insert zeros: 0000006.7000000

- Did the value change? no

- If you have a decimal greater than 1, where can you write zeros without changing the value of the number? Before the whole number part and after the decimal part.

If a zero is written so that it causes a nonzero digit to move to another place, the value of the number will change.

 15 MINUTES

Goal: Discover how the placement of zeros can affect the value of a number.

 NCTM Standards:
Number and Operations
Communication

Teaching Note

What to Expect from Students
Numbers such as 0.6, 42.0 and 42.00 may cause some confusion. Point out that the zeros in these numbers have no effect. In each number, the nonzero digits are in the same places as if the zeros were not there.

Teaching Note

Math Background Explain to students that, for a decimal number less than one, we write a single zero in the ones place to make it easier to notice the decimal point. These numbers all have the value $\frac{67}{100}$, but 0.67 is the best decimal representation:

| .67 | <u>0.67</u> | 00.67 | 000.67 |

Activity 3

Compare Decimals

 10 MINUTES

Goal: Compare decimal numbers.

 NCTM Standards:
Number and Operations
Communication

Teaching Note

Watch For! Some students have difficulty deciding which decimal number is greater because they extend their knowledge of whole number patterns incorrectly. For example, 420 is greater than 85, so they assume that 0.420 must be greater than 0.85. Today's activities will help your students recognize that a *longer* decimal number is not necessarily a *greater* decimal number.

 Ongoing Assessment

Ask students to compare decimal numbers:

Are all these numbers equal?

▶ 0.72, 0.7200, 0.720

Write > or < between each pair of numbers to compare:

▶ 0.5   0.36

▶ 0.16   0.2

▶ 0.78   0.4

▶ Use Inequality Signs to Compare WHOLE CLASS

Inequality Signs Review the meanings of the inequality symbols for comparing numbers. Remind students that each inequality symbol "points to" the smaller number.

15 > 12	12 < 15
15 is greater than 12	12 is less than 15

Write Equivalent Decimals Write these two decimal numbers. Ask the class which is greater.

0.6   0.28

Some students may think that 0.28 is greater than 0.6 because 28 is greater than 6. Remind the class that decimals represent fractions because they show parts of a whole. Ask the class:

● How do we compare unlike fractions, such as $\frac{2}{3}$ and $\frac{3}{4}$? Change them to like fractions.

● How could we make 0.6 and 0.28 like decimals? Write a zero after 0.6.

● Would that change the value of 0.6? no

Write a zero after 0.6.

0.60   0.28

Ask the class to read the numbers aloud and then decide which number is greater. 60 hundredths, 28 hundredths; 60 hundredths is greater.

Write these inequalities on the board and have the class practice reading them aloud:

● 0.60 > 0.28   60 hundredths is greater than 28 hundredths.

● 0.6 > 0.28   6 tenths is greater than 28 hundredths.

Now have the class practice reading these aloud:

● 0.28 < 0.60   28 hundredths is less than 60 hundredths.

● 0.28 < 0.6   28 hundredths is less than 6 tenths.

Have the class compare these decimal numbers by writing either > or <. Remind them to convert to like decimals, if necessary. Have the students work the comparisons out individually on paper and then discuss the results as a class.

0.74	< 0.82
0.56	< 0.7
0.69	> 0.245
0.05	< 0.16
0.82	> 0.082

If students are having trouble determining whether to use the > symbol or the < symbol, suggest that they circle the greater number first. Then they can determine the appropriate symbol as a second step.

② Extending the Lesson

Intervention
for students having difficulty

PAIRS

Equal or Not Equal?

Materials: MathBoard materials

Have students copy and complete this problem set:

Write an equals sign (=) or a not equals sign (≠) between each pair of numbers to compare.	
0.2	0.02
0.5	0.50
60	0.60
0.17	0.71
3.9	3.09
4.0	0.4
0.720	0.72
8.08	8.8
0.045	0.0450
1.010	1.100

Students can model the decimals on the decimal bar of their MathBoards and check each other's answers.

On Level
for students having success

INDIVIDUALS

Decimal Models

Materials: square 10 x 10 sheets of grid paper

Each student needs six square sheets of 10 x 10 grid paper. Explain that each sheet represents one whole. So, each grid square represents one hundredth and each column or row represents one tenth.

Write these pairs of decimals on the board.

0.2 and 0.02

0.71 and 0.17

0.90 and 0.9

Have students model the decimals by shading in their grids. Then students compare and write a comparison statement representing their grids.

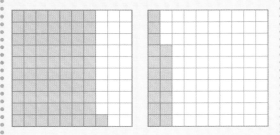

0.71 > 0.17

Challenge
for students seeking a challenge

PAIRS

Inequalities

Materials: MathBoard materials

Introduce the symbols ≤ (is equal to or less than) and ≥ is equal to or greater than). Use real-life situations to demonstrate the symbols:

- An elevator can hold a maximum of 1200 pounds.
- You must be 18 or older to vote.

Then tell students to make up their own sentences and have their partner write the inequalities.

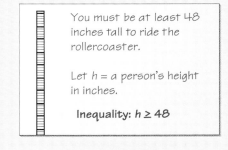

You must be at least 48 inches tall to ride the rollercoaster.

Let *h* = a person's height in inches.

Inequality: *h* ≥ 48

 Math Writing Prompt

Intervention

Show and Tell
Make a drawing of dimes and pennies to show why the decimal 0.5 is greater than 0.05.

 Math Writing Prompt

On Level

Equivalent Decimals
Explain why 3 and 3.00 have the same value.

 Math Writing Prompt

Challenge

Explain Your Thinking
Explain how writing a zero in a decimal number changes or does not change the value of the number. Give examples.

③ Homework and Cumulative Review

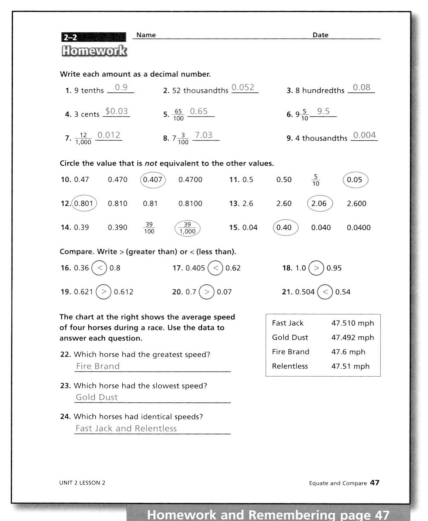

Homework **Goal:** Additional Practice

✓ Include students' work for page 47 as part of their portfolios.

2-2 Homework   Name   Date

Write each amount as a decimal number.

1. 9 tenths __0.9__
2. 52 thousandths __0.052__
3. 8 hundredths __0.08__
4. 3 cents __$0.03__
5. $\frac{65}{100}$ __0.65__
6. $9\frac{5}{10}$ __9.5__
7. $\frac{12}{1,000}$ __0.012__
8. $7\frac{3}{100}$ __7.03__
9. 4 thousandths __0.004__

Circle the value that is *not* equivalent to the other values.

10. 0.47   0.470   ⟨0.407⟩   0.4700
11. 0.5   0.50 $\frac{5}{10}$ ⟨0.05⟩
12. ⟨0.801⟩   0.810   0.81   0.8100
13. 2.6   2.60   ⟨2.06⟩   2.600
14. 0.39   0.390 $\frac{39}{100}$ ⟨$\frac{39}{1,000}$⟩
15. 0.04   ⟨0.40⟩   0.040   0.0400

Compare. Write > (greater than) or < (less than).

16. 0.36 ⟨<⟩ 0.8
17. 0.405 ⟨<⟩ 0.62
18. 1.0 ⟨>⟩ 0.95
19. 0.621 ⟨>⟩ 0.612
20. 0.7 ⟨>⟩ 0.07
21. 0.504 ⟨<⟩ 0.54

The chart at the right shows the average speed of four horses during a race. Use the data to answer each question.

Fast Jack	47.510 mph
Gold Dust	47.492 mph
Fire Brand	47.6 mph
Relentless	47.51 mph

22. Which horse had the greatest speed?
__Fire Brand__

23. Which horse had the slowest speed?
__Gold Dust__

24. Which horses had identical speeds?
__Fast Jack and Relentless__

UNIT 2 LESSON 2   Equate and Compare **47**

Homework and Remembering page 47

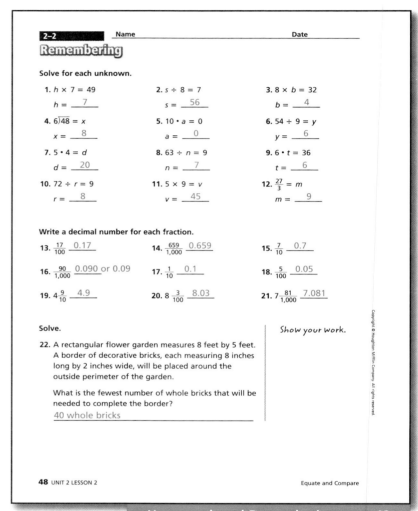

Remembering **Goal:** Cumulative Review

This Remembering Activity would be appropriate anytime after today's lesson.

2-2 Remembering   Name   Date

Solve for each unknown.

1. $h \times 7 = 49$
$h = $ __7__
2. $s \div 8 = 7$
$s = $ __56__
3. $8 \times b = 32$
$b = $ __4__
4. $6\overline{)48} = x$
$x = $ __8__
5. $10 \cdot a = 0$
$a = $ __0__
6. $54 \div 9 = y$
$y = $ __6__
7. $5 \cdot 4 = d$
$d = $ __20__
8. $63 \div n = 9$
$n = $ __7__
9. $6 \cdot t = 36$
$t = $ __6__
10. $72 \div r = 9$
$r = $ __8__
11. $5 \times 9 = v$
$v = $ __45__
12. $\frac{27}{3} = m$
$m = $ __9__

Write a decimal number for each fraction.

13. $\frac{17}{100}$ __0.17__
14. $\frac{659}{1,000}$ __0.659__
15. $\frac{7}{10}$ __0.7__
16. $\frac{90}{1,000}$ __0.090 or 0.09__
17. $\frac{1}{10}$ __0.1__
18. $\frac{5}{100}$ __0.05__
19. $4\frac{9}{10}$ __4.9__
20. $8\frac{3}{100}$ __8.03__
21. $7\frac{81}{1,000}$ __7.081__

Solve.

22. A rectangular flower garden measures 8 feet by 5 feet. A border of decorative bricks, each measuring 8 inches long by 2 inches wide, will be placed around the outside perimeter of the garden.

What is the fewest number of whole bricks that will be needed to complete the border?
__40 whole bricks__

Show your work.

48 UNIT 2 LESSON 2   Equate and Compare

Homework and Remembering page 48

Home or School Activity

 Technology Connection

Calculator Zeros Calculators show that writing zeros before or after a decimal does not change its value. Tell students to enter the decimal 3.10 into a calculator by pressing these keys:

Did the calculator show 3.1 after the equals sign was pressed? This is the calculator's way of showing that 3.10 = 3.1. Have students experiment by copying the chart and entering the decimals shown on the right.

Enter	Calculator Display
0.6 =	
00.7000 =	
010.010 =	
0.500 =	
0000000009. =	
0.20000000000 =	

174 UNIT 2 LESSON 2

Use Decimal Numbers

Lesson Objectives

- Understand place value in decimals and how place value affects addition and subtraction.
- Understand common metric lengths and how they are related. (Optional)

Vocabulary

meter
decimeter
centimeter
millimeter

The Day at a Glance

Today's Goals	Materials	Math Talk
Quick Practice Practice recognizing and saying decimal numbers.	Student Activity Book pages 99-102	In today's activities, the students are involved in discussion as they
1 Teaching the Lesson A1: Add decimals. A2: Subtract decimals. A3: Relate metric lengths to the decimal system and measure objects in meters, decimeters, centimeters, and millimeters. (Optional)	MathBoard materials Place Value Parade Poster Meter stick Make a Meter Stick (Copymaster M21) Colored string or yarn	▶ practice adding and subtracting tenths, hundredths, and thousandths ▶ use the Place Value Parade poster to relate decimals and metric measurements
2 Extending the Lesson ▶ Differentiated Instruction	Scissors and tape Rulers	▶ find approximate metric measurements of real world objects
3 Homework and Cumulative Review	Homework and Remembering pages 49-50 Math Journals	

Quick Practice

⏱ 5 MINUTES **Goal:** Practice recognizing and saying decimal numbers.

Read Decimal Numbers Send two student leaders to the board and have them each write four different decimal numbers. Then each leader points to the numbers in order and says them out loud, omitting the place value name. The class responds with the place value name, emphasizing the –*ths* sound. (No number should be smaller than thousandths.)

> Example:
> Leader writes 0.5
> Leader says "five."
> Class says "tenths."

① Teaching the Lesson

Add Decimal Numbers

 25 MINUTES

Goal: Add decimals.

Materials: MathBoard materials

 NCTM Standards:
Number and Operations
Communication
Representation

Teaching Note

Watch For! If students remember that 4 tenths is 40 hundredths, then adding 2 more hundredths should not pose a problem. However, students might try adding digits in unlike places, and get 6 tenths as an incorrect answer. Make sure that students line up their place values correctly.

▶ Add Decimals ⬚WHOLE CLASS⬚

Tell the students to use the side of the MathBoard with the long bar. Ask them to label the tenths with decimal numbers, just as they did in Lesson 2.

Tenths and Hundredths Have students circle four sections to show 4 tenths.

- 4 tenths is how many hundredths? 4 tenths = 40 hundredths

Now tell the class we want to add 2 hundredths to the 4 tenths. Ask them how we can show the addition on the bar. Circle sections to show 2 more hundredths.

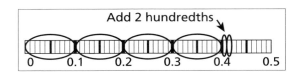

Tell the students that we need a way to add decimals without drawing on a bar every time. Have them write the problem vertically on their MathBoards and solve it. Some students may be more comfortable adding if they write 0.4 as 0.40.

$$\begin{array}{r} 0.4 \\ + 0.02 \\ \hline 0.42 \end{array}$$

Elicit from students that digits in like places are always added together. As with whole numbers, decimal numbers must be lined up properly.

Now give the class another problem of this type to solve on the MathBoard bar, such as 7 tenths + 3 hundredths. When they are finished circling sections on the bar, ask them to solve the problem by writing the numbers vertically, as before.

Regrouping Using the MathBoard, have the class add 7 hundredths and 5 hundredths. Again, have them solve the problem vertically after circling on the MathBoard.

$$\begin{array}{r} \overset{1}{0}.07 \\ + 0.05 \\ \hline 0.12 \end{array}$$

Discuss the result as a class. The answer is 12 hundredths, but students should also notice that they made a new tenth:

$$12 \text{ hundredths} = 1 \text{ tenth} + 2 \text{ hundredths}$$

Extend to Thousandths Without using MathBoards, ask the class to add numbers that involve thousandths, such as 0.028 + 0.93 and 0.867 + 0.34. Discuss alignment and results. Elicit that in the second example they make a new whole.

$$\begin{array}{r} 0.028 \\ + 0.93 \\ \hline 0.958 \end{array} \qquad \begin{array}{r} \overset{1\,1}{0}.867 \\ + 0.34 \\ \hline 1.207 \end{array}$$

Subtract Decimal Numbers

▶ Subtract Decimals `WHOLE CLASS`

Students should use the side of the MathBoard with the long bar. They should leave the labeling of tenths, but all the addition should be wiped away.

Using Models Have students circle 4 sections to show 4 tenths.

Now tell the class we want to subtract 2 hundredths from the 4 tenths. Ask them how we can show the subtraction on the bar. Circle or shade 2 hundredths. Tell them to circle 2 more, and then discuss the result.

Ungrouping Tell the students that we can subtract decimals without drawing on a bar every time. Have them write the problem vertically on their MathBoards.

$$\begin{array}{r} 0.\overset{3\ 10}{\cancel{4}\cancel{0}} \\ -\ 0.0\ 2 \\ \hline 0.3\ 8 \end{array}$$

As with addition decimal numbers must be lined up properly so that digits in like places can be subtracted. Ask, 4 tenths is how many hundredths?

4 tenths = 40 hundredths

Have a student explain how to find the answer.

Give students another example to work through. 0.7 − 0.05. Discuss the result as a class.

$$\begin{array}{r} 0.\overset{6\ 10}{\cancel{7}\cancel{0}} \\ -\ 0.0\ 5 \\ \hline 0.6\ 5 \end{array}$$

Give students other examples to solve.
0.9 − 0.5 and 0.09 − 0.05

Extend to Thousandths Without using MathBoards, ask the class to subtract numbers that involve thousandths, such as:

$$\begin{array}{r} 0.\overset{\ \ \ \ 9}{\overset{3\ 10\,10}{\cancel{4}\cancel{0}\cancel{0}}} \\ -\ 0.0\ 0\ 2 \\ \hline 0.3\ 9\ 8 \end{array} \qquad \begin{array}{r} 0.0\,\overset{3\ 10}{\cancel{4}\cancel{0}} \\ -\ 0.0\ 0\ 2 \\ \hline 0.0\ 3\ 8 \end{array}$$

0.4 − 0.002   0.04 − 0.002
0.7 − 0.003   0.07 − 0.003

Your students may need another day just on decimals to thousandths before going on to billions and billionths. Here are some problems if you wish to spend one more day on decimals to thousandths before moving on.

15.22 + 1.5	45.678 − 33.59	18.3 + 13.34
3.5 + 4.67	7.004 − 4.592	18 − 0.249
33.78 + 0.41	16.72 − 6.99	11 − 0.81

⏱ **25 MINUTES**

Goal: Subtract decimals.

Materials: MathBoard materials

✔ **NCTM Standards:**
Number and Operations
Communication
Representation

123 **Math Talk**

Give students an opportunity to share their solutions.

"I wrote a zero after the 4 because 0.4 and 0.40 have the same value.

Then I ungrouped 1 tenth to make 10 hundredths. Now I can subtract 2 hundredths from 10 hundredths. The answer is 38 hundredths."

Relate Decimals and Metric Lengths

 25 MINUTES

Goal: Relate metric lengths to the decimal system and measure objects in meters, decimeters, centimeters, and millimeters.

Materials: Student Activity Book pages 99–102, Make a Meter Stick (Copymaster M21), Place Value Parade Poster, meter stick, colored string or yarn, scissors, transparent tape

 NCTM Standards:
Measurement
Communication
Representation

Teaching Note

Math Background Metric length can be a helpful visual support for understanding tenths, hundredths, and thousandths. However, using the metric names for these lengths based on 1 meter (decimeters, centimeters, and millimeters) is challenging for some students. Therefore we suggest that you do the metric activities here as initial exposure rather than for mastery. Having the Place Value Parade Poster in your room with the visual examples and terms will permit all students to learn these lengths and their names over time.

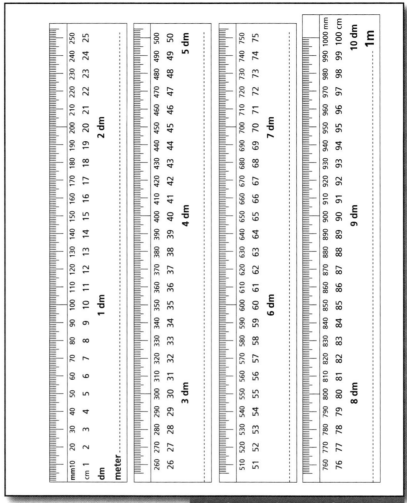

Student Activity Book page 99

▶ Explore Metric Measures of Length WHOLE CLASS

Make Metric Lengths Show the class a meter stick. Have students cut out the rulers on Student Activity Book page 99 or give them Copymaster M21. If you use Copymaster M21 you may want to enlarge it to 105%. When they tape the rulers together, they will have a meter. Invite students to find decimeters, centimeters, and millimeters on their meter stick and discuss the length of 1 decimeter, 1 centimeter, and 1 millimeter.

Have students answer questions 1–6 on Student Activity Book Page 101.

Then have the students look at the Place Value Parade chart in their Student Activity Books. Show students where the Place Value Parade poster is in the classroom. The Place Value Parade poster should remain

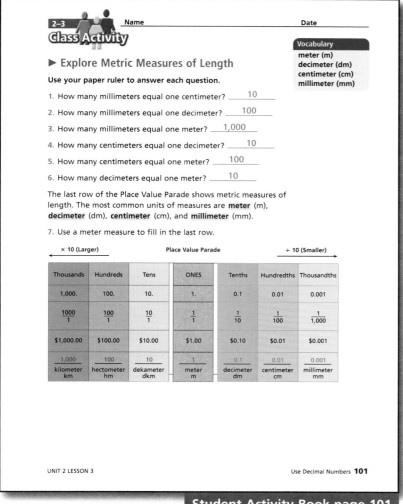

Student Activity Book page 101

on display in the classroom for the duration of this unit.

Direct attention to the last row of the Place Value Parade, which shows metric lengths and their abbreviations. Have students refer to their paper rulers to fill in the blank cells in the chart.

Meters can be divided into tenths (decimeters), hundredths (centimeters), or thousandths (millimeters). Help students relate these units of metric length to the decimal system by asking:

● How are the names for metric units of length like the names of decimal places? As you move to the right, each metric unit of length is one tenth of the unit before it.

Contrast customary units of length with metric units by asking:
● Are yards, feet, and inches based on a decimal system? No, they are not divided into tenths.

For exercises 8–12, have student volunteers read the units aloud.

Activity continued ▶

Teaching Note

Language and Vocabulary Students can brainstorm about other words they know that relate to these prefixes: *deci-* means "ten" and also is in "decimal" and "decade." *Centi-* means one hundred and also is in "cent," "century," and "centipede." *Milli-* means one thousand and also is in "mile" (the Roman mile was one thousand steps), "millennium," and "millipede." Students who speak Spanish will find links to ten (diez), hundred (ciento), and thousand (mil).

Teaching Note

Math Symbols The class may find it helpful if you write equivalent forms on the board.

Example:
7,284 millimeters
728.4 centimeters
72.84 decimeters
7.284 meters

① Teaching the Lesson (continued)

Activity 3 OPTIONAL

Choose Appropriate Units Ask students which metric unit of length they would use to measure each object listed below.

● length of a bulletin board meters

● length of a thumb centimeters

● length of a student desk decimeters

● width of a small paper clip millimeters

Next, have the students actually measure the objects, using their meter rulers. Make a list of measurements on the board, using the appropriate abbreviations.

Estimate Measurements Give students the opportunity to choose an object in the classroom, estimate the length, and record their estimates. Then students can measure the length using their rulers and record the actual length.

Have students measure lengths in the classroom to complete exercises 13 and 14.

Allow time for students to write word problems for exercises 15 and 16. Then ask as many students as possible to share their problems with the class. A different student should be at the board to solve the problem. Encourage students to discuss the solutions to the problems.

② Extending the Lesson

Intervention
for students having difficulty

PAIRS

Metric Lines

Materials: rulers

Write this problem set on the board:

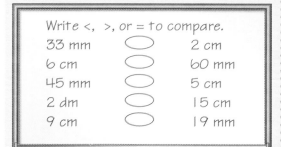

Write <, >, or = to compare.

33 mm	◯	2 cm
6 cm	◯	60 mm
45 mm	◯	5 cm
2 dm	◯	15 cm
9 cm	◯	19 mm

Have students use their rulers to draw line segments and then complete the inequalities.

Example:

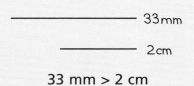

———————— 33mm

———— 2cm

33 mm > 2 cm

On Level
for students having success

PAIRS

Remind students that if the tenths digit is:

• less than 5, round down.

• 5 or greater, round up.

Round and Estimate

Write on the board:

Ira's groceries: Item and weight		Rounded weight
ham	0.87 lb	1 lb
turkey	2.29 lb	2 lb
cheese	1.74 lb	2 lb
Total estimate →		5 lb

Tell each student to make lists with decimals similar to the one on the board. Then have students exchange lists and find estimates of the totals.

Challenge
for students seeking a challenge

SMALL GROUPS

Many Ways

Tell students that they will be showing equivalent forms of the same number. If students need an example, ask them how they can use two different ways to show the number 10. Students might say 5 + 5 or draw 10 dots.

Ask students to use ten different ways to show the number 0.5.

Examples:

0.5, 0.50, 1 ÷ 2, 0.21 + 0.29, $\frac{2}{4}$

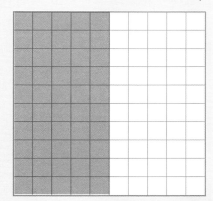

You might want students to create equivalent forms for other numbers, such as 0.4, 0.75, and 0.05. Students can display and share their work with the class.

 Math Writing Prompt

Intervention

Make Lists
Make a list of three objects you would measure in centimeters. Explain why measuring the objects in centimeters makes sense.

 Math Writing Prompt

On Level

Create Your Own
Write two word problems. Each problem should include decimals.

 Math Writing Prompt

Challenge

Explain Your Thinking
Describe how exchanging dimes for a dollar is like regrouping. Describe another way of making change that is like regrouping.

③ Homework and Cumulative Review

2-3

Homework **Goal:** Additional Practice

✓ Use this Homework page to provide students with more practice writing and using decimals and metric units.

Remembering **Goal:** Cumulative Review

This Remembering Activity would be appropriate anytime after today's lesson.

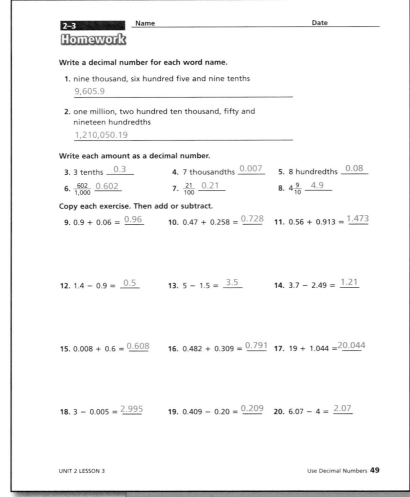

2-3 Name _____ Date _____

Homework

Write a decimal number for each word name.

1. nine thousand, six hundred five and nine tenths
   9,605.9

2. one million, two hundred ten thousand, fifty and nineteen hundredths
   1,210,050.19

Write each amount as a decimal number.

3. 3 tenths __0.3__   4. 7 thousandths __0.007__   5. 8 hundredths __0.08__

6. $\frac{602}{1,000}$ __0.602__   7. $\frac{21}{100}$ __0.21__   8. $4\frac{9}{10}$ __4.9__

Copy each exercise. Then add or subtract.

9. $0.9 + 0.06 =$ __0.96__   10. $0.47 + 0.258 =$ __0.728__   11. $0.56 + 0.913 =$ __1.473__

12. $1.4 - 0.9 =$ __0.5__   13. $5 - 1.5 =$ __3.5__   14. $3.7 - 2.49 =$ __1.21__

15. $0.008 + 0.6 =$ __0.608__   16. $0.482 + 0.309 =$ __0.791__   17. $19 + 1.044 =$ __20.044__

18. $3 - 0.005 =$ __2.995__   19. $0.409 - 0.20 =$ __0.209__   20. $6.07 - 4 =$ __2.07__

UNIT 2 LESSON 3   Use Decimal Numbers **49**

Homework and Remembering page 49

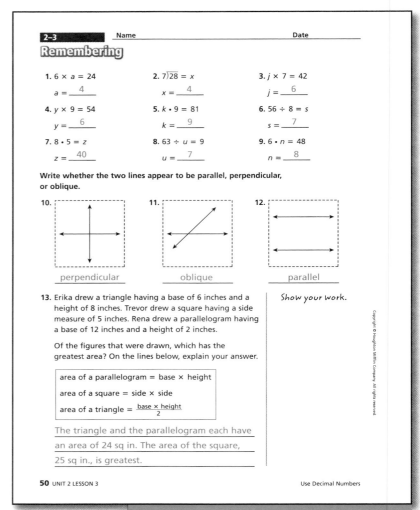

2-3 Name _____ Date _____

Remembering

1. $6 \times a = 24$
   $a =$ __4__

2. $7\overline{)28} = x$
   $x =$ __4__

3. $j \times 7 = 42$
   $j =$ __6__

4. $y \times 9 = 54$
   $y =$ __6__

5. $k \cdot 9 = 81$
   $k =$ __9__

6. $56 \div 8 = s$
   $s =$ __7__

7. $8 \cdot 5 = z$
   $z =$ __40__

8. $63 \div u = 9$
   $u =$ __7__

9. $6 \cdot n = 48$
   $n =$ __8__

Write whether the two lines appear to be parallel, perpendicular, or oblique.

10. __perpendicular__   11. __oblique__   12. __parallel__

13. Erika drew a triangle having a base of 6 inches and a height of 8 inches. Trevor drew a square having a side measure of 5 inches. Rena drew a parallelogram having a base of 12 inches and a height of 2 inches.

Of the figures that were drawn, which has the greatest area? On the lines below, explain your answer.

Show your work.

| area of a parallelogram = base × height |
| area of a square = side × side |
| area of a triangle = $\frac{\text{base} \times \text{height}}{2}$ |

The triangle and the parallelogram each have an area of 24 sq in. The area of the square, 25 sq in., is greatest.

50 UNIT 2 LESSON 3   Use Decimal Numbers

Homework and Remembering page 50

Home or School Activity

Language Arts Connection

Metric Prefixes A *prefix* is added to the beginning of a root word that changes its meaning. In the metric system, all the units of length have a prefix added to the root word *meter*. So, if you know the meaning of the prefix, you also know the meaning of the unit. For example, *kilo–* means "one thousand," so *kilometer* means "one thousand meters."

Have students find words in a dictionary that use the metric prefixes shown in the table at right. Have them write the meanings of the words they find.

Prefix	Meaning
kilo-	one thousand
hecto-	one hundred
deka-	ten
deci-	one tenth
centi-	one hundredth
milli-	one thousandth

182 UNIT 2 LESSON 3

Billions to Billionths

Lesson Objectives

- Recognize whole numbers to billions and decimal numbers to billionths.
- Discover and describe patterns in large whole numbers and decimal numbers.

Vocabulary

billion
billionth

The Day at a Glance

Today's Goals	Materials	Math Talk
Quick Practice Continue practice with decimals and metric lengths.	Student Activity Book pages 103-110	In today's activities, the students are involved in discussion as they
1 Teaching the Lesson **A1:** Recognize place values from billions to billionths. **A2:** Make whole numbers in millions and billions using Secret Code Cards.	Place Value Parade Poster Secret Code Cards (Copymaster M23) Scissors Index cards	▶ expand their knowledge of place value to include billions and billionths ▶ use Secret Code Cards to form numbers to billions
2 Extending the Lesson ▶ Going Further: Different Systems of Numeration ▶ Differentiated Instruction	Paper clips MathBoard Materials Homework and Remembering pages 51-52	
3 Homework and Cumulative Review	Math Journals	

Quick Practice

🕐 **5 MINUTES**   **Goal:** Continue practice with decimals and metric lengths.

Read Decimal Numbers Send two student leaders to the board and have each write four different decimal numbers. Then a leader points to the numbers in order and says them out loud, omitting the place value name. The class responds with the place value name, emphasizing the *–ths* at the end. (No number should be smaller than thousandths.)

Example:
Leader writes 0.32
Leader says "thirty-two."
Class says "hundredths."

Metric Lengths The student leader writes a metric length abbreviation on the board (m, dm, cm, or mm). The other students respond by saying the name of the unit and showing the approximate length with their hands. The leader should try to use all lengths twice, in random order.

① Teaching the Lesson

Place Value Relationships

 20 MINUTES

Goal: Recognize place values from billions to billionths.

Materials: Student Activity Book pages 103–105, Place Value Parade poster

 NCTM Standards:
Number and Operations
Algebra
Communication

Teaching Note

Math Background Each group of 3 digits in a number is usually called a *period*. In this lesson, students learn about the thousands period, the millions period, and the billions period, although they do not use the word *period*.

Patterns From Billions to Billionths

billions	hundred millions	ten millions	millions	hundred thousands	ten thousands	thousands	hundreds	tens	ONES
1,000,000,000	100,000,000	10,000,000	1,000,000	100,000	10,000	1,000	100	10	1

ONES	tenths	hundredths	thousandths	ten thousandths	hundred thousandths	millionths	ten millionths	hundred millionths	billionths
1	0.1	0.01	0.001	0.0001	0.00001	0.000001	0.0000001	0.00000001	0.000000001
	$\frac{1}{10}$	$\frac{1}{100}$	$\frac{1}{1,000}$	$\frac{1}{10,000}$	$\frac{1}{100,000}$	$\frac{1}{1,000,000}$	$\frac{1}{10,000,000}$	$\frac{1}{100,000,000}$	$\frac{1}{1,000,000,000}$

▶ Patterns From Billions to Billionths WHOLE CLASS

Direct students to remove Student Activity Book page 103 from their book.

Focus on the patterns students see in the top half of the page (the whole numbers) and have them circle the words *thousands*, *millions*, and *billions* to clarify the pattern being repeated with tens and hundreds. Then have students look at the decimal places and circle *thousandths*, *millionths*, and *billionths*. Point out the same word patterns but going to the right (getting smaller).

Have students cut (or fold and tear) the page in half horizontally, put the ONES on top of each other, and tape the two parts of the page together so see how the patterns to the left get bigger and to the right get smaller.

From the ones place the students can write an arrow going left that says "getting bigger" and an arrow going right that says "getting smaller."

Lead a discussion about why our system of writing numbers is called a base-ten system. Each place is related to the places beside it by a 1 to 10 trade rule. Ten of any place always make one in the place to the left (the next larger place), and one in any place always makes ten in the place to the right (the next smaller place).

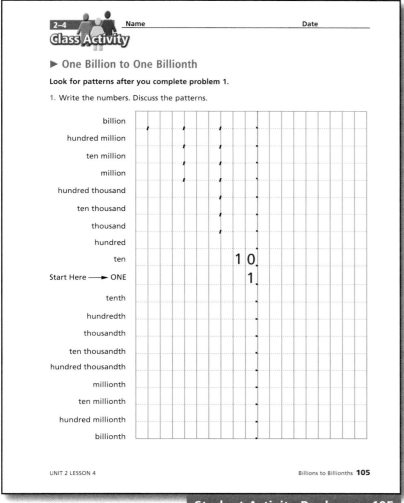

Student Activity Book page 105

▶ One Billion to One Billionth WHOLE CLASS

The grid on page 105 has all the place names from billions to billionths.

Students will write 1s and 0s as they write numbers from 1 to 1 billion in increasing order and from 1 to 1 billionth in decreasing order.

Have the students start in the center with the whole number 1 and build up to 1 billion. Then they can build down to 1 billionth.

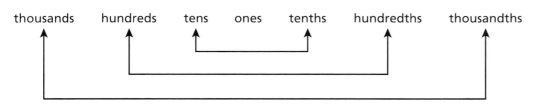

Ask them what they can say about how far the symmetric pattern of place names extends. The symmetry in place value names continues indefinitely.

Teaching Note

What to Expect from Students
During the building up and building down process, make sure students understand that:

- Moving *up* on the Billions to Billionths page corresponds to moving *left* on the Place Value Parade poster.

- Moving *down* on the Billions to Billionths page corresponds to moving *right* on the Place Value Parade poster.

Teaching Note

Math Background In this activity, students generate decimal numbers to one billionth. The symmetric pattern helps them realize:

- By using more and more whole number places, numbers can be made as large as desired.

- By using more and more decimal places, numbers can be made as small as desired.

However, students will not usually be asked to work with decimal numbers smaller than thousandths.

Activity 2

Build Larger Numbers

 35 MINUTES

Goal: Make whole numbers in millions and billions using Secret Code Cards.

Materials: Student Activity Book pages 106–107, Secret Code Cards (Copymaster M23), scissors

 NCTM Standards:
Number and Operations
Communication

Differentiated Instruction

Advanced Learners Once all secret code cards have been cut out, students can make up riddles: "I'm thinking of a number that is greater than one million, but less than one million, two hundred fifty thousand." Other students can build numbers to satisfy the criteria.

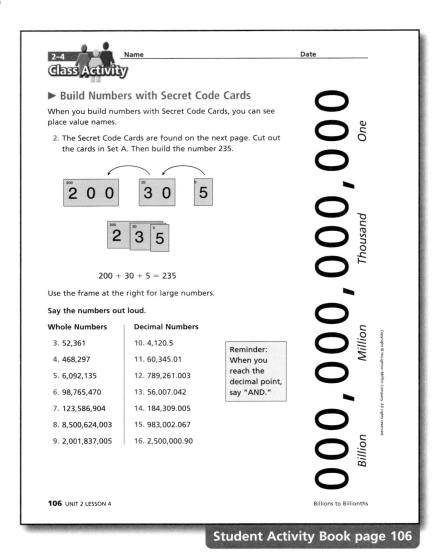

Student Activity Book page 106

▶ Build Numbers With Secret Code Cards [WHOLE CLASS]

Have students find the Secret Code Cards on page 107 and cut out the cards in Set A. Then direct their attention to page 106.

Have students do exercise 2, building the number 235 with their cards. Point out the small numbers in the upper left-hand corners. These numbers allow students to see the hundreds, tens, and ones even after the cards are overlapped.

Have the students turn the book sideways so that they can use the Secret Code Card frame along the edge. Prepare the class for building larger numbers by asking:

● What is the greatest number you can write if you can replace the three zeros at the right end of the frame with other digits? 999

● What three words do you see, reading left to right along the bottom of the frame? billion, million, thousand

- How many places are there between commas? 3 places

Now explain that any number greater than 999 will have one or more of the words *billion, million,* or *thousand.*

Make Different Numbers Tell the class that a three-digit number such as 235 can be called a hundred set. Have students move their 235 so that it is 235 thousands, then move it to be 235 millions, and then move it to be 235 billions.

Generate Random Numbers Have the students put aside the Secret Code Cards in Set A and cut out the cards in Set B.

Invite students to contribute various hundred sets for everyone to place on the frame (such as 692 in the billion section, 876 in the thousand section).

When an entire number has been made, have the class read it out loud while you write it on the board. Repeat this process several times, listing the numbers on the board.

Now ask:

- Which of these numbers is the largest? Which is the smallest?

- What is the largest possible number we could make in this frame, using any numerals we want? 999,999,999,999

Finally, have students say the numbers in exercises 3–16. Students will need to be especially careful when they say the numbers for exercises 10–16 because these numbers have decimal parts. Remind them to say the word *and* before they say the decimal part.

 Math Talk

Students can do library or Web research to find large numbers in the millions and trillions used in real-world settings. They can use this information to write and solve problems and share their problems with the class.

 The Learning Classroom

Building Concepts Using the same hundred set repeatedly allows students to concentrate on the place value names they are learning (billions, millions, and thousands) rather than on the values of the digits.

Ongoing Assessment

What is the largest and smallest place value in each number?

► 2,395

► 87,651

► 0.976

► 1.28

Extending the Lesson

Going Further: Different Systems of Numeration

Goal: Write numbers using different systems of numeration.

Materials: Student Activity Book page 109

✓ **NCTM Standards:**
Communication
Representation

▶ Different Systems of Numeration

WHOLE CLASS

Write this list on the board:

Basketball

Baseball

Hockey

Soccer

Other

Ask students to raise their hand to show their favorite sport to play. Have a volunteer record the numbers of hands raised for each sport on the list using tally marks.

Explain that many groups of people have developed ways of writing numbers, and that several of these systems were based on keeping score of something with tally marks. People would mark short line segments on wood, sand, or other things. These marks gradually became grouped in different ways, and became more complex symbols of numbers.

Have students look at the different number systems shown on Student Activity Book page 109. Discuss where they see the influence of tally marks.

What other patterns do they see?

Have students work in pairs to answer questions 1–5. Discuss students' answers as a class.

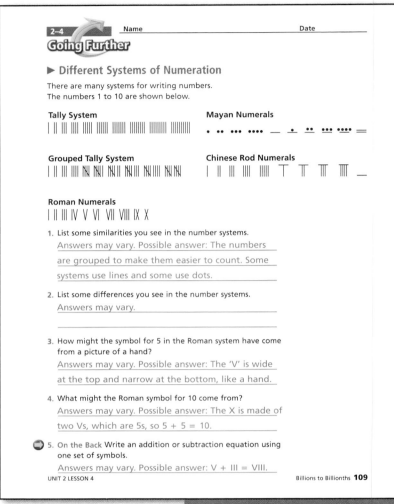

Student Activity Book page 109

Differentiated Instruction

Advanced Learners Some students may be interested in conducting research to find how these groups of people represented numbers greater than 10, or to find number systems developed by other groups of people. If possible, provide resources for them to use, and set aside some time for them to share what they learn with the class.

Intervention
for students having difficulty

PAIRS

One and Zero

Materials: index cards (10 per pair)

Have students write a "1" on one index card and a "0" on the remaining 9 cards.

On the board, write these word names:

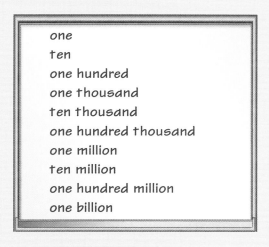

one
ten
one hundred
one thousand
ten thousand
one hundred thousand
one million
ten million
one hundred million
one billion

One student uses the cards to form a number from the list, and the partner tells the word name.

On Level
for students having success

PAIRS

Random Numbers

Materials: index cards (11 per pair), paper clips

Have students write the digits 0–9 on the index cards (1 per card) and a decimal point on the last card.

Students shuffle their number cards, place them in a row, and say the whole number they made. Students can use paper clips or space between the groups of 3 cards to represent commas.

Then students should insert their decimal point between any two cards in the row and say the new number.

Challenge
for students seeking a challenge

SMALL GROUPS

Number Forms

Materials: MathBoard materials, Student Activity Book page 106

Write the following on the board or on a transparency.

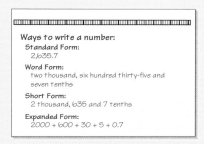

Ways to write a number:
Standard Form:
2,635.7
Word Form:
two thousand, six hundred thirty-five and seven tenths
Short Form:
2 thousand, 635 and 7 tenths
Expanded Form:
2000 + 600 + 30 + 5 + 0.7

Have students work together to write numbers in word form, short word form, and expanded form. They can choose numbers from exercises 3–16 on Student Activity Book page 106.

 Math Writing Prompt

Intervention

Explain Number Names
When you add the sound *–ths* to the end of the word *million*, how does it change its meaning?

 Math Writing Prompt

On Level

Explain Your Thinking
When you write a number, how is inserting a comma different from inserting a decimal point?

Math Writing Prompt

Challenge

How Many Bills?
How many of each type of bill will equal a million dollars?

all $1-bills
all $10-bills
all $100-bills
all $1,000-bills

③ Homework and Cumulative Review

2–4
Homework **Goal:** Additional Practice

✓ Use this Homework page to provide students with more practice with whole numbers and decimals.

2–4
Remembering **Goal:** Cumulative Review

This Remembering Activity would be appropriate anytime after today's lesson.

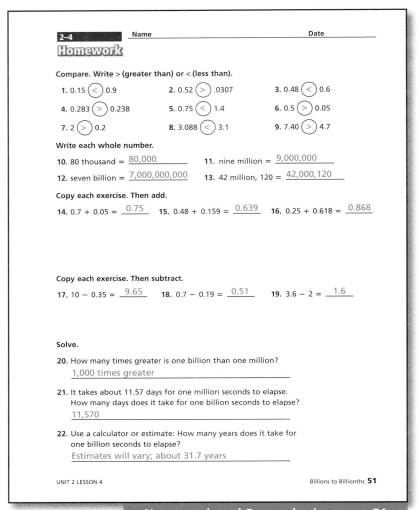

2–4 Name _____ Date _____
Homework

Compare. Write > (greater than) or < (less than).

1. 0.15 ⊖ 0.9   **2.** 0.52 ⊖ .0307   **3.** 0.48 ⊖ 0.6

4. 0.283 ⊖ 0.238   **5.** 0.75 ⊖ 1.4   **6.** 0.5 ⊖ 0.05

7. 2 ⊖ 0.2   **8.** 3.088 ⊖ 3.1   **9.** 7.40 ⊖ 4.7

Write each whole number.

10. 80 thousand = 80,000   **11.** nine million = 9,000,000

12. seven billion = 7,000,000,000   **13.** 42 million, 120 = 42,000,120

Copy each exercise. Then add.

14. 0.7 + 0.05 = 0.75   **15.** 0.48 + 0.159 = 0.639   **16.** 0.25 + 0.618 = 0.868

Copy each exercise. Then subtract.

17. 10 − 0.35 = 9.65   **18.** 0.7 − 0.19 = 0.51   **19.** 3.6 − 2 = 1.6

Solve.

20. How many times greater is one billion than one million?
1,000 times greater

21. It takes about 11.57 days for one million seconds to elapse. How many days does it take for one billion seconds to elapse?
11,570

22. Use a calculator or estimate: How many years does it take for one billion seconds to elapse?
Estimates will vary; about 31.7 years

UNIT 2 LESSON 4   Billions to Billionths **51**

Homework and Remembering page 51

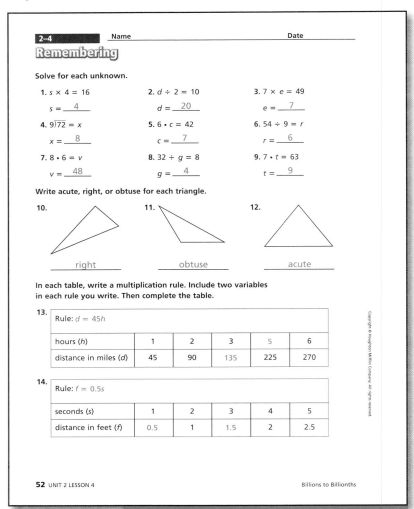

2–4 Name _____ Date _____
Remembering

Solve for each unknown.

1. $s \times 4 = 16$ **2.** $d \div 2 = 10$ **3.** $7 \times e = 49$
$s = 4$ $d = 20$ $e = 7$

4. $9\overline{)72} = x$ **5.** $6 \cdot c = 42$ **6.** $54 \div 9 = r$
$x = 8$ $c = 7$ $r = 6$

7. $8 \cdot 6 = v$ **8.** $32 \div g = 8$ **9.** $7 \cdot t = 63$
$v = 48$ $g = 4$ $t = 9$

Write acute, right, or obtuse for each triangle.

10.   **11.**   **12.**

right   obtuse   acute

In each table, write a multiplication rule. Include two variables in each rule you write. Then complete the table.

13.
Rule: $d = 45h$

hours (h)	1	2	3	5	6
distance in miles (d)	45	90	135	225	270

14.
Rule: $f = 0.5s$

seconds (s)	1	2	3	4	5
distance in feet (f)	0.5	1	1.5	2	2.5

52 UNIT 2 LESSON 4   Billions to Billionths

Homework and Remembering page 52

Home or School Activity

 Social Studies Connection

Commas or Dots? Your students will find it interesting that in many other countries dots are used as we use commas—as separators in whole numbers, and commas are used as we use dots—as decimal points. Invite students to research this topic. Ask them to choose five countries and find out how people in those countries use commas and dots in numbers.

United States

4,020,017.2

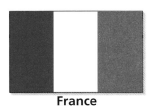
France

4.020.017,2

190 UNIT 2 LESSON 4

Use Place Value

Lesson Objectives

- Understand how to build the largest and the smallest number using a given set of digits.
- Recognize and understand relationships among place value positions to billions.

The Day at a Glance

Today's Goals	Materials	Math Talk
Quick Practice Practice saying decimal and metric length names.	Student Activity Book pages 111–112	In today's activities, the students are involved in discussion as they
1 Teaching the Lesson **A1:** Use place value concepts to increase or decrease numbers. **A2:** Visualize large and small numbers using a dot array.	Calculators Number cubes MathBoard materials Homework and Remembering pages 53–54	► identify place values ► use mental math and place value to change numbers
2 Extending the Lesson ► Differentiated Instruction	Math Journals Quick Quiz 1 (Assessment Guide)	► use a dot array to visualize whole numbers and decimals
3 Homework and Cumulative Review		

Quick Practice

 5 MINUTES **Goal:** Practice saying decimal and metric length names.

Read Decimal Numbers Send two student leaders to the board and have each write four different decimal numbers. Then the leaders point to the numbers in order and say them out loud, omitting the place-value name. The class responds with the decimal name, emphasizing the *–ths* at the end. (No number should be smaller than thousandths.)

> Example:
> Leader writes 0.81.
> Leader says "eighty-one."
> Class says "hundredths."

Metric Lengths The student leader writes a metric length abbreviation (m, dm, cm, or mm) on the board and points to it. The other students respond by saying the name of the unit and showing the approximate length with their hands. The leader should try to use all lengths twice, in random order.

Teaching the Lesson

Apply Place Value Concepts

 25 MINUTES

Goal: Use place value concepts to increase or decrease numbers.

Materials: Student Activity Book page 111

✔ **NCTM Standards:**
Number and Operations
Communication

Differentiated Instruction

Special Needs Tell students to underline or circle the digits in the target place value. For example, in exercise 1, students should underline or circle the 4 after the 7. To increase the number by 2,000 they will need to add 2 to 4.

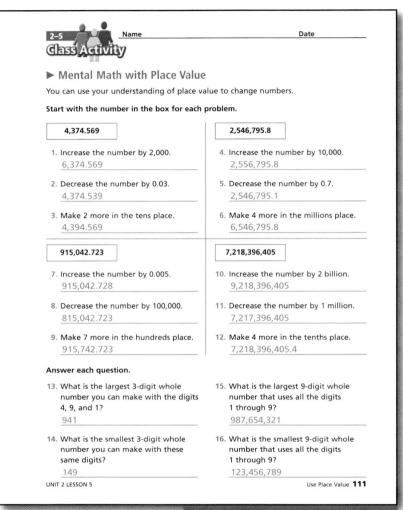

Student Activity Book page 111

▶ Read Large Numbers [WHOLE CLASS]

Ask three or four students to go to the board and write a large number. Then have each student point to each group of digits and read only the numbers. The class responds with the group name.

Example: 68,723,985,103

| **Leader:** 68 | **Leader:** 723 | **Leader:** 985 | **Leader:** 103 |
| **Class:** billion | **Class:** million | **Class:** thousand | **Class:** ones |

▶ Mental Math With Place Value [INDIVIDUALS]

Have the class turn to page 111 and complete exercises 1–12. Write each boxed number on the board. Invite students to work at the board. Notice that in problem 12, students will need to create a tenths place. 7,218,396,405.**4**

Now have the students answer questions 13–16.

Visualize Large and Small Numbers

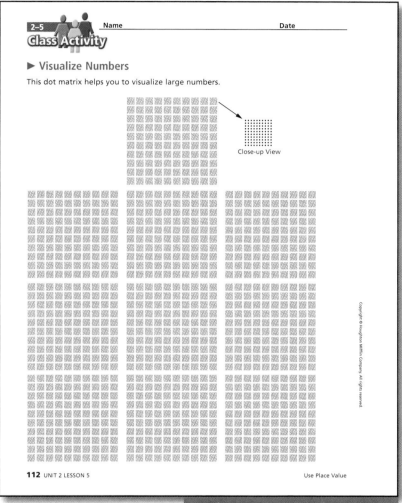

Student Activity Book page 112

---

 25 MINUTES

Goal: Visualize very large and very small numbers using a dot array.

Materials: Student Activity Book page 112

 NCTM Standards:
Number and Operations
Communication

Class Management

Encourage students to label their work on the board (and in their activity books) to help them to see connections while solving problems. Having labels also provides these additional benefits:

► They help other students follow what the explainers are describing.

► They help students to ask specific questions about work.

► They provide assessment feedback to the teacher about student understanding.

► Visualize Numbers [WHOLE CLASS]

Large Numbers Direct students' attention to the dot array on page 112 of the Student Activity Book. Use the questions below to guide students as they find the number of dots on the page, and then the number of pages needed to make a million dots. They can label quantities to keep track. Write each quantity on the board.

● How many dots are in one of the tiny squares? $10 \times 10 = 100$ dots

● How many dots are in one row of tiny squares? $10 \times 100 = 1{,}000$ dots

● How many dots are in one large square? $10 \times 1{,}000 = 10{,}000$ dots

● How many dots are on the whole page? $10 \times 10{,}000 = 100{,}000$ dots

● How many pages will it take to make a million dots? 10 pages

Activity continued ►

Activity 2

Visualize Large and Small Numbers (continued)

Ongoing Assessment

Ask students to:

▶ Increase 5,681,004 by 10,000.

▶ Decrease 40,125.67 by 0.1.

▶ Make the largest 3-digit number possible, using 5, 8, and 2.

Quick Quiz

See Assessment Guide for Unit 2 Quick Quiz 1.

Ask ten students to form a line and show their pages. This will help the class visualize one million. [You may want to create a display later.]

Decimal Numbers Use the same dot array to help students visualize representations of decimal numbers. Ask:

● If one tiny square were one whole, what would one dot be?
  1 hundredth

● If one large square were one whole, what would one dot be?
  1 ten thousandth

● If the entire page were one whole, what would one dot be?
  1 hundred thousandth

● If 10 pages were one whole, what would one dot be? 1 millionth

Conclude this activity by telling students that they will use large whole numbers and decimal numbers every day. Ask them to look for examples in newspapers, magazines, and on the Internet. During the remainder of this unit, encourage students to bring examples to class, with the numbers circled or highlighted. For large numbers that are written as a combination of numerals and words, students should write all numerals. (Example: 23 billion = 23,000,000,000)

② Extending the Lesson

Intervention
for students having difficulty

PAIRS

Powers of Ten

Materials: calculators

Have students do repeated multiplications of 10s on calculators, recording the results with commas and word names.

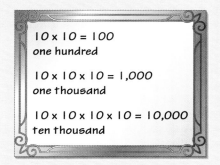

10 x 10 = 100
one hundred

10 x 10 x 10 = 1,000
one thousand

10 x 10 x 10 x 10 = 10,000
ten thousand

Have students continue until they reach one million.

Partners can take turns, one student multiplying and the other student recording results.

On Level
for students having success

PAIRS

Roll With It

Materials: number cube

One student rolls the number cube. The result is the number of times the partner will roll the number cube. Both students then write the greatest whole number and least whole number they can make, using the numbers rolled.

For example, the first student rolls a 5. Then the partner rolls 5 times, getting 3, 1, 1, 6, 5. Both students then write the greatest possible 5-digit number and the least possible 5-digit number.

Greatest: 65,311
Least: 11,356

Challenge
for students seeking a challenge

PAIRS

Place-Value Code

Materials: MathBoard materials

Write the following place-value code key on the board.

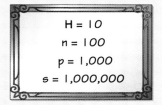

H = 10
n = 100
p = 1,000
s = 1,000,000

Have students use the key to complete the following problem set:

p = 10 x _____

s = 1,000 x _____

p = 100 x _____

Now students can create their own codes and problems to challenge each other.

 Math Writing Prompt

Intervention

Explain Number Names
Which would you rather have: a million $1-bills or a thousand $100-bills? Explain your choice.

 Math Writing Prompt

On Level

Explain Your Thinking
Explain how you can arrange any four digits to make the greatest possible whole number.

 Math Writing Prompt

Challenge

Write Steps
Write four steps that would change 5,420,300 to 6,000,000. Each step can describe only one place value.

③ Homework and Cumulative Review

✓ Use this Homework page to provide students with more practice with place value methods.

This Remembering Activity would be appropriate anytime after today's lesson.

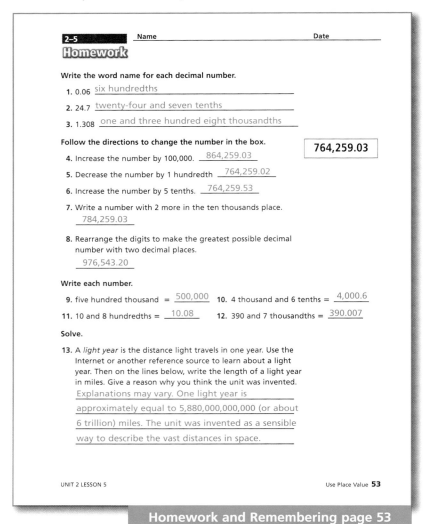

2–5 Homework   Name   Date

Write the word name for each decimal number.

1. 0.06   six hundredths

2. 24.7   twenty-four and seven tenths

3. 1.308   one and three hundred eight thousandths

Follow the directions to change the number in the box.   **764,259.03**

4. Increase the number by 100,000.   864,259.03

5. Decrease the number by 1 hundredth   764,259.02

6. Increase the number by 5 tenths.   764,259.53

7. Write a number with 2 more in the ten thousands place.
764,259.03 → 784,259.03

8. Rearrange the digits to make the greatest possible decimal number with two decimal places.
976,543.20

Write each number.

9. five hundred thousand = 500,000   10. 4 thousand and 6 tenths = 4,000.6

11. 10 and 8 hundredths = 10.08   12. 390 and 7 thousandths = 390.007

Solve.

13. A *light year* is the distance light travels in one year. Use the Internet or another reference source to learn about a light year. Then on the lines below, write the length of a light year in miles. Give a reason why you think the unit was invented. Explanations may vary. One light year is approximately equal to 5,880,000,000,000 (or about 6 trillion) miles. The unit was invented as a sensible way to describe the vast distances in space.

UNIT 2 LESSON 5   Use Place Value **53**

Homework and Remembering page 53

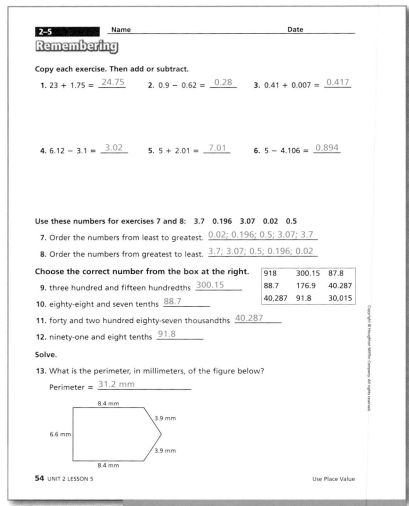

2–5 Remembering   Name   Date

Copy each exercise. Then add or subtract.

1. 23 + 1.75 = 24.75   2. 0.9 − 0.62 = 0.28   3. 0.41 + 0.007 = 0.417

4. 6.12 − 3.1 = 3.02   5. 5 + 2.01 = 7.01   6. 5 − 4.106 = 0.894

Use these numbers for exercises 7 and 8:   3.7   0.196   3.07   0.02   0.5

7. Order the numbers from least to greatest. 0.02; 0.196; 0.5; 3.07; 3.7

8. Order the numbers from greatest to least. 3.7; 3.07; 0.5; 0.196; 0.02

Choose the correct number from the box at the right.

918	300.15	87.8
88.7	176.9	40.287
40,287	91.8	30,015

9. three hundred and fifteen hundredths 300.15

10. eighty-eight and seven tenths 88.7

11. forty and two hundred eighty-seven thousandths 40.287

12. ninety-one and eight tenths 91.8

Solve.

13. What is the perimeter, in millimeters, of the figure below?
Perimeter = 31.2 mm

8.4 mm
3.9 mm
6.6 mm
3.9 mm
8.4 mm

54 UNIT 2 LESSON 5   Use Place Value

Homework and Remembering page 54

Home or School Activity

Science Connection

Millions and Billions of Miles Explain to students that large numbers are used often in astronomy. Ask students to find the distances (in miles) of all the planets from the sun, and then write those distances in order from least to greatest.

Planet Distances	
Planet	**Average Distance from the Sun (in miles)**
Earth	93,000,000
Jupiter	483,600,000
Mars	141,600,000
Mercury	36,000,000
Neptune	2,794,400,000
Pluto	3,674,500,000
Saturn	886,700,000
Uranus	1,784,000,000
Venus	67,200,000

Add Whole Numbers and Decimals

Lesson Objectives

- Align numbers to prepare for addition.
- Explain different methods for addition.

The Day at a Glance

Today's Goals	Materials	Math Talk
Quick Practice Identify place value groups for large numbers and display approximate metric lengths. **1 Teaching the Lesson** A1: Discuss various strategies for making a new ten when adding. A2: Analyze and add different types of numbers. **2 Extending the Lesson** ▶ Differentiated Instruction **3 Homework and Cumulative Review**	Student Activity Book pages 113–114 Centimeter tape measures MathBoard materials Play or real money (dollars, dimes, and pennies) Homework and Remembering pages 55–56 Math Journals	In today's activities, the students are involved in discussion as they ▶ demonstrate how to regroup as they add numbers ▶ set up addition problems that involve different units, money, and the metric system

Quick Practice

5 MINUTES   **Goal:** Identify place values in large numbers and approximate lengths of metric measures.

Read Large Numbers Send three student leaders to the board and have them each write a large number with 6 to 12 digits. Then each leader points to each group of digits and reads the numbers. The class responds with the group name.

Metric Lengths The student leader writes a metric length abbreviation (m, dm, cm, or mm) on the board and points to it. The other students respond by saying the name of the unit and showing the approximate length with their hands. The leader should try to use all lengths twice, in random order.

> *Example:* 5,923,405,172
>
> *Leader:* 5   *Class:* billion
>
> *Leader:* 923   *Class:* million
>
> *Leader:* 405   *Class:* thousand
>
> *Leader:* 172   *Class:* ones

① Teaching the Lesson

Discuss Ways to Regroup

 20–25 MINUTES

Goal: Discuss various strategies for making a new ten when adding.

 NCTM Standards:
Number and Operations
Communication

The Learning Classroom

Building Concepts Some students will make errors in regrouping as they work. Look for correct student work to use as models of the different ways to add. Some students may use a method other than the three shown here. Emphasize that there are many different ways to add.

▶ Student-Generated Addition Methods | WHOLE CLASS |

Send several students to the board as possible and ask them all to solve this problem.

$$769$$
$$+\ 584$$

 Math Talk

Invite several students to explain their methods. Be sure that the explainers use place value words in their explanations. They should not just say, "I carried a one." (Ask them, "One *what?*")

Elicit any different methods your students use and discuss each of them. The most common methods appear below. The New Groups Below and New Groups Above methods involve making one new group of ten in the next larger place whenever there is a total of ten or more in one place.

New Groups Below

Step 1	Step 2	Step 3
769	769	769
$+\ 584$	$+\ 584$	$+\ 584$
3	53	$1{,}353$

New Groups Above

Step 1	Step 2	Step 3
769	769	769
$+\ 584$	$+\ 584$	$+\ 584$
3	53	$1{,}353$

In the Subtotal Method, the hundreds, tens, and ones are added separately.

Subtotal Method

Left to Right	Right to Left
769	769
$+\ 584$	$+\ 584$
1200	13
140	140

You do not need to discuss all of the methods shown above. Focus only on the methods that your students *actually* use. In Lesson 7, the class will be exposed to all three of these methods in the context of adding very large numbers.

Activity 2

Add Unlike Amounts

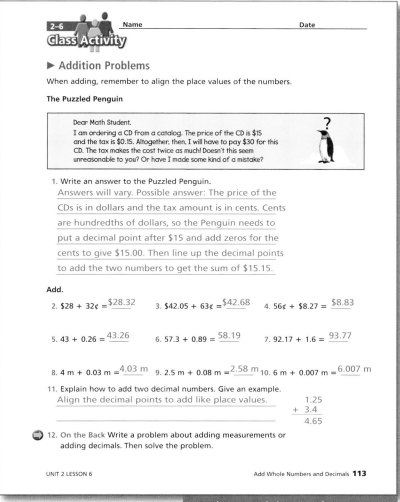

Goal: Add different types of numbers.

Materials: Student Activity Book page 113

✔ **NCTM Standards:**
Number and Operations
Measurement

Teaching Note

What to Expect From Students
Students may readily see the answer without actually aligning and adding. If so, point out that it will not always be this easy to find the answer. For complex problems, they will need to align like place values.

▶ Addition Problems WHOLE CLASS

The Puzzled Penguin Have the class turn to page 113 in the Student Activity Book and discuss the Puzzled Penguin activity. Students should see that the penguin has added *unlike* amounts (dollars and cents) and has therefore arrived at the wrong total. Ask students how they would set up the problem for addition. Have a volunteer write the problem vertically on the board and solve it.

$$\begin{array}{r} \$15.00 \\ +\ 0.15 \\ \hline \$15.15 \end{array}$$

Discuss why the problem is set up this way. Encourage students to justify the alignment by talking about the size of the places rather than simply "lining up the decimal points." If students give a rule about lining up the decimals, ask them the reason for the rule. Elicit from them that only *like* amounts can be added.

Activity continued ▶

① Teaching the Lesson (continued)

Activity 2

The Learning Classroom

Quick Practice This would be a good time to review the relationships among different lengths in the metric system.

- ? cm = 1 m   100
- 1 cm = ? m   0.01
- ? dm = 1 m   10
- 1 dm = ? m   0.1
- ? mm = 1 m   1000
- 1 mm = ? m   0.001

Ask students to talk about patterns that they observe.

✔ Ongoing Assessment

Have students solve these exercises and discuss how to line up the decimal points.

▶ $208.11 + $0.89

▶ 67 dm + 48 cm

▶ 412 + 0.789

Add Money Amounts Invite three students to go to the board and solve exercises 2–4 on page 113 of the Student Activity Book. Give each student a different exercise to solve. The students at their seats can work on all three exercises.

If necessary, review with all students how to write cents as dollars: 32¢ = $0.32 (3 dimes and 2 pennies).

$$\begin{array}{r} \$28.00 \\ + \ 0.32 \\ \hline \$28.32 \end{array}$$

or

When the students at the board have finished, ask each of them to explain how they set up the exercise and why. Most students will use dollars and cents, as shown in the first example at the right. A few students might decide to use all cents, as shown in the second example. That is acceptable, but point out that amounts over one dollar are usually shown as a decimal amount.

$$\begin{array}{r} 2{,}800¢ \\ 32 \\ \hline 2{,}832¢ \end{array}$$

Add Numbers Now have students use Solve and Discuss for exercises 5–7. This time students must align the problems so like amounts are added together.

$$\begin{array}{r} 43.00 \\ + \ 0.26 \\ \hline 43.26 \end{array}$$

Add Metric Units Direct students' attention to exercises 8–10. Again, send three students to the board to solve and discuss these exercises. Students will need to decide which measuring unit they will use for their answer and then convert one of the units. The first exercise, for example, can be set up with either meters or centimeters, as shown at the right.

$$\begin{array}{r} 4.00 \text{ m} \\ + \ 0.03 \text{ m} \\ \hline 4.03 \text{ m} \end{array}$$

or

As each student at the board finishes explaining, ask the seated students if anyone set up the exercise differently. If so, invite that student to explain his or her approach.

$$\begin{array}{r} 400 \text{ cm} \\ + \ \ 3 \text{ cm} \\ \hline 403 \text{ cm} \end{array}$$

In this unit, students will be adding and subtracting like measuring units and like place values. It is important to align numbers so that like place values are added together.

Have students complete exercises 11–12.

② Extending the Lesson

Intervention
for students having difficulty

PAIRS

Metric Sums

Materials: centimeter tape measure, MathBoard materials

Have students use a tape measure to add metric units

Example: 2 dm + 8 cm = 28 cm

One student marks off 2 dm on the tape measure by placing a finger at the appropriate place.

The other student uses a finger to mark off 8 cm more.

Students determine the total length and show the addition.
2 dm + 8 cm = 28 cm, or
20 cm + 8 cm = 28 cm

Have them find these sums. They should use the tape measure if necessary.

11 cm + 5 mm = 11.5 cm
1 dm + 2 cm = 12 cm
2 dm + 10 mm = 21 cm
10 mm + 10 cm = 11 cm

On Level
for students having success

PAIRS

Money Sums

Materials: play money dollars, dimes, and pennies

Have students use play money to model decimal addition.

Example: 56¢ + $2.75 = $3.31
Model each amount.

Combine like money to add.

Trade 10 pennies for a dime and 10 dimes for a dollar.

Have students write other exercises and exchange them. Then have each student model the solution.

Challenge
for students seeking a challenge

INDIVIDUALS

Place the Decimal Point

Materials: MathBoard materials

Have students copy and complete the following exercise set on their MathBoards.

Place the decimal points in each exercise to match its sum.

17.0 + 2.5 = 19.5

3.61 + 14.5 = 18.11

9.1 + 1.09 = 10.19

5.0 + 50.5 = 55.5

86.4 + 32.9 = 119.3

21. + 1.9 = 22.9

10.1 + 1.01 = 11.11

Have students discuss why the decimal points had to be placed the way they did to get each sum.

 Math Writing Prompt

Intervention

Explain Relationships
When adding money amounts, explain when you should regroup pennies for dimes and when you should regroup dimes for dollars.

 Math Writing Prompt

On Level

Write a Correction
Explain why Tyler has the wrong sum for this example and tell how to find the correct sum.

$$\begin{array}{r} 35.2 \\ + 1.46 \\ \hline 4.98 \end{array}$$

 Math Writing Prompt

Challenge

Explain Multi-Step Problems
Write the steps you have to follow to solve 9 m + 5 mm = _____ cm.

 **Homework and Cumulative Review**

✓ Use this Homework page to provide students with more practice with adding whole and decimal numbers.

This Remembering Activity would be appropriate anytime after today's lesson.

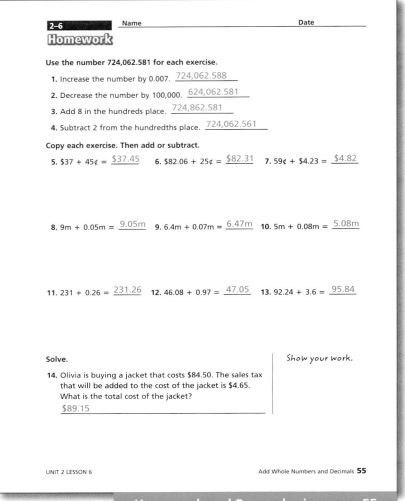

| 2–6 | Name | | Date |

Homework

Use the number 724,062.581 for each exercise.

1. Increase the number by 0.007. ___724,062.588___

2. Decrease the number by 100,000. ___624,062.581___

3. Add 8 in the hundreds place. ___724,862.581___

4. Subtract 2 from the hundredths place. ___724,062.561___

Copy each exercise. Then add or subtract.

5. $37 + 45¢ = ___$37.45___   6. $82.06 + 25¢ = ___$82.31___   7. 59¢ + $4.23 = ___$4.82___

8. 9m + 0.05m = ___9.05m___   9. 6.4m + 0.07m = ___6.47m___   10. 5m + 0.08m = ___5.08m___

11. 231 + 0.26 = ___231.26___   12. 46.08 + 0.97 = ___47.05___   13. 92.24 + 3.6 = ___95.84___

Solve.   *Show your work.*

14. Olivia is buying a jacket that costs $84.50. The sales tax that will be added to the cost of the jacket is $4.65. What is the total cost of the jacket?
___$89.15___

UNIT 2 LESSON 6   Add Whole Numbers and Decimals **55**

Homework and Remembering page 55

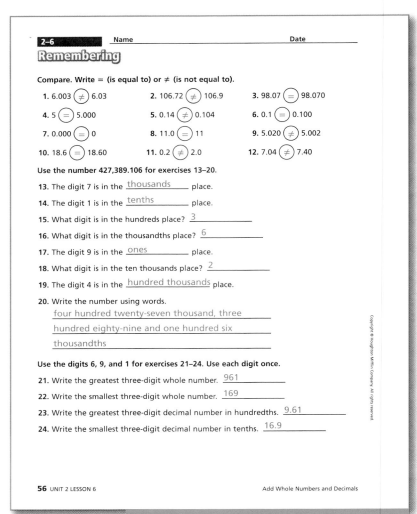

| 2–6 | Name | | Date |

Remembering

Compare. Write = (is equal to) or ≠ (is not equal to).

1. 6.003 (≠) 6.03   2. 106.72 (≠) 106.9   3. 98.07 (=) 98.070

4. 5 (=) 5.000   5. 0.14 (≠) 0.104   6. 0.1 (=) 0.100

7. 0.000 (=) 0   8. 11.0 (=) 11   9. 5.020 (≠) 5.002

10. 18.6 (=) 18.60   11. 0.2 (≠) 2.0   12. 7.04 (≠) 7.40

Use the number 427,389.106 for exercises 13–20.

13. The digit 7 is in the ___thousands___ place.

14. The digit 1 is in the ___tenths___ place.

15. What digit is in the hundreds place? ___3___

16. What digit is in the thousandths place? ___6___

17. The digit 9 is in the ___ones___ place.

18. What digit is in the ten thousands place? ___2___

19. The digit 4 is in the ___hundred thousands___ place.

20. Write the number using words.
___four hundred twenty-seven thousand, three___
___hundred eighty-nine and one hundred six___
___thousandths___

Use the digits 6, 9, and 1 for exercises 21–24. Use each digit once.

21. Write the greatest three-digit whole number. ___961___

22. Write the smallest three-digit whole number. ___169___

23. Write the greatest three-digit decimal number in hundredths. ___9.61___

24. Write the smallest three-digit decimal number in tenths. ___16.9___

56 UNIT 2 LESSON 6   Add Whole Numbers and Decimals

Homework and Remembering page 56

Home or School Activity

 Social Studies Connection

Lots of Time Have students research the length of time for the following.

decade = 10 years
century = 100 years
millennium = 1,000 years

Have students look up several events in history and make a chart estimating how long ago each event happened.

Historical Event	When?
Christopher Columbus sailed to the Americas.	about 5 centuries ago
Paper was invented in China.	about 2 millennia ago
The first known writing system was developed.	about 5 millennia ago
"The Star-Spangled Banner" was written.	about 2 centuries ago

Addition to Millions

Lesson Objectives

- **Align numbers according to their place values to prepare for adding.**
- **Use and explain different methods for addition.**

The Day at a Glance

Today's Goals	Materials	Math Talk
Quick Practice Identify place-value groups for large numbers and display approximate metric lengths. **① Teaching the Lesson** **A1:** Discuss the advantages and disadvantages of different addition methods. **A2:** Solve addition problems using different methods. **② Extending the Lesson** ▶ Differentiated Instruction **③ Homework and Cumulative Review**	Student Activity Book pages 115–116 Place value charts Calculators MathBoard materials Homework and Remembering pages 57–58 Math Journals	In today's activities, the students are involved in discussion as they ▶ examine different methods of regrouping ▶ work through addition exercises with large numbers

Quick Practice

⏱ **5 MINUTES** **Goal:** Identify place-value groups for large numbers and display approximate metric lengths.

Read Large Numbers Send three student leaders to the board and have them each write a large number with 6 to 12 digits. Then each leader points to each group of digits and reads the numbers. The class responds with the group name.

Metric Lengths The student leader writes a metric length abbreviation (m, dm, cm, or mm). The other students respond by saying the name of the unit and showing the approximate length with their hands. The leader should try to use all lengths twice, in random order. If you like, write the abbreviations on the board and let the leader use a pointer.

Example: 42,103,685,093
Leader: 42 *Class:* billion
Leader: 103 *Class:* million
Leader: 685 *Class:* thousand
Leader: 093 *Class:* ones

1 Teaching the Lesson

Addition Methods

 20–25 MINUTES

Goal: Discuss the advantages and disadvantages of different addition methods.

Materials: Student Activity Book page 115

 NCTM Standards:
Number and Operations
Communication

Teaching Note

Math Background Remind students when adding decimal numbers that they should align the numbers by their place values.

 Class Management

Tell students we are going to refer to the horizontal line drawn under the problem as the *problem line.* In the New Groups Below method, the ten groups are written on the problem line.

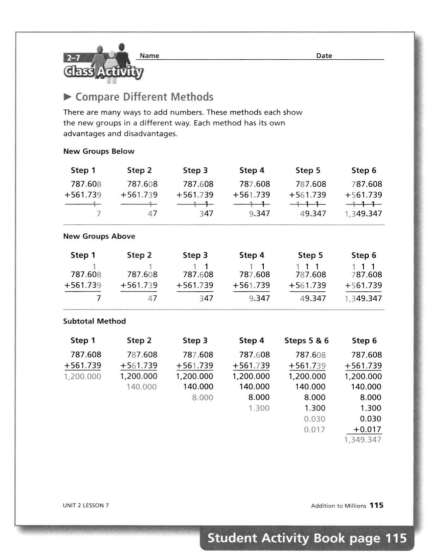

Student Activity Book page 115

▶ **Compare Different Methods** WHOLE CLASS

A Real-World Problem Write the numbers 786,608 and 561,739 on the board. Have a student volunteer read the numbers. Then ask a student to describe an addition word problem that uses the numbers. Write the word problem on the board as the student says it.

Ask the class to verify that the problem is an addition problem.

Share Methods There are three different methods of addition on page 115 in the Student Activity Book. Talk about each method before students look at the student page. Students should notice that each method shows the new group in a different way.

- The first method shows the new groups below the problem line.
- The second method shows the new groups above the top number.
- The third method shows place value groups as subtotals.

After you discuss each method, you may want to have students discuss this page in pairs or in groups of three. Then ask volunteers to share their ideas with the class. Ask students to think about the advantages and disadvantages of each method.

New Groups Below

Advantages:
- Addition is easier because the extra 1 is added last.
- The new teen subtotal can be seen clearly.

Disadvantages:
- The method is not known to many people.

New Groups Above

Advantages:
- The method is known to many people.

Disadvantages:
- Adding can be more difficult if you add the columns from top to bottom.
- Teen subtotals are separated.

Subtotal Method

Advantages:
- You can add in either direction.
- You do not need to insert numbers for new groups.

Disadvantages:
- The problem takes up more space.

The Learning Classroom

Building Concepts This is the perfect place to emphasize that there is more than one way to solve a problem.

Teaching Note

What to Expect From Students
Math Expressions emphasizes New Groups Below over the more traditional New Groups Above because the New Groups Below method is less prone to error. However, by fifth grade, most students have become accustomed to their own methods.

① Teaching the Lesson (continued)

Activity 2

Practice and Explain

 20–25 MINUTES

Goal: Solve addition problems using their preferred method.

Materials: Student Activity Book page 116

 NCTM Standards:
Number and Operations
Communication

Differentiated Instruction

Special Needs Some students have trouble aligning columns of numbers. With longer computation problems such as these, you might want to have these students use lined notebook paper. Before writing the problem, have them turn the paper sideways so that the lines are vertical. The vertical lines will help them align the columns more precisely.

Ongoing Assessment

Tell students to solve each problem and then write the name of the method they chose to use.

► 203.6 + 78,493

► 2,700,508 + 2.009

► 978,859.97 + 4,341.05

► 0.975 + 369.235

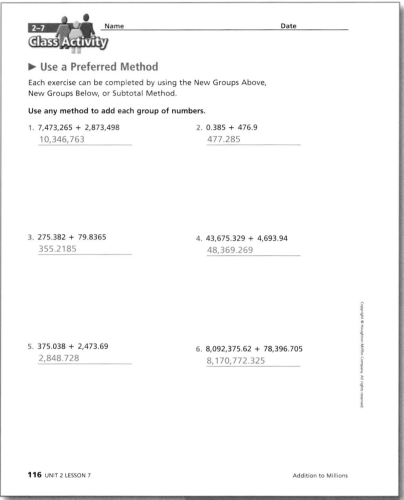

Student Activity Book page 116

►Use a Preferred Method WHOLE CLASS

Have everyone solve exercises 1–6 on page 116 of the Student Activity Book, using any method. Invite as many students as possible to solve at the board while the rest solve at their seats. You may want to have the seated students work in pairs. When explanations are given, emphasize place value language to describe how new groups of tens are made. Invite the class to comment or ask questions when explanations are given.

② Extending the Lesson

Differentiated Instruction
Activities for Individualizing

Intervention
for students having difficulty

PAIRS

Line Up!

Materials: place value charts

Give each pair a place-value chart. Use this example to explain how to use the chart to add large numbers.

4,763,052 + 892,476

	M	HTh	TTh	Th	H	T	O
Regroup	1		1		1		
	4	7	6	3	0	5	2
+		8	2	9	4	7	6
Sum	5	5	9	2	5	2	8

Have pairs take turns writing addition problems of whole numbers to millions. The other student should use the place value chart to find the sum.

 Math Writing Prompt

Intervention

Write Number Names
Use the digits 0 to 9 to write a number in standard form. Use each digit once. Now write the same number in word form.

On Level
for students having success

PAIRS

Choose Your Method

Materials: calculators, MathBoard materials

For each problem below, pairs should discuss which method is best: mental math, paper and pencil, or a calculator. Then use their chosen method to solve.

Problem	Solution	Method
1200 + 700	1,900	(MM)
97.984 + 3.5107	101.4947	(C)
651 + 326	977	(PP)
13,500 + 6,100	19,600	(MM)
15.42 + 6.8	22.22	(PP)
99,999,999 + 999,999	100,999,998	(C)

Have students explain why they chose the method they did.

 Math Writing Prompt

On Level

Explain Your Thinking
Explain when mental math is a good method to choose when you need to add. Give examples.

Challenge
for students seeking a challenge

INDIVIDUALS

Grade a Quiz

Materials: MathBoard materials

Have students copy the following quiz on their MathBoards and check each answer. If the answer is wrong, find the correct sum.

> Name: Puzzled Penguin
> 1. 9.8 + 7.5 = 16.3
> 2. 264,792 + 17,975 = 282,767
> 3. 107.15 + 19.3 = 109.08
> 4. 0.6419 + 64.19 = 64.8319
> 5. 312,546.8 + 894,634 = 313,441.4

For each incorrect answer, students should explain the mistake the Puzzled Penguin made.

 Math Writing Prompt

Challenge

Explain a Process
Explain why it is important to line up digits by place values when you add. Give examples.

③ Homework and Cumulative Review

Homework **Goal:** Additional Practice

✓ Use this Homework page to provide students with more practice with addition to millions.

Remembering **Goal:** Cumulative Review

This Remembering Activity would be appropriate anytime after today's lesson.

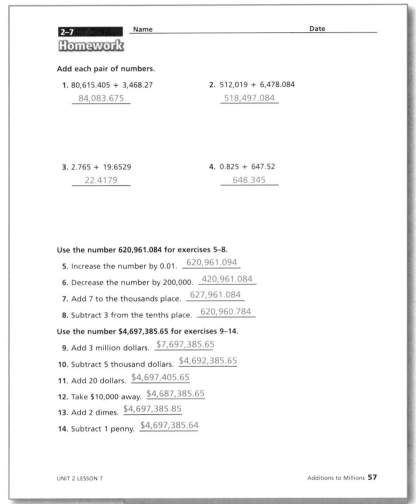

2-7 Name _____ Date _____
Homework

Add each pair of numbers.

1. 80,615.405 + 3,468.27
   84,083.675

2. 512,019 + 6,478.084
   518,497.084

3. 2.765 + 19.6529
   22.4179

4. 0.825 + 647.52
   648.345

Use the number 620,961.084 for exercises 5–8.

5. Increase the number by 0.01. 620,961.094
6. Decrease the number by 200,000. 420,961.084
7. Add 7 to the thousands place. 627,961.084
8. Subtract 3 from the tenths place. 620,960.784

Use the number $4,697,385.65 for exercises 9–14.

9. Add 3 million dollars. $7,697,385.65
10. Subtract 5 thousand dollars. $4,692,385.65
11. Add 20 dollars. $4,697,405.65
12. Take $10,000 away. $4,687,385.65
13. Add 2 dimes. $4,697,385.85
14. Subtract 1 penny. $4,697,385.64

UNIT 2 LESSON 7   Additions to Millions **57**

Homework and Remembering page 57

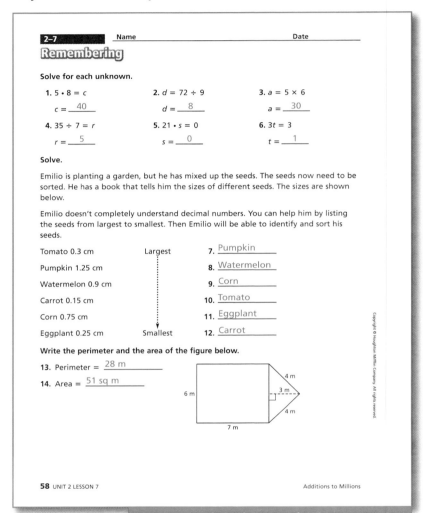

2-7 Name _____ Date _____
Remembering

Solve for each unknown.

1. 5 • 8 = c
   c = 40

2. d = 72 ÷ 9
   d = 8

3. a = 5 × 6
   a = 30

4. 35 ÷ 7 = r
   r = 5

5. 21 • s = 0
   s = 0

6. 3t = 3
   t = 1

Solve.

Emilio is planting a garden, but he has mixed up the seeds. The seeds now need to be sorted. He has a book that tells him the sizes of different seeds. The sizes are shown below.

Emilio doesn't completely understand decimal numbers. You can help him by listing the seeds from largest to smallest. Then Emilio will be able to identify and sort his seeds.

Tomato 0.3 cm   Largest   7. Pumpkin
Pumpkin 1.25 cm   8. Watermelon
Watermelon 0.9 cm   9. Corn
Carrot 0.15 cm   10. Tomato
Corn 0.75 cm   11. Eggplant
Eggplant 0.25 cm   Smallest   12. Carrot

Write the perimeter and the area of the figure below.

13. Perimeter = 28 m
14. Area = 51 sq m

58 UNIT 2 LESSON 7   Additions to Millions

Homework and Remembering page 58

Home or School Activity

Social Studies Connection

Millions of People Every 10 years, the U.S. Census Bureau counts all the people in each state. The Bureau also groups the 50 states into four regions, as shown in the map at right. Have students research to find the population data that the Census Bureau collected for each region in 1990 and 2000 (shown in table). Then have your students calculate the total U.S. population in 1990 and in 2000.

State Region	Population	
	1990	2000
Northeast	50,809,229	53,594,378
Midwest	59,668,632	64,392,776
South	85,445,930	100,236,820
West	52,786,082	63,197,932

U.S. State Regions

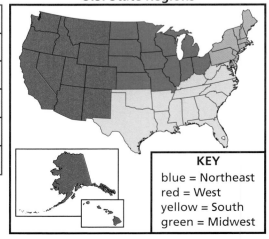

KEY
blue = Northeast
red = West
yellow = South
green = Midwest

Subtract Whole and Decimal Numbers

Lesson Objectives

● Explore the relationship between addition and subtraction.

● Explain solution methods for multi-digit subtraction.

The Day at a Glance

Today's Goals	Materials	Math Talk
Quick Practice Identify place-value groups for large numbers and display approximate metric lengths.	Student Activity Book pages 117–118	In today's activities, the students are involved in discussion as they
1 Teaching the Lesson A1: Discuss regrouping to subtract and relate regrouping in subtraction to addition. A2: Explain subtraction methods and apply them to real-world problems.	Play money Calculators MathBoard materials Homework and Remembering pages 59–60 Math Journals	▶ look at different methods of subtracting and relate them to addition methods ▶ apply subtraction methods to problems
2 Extending the Lesson ▶ Differentiated Instruction		
3 Homework and Cumulative Review		

Quick Practice

🕐 **5 MINUTES** **Goal:** Identify place-value groups for large numbers and display approximate metric lengths using their hands.

Read Large Numbers Send 3 student leaders to the board and have them each write a large number with 6 to 12 digits. Then each leader points to each group of digits and reads the numbers. The class responds with the group name.

Metric Lengths The student leader writes a metric length abbreviation (m, dm, cm, or mm). The other students respond by saying the name of the unit and showing the approximate length with their hands. The leader should try to use all lengths twice, in random order.

Example: 12,983,507,162		
Leader: 12	*Class:* billion	
Leader: 983	*Class:* million	
Leader: 507	*Class:* thousand	
Leader: 162	*Class:* ones	

① Teaching the Lesson

Activity 1

Ungroup With Zeros

 20–25 MINUTES

Goal: Discuss regrouping to subtract and relate regrouping in subtraction to addition.

 NCTM Standards:
Number and Operations
Communication

Teaching Note

Watch For! Remind students to show how they ungroup on their paper, drawing lines through the numbers as they ungroup.

Teaching Note

Math Background Students are given subtraction across zeros first to show that numbers can be ungrouped from the left. Ungrouping all at once from the left is natural because we read from left to right, and this method leads to fewer errors. For these reasons, this method is emphasized in the earlier grades in *Math Expressions*. However, by fifth grade, most students have become adept at one particular method. There is no need to suggest a change unless the student is clearly struggling.

▶ **Discuss Student Methods** WHOLE CLASS

Using Solve and Discuss, have students share methods for subtracting these numbers.

$$\begin{array}{r} 400 \\ -\ 164 \\ \hline \end{array}$$

Ask the students to explain how they would ungroup to get enough tens and ones to subtract 6 tens and 4 ones. Explain that there are two basic methods:

Ungroup Place by Place Ungroup 1 hundred to make 10 tens, leaving 3 hundreds. Then ungroup 1 ten to make 10 ones, leaving 9 tens.

$$\begin{array}{r} {\scriptstyle 9} \\ {\scriptstyle 3\ 1\!\!\!\!/\!0\ 10} \\ 4\!\!\!\!/\,0\!\!\!\!/\,0\!\!\!\!/ \\ -164 \\ \hline \end{array}$$

Ungroup All at Once Ungroup 400 to make 3 hundreds (300), 9 tens (90), and 10 ones.

$$400 = 300 + 90 + 10$$

$$\begin{array}{r} {\scriptstyle 3\ 9\ 10} \\ 4\!\!\!\!/\,0\!\!\!\!/\,0\!\!\!\!/ \\ -164 \\ \hline \end{array}$$

Some students may use drawings to show the ungrouping. Each box in the drawing represents a hundred, each line segment represents a ten, and each circle represents a one. The crossed out hundred-box has been ungrouped as 10 tens, and the crossed out ten-segment has been ungrouped as 10 ones.

1 hundred = 10 tens

1 ten = 10 ones

▶ Relate Addition and Subtraction WHOLE CLASS

Begin by drawing this break-apart drawing on the board.

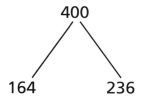

Ask the class to discuss how the drawing shows the relationship between addition and subtraction.

- Which number is the total? the top number

- What do we get if we subtract one of the bottom numbers from the total? We get the other bottom number.

Struggling students may benefit from break-apart drawings as they relate addition and subtraction or solve word problems with unknown addends.

Check Subtraction Using the same set of numbers, ask the class to add the two smaller numbers *without* grouping. Have one student work at the board and ungroup the larger number to subtract. What do we notice about the ungrouped numbers in both problems? They are the same. In subtracting you ungroup to get the numbers you would get if you added without grouping.

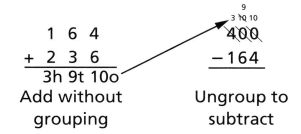

This is a good time to reinforce that addition and subtraction are inverse operations. This example shows why we can use addition to check subtraction work.

Teaching Note

Language and Vocabulary
Students may use a variety of terms for *ungrouping*. Other common terms are *trading* and *borrowing*. Any of these terms is acceptable, as long as students understand what they are used for: ungrouping one unit from a place value to make ten of those units in the next place to the right.

Activity 2

Solve Any Subtraction Problem

 20-25 MINUTES

Goal: Explain subtraction methods and apply them to real-world problems.

Materials: Student Activity Book pages 117–118

 NCTM Standards:
Number and Operations
Measurement
Communication

Teaching Note

What to Expect From Students
With these problems, some students will ungroup from the left, and some from the right. Try to elicit an explanation of both methods, if possible. In addition, some students will ungroup everything before they subtract, while others will subtract as they ungroup. Again, both of these methods are acceptable.

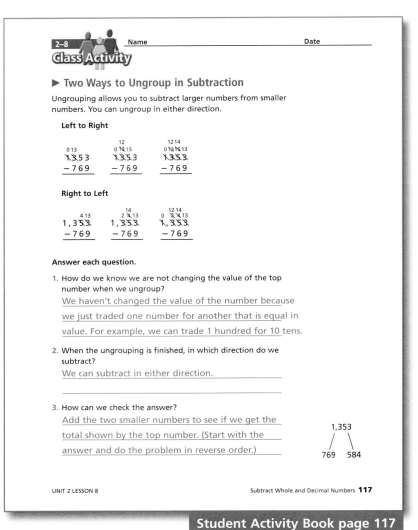

Student Activity Book page 117

▶ Two Ways to Ungroup in Subtraction WHOLE CLASS

Use Solve and Discuss to elicit student solution methods for the problem shown below. Ask students to explain the ungrouping process using place value language. (They should not say "borrowed a one," but "ungrouped [or borrowed or traded] one hundred or one ten.")

$$\begin{array}{r} 1353 \\ -\ 769 \\ \hline \end{array}$$

Ask students to look at page 117 in the Student Activity Book. There they can see the same example ungrouped two ways. If all of your students used the same method, be sure to discuss the other way. Then have students answer the three questions shown.

Practice Subtraction This bank of exercises can be used for mastery of subtraction if students need extra practice. Subsequent days will include more practice on addition and subtraction of decimal numbers, so you don't need to wait for mastery of subtracting decimals.

You may want to suggest that students add to check their subtraction answers, thereby getting addition practice also.

1. $45,384 - 28,946 = 16,438$

2. $137,355 - 18,967 = 118,388$

3. $15,044 - 498 = 14,546$

4. $34,568,999 - 8,479,345 = 26,089,654$

5. $4,508 - 3,305 = 1,203$

6. $7,000 - 4,813 = 2,187$

7. $51,006 - 897 = 50,109$

8. $100,000,000 - 510,000 = 99,490,000$

9. $9,612 - 5,000 = 4,612$

10. $43,080 - 8,948 = 34,132$

11. $17,856 - 96 = 17,760$

12. $73,000 - 37,000 = 36,000$

13. $5,000,000,000 - 493,000,000 = 4,507,000,000$

14. $826,005 - 18,785 = 807,220$

15. $93,000 - 6,130 = 86,870$

16. $5,132 - 4,987 = 145$

17. $7,400,000,034 - 7,300,000,921 = 99,999,113$

18. $651,300 - 85,076 = 566,224$

19. $9,005 - 3,999 = 5,006$

20. $5,000,000 - 3,500,000 = 1,500,000$

Activity continued ▶

Extra Help A few students, even in fifth grade, make this wrong-way error. They do not ungroup, but just subtract the smaller digit from the larger.

Error

$$\begin{array}{r} 52 \\ -\ 18 \\ \hline 46 \end{array}$$

If they use the alternating method (subtracting as they ungroup each column), they may be more prone to this error. If any of your students are making this error, encourage them to do all the ungrouping that is needed before they begin subtracting.

1 Teaching the Lesson (continued)

Activity 2

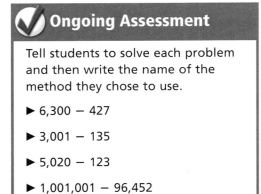

Ongoing Assessment

Tell students to solve each problem and then write the name of the method they chose to use.

▶ 6,300 − 427

▶ 3,001 − 135

▶ 5,020 − 123

▶ 1,001,001 − 96,452

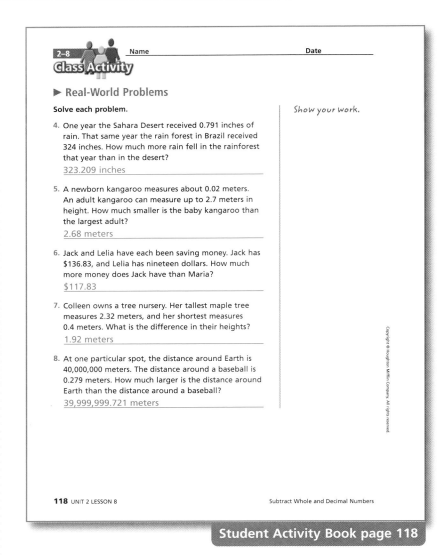

2–8
Class Activity
Name _____ Date _____

▶ **Real-World Problems**

Solve each problem.   *Show your work.*

4. One year the Sahara Desert received 0.791 inches of rain. That same year the rain forest in Brazil received 324 inches. How much more rain fell in the rainforest that year than in the desert?
   323.209 inches

5. A newborn kangaroo measures about 0.02 meters. An adult kangaroo can measure up to 2.7 meters in height. How much smaller is the baby kangaroo than the largest adult?
   2.68 meters

6. Jack and Lelia have each been saving money. Jack has $136.83, and Lelia has nineteen dollars. How much more money does Jack have than Maria?
   $117.83

7. Colleen owns a tree nursery. Her tallest maple tree measures 2.32 meters, and her shortest measures 0.4 meters. What is the difference in their heights?
   1.92 meters

8. At one particular spot, the distance around Earth is 40,000,000 meters. The distance around a baseball is 0.279 meters. How much larger is the distance around Earth than the distance around a baseball?
   39,999,999.721 meters

118 UNIT 2 LESSON 8   Subtract Whole and Decimal Numbers

Student Activity Book page 118

▶ Real-World Problems WHOLE CLASS

Next, have the class solve and discuss the word problems on page 118 of the Student Activity Book. Invite several students to work at the board while the others work at their seats. Students will need to explain, in particular, how they set up each problem and why. Everyone will need to be alert for problems using different metric units of measure.

② Extending the Lesson

Intervention
for students having difficulty

INDIVIDUALS

Across Zeros

Materials: play money

Have students use play money to model subtracting across zeros.

Example: $300 − $279 = $21

Model 3 hundreds with $100-bills and take away 2.

Regroup the remaining hundred as 10 tens and take away 7 tens

Regroup the remaining ten as 10 ones and take away 9 ones.

Have students solve these problems.

$200 − $148

$400 − $327

$500 − $216

On Level
for students having success

SMALL GROUPS

Choose Your Method

Materials: calculators, MathBoard materials

For each problem below, pairs should discuss which method is best: mental math, paper and pencil, or a calculator. Then use their chosen method to solve.

Problem	Solution	Method
950 − 250	700	(MM)
13.402 − 8.979	4.423	(C)
639 − 564	75	(PP)
5000 − 2000	3000	(MM)
9.85 − 2.27	7.58	(PP)
10,213 − 9,999.85	213.15	(C)

Challenge
for students seeking a challenge

PAIRS

Check It!

Remind students that they can use addition to check their answers to subtraction problems.

Have students make their own subtraction exercises and then give them to their partner to solve and check.

> Solve:
>   507.8 − 269.5 = 238.3
>
> Check:
>   238.3 + 269.5 = 507.8 ✓

 Math Writing Prompt

Intervention

Real-World Situation
Write about a real-world situation in which you would need to add or subtract decimals.

 Math Writing Prompt

On Level

Make Connections
Explain how addition and subtraction are related. Give an example.

 Math Writing Prompt

Challenge

Explain a Process
Write a subtraction example that involves regrouping. Then explain how you would regroup to solve it.

③ Homework and Cumulative Review

 **Homework** **Goal:** Additional Practice

✓ Include students' work for page 59 as part of their portfolios.

 **Remembering** **Goal:** Cumulative Review

This Remembering Activity would be appropriate anytime after today's lesson.

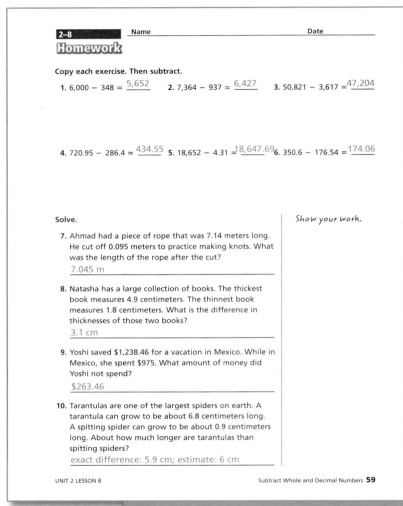

2–8 Homework — Name _____ Date _____

Copy each exercise. Then subtract.

1. $6,000 - 348 = \underline{5,652}$ 2. $7,364 - 937 = \underline{6,427}$ 3. $50,821 - 3,617 = \underline{47,204}$

4. $720.95 - 286.4 = \underline{434.55}$ 5. $18,652 - 4.31 = \underline{18,647.69}$ 6. $350.6 - 176.54 = \underline{174.06}$

Solve.   *Show your work.*

7. Ahmad had a piece of rope that was 7.14 meters long. He cut off 0.095 meters to practice making knots. What was the length of the rope after the cut?
   7.045 m

8. Natasha has a large collection of books. The thickest book measures 4.9 centimeters. The thinnest book measures 1.8 centimeters. What is the difference in thicknesses of those two books?
   3.1 cm

9. Yoshi saved $1,238.46 for a vacation in Mexico. While in Mexico, she spent $975. What amount of money did Yoshi not spend?
   $263.46

10. Tarantulas are one of the largest spiders on earth. A tarantula can grow to be about 6.8 centimeters long. A spitting spider can grow to be about 0.9 centimeters long. About how much longer are tarantulas than spitting spiders?
    exact difference: 5.9 cm; estimate: 6 cm

UNIT 2 LESSON 8   Subtract Whole and Decimal Numbers **59**

Homework and Remembering page 59

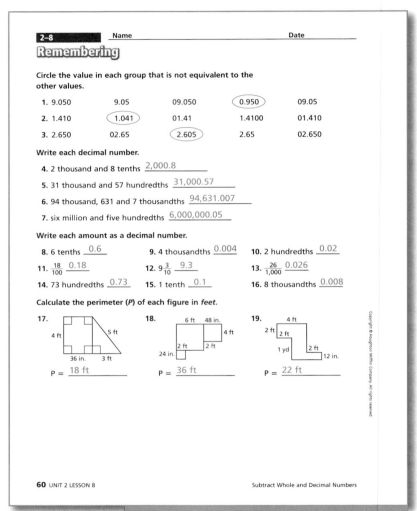

2–8 Remembering — Name _____ Date _____

Circle the value in each group that is not equivalent to the other values.

1. 9.050   9.05   09.050   (0.950)   09.05
2. 1.410   (1.041)   01.41   1.4100   01.410
3. 2.650   02.65   (2.605)   2.65   02.650

Write each decimal number.

4. 2 thousand and 8 tenths _2,000.8_

5. 31 thousand and 57 hundredths _31,000.57_

6. 94 thousand, 631 and 7 thousandths _94,631.007_

7. six million and five hundredths _6,000,000.05_

Write each amount as a decimal number.

8. 6 tenths _0.6_   9. 4 thousandths _0.004_   10. 2 hundredths _0.02_

11. $\frac{18}{100}$ _0.18_   12. $9\frac{3}{10}$ _9.3_   13. $\frac{26}{1,000}$ _0.026_

14. 73 hundredths _0.73_   15. 1 tenth _0.1_   16. 8 thousandths _0.008_

Calculate the perimeter (P) of each figure in feet.

17.   18.   19.

P = _18 ft_   P = _36 ft_   P = _22 ft_

60 UNIT 2 LESSON 8   Subtract Whole and Decimal Numbers

Homework and Remembering page 60

Home or School Activity

 ## Science Connection

Seeing Colors Ask, "Did you know that all the colors we see are just different waves of light?" Then tell students that every color light wave has a different length. Have students research to find the ranges of wave lengths for some common colors. Then ask, Which of these colors has the greatest range of wavelengths? Which color has the smallest range?

Color	Wavelength of Light	
	Shortest	Longest
Blue	0.045 cm	0.05 cm
Green	0.052 cm	0.0565 cm
Yellow	0.0565 cm	0.059 cm
Orange	0.059 cm	0.0625 cm
Red	0.0625 cm	0.074 cm

Place Value Word Problems

Lesson Objectives

● Solve problems with large numbers and decimal numbers.

● Write word problems.

The Day at a Glance

Today's Goals	Materials	Math Talk
Quick Practice Practice counting and saying place-value groups by counting by 10s, 100s, and 1,000s aloud	Student Activity Book pages 119–122 Index cards Homework and Remembering pages 61–62 Math Journals	In today's activities, the students are involved in discussion as they ▶ solve problems that require applying their knowledge of place value and share their strategies with the class ▶ write, solve, and share original problems with the class
1 Teaching the Lesson **A1:** Solve and explain problems with large numbers and decimals. **A2:** Work in pairs or small groups to generate word problems.		
2 Extending the Lesson ▶ Going Further: Is an Exact or Estimated Answer Needed? ▶ Differentiated Instruction		
3 Homework and Cumulative Review		

Quick Practice

🕐 5 MINUTES   **Goal:** Practice counting and saying place-value groups by counting by 10s, 100s, and 1,000s aloud.

Large Count-Bys Have the class count in unison by 10s to 100, by 100s to 1,000, by 1,000s to 10,000, by 10,000s to 100,000, by 100,000s to 1,000,000, and by 1,000,000s to 10,000,000. Write the first several numbers in each series as the students are counting.

10, 20, 30, 40, 50 . . .
100, 200, 300, 400 . . .
1,000, 2,000, 3,000 . . .

Teaching the Lesson

Solve and Explain Word Problems

 15–20 MINUTES

Goal: Solve and explain problems with large numbers and decimals.

Materials: Student Activity Book pages 119–120

✔ **NCTM Standards:**
Problem Solving
Number and Operations
Communication

Teaching Note

What to Expect From Students

Students will use a variety of methods to solve these problems. For example, problem 3 can be solved mentally by some students who have a clear sense of place value. Other students will need to carry out the subtraction on paper. Have students discuss their different solution methods.

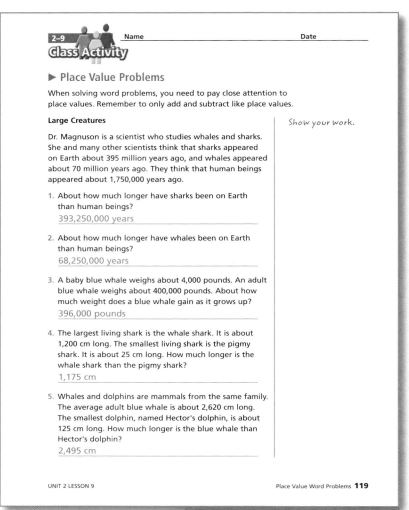

Student Activity Book page 119

► Place-Value Problems WHOLE CLASS

Explain that problems 1–5 on page 119 of the Student Activity Book are like other problems students have seen except that they have large numbers. Invite several students to work at the board while the other students work at their seats. Then ask one or two students at the board to explain how they solved the problem. Some students will need to convert 395 million and 70 million into numerals before they can work with the numbers.

Follow the same basic procedures for problems 6–9. In problems 7, 8, and 9, the alignment of the decimal numbers is crucial to solving the problem. If necessary, have students explain how to correctly set up the problems.

Activity 2

Student-Generated Word Problems

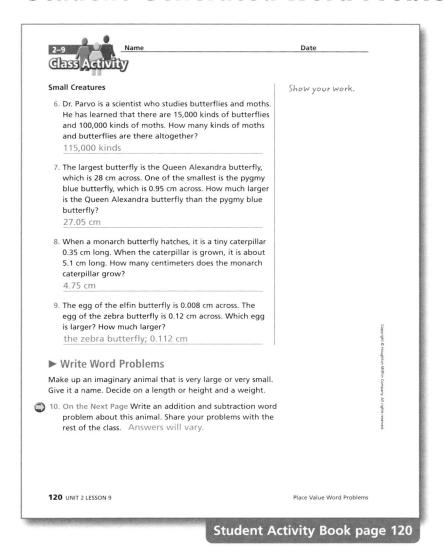

2-9 Class Activity

Name Date

Small Creatures

Show your work.

6. Dr. Parvo is a scientist who studies butterflies and moths. He has learned that there are 15,000 kinds of butterflies and 100,000 kinds of moths. How many kinds of moths and butterflies are there altogether?
   115,000 kinds
7. The largest butterfly is the Queen Alexandra butterfly, which is 28 cm across. One of the smallest is the pygmy blue butterfly, which is 0.95 cm across. How much larger is the Queen Alexandra butterfly than the pygmy blue butterfly?
   27.05 cm
8. When a monarch butterfly hatches, it is a tiny caterpillar 0.35 cm long. When the caterpillar is grown, it is about 5.1 cm long. How many centimeters does the monarch caterpillar grow?
   4.75 cm
9. The egg of the elfin butterfly is 0.008 cm across. The egg of the zebra butterfly is 0.12 cm across. Which egg is larger? How much larger?
   the zebra butterfly; 0.112 cm

▶ **Write Word Problems**

Make up an imaginary animal that is very large or very small. Give it a name. Decide on a length or height and a weight.

10. On the Next Page Write an addition and subtraction word problem about this animal. Share your problems with the rest of the class. Answers will vary.

120 UNIT 2 LESSON 9 Place Value Word Problems

Student Activity Book page 120

▶ Write Word Problems PAIRS

Using the prompt on page 120, students should work together to create some problems of their own. Give them about 10 minutes to come up with two problems about an imaginary animal.

If some groups have trouble getting started, try asking:

- How long is your animal? How much does it weigh?
- Does it have a tail? How long is the tail?
- About how many of these animals are there on Earth? Or does it live on another planet? How far away is that planet?

Then have various groups volunteer to describe their animal and to present some problems for the rest of the class to solve.

20–25 MINUTES

Goal: Students work in pairs or small groups to write their own problems.

Materials: Student Activity Book page 120

NCTM Standards:
Problem Solving
Number and Operations
Communication

The Learning Classroom

Math Talk Emphasize to students that this is a good time to exchange problem solving strategies and to help each other clarify their thinking about problems. Ask students to check each other's work so they can correct their own errors.

Ongoing Assessment

Tell students to write and solve one original problem and note the method they used to solve it.

Extending the Lesson

Going Further: Is an Exact or Estimated Answer Needed?

Goal: Determine whether a problem requires an exact answer or an estimated answer.

Materials: Student Activity Book page 122

✓ **NCTM Standards:**
Number and Operations
Problem Solving

▶ Estimate Sums and Differences

WHOLE CLASS

Review with students how to round decimals and whole numbers to estimate sums and differences.

Have students read the introduction at the top of the page. Discuss the difference between an exact answer and an estimated answer.

Then read the example problem scenario and the first row of questions in the box. Ask:

● How are the questions alike? They both ask about the total number of apples.

● What word is different in the second question? about

● What does that word tell you? I can estimate the answer.

Solve both problems together as a class.

$$
\begin{array}{r} 29 \\ +13 \\ \hline 42 \end{array}
\qquad
\begin{array}{r} 29 \rightarrow 30 \\ +13 \rightarrow +10 \\ \hline 40 \end{array}
$$

Point out that the word *about* is used in the estimated answer sentence.

Then discuss the next example. Have students identify the estimation words. Point out in the last estimation question that since we know the apples cost about $6.00, we know that $10 is enough to buy them.

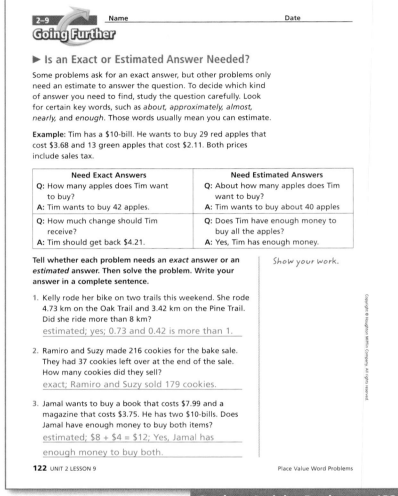

 **Student Activity Book page 122**

Have students solve problems 1–3 independently. Suggest that they underline the question in each problem and circle any key estimation words. Remind students to use estimation words, such as *about,* when they write their estimated answers.

Math Talk

After students solve all the problems, review the answers together as a class. Use Solve and Discuss to encourage students to talk about how they decided whether an exact or estimated answer was needed for each problem.

Intervention
for students having difficulty

INDIVIDUALS

Add or Subtract?

Materials: index cards (12 per student)

Have students write these words on their index cards (1 word per card): *plus, minus, more, less, sum, difference, earn, spend, increase, decrease, up, down.*

Students should shuffle all the cards. Then sort the cards into two groups:

Addition Words

| plus | more | sum |
| earn | increase | up |

Subtraction Words

| minus | less | difference |
| spend | decrease | down |

Have students pick a card and then use the word on the card in a sentence.

 Math Writing Prompt

Intervention

Estimate
Write a word problem that requires an estimated answer. Then solve the problem.

On Level
for students having success

PAIRS

Two Mix

Have students work together to write six addition problems using only the digit 2. Each problem should have a different sum. The problems can add whole numbers or decimals, but each addend must have exactly two digits that are not zero.

Students may switch the order of addends, but they should all get the following six sums.

$$22 + 22 = 44$$
$$22 + 2.2 = 24.2$$
$$22 + .22 = 22.22$$
$$2.2 + 2.2 = 4.4$$
$$2.2 + .22 = 2.42$$
$$.22 + .22 = .44$$

 Math Writing Prompt

On Level

Explain
Use examples to show that addition and subtraction are inverse operations.

Challenge
for students seeking a challenge

INDIVIDUALS

Elapsed Time

Remind students that there are 60 minutes in 1 hour. So, when they subtract time, they must regroup in units of 60, not 100.

$$\begin{array}{r} 85 \\ \cancel{3}\ \text{hr}\ \cancel{2}5\ \text{min} \\ -\ 1\ \text{hr}\ 53\ \text{min} \\ \hline 2\ \text{hr}\ 32\ \text{min} \end{array}$$

Have students write and solve subtraction problems involving time and regrouping. Some sample equations are shown.

1 hr 15 min − 45 min = 30 min

2 hr 7 min − 1 hr 20 min = 47 min

5 hr 30 min − 3 hr 57 min = 1 hr 33 min

8 hr − 4 hr 20 min = 3 hr 40 min

10 hr − 35 min = 9 hr 25 min

 Math Writing Prompt

Challenge

Write a Problem
Write a story problem using your state population and the total population of one other state.

 **Homework and Cumulative Review**

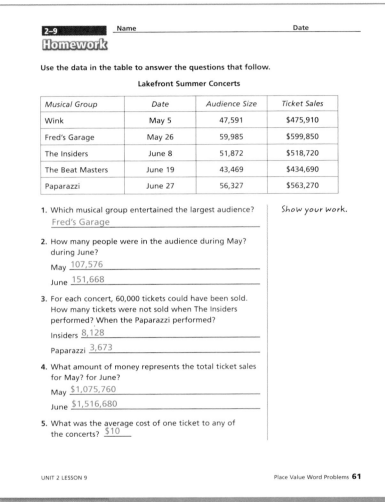

2–9
Homework **Goal:** Additional Practice

✓ Use this Homework page to provide students with more practice with place value problems.

| 2–9 | | Name | Date |
| **Homework** | | | |

Use the data in the table to answer the questions that follow.

Lakefront Summer Concerts

Musical Group	Date	Audience Size	Ticket Sales
Wink	May 5	47,591	$475,910
Fred's Garage	May 26	59,985	$599,850
The Insiders	June 8	51,872	$518,720
The Beat Masters	June 19	43,469	$434,690
Paparazzi	June 27	56,327	$563,270

1. Which musical group entertained the largest audience?   *Show your work.*
   Fred's Garage

2. How many people were in the audience during May? during June?
   May 107,576
   June 151,668

3. For each concert, 60,000 tickets could have been sold. How many tickets were not sold when The Insiders performed? When the Paparazzi performed?
   Insiders 8,128
   Paparazzi 3,673

4. What amount of money represents the total ticket sales for May? for June?
   May $1,075,760
   June $1,516,680

5. What was the average cost of one ticket to any of the concerts? $10

UNIT 2 LESSON 9   Place Value Word Problems **61**

Homework and Remembering page 61

2–9
Remembering **Goal:** Cumulative Review

This Remembering Activity would be appropriate anytime after today's lesson.

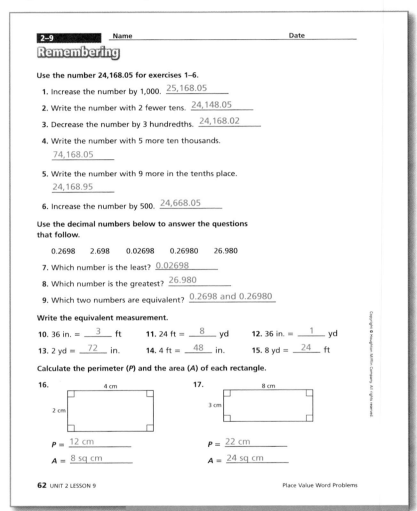

| 2–9 | | Name | Date |
| **Remembering** | | | |

Use the number 24,168.05 for exercises 1–6.

1. Increase the number by 1,000. 25,168.05
2. Write the number with 2 fewer tens. 24,148.05
3. Decrease the number by 3 hundredths. 24,168.02
4. Write the number with 5 more ten thousands.
   74,168.05
5. Write the number with 9 more in the tenths place.
   24,168.95
6. Increase the number by 500. 24,668.05

Use the decimal numbers below to answer the questions that follow.

   0.2698   2.698   0.02698   0.26980   26.980

7. Which number is the least? 0.02698
8. Which number is the greatest? 26.980
9. Which two numbers are equivalent? 0.2698 and 0.26980

Write the equivalent measurement.

10. 36 in. = 3 ft   11. 24 ft = 8 yd   12. 36 in. = 1 yd
13. 2 yd = 72 in.   14. 4 ft = 48 in.   15. 8 yd = 24 ft

Calculate the perimeter (*P*) and the area (*A*) of each rectangle.

16. (4 cm, 2 cm)   17. (8 cm, 3 cm)

P = 12 cm   P = 22 cm
A = 8 sq cm   A = 24 sq cm

62 UNIT 2 LESSON 9   Place Value Word Problems

Homework and Remembering page 62

Home or School Activity

 Science Connection

Animal Facts Scientists divide all animals into groups called *classes,* such as mammals, birds, insects, and fish.

The animal fact cards at right give information about the largest and smallest animals in three different classes.

Have students use the facts to write three addition or subtraction word problems about the animals. Tell students to exchange problems with a friend and solve.

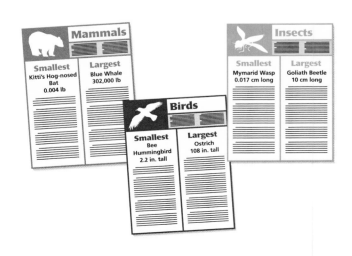

Mammals
| Smallest | Largest |
| Kitti's Hog-nosed Bat 0.004 lb | Blue Whale 302,000 lb |

Insects
| Smallest | Largest |
| Mymarid Wasp 0.017 cm long | Goliath Beetle 10 cm long |

Birds
| Smallest | Largest |
| Bee Hummingbird 2.2 in. tall | Ostrich 108 in. tall |

Properties and Strategies

Lesson Objectives

- Use the Commutative, Associative, and Distributive Properties to compute mentally.
- Apply properties to real-world situations.

Vocabulary
Commutative Property of Addition
Associative Property of Addition
Distributive Property

The Day at a Glance

Today's Goals	Materials	123 Math Talk
Quick Practice Practice counting and saying place-value groups by counting by 10s, 100s, and 1,000s aloud. ① **Teaching the Lesson** **A1:** Use properties to compute mentally with large numbers and decimal numbers. **A2:** Identify Commutative, Associative, and Distributive Properties in real-world contexts. ② **Extending the Lesson** ▶ Differentiated Instruction ③ **Homework and Cumulative Review**	Student Activity Book pages 123-124 Index cards Grid paper Homework and Remembering pages 63-64 Math Journals Quick Quiz 2 (Assessment Guide)	In today's activities, the students are involved in discussion as they ▶ solve problems using the Commutative, Associative, and Distributive Properties ▶ identify which properties apply to specific problems to make solving them easier

Quick Practice

 5 MINUTES   **Goal:** Practice counting and saying place value groups by counting by 10s, 100s, and 1,000s aloud.

Large Count-Bys Have the class count in unison by 10s to 100, by 100s to 1,000, by 1,000s to 10,000, by 10,000s to 100,000, by 100,000s to 1,000,000, and by 1,000,000s to 10,000,000. Write the first several numbers in each series as the students are counting.

10, 20, 30, 40, 50 . . .
100, 200, 300, 400 . . .
1,000, 2,000, 3,000 . . .

① Teaching the Lesson

Activity 1

Use Properties

 20-25 MINUTES

Goal: Use properties to compute mentally with large numbers and decimal numbers.

Materials: Student Activity Book pages 123–124

 NCTM Standards:
Number and Operations
Algebra
Communication

Teaching Note

Language and Vocabulary Remind students about the definitions of the Commutative and Associative Properties of Addition.

Commutative Property:
$a + b = b + a$

Associative Property:
$a + (b + c) = (a + b) + c$

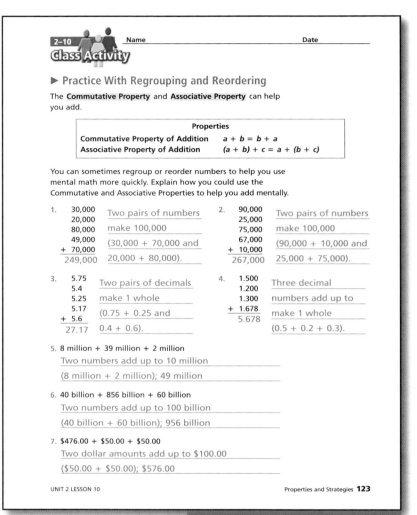

Student Activity Book page 123

▶ Numbers With Multiple Addends WHOLE CLASS

Write this addition problem on the board.

$$\begin{array}{r} 50,000 \\ 25,000 \\ 38,000 \\ 75,000 \\ + \ 50,000 \\ \hline \end{array}$$

Ask the class if there is a quick way to solve it using mental math.

Show students that, by pairing the numbers as shown, we can make two groups of 100,000. Then it is easier to find the total.

$$100,000 + 100,000 + 38,000 = 238,000$$

Ask the students how we know that it is all right to reorder the numbers and to group them together in this way. Students may remember the Commutative Property of Addition and the Associative Property of Addition, which state that numbers can be added in reverse order or regrouped.

▶ Practice With Regrouping and Reordering

WHOLE CLASS

Have students solve and discuss the exercises on pages 123–124 of the Student Activity Book. For exercises 1–7, students need to find meaningful ways to group and reorder numbers so that they can add them mentally.

To best solve exercises 8–10, students need to recognize that the sum of two pairs of factors that share a factor can be simplified into just one pair of factors.

$$(7 \times 25) + (7 \times 75) = 7 \times 100 = 700$$

This is much easier than completing the multiplication first, and then adding the results.

Teaching the Lesson (continued)

Activity 2

Real-World Applications

 20-25 MINUTES

Goal: Apply Commutative, Associative, and Distributive Properties in real-world contexts.

Materials: Student Activity Book page 124

✓ **NCTM Standards:**
Number and Operations
Algebra
Problem Solving

Teaching Note

Language and Vocabulary Help students remember the meanings of Commutative, Associative, and Distributive Properties by associating them with real-world situations. For example, a *commuter* covers the same distance going to and coming from work each day, we *associate* with different groups of people, and we *distribute* grades to everyone in the class, leaving no one out.

 **Quick Quiz**

See Assessment Guide for Unit 2 Quick Quiz 2.

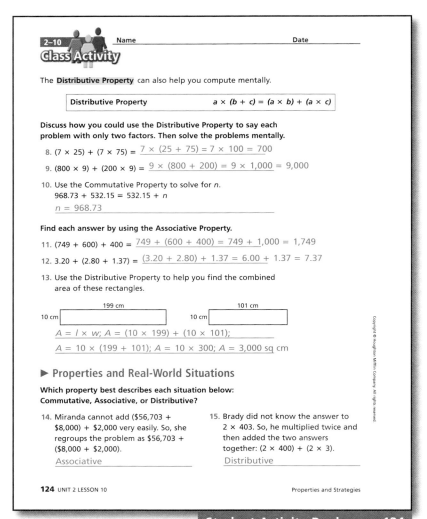

Student Activity Book page 124

▶ Properties of Addition in Real-World Situations

WHOLE CLASS

Have students answer questions 14–15 on page 124 of the Student Activity Book. Tell students to try solving these problems without referring to the definitions on the previous page.

Then tell students to describe a situation that illustrates the Commutative Property. For example,

A school carnival earned $45.00 on Friday morning and $35.00 on Friday afternoon. On Saturday, the carnival earned $35.00 in the morning and $45.00 in the afternoon. The carnival earned exactly the same amount on both days.

② Extending the Lesson

Differentiated Instruction | Activities for Individualizing

Intervention
for students having difficulty
INDIVIDUALS

Hundred Pairs

Materials: index cards (9 per student)

Have students write the hundred numbers 100–900 on their index cards (1 number per card).

Students should pair the cards so it easier to find the sum of all nine numbers using only mental math. Have students find the sum of all the cards.

100	900
200	800
300	700
400	600
500	

Repeat the activity with tens, by erasing a zero in each number.

On Level
for students having success
PAIRS

Area Pairs

Materials: grid paper

Have students draw various sizes of rectangles on grid paper. Tell them to find the area of each, in square units.

Then use the Distributive Property to combine the pair of rectangles to make one larger rectangle and find the combined area. A sample is shown below.

Rectangle A		Rectangle B	
length	width	length	width
5	7	5	4
8	3	6	3
6	9	6	2
4	8	4	7

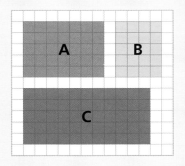

Challenge
for students seeking a challenge
INDIVIDUALS

Backward Distribution

Materials: grid paper

Have students draw each of these rectangles on grid paper and label its area.

length	width
8 units	5 units
7 units	10 units
12 units	3 units
15 units	9 units

Then use the Distributive Property to separate each rectangle to draw two new rectangles, label each length and width, and find each area.

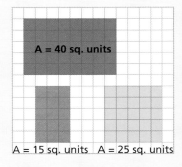

 Math Writing Prompt

Intervention

Draw and Describe
Draw a picture that illustrates the Associative Property of Addition. Explain how the picture shows the property.

 Math Writing Prompt

On Level

Explain Properties
Explain how you can use the Commutative and Associative properties to make it easier to find the sum of the digits 1–9.

 Math Writing Prompt

Challenge

Write Your Own
Write a word problem that can be solved by using the Distributive Property.

 # ③ Homework and Cumulative Review

2–10
Homework **Goal:** Additional Practice

✔ Use this Homework page to provide students with more practice with properties and strategies.

2–10
Remembering **Goal:** Cumulative Review

This Remembering Activity would be appropriate any time after today's lesson.

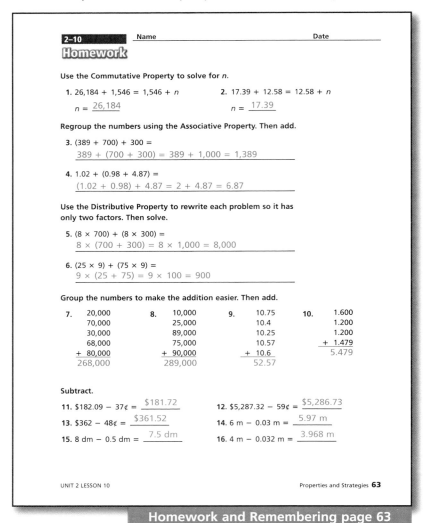

2–10
Homework Name _____ Date _____

Use the Commutative Property to solve for *n*.

1. 26,184 + 1,546 = 1,546 + *n*
   n = 26,184

2. 17.39 + 12.58 = 12.58 + *n*
   n = 17.39

Regroup the numbers using the Associative Property. Then add.

3. (389 + 700) + 300 =
   389 + (700 + 300) = 389 + 1,000 = 1,389

4. 1.02 + (0.98 + 4.87) =
   (1.02 + 0.98) + 4.87 = 2 + 4.87 = 6.87

Use the Distributive Property to rewrite each problem so it has only two factors. Then solve.

5. (8 × 700) + (8 × 300) =
   8 × (700 + 300) = 8 × 1,000 = 8,000

6. (25 × 9) + (75 × 9) =
   9 × (25 + 75) = 9 × 100 = 900

Group the numbers to make the addition easier. Then add.

7.	8.	9.	10.
20,000	10,000	10.75	1.600
70,000	25,000	10.4	1.200
30,000	89,000	10.25	1.200
68,000	75,000	10.57	+ 1.479
+ 80,000	+ 90,000	+ 10.6	5.479
268,000	289,000	52.57	

Subtract.

11. $182.09 − 37¢ = $181.72

12. $5,287.32 − 59¢ = $5,286.73

13. $362 − 48¢ = $361.52

14. 6 m − 0.03 m = 5.97 m

15. 8 dm − 0.5 dm = 7.5 dm

16. 4 m − 0.032 m = 3.968 m

UNIT 2 LESSON 10   Properties and Strategies **63**

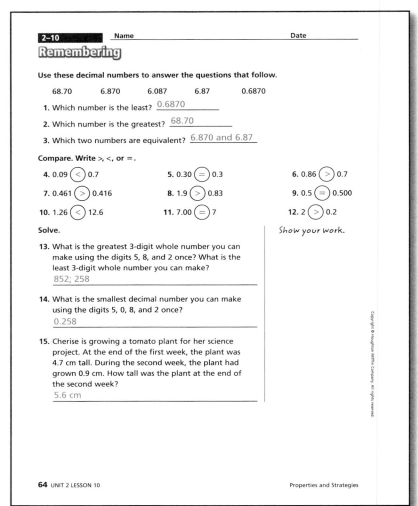

2–10
Remembering Name _____ Date _____

Use these decimal numbers to answer the questions that follow.

68.70   6.870   6.087   6.87   0.6870

1. Which number is the least? 0.6870

2. Which number is the greatest? 68.70

3. Which two numbers are equivalent? 6.870 and 6.87

Compare. Write >, <, or =.

4. 0.09 ⟨<⟩ 0.7

5. 0.30 ⟨=⟩ 0.3

6. 0.86 ⟨>⟩ 0.7

7. 0.461 ⟨>⟩ 0.416

8. 1.9 ⟨>⟩ 0.83

9. 0.5 ⟨=⟩ 0.500

10. 1.26 ⟨<⟩ 12.6

11. 7.00 ⟨=⟩ 7

12. 2 ⟨>⟩ 0.2

Solve.   *Show your work.*

13. What is the greatest 3-digit whole number you can make using the digits 5, 8, and 2 once? What is the least 3-digit whole number you can make?
    852; 258

14. What is the smallest decimal number you can make using the digits 5, 0, 8, and 2 once?
    0.258

15. Cherise is growing a tomato plant for her science project. At the end of the first week, the plant was 4.7 cm tall. During the second week, the plant had grown 0.9 cm. How tall was the plant at the end of the second week?
    5.6 cm

64 UNIT 2 LESSON 10   Properties and Strategies

Homework and Remembering page 63

Homework and Remembering page 64

Home or School Activity

 Music Connection

Orchestra Arrangements Have students research seating arrangements for a symphony orchestra. The instruments are arranged into four "families"—strings, woodwinds, brass, and percussion. A typical number of musicians in the strings family is:

First Violins = 10 musicians
Second Violins = 13 musicians
Violas = 7 musicians

Cellos = 5 musicians
Double Basses = 2 musicians
Harp = 1 musician

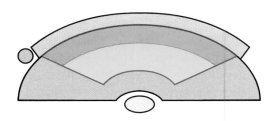

Have students discuss how they can use the properties of addition to find the total number of musicians in the strings section.

UNIT 2 LESSON 11

Pictographs With Large Numbers

Lesson Objectives

- Understand progressively larger increments to one million.
- Read and construct pictographs with large numbers.

The Day at a Glance

Today's Goals	Materials	123 Math Talk
Quick Practice Practice counting aloud by 10s, 100s, and 1,000s. **1 Teaching the Lesson** A1: Discuss pictographs with increasingly large numbers. A2: Read pictographs with large numbers. A3: Construct pictographs with large numbers. **2 Extending the Lesson** ▶ Differentiated Instruction **3 Homework and Cumulative Review**	Student Activity Book pages 125–126 Counters Homework and Remembering pages 65–66 Math Journals	In today's activities, the students are involved in discussion as they ▶ represent large numbers with pictographs ▶ use and interpret rounded numbers in pictographs ▶ draw pictographs

Quick Practice

 5 MINUTES   **Goal:** Practice counting aloud by 10s, 100s, and 1,000s.

Large Count-Bys Have the class count in unison by 10s to 100, by 100s to 1,000, by 1,000s to 10,000, by 10,000s to 100,000, by 100,000s to 1,000,000, and by 1,000,000s to 10,000,000. Write the first several numbers in each series as the students are counting.

10, 20, 30, 40, 50 . . .

100, 200, 300, 400 . . .

1,000, 2,000, 3,000 . . .

Teaching the Lesson

Discuss Pictographs With Large Numbers

 15-20 MINUTES

Goal: Discuss pictographs with increasingly large numbers.

✔ **NCTM Standards:**
Number and Operations
Data Analysis and Probability
Communication

► Pictographs With Weighted Symbols WHOLE CLASS

Make a simple pictograph on the board such as the one shown here. Explain that it shows the number of bagels that two people have.

Bagels

| Dana | ○ ○ ○ |
| Paco | ○ ○ ○ ○ ○ |

Establish a Key Discuss with students what they might do if Dana had 30 bagels and Paco had 50. Help students come to the conclusion that it would take a lot of space and time to draw 30 bagels. Explain that each picture represents 10 bagels. Introduce the concept of a key showing that each bagel on the pictograph represents 10 bagels. Then draw the key on the board below the pictograph.

Bagels

| Dana | ○ ○ ○ |
| Paco | ○ ○ ○ ○ ○ |

Key: ○ =10 bagels

Tell students to count Dana's bagels using the new key: 10, 20, 30. Then have them count Paco's bagels: 10, 20, 30, 40, 50.

Change the Condition Ask the class what could be done if Dana had 300 bagels and Paco had 500. Change the key so that each bagel represents 100. Invite a student to go to the board and fix the key.

Key: ○ =100 bagels

Then ask the student to lead the class in counting Dana's bagels and Paco's bagels using the new key: 100, 200, 300, and so on.

Teaching Note

Math Background Tell students that a pictograph uses the same symbol for each category. A key (value) for that picture is always provided.

Continue to increase the quantity of bagels by a factor of 10 until you reach a million. Have a student adjust the key each time and then lead the class in counting the number of bagels. Point out to the students that the graph itself never changes.

Graphs With Rounded Units Give students some 2- and 3-digit numbers that have not been rounded to the nearest ten, hundred, or thousand, and discuss the implications for making pictographs.

Help students see that pictographs don't always show the exact number of items. Sometimes the numbers have been rounded. Ask students:

● What if Dana had 31 bagels and Paco had 59? What would you do?

Here, 10 is our rounding unit. We would make the key show that 1 bagel picture = 10 bagels. Then, we would round each number to the nearest 10. We would still show 3 bagels on the graph for Dana because 31 is closer to 30 than to 40. But we would show 6 bagels for Paco instead of 5 because 59 is closer to 60 than it is to 50.

● What if Dana had 395 bagels and Paco had 612? What would you do?

We could make the key show that 1 bagel picture = 100 bagels. Then, we would round to the nearest 100. Dana has 395 bagels, which rounds to 400. Paco has 612 bagels, which rounds to 600.

When numbers in any table or graph are very large, they are usually estimates. Very large quantities cannot be counted, so estimates are used. You can include the word estimate or estimated in the title or the key of the graph.

Activity continued ▶

Teaching Note

What to Expect From Students
This discussion should move rapidly if your students have had previous exposure to rounding. At this point, students only need to see that graphs are sometimes based on estimates and that we choose the *nearest rounding* unit when we represent a number in a pictograph.

Teaching Note

Language and Vocabulary When creating a pictograph, it is important to decide what number each symbol will stand for. We call this the *rounding unit*. Every number in the data will need to be rounded to this place value. For example, if the rounding unit is 100, every number will need to be rounded to the nearest 100.

Teaching Note

What to Expect from Students
Some students might have used quarter units in the past. Encourage students to round to the nearest rounding unit or halfway point. For instance, they would round 37 to 35 and 38 to 40.

Find the Halfway Point Restore the key on the bagel graph so that 1 bagel picture = 10 bagels. Now ask how many bagel pictures we would draw if Dana had 35 bagels. Some students may say that they would use the larger rounding unit, 40, because this number is exactly halfway between 30 and 40. Point out that there is another possibility—a half bagel. Explain that half pictures are sometimes used on pictographs to show a number that is right between two rounding units. Demonstrate by drawing a half bagel on the graph.

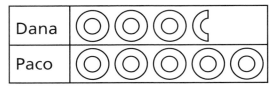

Ask students to identify the halfway point between:

- 200 and 300   250

- 6,000 and 7,000   6500

- 10,000 and 20,000   15,000

Activity 2

Read Pictographs With Large Numbers

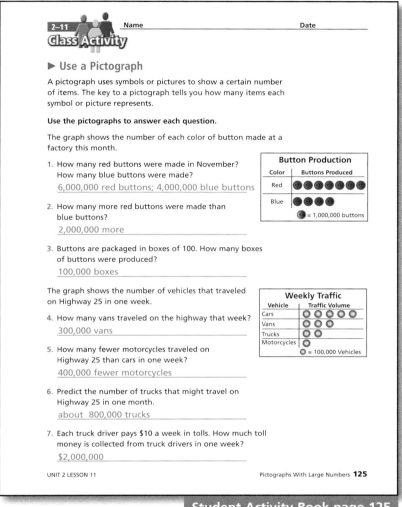

Student Activity Book page 125

Content of the Student Activity Book page:

2–11
Class Activity
Name _____ Date _____

▶ **Use a Pictograph**

A pictograph uses symbols or pictures to show a certain number of items. The key to a pictograph tells you how many items each symbol or picture represents.

Use the pictographs to answer each question.

The graph shows the number of each color of button made at a factory this month.

1. How many red buttons were made in November? How many blue buttons were made?
   6,000,000 red buttons; 4,000,000 blue buttons

2. How many more red buttons were made than blue buttons?
   2,000,000 more

3. Buttons are packaged in boxes of 100. How many boxes of buttons were produced?
   100,000 boxes

The graph shows the number of vehicles that traveled on Highway 25 in one week.

4. How many vans traveled on the highway that week?
   300,000 vans

5. How many fewer motorcycles traveled on Highway 25 than cars in one week?
   400,000 fewer motorcycles

6. Predict the number of trucks that might travel on Highway 25 in one month.
   about 800,000 trucks

7. Each truck driver pays $10 a week in tolls. How much toll money is collected from truck drivers in one week?
   $2,000,000

Button Production

Color	Buttons Produced
Red	●●●●●●
Blue	●●●●

● = 1,000,000 buttons

Weekly Traffic

Vehicle	Traffic Volume
Cars	○○○○○
Vans	○○○
Trucks	○○
Motorcycles	○

○ = 100,000 Vehicles

UNIT 2 LESSON 11   Pictographs With Large Numbers **125**

 10-15 MINUTES

Goal: Read pictographs with large rounded numbers.

Materials: Student Activity Book page 125–126

 NCTM Standards:
Number and Operations
Data Analysis and Probability

Teaching Note

Math Symbols When you reach problem 9, review the halfway point. Elicit from students that the half-figure on the graph shows the halfway point between 60,000,000 and 70,000,000.

▶ Use a Pictograph WHOLE CLASS

Have students turn to page 125 and answer the questions about the three pictographs. Direct their attention to the key for each graph. Have students identify the rounding unit and then use count-bys to answer exercises 1–7. The rounding unit in the first graph, for example, is a million, so the first question can by answered by counting: 1 million, 2 million, 3 million, and so on.

As each question is answered, ask a volunteer to write the number on the board. Check the position of the commas.

Next, have students turn to page 126 and complete exercises 8–10.

① Teaching the Lesson (continued)

Construct Pictographs With Large Numbers

 15-20 MINUTES

Goal: Construct pictographs with large numbers.

Materials: Student Activity Book page 126

✓ **NCTM Standards:**
Number and Operations
Data Analysis and Probability
Representation

Teaching Note

What to Expect From Students
Students should keep their drawings simple and neat while they work on making their graphs mathematically accurate. Tell students that one of the important advantages of using pictographs is that the reader can quickly read and interpret the data. It is imperative that the presentation be neat and accurate, and that it include details such as the title and key.

 Ongoing Assessment

▶ Observe the students as they construct their pictographs. Ensure that all students round correctly and include appropriate keys.

▶ Ask students to explain what the key is used for in a pictograph.

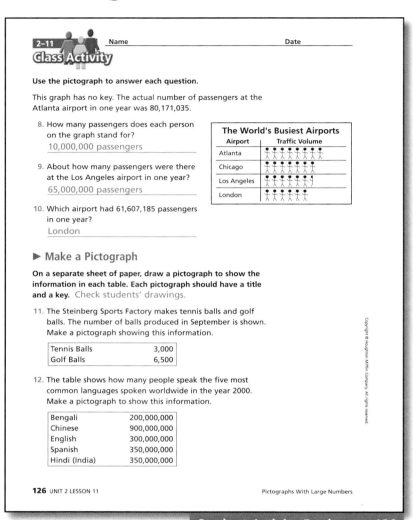

Student Activity Book page 126

▶ Make a Pictograph WHOLE CLASS

Have students turn to page 126 in the Student Activity Book. Ask students to draw pictographs to show the information in each table. Have them use simple grids with crossed lines.

Discuss what rounding unit should be shown in the key. Ask students if there will be any halfway points. Have students discuss the results when they are finished.

② Extending the Lesson

Intervention
for students having difficulty

PAIRS

Counter Pictographs

Materials: counters (25 per student)

Write the data on the board or transparency.

Books in the Library	
Art	40
Fiction	100
History	60
Science	20

Each students choose a different value for a key.

Then they use their own key to represent the data of the pictograph using counters.

Books in the Library

Art	●●●●
Fiction	●●●●●●●●●●
History	●●●●●●
Science	●●

● = 10 books

On Level
for students having success

SMALL GROUPS

Half Pictures

Give students the following keys.

■ = 50 balls

▼ = 100 balls

● = 500 balls

Have each student make up data and draw a pictograph with the keys provided. Students may substitute the key symbols with a picture of their choice.

Sample Pictograph:

Number of Balls Collected

Tom	🏀🏀
Aisha	🏀🏀🏀
Pete	🏀🏀🏀
Sharon	🏀🏀🏀🏀🏀

🏀 = 50 balls

Challenge
for students seeking a challenge

PAIRS

Compare Graphs

Give each pair the following data:

- Baseballs: 8
- Footballs: 4
- Basketballs: 6

Then have one student make a bar graph and one student make a pictograph (with a key).

Examples of student graphs:

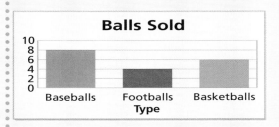

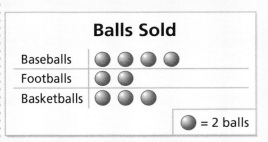

Have partners discuss how the two graphs are alike and how they are different. Students should list at least three similarities and three differences between the graphs.

 Math Writing Prompt

Intervention

Make Connections

Why do you think a pictograph key is called a key? Explain.

 Math Writing Prompt

On Level

Same and Different

Explain the similarities and differences between a bar graph and a pictograph.

 Math Writing Prompt

Challenge

Explain Your Thinking

Explain why you sometimes have to draw half or a quarter of a picture on a pictograph.

③ Homework and Cumulative Review

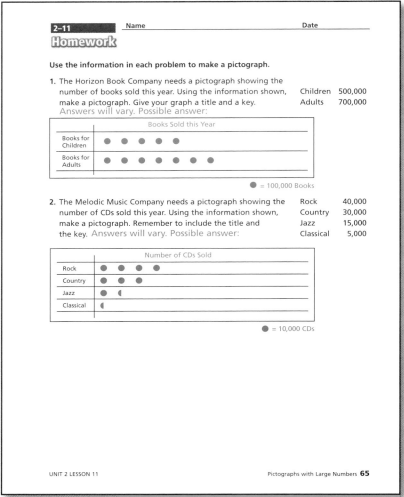

Homework Goal: Additional Practice

✓ Use this Homework page to provide students with more practice interpreting and constructing pictographs.

Remembering Goal: Cumulative Review

This Remembering Activity would be appropriate anytime after today's lesson.

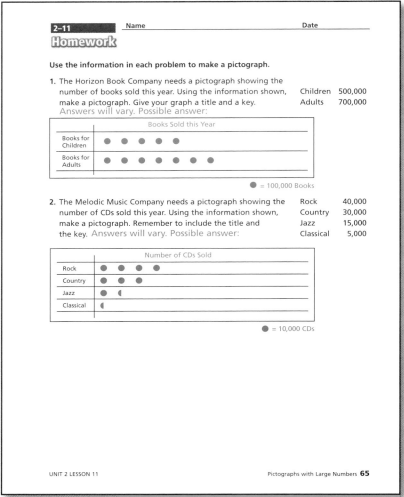

Homework and Remembering page 65

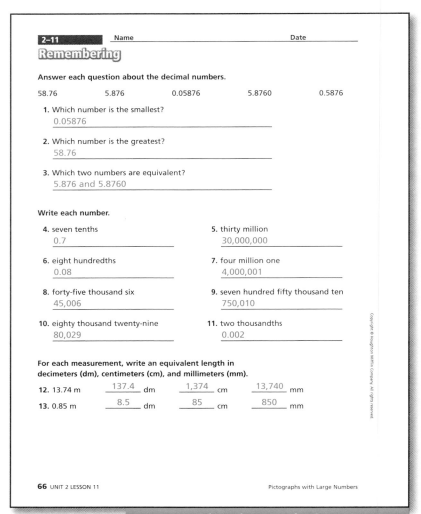

Homework and Remembering page 66

Home or School Activity

Art Connection

Stone Age Art Discuss ancient rock art with students. Thousands of years ago, ancient peoples made art on rocks. Today, people call these images petroglyphs or petrographs. Petroglyphs and petrographs are found all over the world. Some are more than 20,000 years old! Common images include people, animals, and handprints. Experts believe these images may have been used to record history. In Greek, *petro* means "stone," *glyph* means "to carve," and *graph* means "to record."

Have students create their own rock art to show something about their family.

UNIT 2 LESSON 11

Round Numbers on Graphs

Lesson Objectives

- Read scales that show large rounded numbers to 100 million.
- Identify the halfway point between two numbers that are multiples of ten.
- Estimate by rounding large numbers.

Vocabulary
scale
estimate
elapsed time

The Day at a Glance

Today's Goals	Materials	Math Talk
Quick Practice Use the halfway point of a group of numbers to facilitate rounding. **1** **Teaching the Lesson** **A1:** Round large numbers with the aid of a scale or number line, then round without visual aids. **A2:** Round large numbers for the purpose of estimation in real-world contexts. **2** **Extending the Lesson** ► Going Further: Elapsed Time ► Differentiated Instruction **3** **Homework and Cumulative Review**	Student Activity Book pages 127–130 Secret Code Cards (Copymaster M23) Homework and Remembering pages 67–68 Math Journals	In today's activities, the students are involved in discussion as they ► practice using scales to help round large numbers ► decide whether a safe or ordinary estimate is needed ► estimate mentally by rounding numbers

Quick Practice

🕐 **5 MINUTES** **Goal:** Use the halfway point of a group of numbers to facilitate rounding.

The Halfway Point Send 3 student leaders to the board. The first student writes the numbers vertically as the class counts by 100s to 1,000. Then another writes the numbers as the class counts by 1,000s to 10,000. Then another student writes the numbers as the class counts by 10,000s to 100,000.

Now have each student leader take turns circling several pairs of consecutive numbers in the list. As they do so, they should ask, "What is the halfway point?" The class responds with the number: "350."

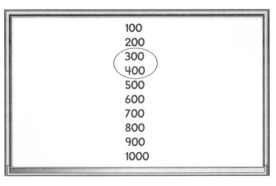

Teaching the Lesson

Use Scales to Round Large Numbers

 25 MINUTES

Goal: Round large numbers with the aid of a scale or number line, then round without visual aids.

Materials: Student Activity Book page 127

✔ **NCTM Standards:**
Number and Operations
Communication

Differentiated Instruction

Extra Help When working through the first example, the answer may not be apparent to everyone. If students hesitate, ask them to identify the halfway point. 75 Then ask if 76 is larger or smaller than 75. larger Because 76 is larger than 75, it is closer to 80 than to 70.

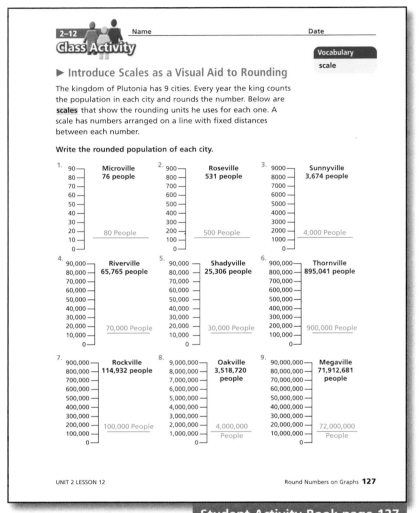

Student Activity Book page 127

▶ Introduce Scales as a Visual Aid to Rounding

WHOLE CLASS

Have the class turn to page 127. Introduce the word *scale* (numbers arranged in equal "increments"). Have students discuss how the scales on this page are similar to the count-bys that they have been practicing in the Quick Practice.

Ask students to round the population of each city in Plutonia, using the scale to help them position the number. Then ask:

● What is the rounding unit of the scale in exercise 1? 10

● What are we counting by? 10s

● Between which 2 numbers on the scale does the population of Microville fall? between 70 and 80

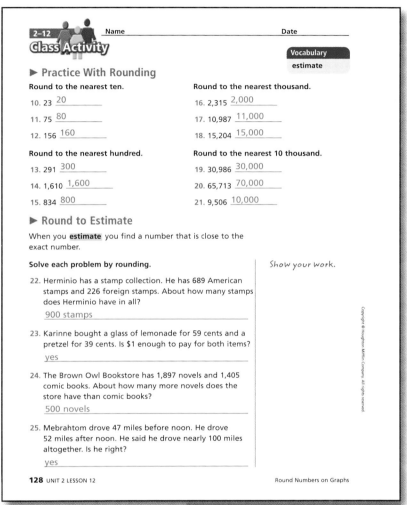

Student Activity Book page 128

The page 128 shows:

2–12 **Class Activity** Name _____ Date _____

Vocabulary
estimate

▶ **Practice With Rounding**

Round to the nearest ten.

10. 23 _20_

11. 75 _80_

12. 156 _160_

Round to the nearest hundred.

13. 291 _300_

14. 1,610 _1,600_

15. 834 _800_

Round to the nearest thousand.

16. 2,315 _2,000_

17. 10,987 _11,000_

18. 15,204 _15,000_

Round to the nearest 10 thousand.

19. 30,986 _30,000_

20. 65,713 _70,000_

21. 9,506 _10,000_

▶ **Round to Estimate**

When you **estimate** you find a number that is close to the exact number.

Solve each problem by rounding.

Show your work.

22. Herminio has a stamp collection. He has 689 American stamps and 226 foreign stamps. About how many stamps does Herminio have in all?
900 stamps

23. Karinne bought a glass of lemonade for 59 cents and a pretzel for 39 cents. Is $1 enough to pay for both items?
yes

24. The Brown Owl Bookstore has 1,897 novels and 1,405 comic books. About how many more novels does the store have than comic books?
500 novels

25. Mebrahtom drove 47 miles before noon. He drove 52 miles after noon. He said he drove nearly 100 miles altogether. Is he right?
yes

128 UNIT 2 LESSON 12   Round Numbers on Graphs

- Is it closer to 70 or closer to 80? closer to 80

- So, what would we round the population of Microville to? 80

Tell students that as the numbers get larger, the process still remains the same. Before they begin each exercise, have them identify the rounding unit.

Repeatedly use the term "nearest 10,000," "nearest 100,000," or "nearest million" to help students associate this word with scales arranged in these increments.

▶ **Practice With Rounding** [WHOLE CLASS]

Direct students' attention to Student Activity Book page 128. Ask them to round each number as indicated in the directions.

Teaching the Lesson (continued)

Activity 2

Round to Estimate

 25 MINUTES

Goal: Round large numbers for the purpose of estimation in real-world contexts.

Materials: Student Activity Book pages 128-129

✔ **NCTM Standard:**
Number and Operations

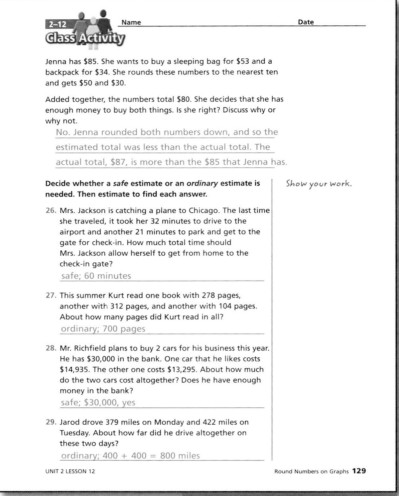

| 2-12 | Name _____ Date _____ |

Class Activity

Jenna has $85. She wants to buy a sleeping bag for $53 and a backpack for $34. She rounds these numbers to the nearest ten and gets $50 and $30.

Added together, the numbers total $80. She decides that she has enough money to buy both things. Is she right? Discuss why or why not.

No. Jenna rounded both numbers down, and so the estimated total was less than the actual total. The actual total, $87, is more than the $85 that Jenna has.

Decide whether a *safe* estimate or an *ordinary* estimate is needed. Then estimate to find each answer.   *Show your work.*

26. Mrs. Jackson is catching a plane to Chicago. The last time she traveled, it took her 32 minutes to drive to the airport and another 21 minutes to park and get to the gate for check-in. How much total time should Mrs. Jackson allow herself to get from home to the check-in gate?
safe; 60 minutes

27. This summer Kurt read one book with 278 pages, another with 312 pages, and another with 104 pages. About how many pages did Kurt read in all?
ordinary; 700 pages

28. Mr. Richfield plans to buy 2 cars for his business this year. He has $30,000 in the bank. One car that he likes costs $14,935. The other one costs $13,295. About how much do the two cars cost altogether? Does he have enough money in the bank?
safe; $30,000, yes

29. Jarod drove 379 miles on Monday and 422 miles on Tuesday. About how far did he drive altogether on these two days?
ordinary; 400 + 400 = 800 miles

UNIT 2 LESSON 12   Round Numbers on Graphs **129**

Student Activity Book page 129

▶ Round Numbers to Estimate [WHOLE CLASS]

Explain that we often round numbers because it allows us to solve problems faster. The answer won't be an exact answer, but an estimate. Sometimes an estimate, something close to the real answer, is good enough. Discuss each problem on pages 128–129 of the Student Activity Book with your students.

● Look at problem 22. Are these numbers easy to work with? no

● If we rounded each number to the nearest ten, would these numbers be easier to work with? yes

● What are the rounded numbers? 690 and 230

● Look at problem 23. Can you estimate to answer the question? yes

● What would be a good rounding unit for these numbers? ten

● What are the rounded numbers? 60 and 40

Safe Estimates Have students read and discuss the problem at the top of on page 129 of the Student Activity Book. Ask questions to help the class discover Jenna's mistake:

- Did Jenna round correctly? yes

- Did she add correctly? yes

- Then what went wrong? An estimate is always slightly off. In this case, Jenna rounded both numbers down, and so the estimated total was less than the actual total. The actual total, $87, is more than the $85 that Jenna has.

Elicit from students the idea that in some cases, such as when time or money are involved, we need to make sure that our estimates make sense—we round up or down to make sure that we will have enough time or money.

Make an Appropriate Estimate Discuss problems 26–29 in Student Activity Book page 129. Before making an estimate, students should first decide whether a *safe estimation* or an *ordinary estimation* should be used. Have students decide whether they need to round up to be safe.

Problem 26: Safe Estimation

- Getting to the airport on time is crucial, and traffic conditions can vary widely. Therefore, Mrs. Jackson should leave plenty of time and make a safe estimation. If she just followed the normal rules of rounding, she would add 20 + 30 = 50 minutes. This is not going to be enough time. It took longer than that to reach the airport last time she made the trip, and it could take even longer this time.

Problem 27: Ordinary Estimation

- Rounding to the nearest hundred, we can figure out that Kurt read 300 + 300 + 100 = 700 pages this summer.

Problem 28: Safe Estimation

- A safe estimation is needed because Mr. Richfield cannot spend more money than he has. Some students will be able to see immediately that he has enough money to buy the 2 cars because both amounts are less than half ($15,000) of the whole ($30,000). Other students will estimate the long way, rounding both amounts up to play it safe. To the nearest thousand, $15,000 + $14,000 = $29,000.

Problem 27: Ordinary Estimation

- Rounding to the nearest hundred, we can figure out that Jarod drove 400 + 400 = 800 miles.

Teaching Note

What to Expect From Students
Emphasize that students should find the most exact rounding unit that still allows them to do the computation in their heads. Making every digit zero except the first one is a good general rule, but sometimes they will need to be more exact.

 Ongoing Assessment

Ask questions such as:

► Michelle read 347 pages of her Science book in one week, and 651 pages the next week. About how many pages has she read in all?

► Katie has $20.00 to spend on a field trip. If she buys a book for $13.74 and a souvenir for $5.18, can she afford to buy a magnet for $1.99?

② Extending the Lesson

Going Further: Elapsed Time

Goal: Use addition and subtraction to find elapsed time, start time, and end time.

Materials: Student Activity Book page 130

✓ **NCTM Standards:**
Measurement
Problem Solving

Differentiated Instruction

Advanced Learners None of the problems on this page involve regrouping units of time to add or subtract. You may wish to provide such problems for advanced students to solve.

▶ Review Time │WHOLE CLASS│

Ask students:

● How many hours are in a day?

● How many minutes are in an hour?

● How many seconds are in a minute?

● What hours of the day are labeled A.M.? P.M.?

Have students read the text at the top page 130. Challenge students to describe time periods they know, such as how long their school lunch period is. Lead students to understand that they know how long their lunch period is because they know what time lunch starts and what time it ends.

Read the example problems together as a class. Point out that the times are rewritten as hours (hr) and minutes (min) when they are added and subtracted. Ask:

● Do you add or subtract to find the elapsed time? subtract; count on to add

● What do you subtract? the start time from the end time

Repeat the questioning for finding the end time and start time.

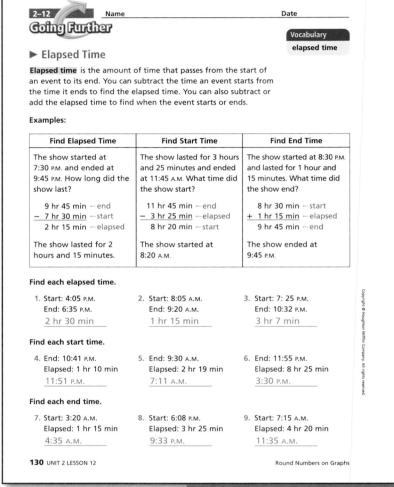

Student Activity Book page 130

✋ Alternate Approach

Act it Out It may help some students to act out these problems by moving the hands of an analog clock or by counting up or counting back on a number line labeled in units of time.

▶ Practice With Elapsed Time │PAIRS│

Have students work together to complete exercises 1–9. Remind them to write A.M. or P.M. in all of their time answers. Tell students to refer to the boxed examples to help them remember what to add or subtract to find each answer. Students can estimate to check their answers.

Intervention
for students having difficulty

PAIRS

About Time
Have students copy and complete this chart.

Round to estimate each amount of time.

17 minutes

about _____ minutes

3 hours, 42 minutes

about _____ hours

41 hours

about _____ days

23 days

about _____ weeks

Then have students take turns giving an amount of time that their partner should round.

 Math Writing Prompt

Intervention

Make Connections
Describe a situation when you might want to round numbers.

On Level
for students having success

PAIRS

More Is Better
Write the following on the board.

- Your bus to school leaves at 8:30 A.M.

- A movie you want to see starts at 7:00 P.M.

- You have exactly $10 to buy school supplies.

- 12 people are coming to your birthday party.

Have partners discuss why each of these situations might require overestimating. For example, you probably want to have more than 12 pieces of birthday cake in case someone wants more than one piece.

Challenge students to come up with situations in which they may want to underestimate.

 Math Writing Prompt

On Level

Write Rules
Write three rules for rounding whole numbers to the nearest ten. Use examples to illustrate the rules.

Challenge
for students seeking a challenge

INDIVIDUALS

Schedules
Have students think about everything they have to do tomorrow. Then make a schedule for the day, which shows what time they plan on starting each activity. Remind students to include times for sleeping and meals.

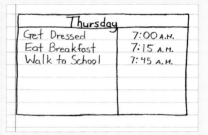

Have students describe how much time their schedule leaves for each activity they will do.

Math Writing Prompt

Challenge

Reasoning
When you round 199 to the nearest ten and to the nearest hundred, why do you get the same result?

③ Homework and Cumulative Review

 **Homework** **Goal:** Additional Practice

✔ Use this Homework page to provide students with more practice with rounding methods.

 **Remembering** **Goal:** Cumulative Review

This Remembering Activity would be appropriate anytime after today's lesson.

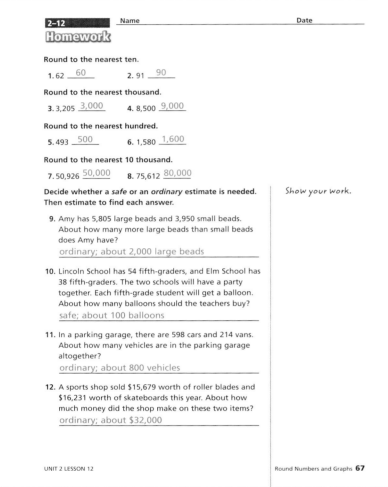

2–12 Name ____ Date ____
Homework

Round to the nearest ten.

1. 62 __60__   2. 91 __90__

Round to the nearest thousand.

3. 3,205 __3,000__   4. 8,500 __9,000__

Round to the nearest hundred.

5. 493 __500__   6. 1,580 __1,600__

Round to the nearest 10 thousand.

7. 50,926 __50,000__   8. 75,612 __80,000__

Decide whether a *safe* or an *ordinary* estimate is needed. Then estimate to find each answer.   *Show your work.*

9. Amy has 5,805 large beads and 3,950 small beads. About how many more large beads than small beads does Amy have?
   __ordinary; about 2,000 large beads__

10. Lincoln School has 54 fifth-graders, and Elm School has 38 fifth-graders. The two schools will have a party together. Each fifth-grade student will get a balloon. About how many balloons should the teachers buy?
   __safe; about 100 balloons__

11. In a parking garage, there are 598 cars and 214 vans. About how many vehicles are in the parking garage altogether?
   __ordinary; about 800 vehicles__

12. A sports shop sold $15,679 worth of roller blades and $16,231 worth of skateboards this year. About how much money did the shop make on these two items?
   __ordinary; about $32,000__

UNIT 2 LESSON 12   Round Numbers and Graphs **67**

Homework and Remembering page 67

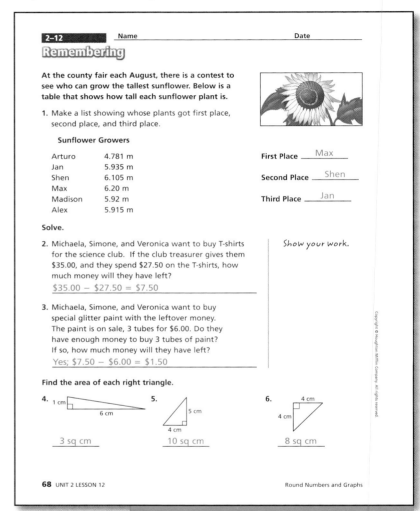

2–12 Name ____ Date ____
Remembering

At the county fair each August, there is a contest to see who can grow the tallest sunflower. Below is a table that shows how tall each sunflower plant is.

1. Make a list showing whose plants got first place, second place, and third place.

   Sunflower Growers

Arturo	4.781 m
Jan	5.935 m
Shen	6.105 m
Max	6.20 m
Madison	5.92 m
Alex	5.915 m

   First Place __Max__

   Second Place __Shen__

   Third Place __Jan__

Solve.

2. Michaela, Simone, and Veronica want to buy T-shirts for the science club. If the club treasurer gives them $35.00, and they spend $27.50 on the T-shirts, how much money will they have left?   *Show your work.*
   __$35.00 − $27.50 = $7.50__

3. Michaela, Simone, and Veronica want to buy special glitter paint with the leftover money. The paint is on sale, 3 tubes for $6.00. Do they have enough money to buy 3 tubes of paint? If so, how much money will they have left?
   __Yes; $7.50 − $6.00 = $1.50__

Find the area of each right triangle.

4. 1 cm / 6 cm   5. 5 cm / 4 cm   6. 4 cm / 4 cm

   __3 sq cm__   __10 sq cm__   __8 sq cm__

68 UNIT 2 LESSON 12   Round Numbers and Graphs

Homework and Remembering page 68

Home or School Activity

 Real-World Connection

Shopping Trip Tell students that nearly everyone uses rounding and estimation when they shop. Explain that when shopping, you need to make sure you have enough money to pay for all the items, including the tax, which adds to the total. For this reason, it's usually best to round up each item's price so that you don't go over your limit.

Have students use grocery store advertisements to practice estimating. Tell them to pick five or more items and estimate the total cost. Then find the exact cost to compare.

Students can also try the skill in the real world. Tell them to try to estimate the total cost as they shop the next time they go to the grocery store with their family.

Bar Graphs and Rounding

Lesson Objectives

- Read and construct bar graphs with large numbers.
- Round numbers to the hundred millions.
- Identify the halfway point with numbers to the hundred millions.

Vocabulary
bar graph
double-bar graph

The Day at a Glance

Today's Goals	Materials	Math Talk
Quick Practice Use the halfway point of a group of numbers to facilitate rounding.	Student Activity Book pages 131–132	In today's activities, the students are involved in discussion as they
1 Teaching the Lesson **A1:** Discuss bar graphs with large numbers. **A2:** Make bar graphs.	Connecting cubes Grid paper Homework and Remembering pages 69–70	▶ use their rounding skills to interpret bar graph scales
2 Extending the Lesson ▶ Differentiated Instruction	Math Journals	▶ complete bar graphs when scales and labels are supplied
3 Homework and Cumulative Review		▶ construct a scale for a bar graph

Quick Practice

🕐 **5 MINUTES** **Goal:** Use the halfway point of a group of numbers to facilitate rounding.

The Halfway Point Send 3 student leaders to the board. One student writes the numbers vertically as the class counts by 100,000 to a million. Then another student writes the numbers as the class counts by millions to 10 million. Then another student writes the numbers as the class counts by 10 million to 100 million.

Now have each student leader take turns circling several pairs of consecutive numbers in the list. As they do so, they should ask, "What is the halfway point?" The class responds with the number.

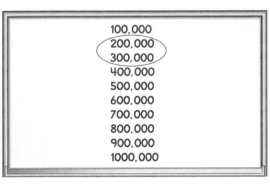

Teaching the Lesson

Interpret Bar Graphs

 20 MINUTES

Goal: Discuss bar graphs with large numbers.

Materials: Student Activity Book page 131

✓ **NCTM Standards:**
Number and Operations
Algebra
Communication

Teaching Note

Extra Help You can help strugglers while students are solving any problems, and you can invest time in helping students learn to help other students. Many teachers find that after several days on an important topic, they can work at the board with a small group of strugglers while the others work productively practicing problems (with some students helping others).

Differentiated Instruction

English Learners Some students learning English develop oral English skills well before they are able to write English fluently. Since many answers in this activity require writing words and sentences, consider writing each answer on the board after a student provides it. This provides English learners with a model of written English.

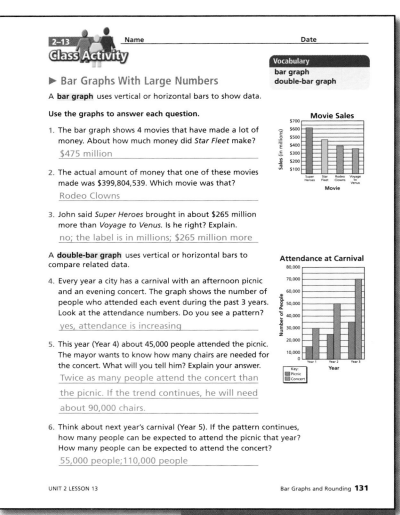

Student Activity Book page 131

▶ Bar Graphs With Large Numbers WHOLE CLASS

Begin by having your students look at the scale on the "Movie Sales" graph on Student Activity Book page 131. Ask:

● What is the rounding unit on this scale? Hundred millions

● What are we counting by on this scale? 100 millions

Be sure everyone notices the word millions in the label on the left. Explain that on a bar graph, large numbers are often represented this way. Explain that writing all the zeros would take up too much space.

 **Math Talk**

Now have students discuss the problems that go with each bar graph.

- **Problem 1** Have a student read problem 1 aloud. Explain to the students that reading a bar graph where the bar does not touch any line exactly is always a matter of estimation. This bar is about halfway between the dotted lines for $450 million and $500 million. A good estimate would be $475 million. Ask a volunteer to write $475 million on the board.

- **Problem 2** Have a student read problem 2 aloud. $399,804,539 is just under $400 million. The movie *Star Fleet* is the answer because the bar for *Star Fleet* is just under the $400 million line.

- **Problem 3** Ask a student to read problem 3 aloud. John is wrong because the label on the left indicates the dollars are in millions. So the answer is $265 million, not $265.

Before talking about the second graph, which is a double-bar graph, direct students' attention to the key. Be sure they understand that the darker bar represents the number of people who attended the picnic and the lighter bar represents the number people who attended the band concert. Then ask them what the rounding unit is. 10,000

- **Problem 4** Have a student read problem 4 aloud. Ask students to look at the bars on the graph and describe any patterns they see. Students might notice that about twice as many people attend the concert as the picnic each year, that attendance at the picnic increases by about 10,000 each year, and that attendance at the concert increases by about 20,000 each year.

- **Problem 5** Ask a student to read problem 5 aloud. Remind students that they can use any of the patterns they recognized in problem 4 to make an estimate for the number of chairs for the concert. Students might notice that the number will probably be twice as much as 45,000 or 20,000 more than the year before, which was 70,000. So, the best estimate is 90,000 chairs.

- **Problem 6** Have a student read problem 6 aloud. Remind students that we already concluded that the Year 4 figures would be 45,000 people at the picnic and 90,000 people at the band concert. We can find the Year 5 figures by calculating that 10,000 more than 45,000 is 55,000 and 20,000 more than 90,000 is 110,000. We also know that the second bar must be twice as long as the first. $55,000 \times 2 = 110,000$. So, we know that if the pattern continues, the Year 5 figures will be 55,000 and 110,000.

Activity 2

Make Bar Graphs

 **30 MINUTES**

Goal: Make bar graphs.

Materials: Student Activity Book page 132

✔ **NCTM Standard:**
Data Analysis and Probability

✔ **Ongoing Assessment**

Ask students to:

▶ explain the difference between a bar graph and a double-bar graph.

▶ define scale.

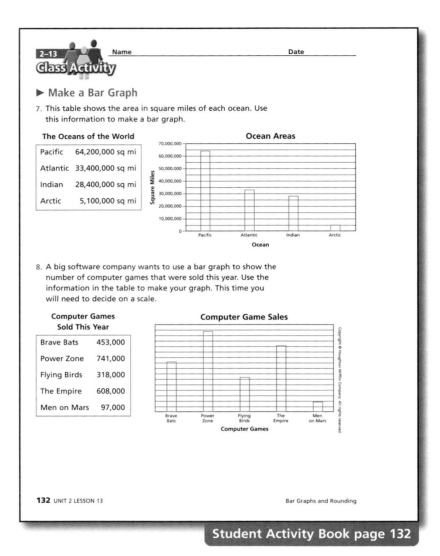

Student Activity Book page 132

▶ Make a Bar Graph WHOLE CLASS

Oceans of the World Have everyone turn to Student Activity Book page 132. The first bar graph has a scale and labels for the students. Their task is to draw the bars. Discuss the rounding units on the scale (10 million) and have students identify the halfway point that is shown by each thin dotted line. Then, discuss how the numbers in the table might be rounded to make them easier to graph.

Computer Games The second bar graph does not have a scale indicated—only the calibration lines and labels. Students will need to determine their own scale.

Discuss what rounding units would make a good scale. Increments of 100,000 would work out best. If students propose something else, let them give it a try. They will discover if it is not workable.

Have students work independently on their graphs. Offer help as needed. Then discuss the results as a class.

② Extending the Lesson

Intervention
for students having difficulty

| PAIRS |

3-D Bar Graphs

Materials: connecting cubes

Have students make a 3-dimensional version of the Trees bar graph in their Homework.

Students should first copy the axis labels on a large sheet of paper. Then they can lay stacks of connecting cubes on the graph to model the bars, and write a scale to fit their stacks.

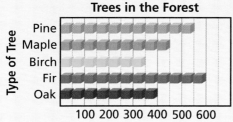

Trees in the Forest

On Level
for students having success

| SMALL GROUPS |

Survey It

Materials: grid paper

Have students think of something they want to know about their classmates, such as what color students like best. Then work together to conduct a class survey to collect that information. Finally, students should display the survey data they collected on a bar graph.

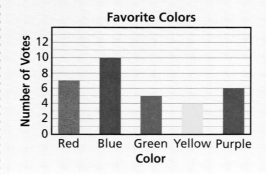

Favorite Colors

Challenge
for students seeking a challenge

| PAIRS |

Double Display

Materials: grid paper

Have students choose a topic such as favorite color and collect data about their class in a survey and display it on a bar graph. Then display the same data on a pictograph.

Favorite Color Survey

Color	Number of Colors
Red	● ● ● ◖
Blue	● ● ● ● ●
Green	● ● ◖
Yellow	● ●
Purple	● ● ●

 = 2 votes

Ask students to explain which kind of graph they think best displays the data.

Math Writing Prompt

Intervention

Make Connections

Explain how a bar graph is like a pictograph.

Math Writing Prompt

On Level

Explain Your Thinking

Explain why some bar graphs need keys, while others do not.

Math Writing Prompt

Challenge

In Your Own Words

Explain how you choose the scale when making a bar graph.

 # Homework and Cumulative Review

2-13 Homework Goal: Additional Practice

✓ Use this Homework page to provide students with more practice with graphing methods.

2-13 Remembering Goal: Cumulative Review

This Remembering Activity would be appropriate any time after today's lesson.

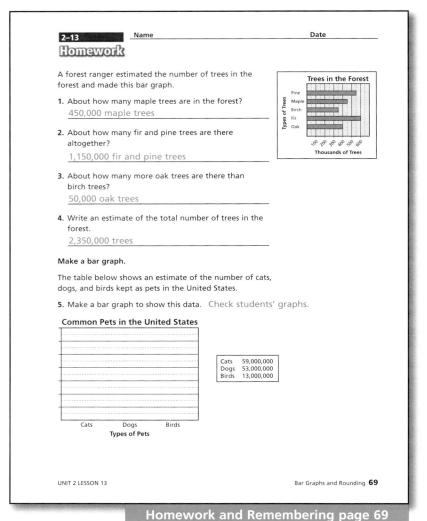

2-13 Name _____ Date _____
Homework

A forest ranger estimated the number of trees in the forest and made this bar graph.

1. About how many maple trees are in the forest?
   450,000 maple trees

2. About how many fir and pine trees are there altogether?
   1,150,000 fir and pine trees

3. About how many more oak trees are there than birch trees?
   50,000 oak trees

4. Write an estimate of the total number of trees in the forest.
   2,350,000 trees

Make a bar graph.

The table below shows an estimate of the number of cats, dogs, and birds kept as pets in the United States.

5. Make a bar graph to show this data. Check students' graphs.

Common Pets in the United States

Cats 59,000,000
Dogs 53,000,000
Birds 13,000,000

UNIT 2 LESSON 13   Bar Graphs and Rounding **69**

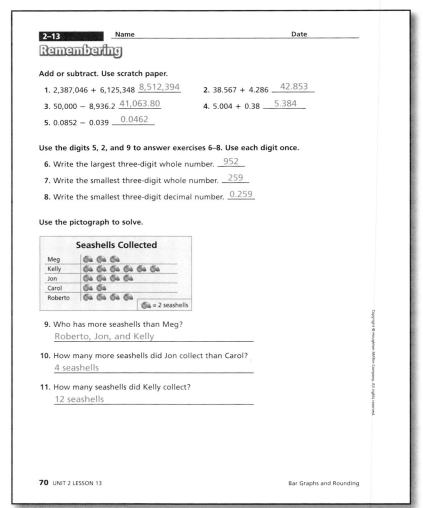

2-13 Name _____ Date _____
Remembering

Add or subtract. Use scratch paper.

1. 2,387,046 + 6,125,348 8,512,394
2. 38.567 + 4.286 42.853
3. 50,000 − 8,936.2 41,063.80
4. 5.004 + 0.38 5.384
5. 0.0852 − 0.039 0.0462

Use the digits 5, 2, and 9 to answer exercises 6–8. Use each digit once.

6. Write the largest three-digit whole number. 952
7. Write the smallest three-digit whole number. 259
8. Write the smallest three-digit decimal number. 0.259

Use the pictograph to solve.

Seashells Collected

Meg	🐚 🐚 🐚
Kelly	🐚 🐚 🐚 🐚 🐚 🐚
Jon	🐚 🐚 🐚 🐚 🐚
Carol	🐚 🐚
Roberto	🐚 🐚 🐚 🐚

🐚 = 2 seashells

9. Who has more seashells than Meg?
   Roberto, Jon, and Kelly

10. How many more seashells did Jon collect than Carol?
    4 seashells

11. How many seashells did Kelly collect?
    12 seashells

70 UNIT 2 LESSON 13   Bar Graphs and Rounding

Homework and Remembering page 69

Homework and Remembering page 70

Home or School Activity

 ### Multicultural Connection

Melting Pot Explain to students that people sometimes call the United States a "melting pot" because people from so many different places and cultures live here. Suggest to students that they ask their parents or other family members to tell them about where their ancestors came from. Then invite students to discuss some traditions their family practices that reflect their ancestry.

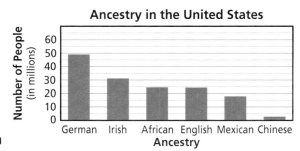

The bar graph shows population data for five common ancestries in the United States. Have students work in small groups to make a class graph about their ancestry. Students can write word problems that can be solved using the graph.

Introduce Line Graphs

Lesson Objectives

- Read single and double line graphs.
- Construct line graphs with large numbers.
- Distinguish between the kind of information that is shown on a bar graph and the kind that is usually shown on a line graph.

The Day at a Glance

Today's Goals	Materials	Math Talk

Quick Practice Round decimals to the nearest tenth, hundredth, or thousandth.	MathBoard Materials
	Grid paper
	Student Activity Book
	    pages 133-136
	Homework and
	    Remembering pages 71-72
	Math Journals
		In today's activities, the students are involved in discussion as they
		
		▶ differentiate between bar graphs and line graphs
		
		▶ use more advanced line graphs that show large numbers or use double lines
		
		▶ create line graphs from given information

1 Teaching the Lesson A1: Read and discuss single line graphs. A2: Interpret a double line graph. A3: Construct line graphs with large numbers.		
2 Extending the Lesson ▶ Differentiated Instruction		
3 Homework and Cumulative Review		

Quick Practice

🕐 **5 MINUTES**   **Goal:** Round decimals to the nearest tenth, hundredth, or thousandth.

Round Decimals Start by asking the class:

▶ If we rounded to the nearest tenth, how many numbers would we have after the decimal point? only 1 number

▶ If we rounded to the nearest hundredth, how many numbers would we have after the decimal point? 2 numbers

▶ What if we rounded to the nearest thousandth? 3 numbers after the decimal point

Now send several students to the board. Each one writes a decimal number with 4 digits after the decimal point and asks the class to round to the nearest thousandth, the nearest hundredth, and the nearest tenth. After each response, the leader writes the rounded decimal.

Teaching the Lesson

The Function of Line Graphs

 15 MINUTES

Goal: Read and discuss single line graphs.

Materials: Student Activity Book page 133

✔ **NCTM Standards:**
Algebra
Data Analysis

Teaching Note

Math Symbols Remind students that a rounded decimal number will always have the same number of digits after the decimal point as there are zeros in the whole number. For example:

- Tenths have 1 digit after the decimal point, just as ten has 1 zero.

- Hundredths have 2 digits after the decimal point, just as a hundred has 2 zeros.

The Learning Classroom

Math Talk To continue to keep students in their seats engaged and to move this engagement to a deeper level, challenge them to listen carefully so that they might say the explainers' statements in their own words. Ask several students to "repeat" in their own words what has been explained by the student explainer.

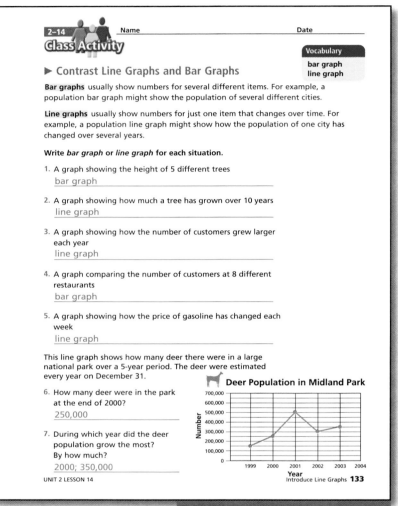

Student Activity Book page 133

▶ Contrast Line Graphs and Bar Graphs WHOLE CLASS

Read the introduction on page 133 of the Student Activity Book about bar graphs and line graphs with the students. Then discuss the difference between a line graph and a bar graph.

Now have students complete exercises 1–5. Bar graphs are used to compare several items that do not change. Line graphs show a single item that changes over time.

Single Line Graphs Using the line graph on Student Activity Book page 133 have students complete exercises 6–7. If there is confusion, remind them that each dot shows the number of deer at the end of the year. The answers all involve direct reading of the points and require no estimation.

Graphs With More Than One Line

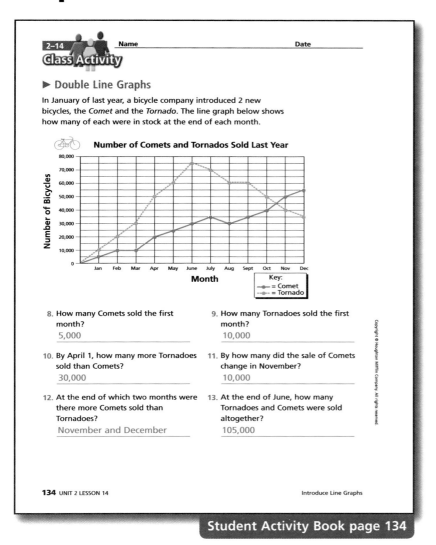

Student Activity Book page 134

The content within the activity book page:

2–14 Class Activity   Name _____   Date _____

▶ **Double Line Graphs**

In January of last year, a bicycle company introduced 2 new bicycles, the *Comet* and the *Tornado*. The line graph below shows how many of each were in stock at the end of each month.

Number of Comets and Tornados Sold Last Year

Key:
--●-- = Comet
--●-- = Tornado

8. How many Comets sold the first month?
   5,000

9. How many Tornadoes sold the first month?
   10,000

10. By April 1, how many more Tornadoes sold than Comets?
    30,000

11. By how many did the sale of Comets change in November?
    10,000

12. At the end of which two months were there more Comets sold than Tornadoes?
    November and December

13. At the end of June, how many Tornadoes and Comets were sold altogether?
    105,000

134 UNIT 2 LESSON 14   Introduce Line Graphs

▶ **Double Line Graphs** WHOLE CLASS

Have students turn to Student Activity Book page 134 and look at the graph with the double lines. Direct their attention to the key, which explains the two lines. Discuss the questions as a class.

When the discussion is over, point out to students that line graphs allow us to see general trends. Sometimes the trend is more important than the specific numbers.

 15 MINUTES

Goal: Interpret a line graph with a double line.

Materials: Student Activity Book page 134

 NCTM Standards:
Algebra
Data Analysis

 Math Talk

If you were the owner of a small bicycle shop and planning to buy both types of bicycles for your store, which would you order more of, Comets or Tornadoes?

Encourage students to discuss the issue. Both answers can be justified, though the Comet is probably the better choice. The Tornado made more money but its popularity peaked and started to decline. The Comet is catching on fast and will probably outsell the Tornado in the coming year.

Point out to students that line graphs can help us identify a trend. Sometimes, a trend is more important than all the numbers.

Activity 3

Construct Line Graphs

 15 MINUTES

Goal: Construct line graphs with large numbers.

Materials: Student Activity Book page 135

✔ **NCTM Standards:**
Algebra
Data Analysis

Ongoing Assessment

Ask students to decide which type of graph to use to graph the information below and have them explain their reasoning.

▶ Birds Stopping at Bird Feeder, March: 82 birds per day, June: 108 birds per day, September: 74 birds per day, January: 29 birds per day

---

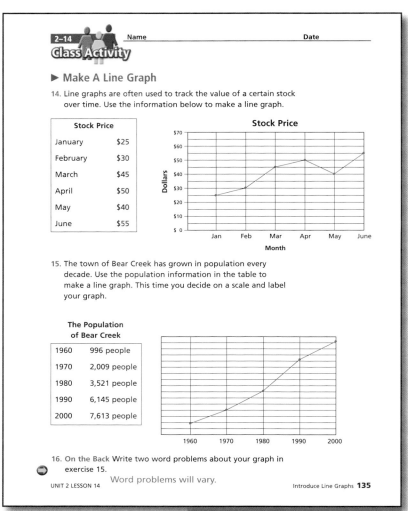

Student Activity Book page 135

▶ Make A Line Graph INDIVIDUALS

For exercise 15 on page 135 of the Student Activity Book, the numbers are rounded and the scale is provided. Students simply plot the points and make the lines.

For exercise 16, students will need to make the scale themselves. They should discuss the options as a class. A good choice would be to use increments of 1,000. Offer help as needed.

Students who have trouble can work with a partner.

② Extending the Lesson

Intervention
for students having difficulty

INDIVIDUALS

Count and Graph

Materials: grid paper

Have students count the number of boys and girls in their class. Then, ask whether they would use a bar graph or a line graph to show this data. Next, have them use grid paper to draw the graph.

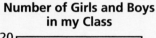
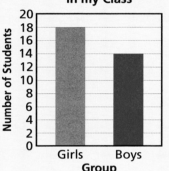

Number of Girls and Boys in my Class

On Level
for students having success

INDIVIDUALS

Change the Scale

Materials: grid paper

Have students remake the Deer Population line graph they read in Activity 1 by using the scale 0–1,000,000 in intervals of 200,000. Tell students that in addition to finding the halfway points on their scale, they will also have to find the quarter-way points to graph some data.

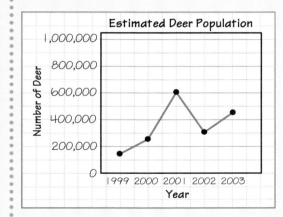

Challenge
for students seeking a challenge

PAIRS

Misleading Graphs

Give students a copy of this double-line graph. Then have partners work together to identify three errors on the graph that make it misleading.

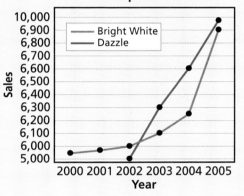

Challenge students to make a correct version of the graph so it is not misleading.

 Math Writing Prompt

Intervention

Make Connections

Describe data that would be best shown on a line graph.

 Math Writing Prompt

On Level

Explain Your Thinking

Explain how you choose the scale for a line graph. Use an example.

Math Writing Prompt

Challenge

Collect Data

Collect some data about your family. Choose a graph to display your data.

③ Homework and Cumulative Review

Homework and Remembering page 71

2–14
Homework **Goal:** Additional Practice

✓ Include students' work for page 71 as part of their portfolios.

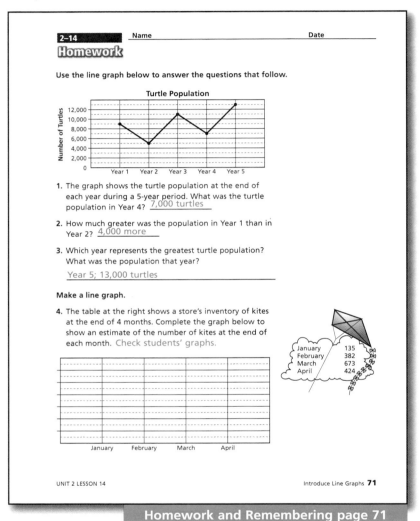

2–14 Name _____ Date _____
Homework

Use the line graph below to answer the questions that follow.

Turtle Population

1. The graph shows the turtle population at the end of each year during a 5-year period. What was the turtle population in Year 4? __7,000 turtles__

2. How much greater was the population in Year 1 than in Year 2? __4,000 more__

3. Which year represents the greatest turtle population? What was the population that year?
__Year 5; 13,000 turtles__

Make a line graph.

4. The table at the right shows a store's inventory of kites at the end of 4 months. Complete the graph below to show an estimate of the number of kites at the end of each month. Check students' graphs.

January	135
February	382
March	673
April	424

| January | February | March | April |

UNIT 2 LESSON 14   Introduce Line Graphs **71**

Homework and Remembering page 71

2–14
Remembering **Goal:** Cumulative Review

This Remembering Activity would be appropriate any time after today's lesson.

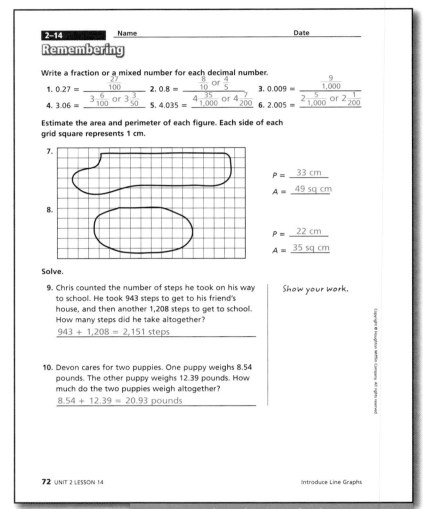

2–14 Name _____ Date _____
Remembering

Write a fraction or a mixed number for each decimal number.

1. $0.27 = \frac{27}{100}$ 2. $0.8 = \frac{8}{10}$ or $\frac{4}{5}$ 3. $0.009 = \frac{9}{1,000}$
4. $3.06 = 3\frac{6}{100}$ or $3\frac{3}{50}$ 5. $4.035 = 4\frac{35}{1,000}$ or $4\frac{7}{200}$ 6. $2.005 = 2\frac{5}{1,000}$ or $2\frac{1}{200}$

Estimate the area and perimeter of each figure. Each side of each grid square represents 1 cm.

7.

$P = $ __33 cm__
$A = $ __49 sq cm__

8.

$P = $ __22 cm__
$A = $ __35 sq cm__

Solve.

9. Chris counted the number of steps he took on his way to school. He took 943 steps to get to his friend's house, and then another 1,208 steps to get to school. How many steps did he take altogether?
__943 + 1,208 = 2,151 steps__

Show your work.

10. Devon cares for two puppies. One puppy weighs 8.54 pounds. The other puppy weighs 12.39 pounds. How much do the two puppies weigh altogether?
__8.54 + 12.39 = 20.93 pounds__

72 UNIT 2 LESSON 14   Introduce Line Graphs

Homework and Remembering page 72

Home or School Activity

 Technology Connection

Computer Graphing There are many kinds of computer software available for making graphs. You may have such software in your school. Graphing software is a good tool for enhancing your students' projects.

Have students do research at the library or on the Internet to find the population of your state for the five past years. Then have them use a computer to make a graph of that data.

Have students explain:

● the kind of graph they made.

● why they chose that graph for their data.

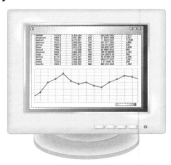

UNIT 2 LESSON 15

Graphs With Decimal Numbers

Lesson Objectives

- Round decimal numbers to the nearest tenth, hundredth, and thousandth.
- Read and construct graphs with decimal scales and decimal numbers.

Vocabulary
histogram

The Day at a Glance

Today's Goals	Materials	Math Talk
Quick Practice Review rounding decimals to the nearest tenth, hundredth, and thousandth. **1 Teaching the Lesson** **A1:** Read and discuss line graphs and bar graphs with decimal numbers. **A2:** Round decimal numbers and construct a bar graph with the results. **2 Extending the Lesson** ▸ Going Further: Histograms ▸ Differentiated Instruction **3 Homework and Cumulative Review**	Grid paper Meter sticks Student Activity Book pages 137–140 Homework and Remembering pages 73–74 Math Journals Quick Quiz 3 (Assessment Guide)	In today's activities, the students are involved in discussion as they ▸ use decimal numbers in a graph's scale ▸ review rounding decimal numbers in order to create a bar graph ▸ create their own scale and bar graph for given information

Quick Practice

 5 MINUTES **Goal:** Review rounding decimals to the nearest tenth, hundredth, and thousandth.

Round Decimals If you think it is necessary, repeat these questions:

▸ If we rounded to the nearest tenth, how many numbers would we have after the decimal point? 1 number

▸ If we rounded to the nearest hundredth, how many numbers would we have after the decimal point? 2 numbers

▸ What if we rounded to the nearest thousandth? 3 numbers

Now send several students to the board. Each one writes a decimal number with 4 digits after the decimal point and asks the class to round to the nearest thousandth, the nearest hundredth, and the nearest tenth. After each response, the leader writes the rounded decimal.

Teaching the Lesson

Discuss Decimal Graphs

 20 MINUTES

Goal: Read and discuss line graphs and bar graphs with decimal numbers.

Materials: Student Activity Book page 137

✔ **NCTM Standards:**
Algebra
Data Analysis and Probability

Teaching Note

Language and Vocabulary
Students may be familiar with the terms "*x*-axis" and "*y*-axis" used when describing data on a graph. The *x*-axis is the horizontal axis. Remind students that a horizontal line is like the horizon line when they look at a sunset. The *y*-axis is the vertical axis. Remind students that a vertical line is straight up and down. Students should get used to this terminology since it will be used in later grades.

The Learning Classroom

Math Talk Encourage students to discuss some of the places they would commonly see bar graphs used. Many of them will say newspapers or magazines. Ask them to brainstorm several situations when a graph would be helpful.

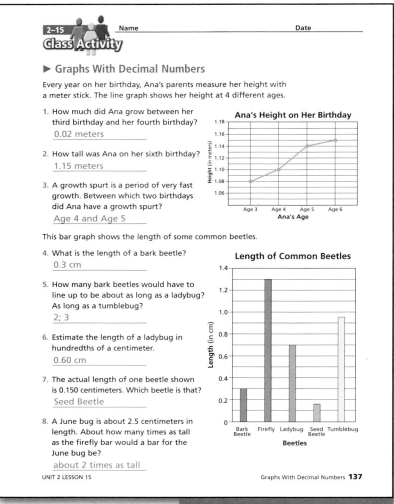

Student Activity Book page 137

▶ **Graphs With Decimal Numbers** WHOLE CLASS

Line Graphs With Decimal Numbers Discuss the scale of the line graph on page 137 in the Student Activity Book.

● What decimal numbers does it have? hundredths

● How far apart are the numbers on the scale? 0.02 apart

Have students discuss and answer exercises 1–3.

Bar Graphs With Decimal Numbers Discuss the scale of the bar graph on page 137 in the Student Activity Book.

● What decimal numbers does it have? tenths

● How far apart are the numbers on the scale? 0.2 apart

Have students discuss and answer exercises 4–8.

Construct a Decimal Graph

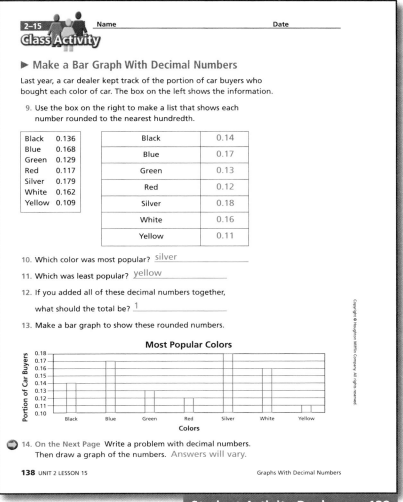

Student Activity Book page 138

The worksheet shows:

2–15 **Class Activity** Name _____ Date _____

▶ **Make a Bar Graph With Decimal Numbers**

Last year, a car dealer kept track of the portion of car buyers who bought each color of car. The box on the left shows the information.

9. Use the box on the right to make a list that shows each number rounded to the nearest hundredth.

Black	0.136
Blue	0.168
Green	0.129
Red	0.117
Silver	0.179
White	0.162
Yellow	0.109

Black	0.14
Blue	0.17
Green	0.13
Red	0.12
Silver	0.18
White	0.16
Yellow	0.11

10. Which color was most popular? _silver_

11. Which was least popular? _yellow_

12. If you added all of these decimal numbers together, what should the total be? _1_

13. Make a bar graph to show these rounded numbers.

Most Popular Colors

14. On the Next Page Write a problem with decimal numbers. Then draw a graph of the numbers. Answers will vary.

138 UNIT 2 LESSON 15   Graphs With Decimal Numbers

▶ Make a Bar Graph With Decimal Number

WHOLE CLASS

Ask students to explain the data:

● What does the entry 0.136 mean? one hundred thirty-six thousandths, which is the fraction of all the car-buyers who bought black cars

● What number would represent all the data? one

Now work together to round the decimals in the table to the nearest hundredth. Ask the class how many digits there will be after the decimal point. 2 digits

Make a Bar Graph Let each student work independently to construct the bar graph of car colors. Remind everyone that the colors should be presented in order of popularity. If necessary, work together to list the cars in order from most popular to least popular.

 30 MINUTES

Goal: Round decimal numbers and construct a bar graph with the results.

Materials: Student Activity Book pages 138–139

 NCTM Standards:
Number and Operations
Algebra
Data Analysis and Probability

 Ongoing Assessment

Give students the following data: 0.59, 0.0304, 1.98, 0.78 Ask students to:

▶ choose the number that is closest to one whole.

▶ draw a vertical axis starting at 0 with a scale of 0.04.

 Quick Quiz

See Assessment Guide for Unit 2 Quick Quiz 3.

Differentiated Instruction

Sometimes it helps to write both choices above and below the number to be rounded, and to fill in with the extra zero.

0.180

0.179

0.170

Remind the class that a number ending in 5 (the halfway point) will be rounded up to the next larger hundredth.

Extending the Lesson

Going Further: Histograms

Goal: Understand the difference between bar graphs and histograms and read histograms to solve problems.

Materials: Student Activity Book page 140

✔ **NCTM Standards:**
Data and Analysis
Problem Solving

► **Read a Histogram** WHOLE CLASS

Have students look at the population bar graph on page 140. Then read the text at the top of this page.

Point out that the first and last age intervals on this histogram have larger ranges than the rest. The first interval is limited (by 0 and 14), but the last interval is only limited by the lowest age, 75. The rest of the intervals cover ranges of 10 years.

Solve and Discuss Work together as a class to answer questions 1–7. Lead students to use the space between two marks on the vertical scale to estimate the data shown by each bar's height. For example, the bar for ages 65–74 ends about halfway between 10 and 20 on the scale. So, 18 million is a good estimate for that data. Point out that some of the questions involve adding data for two intervals.

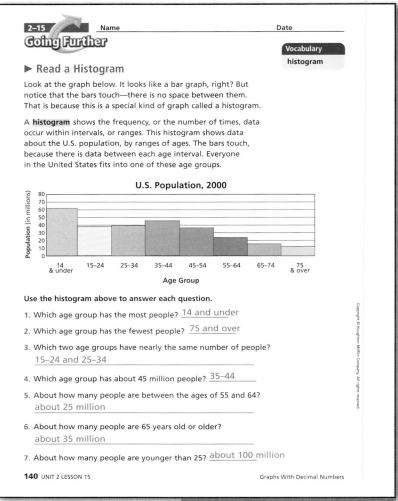

Student Activity Book page 140

► **Extend** WHOLE CLASS

You can extend this activity by showing students how to make a histogram. Write the following data table on the board. Then graph the data on a histogram on an overhead transparency.

Football Game Points Scored	
Point Range	**Number of Games**
0–9	3
10–19	7
20–29	9
30–39	5

Differentiated Instruction   Activities for Individualizing

Intervention
for students having difficulty

PAIRS

Coin Scale

Materials: grid paper

Have students make a bar graph on grid paper with a decimal scale to show the decimal value of a U.S. penny, nickel, dime, quarter, and half-dollar. Remind students to give their graph a title.

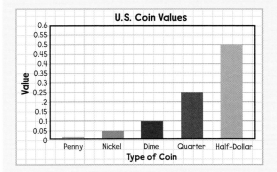

Encourage students to explain how they chose their graph's scale.

On Level
for students having success

SMALL GROUPS

Metric Lengths

Materials: grid paper, meter sticks (1 per group)

Have students work in groups of five to measure the length of their stride in meters. Then make a bar graph with a decimal scale to show all of their strides.

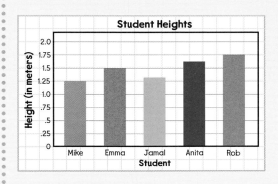

Encourage students to use their completed graphs to compare their stride lengths.

Challenge
for students seeking a challenge

PAIRS

Decimal Billions

Materials: grid paper

Have students find the world population for the years 1950, 1960, 1970, 1980, 1990, and 2000. Then have them use this information to draw a line graph. Tell them to use a scale interval of 0.5 billion.

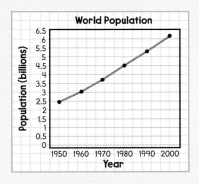

Ask students to explain how they chose their graph's scale and interval.

 Math Writing Prompt

Intervention

Number Sense
If a graph has a scale of 0 to 1, why do you think most of the data graphed is decimals? Explain your thinking.

 Math Writing Prompt

On Level

Make Connections
Describe a set of data that you could use a decimal scale to graph.

 Math Writing Prompt

Challenge

Draw Conclusions
Write a conclusion based on a graph you have drawn in this unit.

③ Homework and Cumulative Review

2-15
Homework **Goal:** Additional Practice

✓ Use this Homework page to provide students with more practice with graphing methods.

2-15
Remembering **Goal:** Cumulative Review

This Remembering Activity would be appropriate any time after today's lesson.

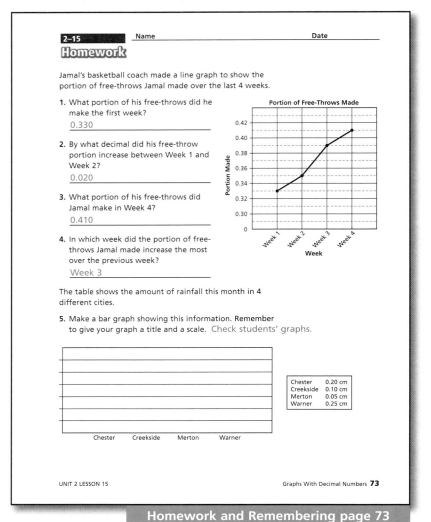

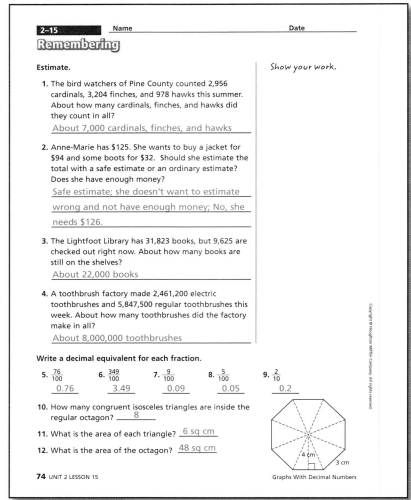

Home or School Activity

Science Connection

Your Weather Explain to students that scientists called meteorologists collect and study data about weather. Since weather changes over time, they often display the data they collect on line graphs and histograms.

Have students collect weather data for your community for one week. Each day, they should record the amount of precipitation (rain or snow) and the high temperature. At the end of the week, have them make one line graph (and possibly one histogram) to show each set of data that they collected. Then tell them to use their completed graphs to describe the weather in their community that week.

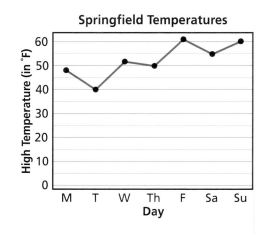

Classify Word Problems

Lesson Objectives

- Understand and apply a classification system for common addition and subtraction situations.
- Solve word problems with both additive and multiplicative comparisons.

The Day at a Glance

Today's Goals	Materials	Math Talk
Quick Practice Practice rounding decimals.	Counters	In today's activities, the students are involved in discussion as they
❶ **Teaching the Lesson** **A1:** Classify addition and subtraction word problems. **A2:** Represent, solve, and discuss various kinds of comparison word problems.	Student Activity Book pages 141–144 Homework and Remembering pages 75–76 Math Journals	▶ classify different types of addition and subtraction problems
❷ **Extending the Lesson** ▶ Differentiated Instruction		▶ solve word problems involving additive and multiplicative comparisons
❸ **Homework and Cumulative Review**		

Quick Practice

🕐 **5 MINUTES**   **Goal:** Practice rounding decimals.

Round Decimals Invite several student leaders to go to the board. Each one should write a decimal number with 4 digits after the decimal point (for example, 0.1752). They ask the class to round to the nearest thousandth, the nearest hundredth, and then the nearest tenth. After each response, the leader writes the rounded decimal.

Teaching the Lesson

Addition and Subtraction Situations

 30 MINUTES

Goal: Classify addition and subtraction word problems.

Materials: Student Activity Book pages 141–143

✔ **NCTM Standards:**
Number and Operations
Algebra
Representation
Communication

Differentiated Instruction

English Learners Encourage English learners to ask about word meanings if they are unsure. Ask them what words tell them that a problem is change plus or change minus. For example, in problems 1–3, *picked more* indicates change plus. In problems 4–6, *ate* indicates change minus.

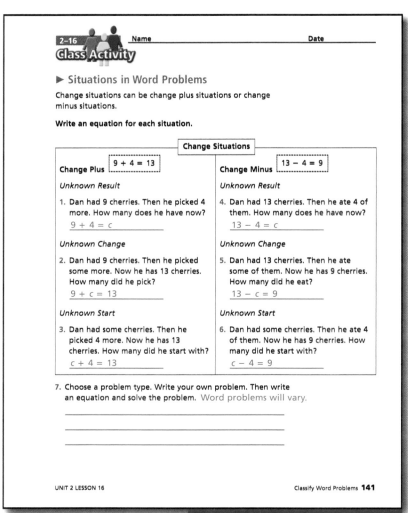

Student Activity Book page 141

▶ Situations in Word Problems WHOLE CLASS

Change Situations Direct students' attention to page 141 of the Student Activity Book. Explain that situation equations are a good way to represent these change problems. Have someone read each word problem out loud, and then have everyone write an equation that shows the unknown quantity in each situation. Students can use the letter *c* for the unknown number of cherries. Invite a few students to work at the class board.

Change Plus	Change Minus
1. $9 + 4 = c$	4. $13 - 4 = c$
2. $9 + c = 13$	5. $13 - c = 9$
3. $c + 4 = 13$	6. $c - 4 = 9$

Collection situations can have an unknown total or an unknown partner.

Write an equation for each situation.

Collection Situations

```
        13
       /  \
      9    4
```

Unknown Total

Put Together

8. Ana put 9 dimes and 4 nickels in her pocket. How many coins did she put in her pocket?

   $9 + 4 = c$

Take Apart

9. Ana put 9 coins in her purse and 4 coins in her bank. How many coins did she have in the beginning?

   $9 + 4 = c$

No Action

10. Ana has 9 dimes and 4 nickels. How many coins does she have in all?

    $9 + 4 = c$

Unknown Partner

Put Together

11. Ana put 13 coins in her pocket. Nine are dimes and the rest are nickels. How many nickels are in her pocket?

    $9 + n = 13$

Take Apart

12. Ana had 13 coins. She had 9 dimes and the rest were nickels. She put all 9 dimes in her purse and all the nickels in her bank. How many nickels did she put in her bank?

    $9 + n = 13$

No Action

13. Ana has 13 coins. She has 9 dimes and the rest are nickels. How many are nickels?

    $9 + n = 13$

14. Choose a problem type. Write your own problem. Then write an equation and solve the problem.

    Answers will vary.

142 UNIT 2 LESSON 16   Classify Word Problems

Teaching Note

Math Background This activity gives students a comprehensive view of all the basic addition and subtraction situations that they may have encountered. That, in turn, helps them build a context for any new addition or subtraction situation they encounter in the future.

Collection Situations   Ask the class to look at student page 142. Have students quickly read the word problems to themselves. Then discuss how collection situations differ from change situations. Ask:

● **What is the difference between a collection situation and a change situation?** In a collection situation, all of the objects are there from the beginning. We don't add or subtract anything. We just move them around or classify them.

Activity continued ▶

① Teaching the Lesson (continued)

Activity 1

Teaching Note

Math Background Students are exposed to these different addition and subtraction problem types so that they will be aware of the many variations. They are definitely not expected to internalize all the subcategories or to label each word problem they encounter. This classification system will help them to understand the unknown quantity in a word problem and how it can be related to the known quantities. Equations, break-apart drawings, and comparison bars are all representations that help students to see these relationships.

Explain that break-apart drawings are a good way to represent collection problems because they show the total and the parts without showing any change (plus or minus). Ask the students to draw a break-apart drawing for each of these collection situations. They can use the letter c for coins, n for nickels, and d for dimes. (There are only two kinds of break-apart drawings for these six problems—one for an unknown total and one for an unknown addend.)

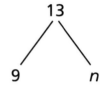

Unknown Total	Unknown Partner
c	13
9 4	9 n

Unknown Total	Unknown Addend
8. $9 + 4 = c$	11. $9 + n = 13$
9. $9 + 4 = c$	12. $9 + n = 13$
10. $9 + 4 = c$	13. $9 + n = 13$

In problems 11–13, the unknown addend is always 4. Ask the class to invent a word problem about Ana and her coins in which the unknown addend is 9. Ana has 13 coins. 4 are nickels and the rest are dimes. How many are dimes? Then have everyone make a break-apart drawing and write an equation for that situation.

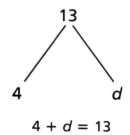

$$4 + d = 13$$

2-16

Class Activity

Name _____ Date _____

Comparison situations can have an unknown quantity or an unknown difference.

Write an equation for each situation.

Comparison Situations

| 13 |
| 9 | 4 |

Unknown Difference

How Many More?

15. Ali has 9 balloons. Lisa has 13 balloons. How many more balloons does Lisa have than Ali?

   $13 - 9 = c$

How Many Fewer?

16. Ali has 9 balloons. Lisa has 13 balloons. How many fewer balloons does Ali have than Lisa?

   $13 - 9 = c$

Unknown Quantity

Leading Language

17. Ali has 9 balloons. Lisa has 4 more than Ali. How many balloons does Lisa have?

   $9 + 4 = c$

Misleading Language

18. Ali has 9 balloons. He has 4 fewer than Lisa. How many balloons does Lisa have?

   $9 + 4 = c$

19. Write a comparison problem with an unknown difference. Then write an equation and solve the problem.

   Answers will vary. _____
   _____
   _____

20. Write a comparison problem with an unknown quantity. Then write an equation and solve the problem.

   Answers will vary. _____
   _____
   _____

UNIT 2 LESSON 16   Classify Word Problems **143**

Teaching Note

Math Background Different equations are possible for any word problem. For problem 13, the equation $13 - 9 = n$ is also correct. Equations such as $13 - 9 = n$ and $9 + n = 13$ are called *equivalent equations* because they have the same solution.

Comparison Situations Direct everyone's attention to exercises 15–20 on page 143. Remind students of the comparison bars they have been using to represent these comparison situations. Ask the class to read each problem and then draw comparison bars showing which quantity is unknown.

Unknown Difference

| 13 |
| 9 | C |

Unknown Quantity

| C |
| 9 | 4 |

Have students write and solve word problems for exercises 19 and 20 with a partner.

Activity 2

Mixed Practice With Comparisons

 25 MINUTES

Goal: Represent, solve, and discuss various kinds of comparison word problems.

Materials: Student Activity Book page 144

 NCTM Standards:
Number and Operations
Algebra
Communication
Problem Solving
Representation

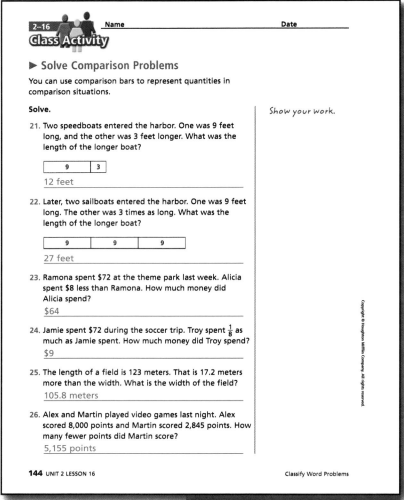

2–16
Class Activity

Name _____ Date _____

▶ **Solve Comparison Problems**

You can use comparison bars to represent quantities in comparison situations.

Solve.   *Show your work.*

21. Two speedboats entered the harbor. One was 9 feet long, and the other was 3 feet longer. What was the length of the longer boat?

| 9 | 3 |

12 feet

22. Later, two sailboats entered the harbor. One was 9 feet long. The other was 3 times as long. What was the length of the longer boat?

| 9 | 9 | 9 |

27 feet

23. Ramona spent $72 at the theme park last week. Alicia spent $8 less than Ramona. How much money did Alicia spend?

$64

24. Jamie spent $72 during the soccer trip. Troy spent $\frac{1}{8}$ as much as Jamie spent. How much money did Troy spend?

$9

25. The length of a field is 123 meters. That is 17.2 meters more than the width. What is the width of the field?

105.8 meters

26. Alex and Martin played video games last night. Alex scored 8,000 points and Martin scored 2,845 points. How many fewer points did Martin score?

5,155 points

144 UNIT 2 LESSON 16   Classify Word Problems

Student Activity Book page 144

The Learning Classroom

Math Talk Ask the class to discuss the difference between these two comparison problems. The comparison drawing for problem 21 shows addition. The comparison drawing for problem 22 shows multiplication. Point out that any comparison drawing for multiplication by a whole number will have equal sections.

▶ **Solve Comparison Problems** WHOLE CLASS

Have students turn to the word problems on page 144 and solve problems 21 and 22. Then ask the class to discuss the difference between these two comparison problems. Problem 21 may cause some confusion because it is a comparison with misleading language. For this type of problem, the comparison bars are especially helpful.

Now ask the class to solve problems 23 and 24. In each of these problems, the unknown amount is the *smaller* amount.

Discuss the rest of the problems on the page, which are a mixture of types. Invite some students to solve and explain at the board while the others work at their seats.

② Extending the Lesson

Differentiated Instruction
Activities for Individualizing

Intervention
for students having difficulty

PAIRS

Counter Models

Materials: counters

Have students use counters to model the equations for word problems 1–3. For each equation, they should write the solution.

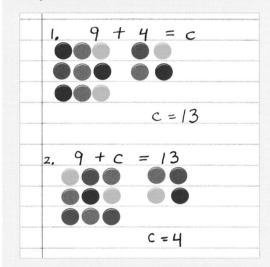

If there is time, students can write their own change plus equations and model them.

On Level
for students having success

INDIVIDUALS

All Possible Equations

Ask students to write and solve all possible addition and subtraction equations using the whole numbers 4 and 9 and the letter a.

$$a + 4 = 9$$
$$a = 5$$

$$a + 5 = 9$$
$$a = 4$$

$$4 + a = 9$$
$$a = 5$$

$$5 + a = 9$$
$$a = 4$$

$$a - 4 = 9$$
$$a = 13$$

$$a - 9 = 4$$
$$a = 13$$

Challenge
for students seeking a challenge

PAIRS OR INDIVIDUALS

Comparison Sentences

Have students copy the following:

__ _____ __ is __.

Tell them to write as many sentences as possible, using 3 and 5 for two of the "short" blanks, and one of these phrases for the "long" blank:

- more than
- times as much as

> 5 more than 3 is 8
>
> 5 times as much as 3 is 15
>
> 2 more than 3 is 5
>
> ⋮

Variation: If students are working in pairs, they can challenge each other by using different numbers.

 Math Writing Prompt

Intervention

Compare and Contrast
How are addition and subtraction alike? How are they different?

 Math Writing Prompt

On Level

Write Your Own
Use the numbers 7, 5, and 12 to write a change, a collection, and a comparison word problem.

 Math Writing Prompt

Challenge

Explain Your Thinking
Make a list of words or phrases that might be in multiplication comparison word problems. Make another list for addition comparison word problems.

③ Homework and Cumulative Review

 2-16
Homework **Goal:** Additional Practice

✓ Include students' work for page 75 as part of their portfolios.

 2-16
Remembering **Goal:** Cumulative Review

This Remembering Activity would be appropriate any time after today's lesson.

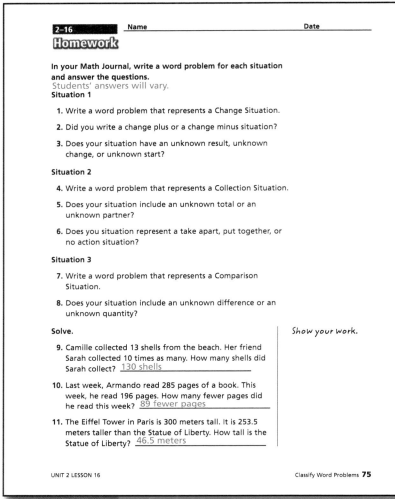

Homework and Remembering page 75

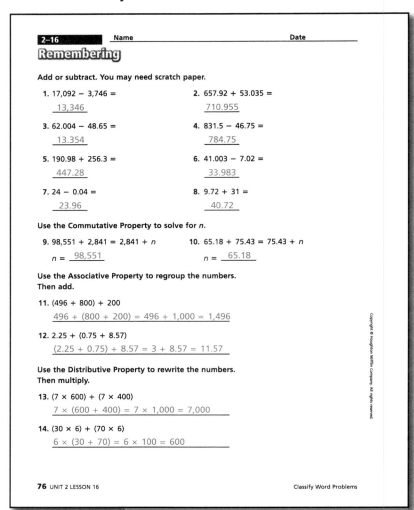

Homework and Remembering page 76

Home or School Activity

 Language Arts Connection

Comparison Suffixes Tell students that a suffix is a word ending. Two suffixes that indicate comparison are *-er* and *–est*.

Have students make a list of words that describe measurement, such as *tall, short, heavy, cold, small,* etc. Then they should attach suffixes and use the new comparison words to write word problems.

> The low temperature on Wednesday was 15°. That was 12° colder than the low temperature on Tuesday. What was the low temperature on Tuesday?

Situation and Solution Equations

Lesson Objectives

- Solve word problems with unknown addends.
- Write a situation equation and convert it to a solution equation.

Vocabulary

situation equation
solution equation

The Day at a Glance

Today's Goals	Materials	Math Talk
Quick Practice Practice rounding four-digit decimals.	Student Activity Book pages 145–148	In today's activities, the students are involved in discussion as they
1 Teaching the Lesson A1: Solve problems that require converting situation equations to solution equations. A2: Practice solving for a variety of unknowns in charts and word problems.	Index cards Centimeter rulers Grid paper (optional) Homework and Remembering pages 77–78	► create situation equations and convert to solution equations ► solve word problems
2 Extending the Lesson ► Differentiated Instruction	Math Journals	
3 Homework and Cumulative Review		

Quick Practice

🕐 **5 MINUTES** **Goal:** Practice rounding four-digit decimals.

Read Decimals Invite several student leaders to go to the board. Each one should write a decimal number with 4 digits after the decimal place (for example, 0.6752). They ask the class to round to the nearest thousandth, the nearest hundredth, and the nearest tenth. After each response, the leader writes the rounded decimal.

Teaching the Lesson

Convert to Solution Equations

 25 MINUTES

Goal: Solve problems that require converting situation equations to solution equations.

Materials: Student Activity Book pages 145-146

✔ **NCTM Standards:**
Number and Operations
Algebra
Communication
Problem Solving

The Learning Classroom

Helping Community Students at the board may get stuck. They usually welcome help from another student at that point. Allowing other students to help (instead of you) will lead them to assume responsibility for one another's learning. Ask who they would like to come help them. You can move on to another explainer while the students redo their work at the board. Of course, sometimes it is fine to have the whole class help the student as you guide the process.

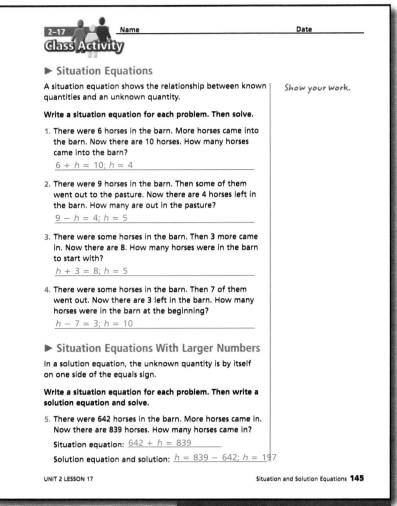

Student Activity Book page 145

▶ Situation Equations WHOLE CLASS

Problems 1–4 have been made deliberately easy so that students can see the relationship between the unknown and the known quantities.

Using the letter h as the unknown number of horses, ask students to write the equation that shows each situation. Ask a few student volunteers to work at the classroom board. Tell students not to solve the equations yet.

Now discuss how these equations can be solved. Many students will automatically know the answers. Others will count on to find the unknown number.

Example: 6 + *what number* = 10? It takes 4 to get from 6 to 10, so $h = 4$. Give students time to solve the equations in problems 1–4. Leave the equations and answers on the board.

Discuss the term *situation equation*. Explain that an equation that shows the real-life situation, as these equations do, can be called a situation equation.

▶ Situation Equations With Larger Numbers

WHOLE CLASS

Direct students' attention to problems 5–8.

Again, work together as a class to write situation equations, using the letter *h* for the unknown number of horses.

When the equations have all been written, discuss how they can be solved. For these equations, students will *not* be able to perform mental math or count on to find the answers. Students should realize at this point that solving situation equations with large numbers requires a method other than mental math or counting on.

The method will be to convert situation equations to solution equations, as described on the following page.

Activity continued ▶

The Learning Classroom

Building Concepts Some students may be able to explain details about their solving strategies. You may want to have these students explain their strategies to other students. Their "peer-friendly" language may be more meaningful than your own way of talking about a concept.

Differentiated Instruction

Extra Help Some students may need more structure when identifying the total and the parts. It may be helpful to start by circling or underlining the total in the equation.

Making a drawing that shows the total on top and the two parts on the bottom could also be helpful.

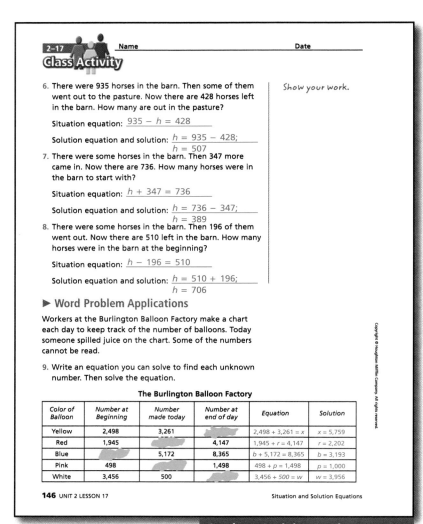

Solution Equations In problem 5, we can think 642 + *what* = 839? However, we cannot easily produce the answer by mental math. This equation must be changed into a solution equation. In a solution equation the unknown number is alone on one side of the equals sign.

Discuss how to rewrite each equation in problems 5–8 as a solution equation. If students have trouble, return to the easier equations in problems 1–4 and ask the class how they could be rewritten. Elicit from students that subtracting the known part from the total will give us the unknown part. Problems 5–7 each have an unknown part. Problem 8 has an unknown total. Solve each equation for *h*.

Solve With Various Unknowns

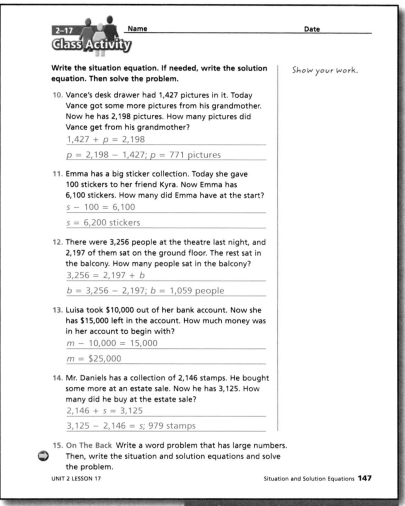

Student Activity Book page 147

2–17
Class Activity

Name _____ Date _____

Write the situation equation. If needed, write the solution equation. Then solve the problem.

Show your work.

10. Vance's desk drawer had 1,427 pictures in it. Today Vance got some more pictures from his grandmother. Now he has 2,198 pictures. How many pictures did Vance get from his grandmother?
$1,427 + p = 2,198$
$p = 2,198 − 1,427; p = 771$ pictures

11. Emma has a big sticker collection. Today she gave 100 stickers to her friend Kyra. Now Emma has 6,100 stickers. How many did Emma have at the start?
$s − 100 = 6,100$
$s = 6,200$ stickers

12. There were 3,256 people at the theatre last night, and 2,197 of them sat on the ground floor. The rest sat in the balcony. How many people sat in the balcony?
$3,256 = 2,197 + b$
$b = 3,256 − 2,197; b = 1,059$ people

13. Luisa took $10,000 out of her bank account. Now she has $15,000 left in the account. How much money was in her account to begin with?
$m − 10,000 = 15,000$
$m = $25,000$

14. Mr. Daniels has a collection of 2,146 stamps. He bought some more at an estate sale. Now he has 3,125. How many did he buy at the estate sale?
$2,146 + s = 3,125$
$3,125 − 2,146 = s; 979$ stamps

15. On The Back Write a word problem that has large numbers. Then, write the situation and solution equations and solve the problem.

UNIT 2 LESSON 17   Situation and Solution Equations **147**

30 MINUTES

Goal: Practice solving for a variety of unknowns in charts and word problems.

Materials: Student Activity Book page 147

✔ **NCTM Standards:**
Number and Operations
Algebra
Communication
Problem Solving

▶ Word Problem Applications WHOLE CLASS

Have your students read exercise 9 and look at the balloon factory chart. Every row has a missing number. Have students first write the situation equation, using any letter for the unknown that is meaningful to them. If necessary, they can convert it to a solution equation and solve for the missing number. Encourage your students to use mental math for the last two rows.

Yellow: situation: $2,498 + 3,261 = x$ $x = 5,759$

Red: situation: $1,945 + r = 4,147$ $r = 2,202$

Blue: situation: $b + 5,172 = 8,365$ $b = 3,193$

Pink: situation: $498 + p = 1,498$ $p = 1,000$

White: situation: $3,456 + 500 = w$ $w = 3,956$

Differentiated Instruction

English Learners Pair English learners with helping partners as students solve word problems. Words such as *theatre*, *balcony*, and *bank account* may not be familiar to all students. Problem solving is more meaningful when the student understands the context.

Activity continued ▶

Activity 2

Working together as a class, solve problems 10–15 on page 147 of the Student Activity Book. Invite some students to work at the class board. Situation equations that cannot be solved mentally will need to be converted to solution equations.

Again, encourage students to solve problems mentally if they can. Problems 11 and 13 can be solved mentally by many students.

► Use Mental Math to Solve Equations | WHOLE CLASS |

Write these equations on the board and have the class find the unknown number quickly. If students have trouble, emphasize the meaning of the equation. *Example:* 500,000 + *what* will give us 600,000?

$500,000 + g = 600,000$ $g = 100,000$

$d + 788 = 6,788$ $d = 6,000$

$c - 20,000 = 30,000$ $c = 50,000$

$0.45 + l = 38.45$ $l = 38$

$k - 0.40 = 0.50$ $k = 0.90$

Students will be using mental math to solve equations as part of their homework today. Solving equations such as these helps reinforce place value concepts.

② Extending the Lesson

Intervention
for students having difficulty

PAIRS

Card Equations

Materials: MathBoard materials, index cards (14 per pair)

Give each pair of students 14 index cards. Have students write the numbers 1–10 on 10 of the cards and +, −, =, and n on the other 4 cards. Students shuffle the 10 numbered cards and place them face down. One student chooses 2 of the numbered cards and 3 of the other cards to form an equation on the MathBoard. The partner solves the equation.

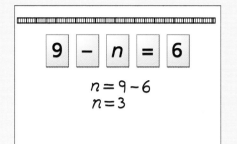

$$9 - n = 6$$
$$n = 9 - 6$$
$$n = 3$$

On Level
for students having success

PAIRS

Inverse Operations

Write on the board:

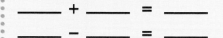

_____ + _____ = _____

_____ − _____ = _____

A student chooses one of the equation forms, and writes a situation equation with two decimal numbers and a letter. The partner then converts to a solution equation and solves.

$$a + 1.2 = 5.75$$
$$a = 5.75 - 1.2$$
$$a = 4.55$$

Challenge
for students seeking a challenge

PAIRS

Equations for Geometry

Materials: centimeter ruler, grid paper (optional)

Each student uses a centimeter ruler to draw a polygon that has all right angles. (Grid paper will make it easier to draw accurate right angles.) The student labels all side lengths except one; that side gets labeled with a letter. Students put away the rulers and exchange drawings. Each student then writes an equation and solves it to find the unknown side length.

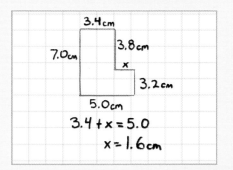

$$3.4 + x = 5.0$$
$$x = 1.6 cm$$

 Math Writing Prompt

Intervention

Explain Your Thinking

If two numbers in a situation equation are 18 and 3, what is a possible solution? Explain your answer.

 Math Writing Prompt

On Level

Support Your Answer

If a situation equation has a subtraction sign, will the solution equation always have an addition sign? Give an example to support your answer.

 Math Writing Prompt

Challenge

Write Your Own

Describe how to find the area of a figure you worked with in your activity.

③ Homework and Cumulative Review

2-17

Homework **Goal:** Additional Practice

✔ Use this Homework page to provide students with more practice with situation and solution equations.

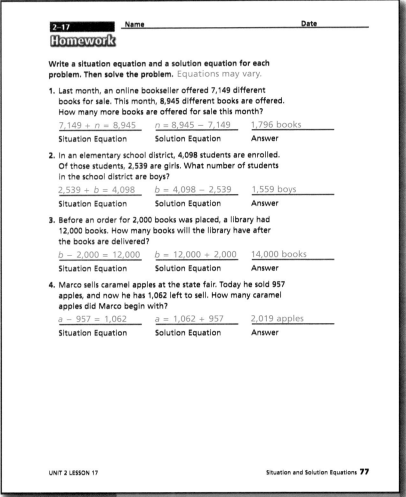

2-17 Name _____ Date _____
Homework

Write a situation equation and a solution equation for each problem. Then solve the problem. Equations may vary.

1. Last month, an online bookseller offered 7,149 different books for sale. This month, 8,945 different books are offered. How many more books are offered for sale this month?

   7,149 + n = 8,945   n = 8,945 − 7,149   1,796 books
   Situation Equation   Solution Equation   Answer

2. In an elementary school district, 4,098 students are enrolled. Of those students, 2,539 are girls. What number of students in the school district are boys?

   2,539 + b = 4,098   b = 4,098 − 2,539   1,559 boys
   Situation Equation   Solution Equation   Answer

3. Before an order for 2,000 books was placed, a library had 12,000 books. How many books will the library have after the books are delivered?

   b − 2,000 = 12,000   b = 12,000 + 2,000   14,000 books
   Situation Equation   Solution Equation   Answer

4. Marco sells caramel apples at the state fair. Today he sold 957 apples, and now he has 1,062 left to sell. How many caramel apples did Marco begin with?

   a − 957 = 1,062   a = 1,062 + 957   2,019 apples
   Situation Equation   Solution Equation   Answer

UNIT 2 LESSON 17   Situation and Solution Equations **77**

Homework and Remembering page 77

2-17

Remembering **Goal:** Cumulative Review

This Remembering Activity would be appropriate any time after today's lesson.

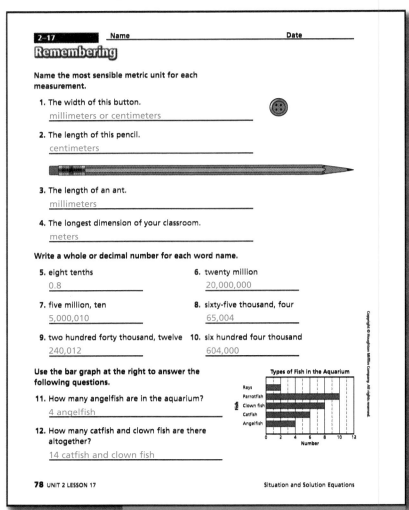

2-17 Name _____ Date _____
Remembering

Name the most sensible metric unit for each measurement.

1. The width of this button.
   millimeters or centimeters

2. The length of this pencil.
   centimeters

3. The length of an ant.
   millimeters

4. The longest dimension of your classroom.
   meters

Write a whole or decimal number for each word name.

5. eight tenths   6. twenty million
   0.8   20,000,000

7. five million, ten   8. sixty-five thousand, four
   5,000,010   65,004

9. two hundred forty thousand, twelve   10. six hundred four thousand
   240,012   604,000

Use the bar graph at the right to answer the following questions.

11. How many angelfish are in the aquarium?
    4 angelfish

12. How many catfish and clown fish are there altogether?
    14 catfish and clown fish

78 UNIT 2 LESSON 17   Situation and Solution Equations

Homework and Remembering page 78

Home or School Activity

Social Studies Connection

Morse Code In 1840, Samuel Morse invented a code that was used to send telegraph messages. There is a Morse code for every letter and digit.

Give several of the digit codes to your students. Have them research to find the remaining digit codes, and then write equations "in Morse code." Students can exchange equations and solve them. For example:

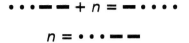

$$\cdots\!=\!= + n = \!=\cdots\cdots$$

$$n = \cdots\!=\!=$$

MORSE CODE DIGITS	
Digit	Code
0	━ ━ ━ ━ ━
1	• ━ ━ ━ ━
2	• • ━ ━ ━
3	• • • ━ ━
4	• • • • ━
5	• • • • •
6	━ • • • •

Comparison Problems

Lesson Objectives

- Solve addition and subtraction problems mentally using place value concepts.
- Represent and solve comparison word problems.
- Understand and apply comparing language.

The Day at a Glance

Today's Goals	Materials	Math Talk
Quick Practice Practice rounding four-digit decimals.	Student Activity Book pages 149–150	In today's activities, the students are involved in discussion as they
① Teaching the Lesson **A1:** Solve a variety of comparison problems, including those with misleading language. **A2:** Solve and discuss mixed word problems with comparisons.	Counters Homework and Remembering pages 79–80 Math Journals	► state comparisons in two ways ► work through misleading comparison language
② Extending the Lesson ► Differentiated Instruction		► use mental math to solve additions and subtractions
③ Homework and Cumulative Review		

Quick Practice

🕐 **5 MINUTES**   **Goal:** Practice rounding four-digit decimals.

Round Decimals Invite several student leaders to go to the board. Each one should write a decimal number with 4 digits after the decimal point (for example, 0.9743). They ask the class to round to the nearest thousandth, the nearest hundredth, and the nearest tenth. It would be a good idea for students to do these tasks in random order this time. After each response, the leader writes the rounded decimal.

Teaching the Lesson

Explore Comparison Situations

 25 MINUTES

Goal: Solve a variety of comparison problems, including those with misleading language.

Materials: Student Activity Book page 149

✔ **NCTM Standards:**
Number and Operations
Problem Solving
Communication
Representation

The Learning Classroom

Math Talk Try to use *less* or *fewer* in appropriate contexts. For a continuous quantity, such as water, we use *less*. For a quantity that can be counted, such as a number of cookies, we use *fewer*. (So, we say "less water," but "fewer cookies.") We also use less for whole numbers and for dollar amounts—5 is less than 7; 3 dollars is less than 4 dollars.

Try to use these terms correctly when you speak. However, it is not necessary to correct students when they use the wrong word. The distinction between *less* and *fewer* is difficult even for some adults.

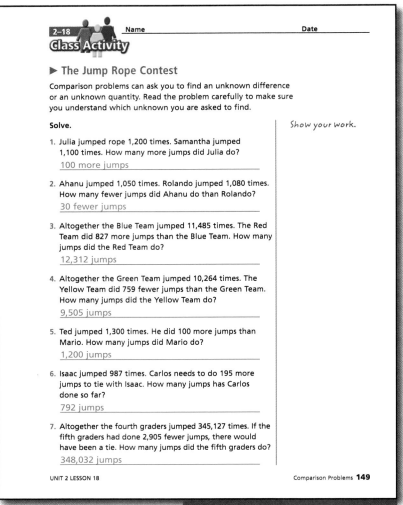

Student Activity Book page 149

▶ The Jump Rope Contest WHOLE CLASS

Unknown Difference Problems Have the class solve problems 1 and 2 on page 149 of the Student Activity Book. This will be familiar territory to most students. They have already solved this type of problem in connection with graphs. Encourage students to solve the problems in their heads.

Discuss how comparisons can be stated two ways. Have students practice describing each situation using two comparisons:

1. If Julia did 100 *more* jumps than Samantha, then Samantha did 100 *fewer* jumps than Julia.

2. If Ahanu did 30 *fewer* jumps than Rolando, then Rolando did 30 *more* jumps than Ahanu.

Unknown Quantity Problems From a conceptual point of view, problems 3 and 4 will likely be easy for students. The word *more* will signal addition, and the word *fewer* will signal subtraction. However, the computation might be a challenge. Invite several students to work at the class board while the others work at their seats. Be sure all students check their answers.

3. 12,312 jumps

4. 9,505 jumps

Comparison Problems With Misleading Language Ask students to solve problem 5 on their own. This problem may be tricky for your class. The word *more* might lead students to believe that they should add, but they actually need to subtract. They know the larger quantity and the difference, so subtraction will give them the smaller quantity. Discuss the results.

Emphasize to your class that the two most important questions to ask in a comparison problem are:

● Who has more (or less)?

● How much more (or less)?

If they focus on these questions, instead of just on the words *more* or *less*, they will be more likely to solve the problem correctly.

Activity continued ▶

Activity 1

The Learning Classroon

Building Concepts Constructing thoughtful questions and probing statements is often challenging while teaching a lesson. Here are some questions and statements that teachers have found useful. It is fine to use a few questions or statements repeatedly with your students. Students will begin to predict your probes and grow more comfortable responding to them.

▶ What is this problem about?

▶ Tell us what you see.

▶ Tell us your thinking.

▶ What would happen if...?

▶ Is that true for all cases?

▶ How can we check to be sure that this is a correct answer?

▶ What did you mean when you said ...?

▶ What were you thinking when you decided to ...?

Comparison Bars Direct students' attention to problem 5. Ask:

● Who jumped more times?

● How can we show this?

Draw these comparison bars on the board and tell students to copy them. Explain that comparison bars such as these can help us see who has the larger quantity.

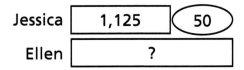

Have all students draw comparison bars to help them solve problem 6. Then have volunteers draw theirs at the board so that everyone can compare and discuss.

Tell students to draw comparison bars to help them solve the rest of the problems with misleading language. See Math Talk in Action below for a sample of classroom dialogue.

Math Talk in Action

How did you solve problem 6?

Jenna: For problem 6, I asked myself, "Who jumped more?" Since Carlos needs to jump more to tie Isaac, then Isaac jumped more times than Carlos. Then I needed to find how many times Carlos has jumped already. So, I subtracted 195 from 987 and the difference is 792. So, Carlos has jumped 792 times so far.

How did you solve problem 7?

Thomas: Problem 7 said that if the fifth-graders had jumped 2,905 fewer it would have tied. That means that the fifth-graders jumped 2,905 more than the fourth-graders. So I added 345,127 and 2,905 and the sum is 348,032. So, the fifth-graders jumped 348,032 times.

Activity 2

Mixed Practice With Comparisons

2-18 Class Activity

Name ______________________ Date ____________

▶ Solve Mixed Word Problems

Show your work.

8. Last night 45,239 people attended the soccer game. This is 5,856 more people than were at the baseball game. How many people attended the baseball game?
   39,383 people

9. Eva earned $1,268 over the summer. That was $145.60 less than Daria earned. How much did Daria earn?
   $1,413.60

10. A chef has 935 plates for a banquet with 1,086 guests. How many more plates does he need?
    151 plates

11. Ramon worked 1,910 hours this year. His sister worked 45.5 fewer hours than Ramon did. How many hours did Ramon's sister work?
    1,864.5 hours

▶ Solve With Mental Math

Say and write the answer.

12. 7,000 + 10 = 7,010
13. 7,000 − 10 = 6,990
14. 20,000 + 5,000 = 25,000
15. 20,000 − 5,000 = 15,000
16. 500 thousand + 1,000 = 501,000
17. 500 thousand + 10 = 500,010
18. 40 million + 1 = 40,000,001
19. 40 million − 1 = 39,999,999

▶ Challenging Comparison Problems

20. The hottest temperature recorded on Earth is 132°F. The temperature on the sun is 720,000,000°F. How much hotter is the sun than the hottest place on Earth?
    719,999,868°F

21. An inch is 2.54 centimeters. That is about 27.46 centimeters less than a foot. About how many centimeters are in a foot?
    about 30 centimeters

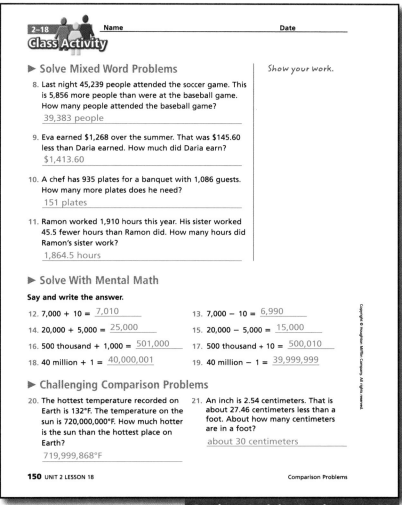

Student Activity Book page 150

▶ Solve Mixed Word Problems WHOLE CLASS

The different types of comparison problems are mixed together in problems 8–11. For each problem, send several students to work at the board while the other students work at their seats. Encourage students to use the comparison bars any time they are unsure of themselves.

30 MINUTES

Goal: Solve and discuss mixed word problems with comparisons.

Materials: Student Activity Book page 150

NCTM Standards:
Number and Operations
Problem Solving
Communication

Teaching Note

Watch For! Some students may still be inclined to simply look for key words in problems, instead of thinking about what is being asked. Watch for students who get the wrong answer because they always add when they see the word "more", for example.

Activity continued ▶

Activity 2

✔ Ongoing Assessment

Watch your students closely as they are working through the mental math exercises. Are there some students who do not join in to answer? These students might require extra assistance with their mental math skills.

Problems 8 and 9 have misleading language. Say the comparing sentence out loud. Ask students to respond with the other comparing sentence that means the same thing:

8. **Teacher:** There were 5,856 *more* people at the soccer game than at the baseball game.

   Students: There were 5,856 *fewer* people at the baseball game than at the soccer game.

9. **Teacher:** Eva earned $145.60 *less* than Daria earned.

   Students: Daria earned $145.60 *more* than Eva earned.

▶ Solve With Mental Math WHOLE CLASS

Exercises 12–19 on page 150 of the Student Activity Book are designed to improve students' number sense. Send several students to the board. Read each problem aloud, and then give a hand signal when everyone can answer. At that point, the students at their seats say the answer in unison while the students at the board write the answer. After two or three problems, replace the students at the board with other students.

▶ Challenging Comparison Problems WHOLE CLASS

This is an optional activity. If time permits, and your students are fairly secure with comparisons, let them try these challenging problems. You can also assign these problems as optional homework.

② Extending the Lesson

Differentiated Instruction ⟩ Activities for Individualizing

Intervention
for students having difficulty

PAIRS

Counter Comparisons

Materials: counters

Have each student take a handful of counters from a bag and count them. Then partners should work together to make up a comparison problem about the counters, using their names.

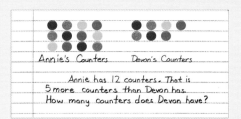

Have students repeat the activity by grabbing different amounts of counters.

On Level
for students having success

PAIRS

Combine Problems

Have one student write an equation with a variable. The partner writes a word problem for the equation. Both students solve it together.

$$987 + c = 1,910$$

Meg earned $987 during her first month at a new job. After two months, she had earned $1,910 altogether. How much did she earn during the second month?

Challenge
for students seeking a challenge

PAIRS

Number Patterns

Ask students to predict the next number in this pattern:

3, 6, 10, 15, ___

Ask students to describe the pattern. (Add 1 more each time than you added the time before.)

Point out that you *do not* add the same number each time. Tell the students to take turns creating number patterns for partners to solve. The only rule is to not have a pattern with the same number added each time.

✎ Math Writing Prompt

Intervention

Write a Word Problem
Write a word problem that has the word *less*, but that you *add* to solve.

✎ Math Writing Prompt

On Level

Write an Equation
Write an equation where the sum is 356. Then write a word problem for the equation.

✎ Math Writing Prompt

Challenge

Make a Table
Create a function table to show the price of 15 tickets when one ticket costs $2.25.

 **Homework and Cumulative Review**

Homework **Goal:** Additional Practice

✓ Use this Homework page to provide students with more practice with comparison problems.

Remembering **Goal:** Cumulative Review

This Remembering Activity would be appropriate any time after today's lesson.

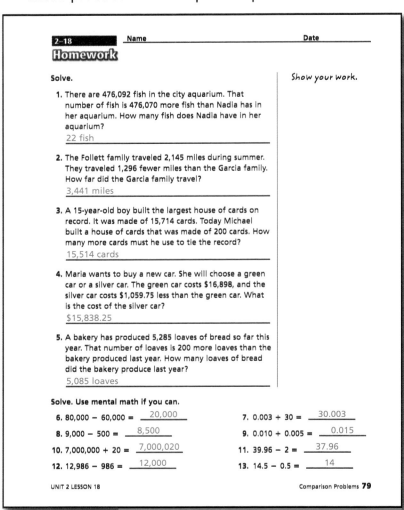

2-18 Name _____ Date _____
Homework

Solve. *Show your work.*

1. There are 476,092 fish in the city aquarium. That number of fish is 476,070 more fish than Nadia has in her aquarium? How many fish does Nadia have in her aquarium?
   22 fish

2. The Follett family traveled 2,145 miles during summer. They traveled 1,296 fewer miles than the Garcia family. How far did the Garcia family travel?
   3,441 miles

3. A 15-year-old boy built the largest house of cards on record. It was made of 15,714 cards. Today Michael built a house of cards that was made of 200 cards. How many more cards must he use to tie the record?
   15,514 cards

4. Maria wants to buy a new car. She will choose a green car or a silver car. The green car costs $16,898, and the silver car costs $1,059.75 less than the green car. What is the cost of the silver car?
   $15,838.25

5. A bakery has produced 5,285 loaves of bread so far this year. That number of loaves is 200 more loaves than the bakery produced last year. How many loaves of bread did the bakery produce last year?
   5,085 loaves

Solve. Use mental math if you can.

6. 80,000 − 60,000 = __20,000__   7. 0.003 + 30 = __30.003__

8. 9,000 − 500 = __8,500__   9. 0.010 + 0.005 = __0.015__

10. 7,000,000 + 20 = __7,000,020__   11. 39.96 − 2 = __37.96__

12. 12,986 − 986 = __12,000__   13. 14.5 − 0.5 = __14__

UNIT 2 LESSON 18   Comparison Problems **79**

Homework and Remembering page 79

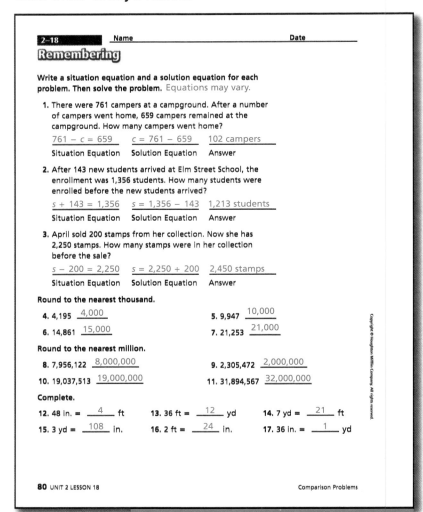

2-18 Name _____ Date _____
Remembering

Write a situation equation and a solution equation for each problem. Then solve the problem. Equations may vary.

1. There were 761 campers at a campground. After a number of campers went home, 659 campers remained at the campground. How many campers went home?
   __761 − c = 659__ __c = 761 − 659__ __102 campers__
   Situation Equation Solution Equation Answer

2. After 143 new students arrived at Elm Street School, the enrollment was 1,356 students. How many students were enrolled before the new students arrived?
   __s + 143 = 1,356__ __s = 1,356 − 143__ __1,213 students__
   Situation Equation Solution Equation Answer

3. April sold 200 stamps from her collection. Now she has 2,250 stamps. How many stamps were in her collection before the sale?
   __s − 200 = 2,250__ __s = 2,250 + 200__ __2,450 stamps__
   Situation Equation Solution Equation Answer

Round to the nearest thousand.

4. 4,195 __4,000__   5. 9,947 __10,000__

6. 14,861 __15,000__   7. 21,253 __21,000__

Round to the nearest million.

8. 7,956,122 __8,000,000__   9. 2,305,472 __2,000,000__

10. 19,037,513 __19,000,000__   11. 31,894,567 __32,000,000__

Complete.

12. 48 in. = __4__ ft   13. 36 ft = __12__ yd   14. 7 yd = __21__ ft

15. 3 yd = __108__ in.   16. 2 ft = __24__ in.   17. 36 in. = __1__ yd

80 UNIT 2 LESSON 18   Comparison Problems

Homework and Remembering page 80

Home or School Activity

 Social Studies Connection

Great Lakes The Great Lakes are located in the northeastern part of the United States along the Canadian border. Have students research the different lakes that make up the Great Lakes.

Then have students make a bar graph to display their data.

Lake	Total Area (in square miles)	Greatest Depth (in feet)
	GREAT LAKES FACTS	
Erie	9,940	210
Huron	23,010	750
Michigan	22,178	923
Ontario	7,540	778
Superior	31,820	1,302

Two-Step Word Problems

Lesson Objectives

- Solve word problems that involve two steps.
- Explain a solution method to the class and answer any questions.

Vocabulary

range
median
mode

The Day at a Glance

Today's Goals	Materials	Math Talk
Quick Practice Pracitce rounding four-digit decimals.	Student Activity Book pages 151–152	In today's activities, the students are involved in discussion as they
❶ Teaching the Lesson **A1:** Solve and explain word problems with two or more steps. **A2:** Work in pairs or small groups to write word problems from a map.	Grid paper Play money (optional) Homework and Remembering pages 81–82 Math Journals	▶ solve multi-step word problems ▶ create word problems based on a map
❷ Extending the Lesson ▶ Going Further: Find Range, Median, and Mode ▶ Differentiated Instruction	Quick Quiz 4 (Assessment Guide)	
❸ Homework and Cumulative Review		

Quick Practice

🕐 **5 MINUTES** **Goal:** Practice rounding four-digit decimals.

Round Decimals Invite several student leaders to go to the board. Each one should write a decimal number with 4 digits after the decimal point (for example, 0.5384). They ask the class to round to the nearest thousandth, the nearest hundredth, and then the nearest tenth. It would be a good idea for students to do these tasks in random order this time. After each response, the leader writes the rounded decimal.

Teaching the Lesson

Solve and Explain Two-Step Problems

 25 MINUTES

Goal: Solve and explain word problems with two or more steps.

Materials: Student Activity Book page 151

✔ **NCTM Standards:**
Number and Operations
Problem Solving
Communication

The Learning Classroom

Math Talk Have students practice explaining one another's work in their own words from their seats, or have them go to the board and point to the parts of a student's work as you or another student explains those parts.

Teaching Note

Math Background The two methods described for problem 5 illustrate the distributive property:

$10 \times (6,125 - 5,450) =$
$10 \times 6,125 - 10 \times 55,4500$

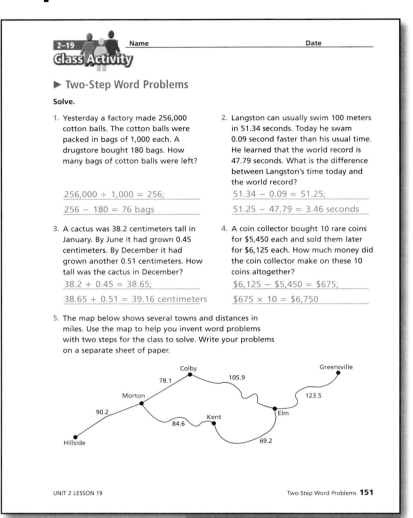

Student Activity Book page 151

▶ **Two-Step Word Problems** WHOLE CLASS

Have students work individually to solve problems 1–4. Explain that for these problems, most solution methods will take two steps. Invite several students to work at the board while the other students work at their seats. Then ask two students at the board to explain how they solved the problem. Choose students who had somewhat different approaches, if possible.

Note that there are sometimes different ways to solve a problem. Problem 4, for example, can be solved by writing:

$(\$6,125 - \$5,450) \times 10 = \$6,750$

or

$10(\$6,125 - \$5,450) = (10 \times 6,125) - (10 \times 5,450).$

Write Word Problems

Divide students into pairs or small groups for problem 5. Using the map, students should work together to create some problems of their own. Give them about 10 minutes to write three problems that are based on the map. [If you are running short on time, have the whole class brainstorm to make up problems instead of dividing students into small groups.]

Remind the class to write both addition and subtraction problems. Below are a few examples:

- We drove from Elm to Greensville and back again. How far did we drive?

- I am driving from Hillside to Morton. I have gone 9.6 miles. How far do I still have to go before I reach Morton?

- Ella wants to drive from Morton to Elm. There are two routes. Which route will be shorter? How much shorter will it be?

After the allotted time, have various groups volunteer to present some of their map problems for the rest of the class to solve.

 30 MINUTES

Goal: Work in pairs or small groups to write word problems from a map.

 NCTM Standards:
Number and Operations
Problem Solving
Communication

 Ongoing Assessment

Write the following problem on the board. Have students solve it two different ways.

▶ Jose earned $4.75 each day for 10 days. Paul earned $3.95 each day for 10 days. How much more did Jose earn than Paul?

 Quick Quiz

See Assessment Guide for Unit 2 Quick Quiz 4.

② Extending the Lesson

Going Further: Find Range, Median, and Mode

Goal: Find the range, median, and mode of a data set.

Materials: Student Activity Book page 152

✔ **NCTM Standards:**
Data Analysis and Probability

▶ Range, Median, and Mode [WHOLE CLASS]

Range, median, and mode are measures of central tendency, which are used to describe important features of a data set. This activity focuses on the process of finding each measure. In a later lesson, students will solve problems involving range, median, and mode.

Order Numbers Review with students how to order a set of numbers from least to greatest. You may wish to use a number line in the review.

Have students read the text at the top of Student Activity Book page 152. After you read the definitions, explain that all data sets have exactly one range and one median, but the number of modes varies. Data sets can have one or more modes or no mode at all.

As you read through the two examples, make sure students understand that each row shows one of the four steps listed above the box. Ask:

● How does listing the data in order from least to greatest help you find the range? *It is easier to find the least and greatest numbers.*

● How does it help you find the mode? *It makes it easier to find repeated numbers in the set.*

● How does it help you find the median? *It makes it easier to identify what number is in the middle.*

Explain that if a set has an *odd* number of data, the median will be the middle number in the set. If the set has an *even* number of data, the median will be halfway between the two middle numbers. To find the number halfway between two numbers, you divide the sum of those two numbers by 2. (In other words, you find the mean of the two numbers.)

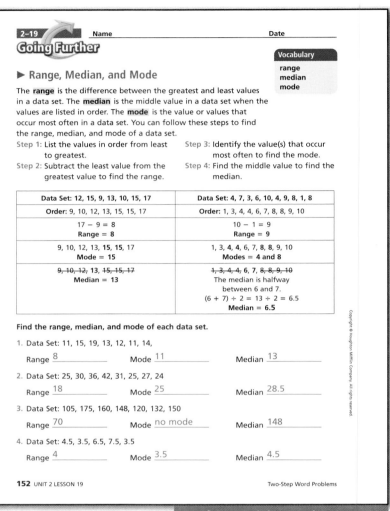

Student Activity Book page 152

▶ Practice Finding Range, Median, and Mode [PAIRS]

Have students work in pairs to complete exercises 1–4. Remind them to follow the four listed steps. To order their numbers, suggest that students first identify the smallest number in the set. Then find the next smallest number, and so on.

▶ Critical Thinking [WHOLE CLASS]

After students solve all the problems, review their answers together as a class. Then challenge students to take a survey to find the age of each student in their class. Have students find the range, median, and mode age of their class.

Intervention
for students having difficulty

`PAIRS`

Shopping Spree

Materials: play money (optional)

Tell students to make a list of items and prices for a store. Have them take turns being shopper and cashier. The shopper buys two or three items. The cashier gives (or computes) the correct change. The shopper checks the amount.

SCHOOL STORE	
Item	Price
Folder	$3.79
Box of Pencils	$2.39
Pen	$4.50
3-Ring Binder	$8.99
Spiral Notebook	$4.29
Ruler	$2.15

 Math Writing Prompt

Intervention

How Many Steps?

If you buy two items and get change in return, how many steps do you need to find the correct change? Explain.

On Level
for students having success

`INDIVIDUALS`

Problems for Equations

Have students write a word problem for each equation:

1. $s + 1.25 = 20.4$

2. $a = 129 + 26 - 33$

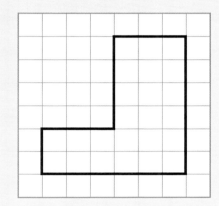

> 1. Tyra ran a race in 20.4 seconds. That was 1.25 seconds more than it took Sonya to run the same race. What was Sonya's time?
>
> 2. Alan had $129. He earned $26 more. Then he spent $33. How much money did Alan have left?

1. Tyra ran a race in 20.4 seconds. That was 1.25 seconds more than it took Sonya to run the same race. What was Sonya's time?

2. Alan had $129. He earned $26 more. Then he spent $33. How much money did Alan have left?

If students work in pairs, they can make up their own equations, exchange, and write word problems for the equations they receive.

 Math Writing Prompt

On Level

Write a Problem

Write a two-step word problem that can be solved in more than one way.

Challenge
for students seeking a challenge

`INDIVIDUALS`

Draw a Picture

Materials: grid paper

Ask students to draw a polygon that has:

- all right angles
- perimeter 24 units
- area 24 square units

Variation if students are working in pairs: One student draws a polygon with all right angles on grid paper and tells the partner the area and perimeter. The partner tries to draw it.

Math Writing Prompt

Challenge

Too Much Information

Write a two-step word problem. Include more information than is needed to solve the problem.

 # **Homework and Cumulative Review**

2-19
Homework **Goal:** Additional Practice

✔ Use this Homework page to provide students with more practice with two-step word problems.

2-19
Remembering **Goal:** Cumulative Review

This Remembering Activity would be appropriate any time after today's lesson.

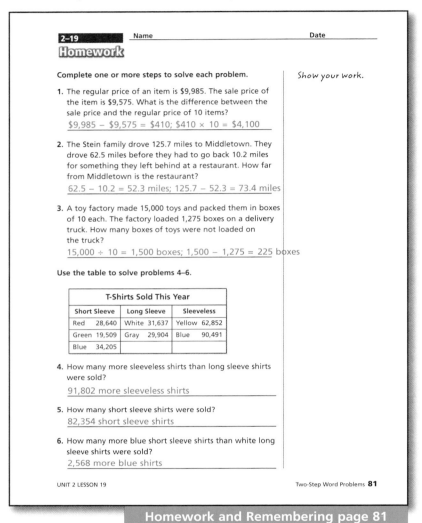

2-19
Homework

Name _____ Date _____

Complete one or more steps to solve each problem.

Show your work.

1. The regular price of an item is $9,985. The sale price of the item is $9,575. What is the difference between the sale price and the regular price of 10 items?
   $9,985 − $9,575 = $410; $410 × 10 = $4,100

2. The Stein family drove 125.7 miles to Middletown. They drove 62.5 miles before they had to go back 10.2 miles for something they left behind at a restaurant. How far from Middletown is the restaurant?
   62.5 − 10.2 = 52.3 miles; 125.7 − 52.3 = 73.4 miles

3. A toy factory made 15,000 toys and packed them in boxes of 10 each. The factory loaded 1,275 boxes on a delivery truck. How many boxes of toys were not loaded on the truck?
   15,000 ÷ 10 = 1,500 boxes; 1,500 − 1,275 = 225 boxes

Use the table to solve problems 4–6.

T-Shirts Sold This Year		
Short Sleeve	Long Sleeve	Sleeveless
Red 28,640	White 31,637	Yellow 62,852
Green 19,509	Gray 29,904	Blue 90,491
Blue 34,205		

4. How many more sleeveless shirts than long sleeve shirts were sold?
   91,802 more sleeveless shirts

5. How many short sleeve shirts were sold?
   82,354 short sleeve shirts

6. How many more blue short sleeve shirts than white long sleeve shirts were sold?
   2,568 more blue shirts

UNIT 2 LESSON 19

Two-Step Word Problems **81**

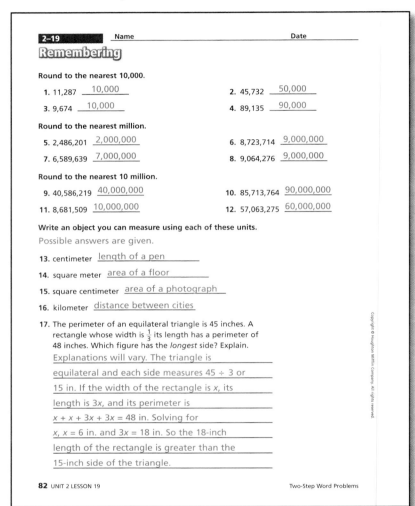

2-19
Remembering

Name _____ Date _____

Round to the nearest 10,000.

1. 11,287 _10,000_
2. 45,732 _50,000_
3. 9,674 _10,000_
4. 89,135 _90,000_

Round to the nearest million.

5. 2,486,201 _2,000,000_
6. 8,723,714 _9,000,000_
7. 6,589,639 _7,000,000_
8. 9,064,276 _9,000,000_

Round to the nearest 10 million.

9. 40,586,219 _40,000,000_
10. 85,713,764 _90,000,000_
11. 8,681,509 _10,000,000_
12. 57,063,275 _60,000,000_

Write an object you can measure using each of these units.
Possible answers are given.

13. centimeter _length of a pen_
14. square meter _area of a floor_
15. square centimeter _area of a photograph_
16. kilometer _distance between cities_

17. The perimeter of an equilateral triangle is 45 inches. A rectangle whose width is $\frac{1}{3}$ its length has a perimeter of 48 inches. Which figure has the *longest* side? Explain.
   Explanations will vary. The triangle is equilateral and each side measures 45 ÷ 3 or 15 in. If the width of the rectangle is x, its length is $3x$, and its perimeter is $x + x + 3x + 3x = 48$ in. Solving for x, $x = 6$ in. and $3x = 18$ in. So the 18-inch length of the rectangle is greater than the 15-inch side of the triangle.

82 UNIT 2 LESSON 19

Two-Step Word Problems

Homework and Remembering page 81

Homework and Remembering page 82

Home or School Activity

 ### **Real-World Connection**

Perimeter and Area Ask your students to make up and solve a word problem about the perimeter and area of some part of their house. For example: a yard, garden, or driveway.

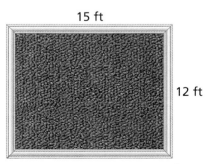

15 ft

12 ft

Carpet: Area = 12 × 15 = 180 square feet

Unit Review and Test

Lesson Objective

● **Assess student progress on unit objectives.**

The Day at a Glance

Today's Goals	Materials
1 Assessing the Unit ► Assess student progress on unit objectives. ► Use activities from unit lessons to reteach content. **2 Extending the Assessment** ► Use remediation for common errors. There is no homework assignment on a test day.	Unit 2 Test, Student Activity Book pages 153–154 Unit 2 Test, Form A or B, Assessment Guide pages A28–A34 (optional) Unit 2 Performance Assessment, Assessment Guide pages A35–A38 (optional)

Quick Practice

 5 MINUTES **Goal:** Review any skills you choose to meet the needs of your students

Choose any Quick Practice activities that provide support for your students. The following may be helpful:

Reading Decimal Numbers and Metric Lengths, Unit 2, Lessons 2–5

Reading Large Numbers and Metric Lengths, Unit 2, Lessons 6–8

Large Count-Bys, Unit 2, Lessons 9–11

The Halfway Point, Unit 2, Lessons 12–13

 Class Management

Review and Test Day You may want to choose a quiet game or other activity (reading a book or working on homework for another subject) for students who finish early.

① Assessing the Unit

Assess Unit Objectives

🕐 **45 MINUTES** (more if schedule permits)

Goal: Assess student progress on unit objectives

Materials: Student Activity Book page 153; Assessment A28–A34 (optional)

▶ Review and Assessment

If your students are ready for assessment on the unit objectives, you may use either the test on the Student Activity Book pages or one of the forms of the Unit 2 Test in the Assessment Guide to assess student progress.

If you feel that students need some review first, you may use the test on the Student Activity Book pages as a review of unit content, and then use one of the forms of the Unit 2 Test in the Assessment Guide to assess student progress.

To assign a numerical score for all of these test forms, use 5 points for each question. You may also choose to use the Unit 2 Performance Assessment. Scoring for that assessment can be found in its rubric in the Assessment Guide.

▶ Reteaching Resources

The chart at the right lists the test items, the unit objectives they cover, and the lesson activities in which the objective is covered in this unit. You may revisit these activities with students who do not show mastery of the objectives.

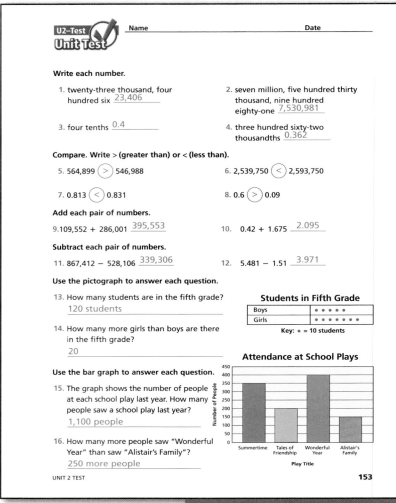

Student Activity Book page 153

Unit Test Items	Unit Objectives Tested	Activities to Use for Reteaching
1–4	**2.1** Read, write, and identify the place value of decimals and whole numbers.	Lesson 1, Activities 1–2 Lesson 4, Activities 1–2 Lesson 5, Activity 1
5–8	**2.2** Compare, order, and round numbers and estimate sums and differences.	Lesson 2, Activities 2–3 Lesson 12, Activities 1–2 Lesson 15, Activity 2
9–12	**2.3** Add and subtract whole numbers and decimals.	Lesson 3, Activities 1–2 Lesson 6, Activities 1–2 Lesson 7, Activity 1 Lesson 8, Activities 1–2 Lesson 10, Activity 1

Student Activity Book page 154

U2–Test
Unit Test

Name _____ Date _____

Use the line graph to answer each question.

Fish Population in Potter's Pond

17. The graph shows the fish population at the end of each year. What was the fish population at the end of 2002?

   45 fish

18. How much greater was the fish population in 2004 than it was in 1999?

   25 fish

Solve.

19. Marco earns $7.50 per hour at his summer job. Last week, he worked 22 hours. He bought a skateboard for $35 and put the rest into his savings account. How much did he put into his savings account?

   $7.50 × 22 = $165; $165 − $35 = $130

   Show your work.

20. **Extended Response** The distance between Chicago and Los Angeles is 1,742 miles. The distance between Chicago and Philadelphia is 665 miles. The distance between Chicago and Detroit is 427 miles less than the distance between Chicago and Philadelphia. Explain how to find how much greater the distance between Chicago and Los Angeles is than the distance between Chicago and Detroit.

   First find the distance between Chicago and Detroit, 665 − 427 = 238. Then subtract the distance from 1,742, 1,742 − 238 = 1,504. The distance between Chicago and Los Angeles is 1,504 miles more than the distance between Chicago and Detroit.

154 UNIT 2 TEST

Unit Test Items	Unit Objectives Tested	Activities to Use for Reteaching
13–18	**2.4** Interpret and make pictographs, bar graphs, and line graphs.	Lesson 11, Activities 1–3 Lesson 12, Activity 1 Lesson 13, Activities 1–2 Lesson 14, Activities 1–3 Lesson 15, Activity 1
19–20	**2.5** Solve a variety of problems involving addition and subtraction of whole numbers and decimals.	Lesson 9, Activity 1 Lesson 16, Activities 1–2 Lesson 17, Activities 1–2 Lesson 18, Activities 1–2 Lesson 19, Activity 1

▶ Assessment Resources

Free Response Tests
Unit 2 Test, Student Activity Book page 154
Unit 2 Test, Form A, Assessment Guide, pages A28–A30

Extended Response Item
The last item in the Student Activity Book test and in the Form A test will require an extended response as an answer.

Multiple Choice Test
Unit 2 Test, Form B, Assessment Guide, pages A31–A34

Performance Assessment
Unit 2 Performance Assessment, Assessment Guide, page A35
Unit 2 Performance Assessment Rubric, Assessment Guide, page A38

▶ Portfolio Assessment

Teacher-selected Items for Student Portfolios:

- Homework, Lesson 2, 8, 14, and 16
- Class Activity work, Lessons 8, 13, and 18

Student-selected Items for Student Portfolios:

- Favorite Home or School Activity
- Best Writing Prompt

Copyright © Houghton Mifflin Company. All rights reserved.

UNIT 2 UNIT REVIEW AND TEST **295**

② Extending the Assessment

Unit Objective 2.1
Read, write, and identify the place value of decimals and whole numbers.

Common Error: Omits zeros.

Remediation Students may sometimes omit one or more zeros when writing the standard form of a number given in word form. Have these students use a place value chart or grid to record the standard form of the number. This will help them recognize and understand that zeros are sometimes used as placeholders in a number.

Unit Objective 2.2
Compare, order, and round numbers and estimate sums and differences.

Common Error: Compares digits in different places.

Remediation Have these students use grid paper to complete their comparisons. For each comparison, have students write the numbers, one above the other, and align the numbers by place value. Remind students to compare digits beginning at the greatest, or leftmost, place of the numbers.

Unit Objective 2.3
Add and subtract whole numbers and decimals.

Common Error: Aligns places incorrectly.

Remediation Some students may have difficulty adding and subtracting decimals that have a different number of places, especially when the computations are presented horizontally. Have students carefully rewrite the computations vertically on grid paper or lined paper turned sideways. This will enable them to use a column or a line for vertical alignment of the decimal points as well as the various places in the numbers.

Unit Objective 2.4
Interpret and make pictographs, bar graphs, and line graphs.

Common Error: Misreads pictographs.

Remediation Some students do not use the information in the key when reading the data presented in pictographs. For students to learn to read the key, they need to see a number of pictographs and practice including the information in the key when interpreting the data.

Unit Objective 2.5
Solve a variety of problems involving addition and subtraction of whole numbers and decimals.

Common Error: Has difficulty with multistep problems.

Remediation Have students act out problems using lists, drawings, manipulatives, or money. This will allow them to see concretely the steps, and the order of the steps, that must be performed.

Common Error: Doesn't know how to begin.

Remediation Have students work in pairs to work through a problem. Students should list the steps they must complete to find the solution. Then have students solve similar problems in which they can apply a similar strategy.

Circles, Polygons, and Angles

IN THIS UNIT, students explore various aspects of angles, including the formation of angles by lines and rays and how knowledge of angles helps students learn about polygons and circles.

Students are involved in hands-on activities to investigate how angles and lines combine in polygons and circles. They apply their discoveries about angles in a circle to describe rotational symmetry and to interpret and create circle graphs.

Students then use what they have learned about circumference in previous units to investigate and describe the relationship between diameter and circumference of a circle.

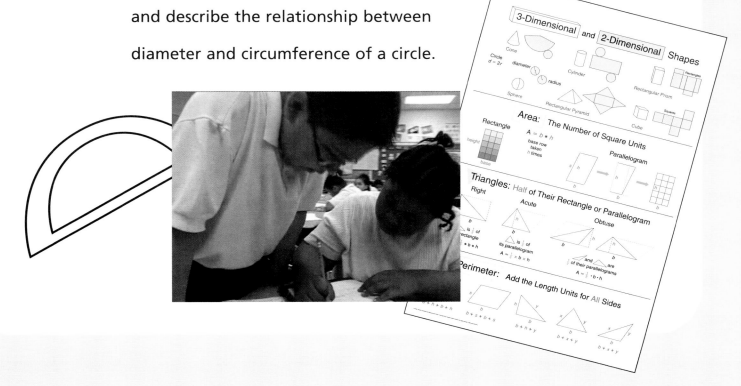

UNIT B CONTENTS

Big Idea **Using Angles to Learn About Polygons and Circles**

Planning Unit B Unit Pacing: 10–14 days

Lesson Title	Lesson Resources	Materials and Manipulatives		
		Math Expressions	Other	
1 Lines and Angles	Family Letter Student Activity Book pages 155–160 Homework and Remembering pages 83–84	Rulers	Protractors or Protractors (Copymaster M24), rectangular sheet of paper, Math Journals	
2 Polygons and Angles	Student Activity Book pages 161–164 Homework and Remembering pages 85–86	Rulers	Scissors, protractors or Protractors (Copymaster M24), Math Journals	
3 Compare and Contrast Polygons	Student Activity Book pages 165–168 Homework and Remembering pages 87–88	MathBoard materials (optional)	Dot paper, scissors, Centimeter-Dot Paper (Copymaster M25), 1 regular pentagon, 1 regular hexagon, Math Journals	
4 Circles and Angles	Student Activity Book pages 169–172 Homework and Remembering pages 89–90	Rulers	Protractors or Protractors (Copymaster M24), grid paper or dot paper, scissors, Math Journals	
5 Symmetry	Student Activity Book pages 173–176 Homework and Remembering pages 91–92		Rectangular sheet of unlined paper, scissors, Centimeter-Dot Paper (Copymaster M25), Math Journals	
6 Circle Graphs	Student Activity Book pages 177–178, Homework and Remembering pages 93–94	Rulers	Protractor or Protractors (Copymaster M24), Math Journals	
7 Circumference	Student Activity Book pages 179–180, Homework and Remembering pages 95–96	Rulers	Cans of various sizes, string, strip of paper, scissors, circular object, Math Journals	
✔ Unit Review and Test	Student Activity Book pages 181–182 Assessment Guide			

Unit B Assessment

✓ Unit Objectives Tested	Unit Test Items	Lessons
B.1 Identify and measure angles.	1–2	1
B.2 Find the measure of an unknown angle in a polygon.	3–4	1, 2
B.3 Identify congruent figures.	5	3
B.4 Identify the position of an object after it has been turned.	6	4
B.5 Identify lines of symmetry.	7	5
B.6 Solve problems using a circle graph.	8–10	6

Formal Assessment

Open or Free Response Tests

- Unit Review and Test (Student Activity Book pages 181–182, Teacher's Guide pages 341–344)
- Unit B Test Form A (Assessment Guide)
- Unit B Open Response Test (Test Generator)
- Test Bank Items for Unit B (Test Generator)

Multiple Choice Tests

- Unit B Test Form B (Assessment Guide)
- Unit B Multiple Choice Test (Test Generator)
- Test Bank Items for Unit B (Test Generator)

Performance Tasks

- Unit B Performance Assessment (Assessment Guide)
- Unit B Performance Assessment (Test Generator)

Informal Assessment

Ongoing Assessment

In every Teacher's Guide lesson

Performance Assessment

- Class discussions
- Small-group work
- Individual work on teacher-selected tasks

Portfolios

- See Unit B Review and Test for suggestions for selecting items for portfolios.
- Some Homework pages are noted as suitable for portfolio inclusion.

Review Opportunities

Homework and Remembering

- Homework pages provide review of recently taught topics.
- Remembering pages provide cumulative review.

Teacher's Guide

- Unit Review and Test (page 341–344)

Teacher's Resource Book

- Problem Bank

Test Generator CD-ROM

- Test Bank Items can be used to create custom review sheets.

Unit B Teaching Resources

Reaching All Learners

Extra Help
Lesson 5, page 325

Advanced Learners
Lesson 4, page 319

Individualizing Instruction

Activities
- Intervention (in every lesson)
- On Level (in every lesson)
- Challenge (in every lesson)

Math Writing Prompts
- Intervention (in every lesson)
- On Level (in every lesson)
- Challenge (in every lesson)

Cross-Curricular Links • Home or School Activities

 Art Connection
Mathematics and Art (Lesson 2, page 310)

 Language Arts Connection
Names for Polygons (Lesson 3, page 316)

 Science Connections
Rotations in Our World (Lesson 4, page 322)
Symmetry in Nature (Lesson 5, page 328)

 Social Studies Connection
Graphs in the Media (Lesson 6, page 334)

 Literature Connection
Math and Literature (Lesson 7, page 340)

Teaching Unit B

Putting Research Into Practice for Unit B

From Current Research: Developing Angle Concepts

An important and difficult geometric figure for students to understand and be able to use is the angle. In the course of schooling, students need to encounter multiple mathematical conceptions of angle, including: (a) angle as movement, as in rotation or sweep; (b) angle as a geometric shape, a delineation of space by two intersecting lines; and (c) angle as a measure, a perspective that encompasses the other two. Although as preschoolers, they encounter and use angles intuitively in their play, children have many misconceptions about angles. They typically believe that angle measures are influenced by the lengths of the intersecting lines or by the angle's orientation in space. The latter conception decreases with age, but the former is robust at every age. Some researchers have suggested that students in the elementary grades should develop separate mental models of angle as movement and angle as shape.

There is some research on instructional approaches that attempt to develop the two models of angles. With appropriate instruction, Logo's Turtle Geometry can support the development of measures of rotations. The students, however, rarely connected these rotations to models of the space in the interior of figures traced by the turtle. Simple modifications to Logo helped students perceive the relationship between turns and traces (the path made by Logo's turtle), and the students could then use turns to measure static intersections of lines. Another approach used multiple concrete analogies such as turns, slopes, meetings, bends, directions, corners, and openings to help children develop general angle concepts by recognizing common features of these situations. Other research took as the starting point children's experience with physical rotations, especially rotations of their own bodies. In time, students were able to assign numbers to certain turns and integrate turn-as-body-motion with turn-as-number.

An understanding of angle requires novel forms of mental structuring, the coordination of several potential models, and an integration of those models. The long developmental process is best begun in the early grades. Common admonitions to teach angles as turns run the risk of students developing only one concept of angle since they rarely spontaneously relate situations involving rotations to those involving shape and form.

Kilpatrick, Jeremy, Jane Swafford, Bradford Findell, eds. *Adding It Up: Helping Children Learn Mathematics.* Mathematics Learning Study Committee, National Research Council. Washington: NAP, 2001. 286.

Other Useful References: Perimeter and Area

Learning Math: Geometry. Annenberg/CPB Learner.org. 1997–2004. <www.learner.org/resources/series167.html>.

Learning Math: Measurement. Annenberg/CPB Learner.org. 1997–2004. <www.learner.org/resources/series184.html>.

National Council of Teachers of Mathematics. *Learning and Teaching Measurement* (NCTM 2003 Yearbook). Ed. Douglas H. Clements. Reston: NCTM, 2003.

National Council of Teachers of Mathematics. *Mathematics Teaching in the Middle School* (Focus Issue: Measurement) 9.8 (Apr. 2004).

National Council of Teachers of Mathematics. *Mathematics Teaching in the Middle School* (Focus Issue: Geometry) 3.6 (Mar. 1998).

National Council of Teachers of Mathematics. *Principles and Standards for School Mathematics.* Reston: NCTM, 2000.

Math Background

Characteristics of Lines and Angles

In order to classify polygons, students need to be familiar with certain characteristics of lines and angles. Parallel line segments run in the same direction, and will never meet, even if extended.

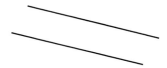

Perpendicular line segments will intersect and form a 90° angle.

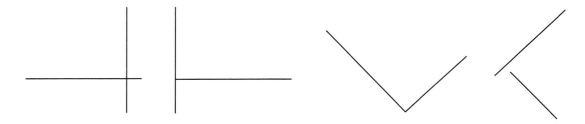

Measuring Angles With a Protractor

In this unit, students will measure angles with a protractor. In order to use a protractor accurately, students need to align the vertex of the angle carefully with the center mark on the protractor and align one ray with the zero line. Some protractors are labeled clockwise *and* counterclockwise. Students should use what they already know about angles to choose which scale to read. Some practice as a class may be useful.

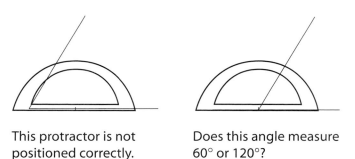

This protractor is not positioned correctly.

Does this angle measure 60° or 120°?

Building Concepts of Angles

In Lesson 4, students are asked to make a connection between angles as shapes—two line segments and the space between them—and angles as turns—the movement between one position and another. Seeing angles as turns will help students to describe rotational symmetry in Lesson 5.

Circle graphs are commonly used to show data. To read a circle graph, we need to have a fundamental understanding of angles in a circle. To create a circle graph, we also need a sense of proportion. If I survey 72 people, and 360° represents all of them, what angle in the circle represents each person? ($360° = 72 = 5°$. Each response is represented by 5° on a circle graph.)

Lines and Angles

Lesson Objectives

- Identify and draw lines, rays, and line segments.
- Measure angles.
- Classify angles according to their measures.

The Day at a Glance

Today's Goals	Materials	123 Math Talk
1 Teaching the Lesson A1: Name the characteristics of, and draw, various lines, rays, and angles. A2: Use a protractor to measure angles. A3: Identify vertical, complementary, and supplementary angles. **2 Extending the Lesson** ▶ Differentiated Instruction **3 Homework and Cumulative Review**	Student Activity Book pages 155–160 Rulers Protractors or Protractors (Copymaster M24) Rectangular sheet of paper Math Journals Homework and Remembering pages 83–84 Family Letter	In today's activities, the students are involved in discussion as they ▶ define characteristics of lines ▶ measure and identify types of angles

Teaching the Lesson

Draw Lines, Rays, and Angles

 15 MINUTES

Goal: Name the characteristics of, and draw, various lines, rays, and angles.

Materials: Student Activity Book page 155, rulers (1 per student)

✔ **NCTM Standards:**
Geometry
Representation

▶ Identify Lines WHOLE CLASS

Divide the board into six columns. Label the columns 1–6. Have students look at the instructions on Student Activity Book page 155. Invite volunteers to come to the board and to record two characteristics of each figure 1–6. Some characteristics may be named more than once.

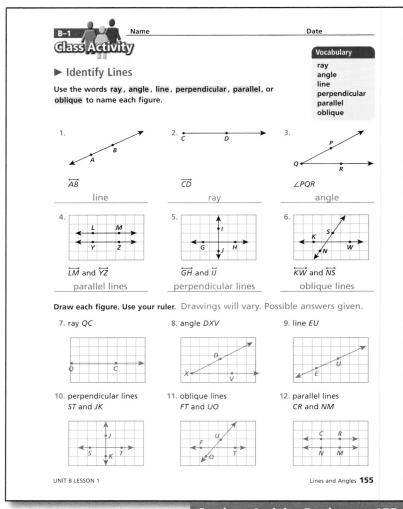

Student Activity Book page 155

Definition	Sample of Characteristics
A *line* is set of points that form a straight path that extends infinitely in opposite directions.	a set of points; straight path; infinite length in opposite directions; length goes on and on
A *ray* is part of a line that begins at an endpoint and extends infinitely in one direction.	a set of points; part of a line; one endpoint; infinite length in one direction
An *angle* is formed by two rays sharing a common endpoint.	two rays; common endpoint
Parallel lines are lines that are equidistant from each other and in the same plane.	lines that do not intersect; always the same distance from each other
Perpendicular lines are lines in the same plane that intersect or meet to form right (90°) angles.	lines that intersect; form right (90°) angles; square corners
Oblique lines are lines in the same plane that intersect to form nonright (acute or obtuse) angles.	lines that intersect; form nonright (acute or obtuse) angles

With a completed list of characteristics on the board, invite the students to discuss the characteristics and, by consensus, erase those that are not correct. Have volunteers write the name of each geometric figure at the top of each column, and draw several different examples of that kind of figure, while the rest of the students complete exercises 1– 6.

Teaching Note

Watch For! Some students may believe that a point of intersection can be formed only when two lines cross. Explain that a point of intersection is formed whenever two lines, rays, or line segments cross or meet. This figure shows that the line and the ray share a common point: they intersect but do not cross.

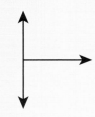

Teaching Note

Math Symbols Discuss how the mathematical notation for these geometric figures shows the aspects of the figure.

line *AB*	$\overleftrightarrow{AB}$
parallel lines *ST* and *JK*	*ST* ‖ *JK*
ray RT	$\overrightarrow{RT}$
perpendicular lines *GH* and *UV*	$\overleftrightarrow{GH} \perp \overleftrightarrow{UV}$
segment *LM*	$\overline{LM}$
angle *PQR*	$\angle PQR$

Ask students to complete exercises 7–12. As a class, discuss where we can see these figures in the world around us.

① Teaching the Lesson (continued)

Activity 2

Measure Angles With a Protractor

 20 MINUTES

Goal: Use a protractor to measure angles.

Materials: protractors or Protractors (Copymaster M24), Student Activity Book page 156

 NCTM Standards:
Geometry
Measurement

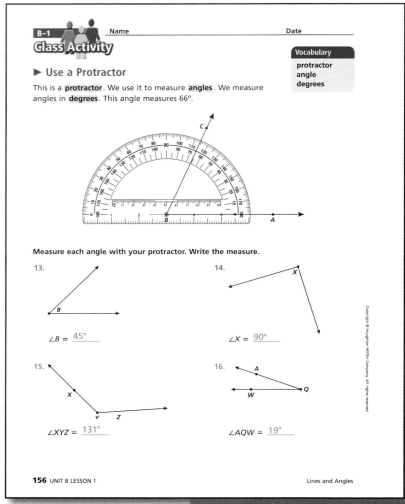

B–1
Class Activity   Name _____   Date _____

Vocabulary
protractor
angle
degrees

▶ Use a Protractor

This is a **protractor**. We use it to measure **angles**. We measure angles in **degrees**. This angle measures 66°.

Measure each angle with your protractor. Write the measure.

13.   14.

∠B = __45°__   ∠X = __90°__

15.   16.

∠XYZ = __131°__   ∠AQW = __19°__

156 UNIT B LESSON 1   Lines and Angles

Student Activity Book page 156

▶ Use a Protractor WHOLE CLASS

Briefly review the idea of using units to label a measurement.

● What units would you use to measure the length of your pencil? centimeters, millimeters, inches

● What units would you use to measure the distance from school to home? miles, kilometers

● What units and symbol do we use when we measure an angle? degrees; °

Discuss the protractor on Student Activity Book page 156. Allow students time to find the 0° mark on their protractors. Students may discover that some protractors have two scales.

Help students align the base ray of the angle with the 0° mark of the scale. Then demonstrate how to read the scale where the remaining ray of the angle intersects the scale.

Have students use their protractors to measure the angles in exercises 13–16.

 Class Management

Copymaster M24 shows a protractor with a clockwise scale and a protractor with a counter-clockwise scale. It also includes a full-circle protractor that you can use to measure angles greater than 180°.

Teaching Note

Math Symbols Point out the degree symbol (°) and explain that this symbol represents the word *degrees*. The angle symbol (∠) is used to represent the word *angle*. Students may occasionally see a statement like m∠S = 70°. This is a way of using mathematical notation to show that the measure of angle *S* is 70 degrees. For simplicity, the notation "m" is not used in this resource. When students see ∠S = ____, they should understand that it refers to the measure of an angle. When they see ∠S + ∠T = ____, they should understand that it refers to the total of the measures of two angles.

 Ongoing Assessment

Ask students to use a ruler to draw two line segments that cross each other. Have them label the endpoints of the segments and the point where they cross, measure, and record the angles in the drawing, and name pairs of angles with equal measures.

300 UNIT B LESSON 1

Find Unknown Angles

25 MINUTES

Goal: Identify vertical, complementary, and supplementary angles.

Materials: protractors or Protractors (Copymaster M24), Student Activity Book pages 157–158

 NCTM Standards:
Geometry
Reasoning and Proof

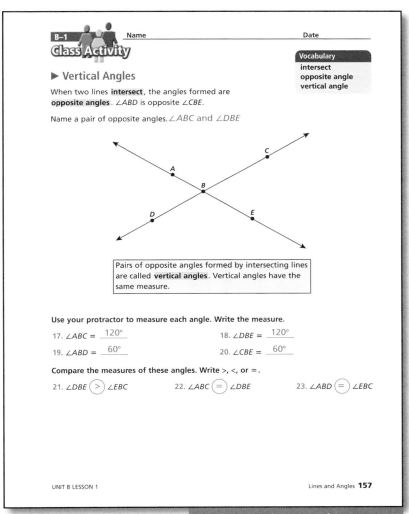

Student Activity Book page 157

▶ **Vertical Angles** WHOLE CLASS

Discuss the intersecting lines at the top of Student Activity Book page 157.

● Name the angles formed by the intersecting lines. ∠ABD, ∠DBE , ∠CBE, ∠ABC

● Which pairs of angles are opposite each other? ∠ABD is opposite ∠CBE; ∠DBE is opposite ∠ABC

Read the definition of vertical angles given on the page. Ask students to apply the definition and to name the vertical angles in the figure. Have them complete exercises 17–23.

▶ **Complementary and Supplementary Angles** WHOLE CLASS

Explain that a right angle has a measure of 90° and a straight angle has a measure of 180°. Draw an example of each angle on the board.

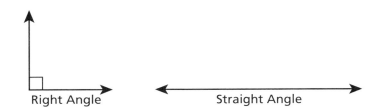

Point out the symbol located at the vertex of the right angle. Explain that this symbol represents a right, or 90°, angle, and indicates perpendicular lines, rays, and line segments.

Activity continued ▶

❶ Teaching the Lesson (continued)

Activity 3

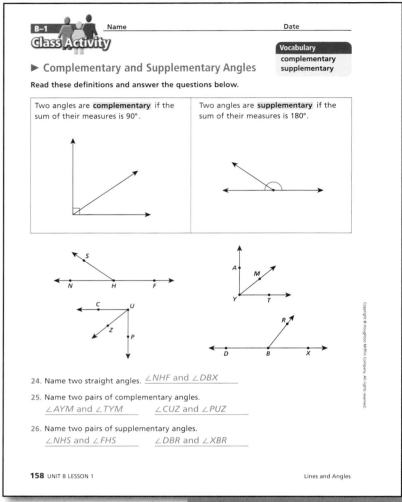

Teaching Note

Language and Vocabulary Discuss the difference between *compliment* and *complement*. When you admire someone you are being *complimentary*. When angles are *complementary*, their measures total 90°. *Complementary* comes from the same root as *complete*. Together, the two angles complete a right angle.

A way to remember that supplementary angles form a straight angle is that both words begin with the letter *s*.

Student Activity Book page 158

Read the definitions of complementary and supplementary angles given on the page. Ask students to apply the definitions to complete exercises 24–26.

② Extending the Lesson

Intervention
for students having difficulty

`PAIRS`

Paper Folding

Materials: rectangular sheet of paper

One partner folds the sheet of paper in half, folds it again from a corner at any angle, and then unfolds it.

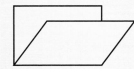

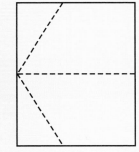

Students trace the line segments created, label all the corners and endpoints, and name all the angles they see. They identify the angles as acute, obtuse, right, supplementary, or complementary.

On Level
for students having success

`INDIVIDUALS`

Investigate Math

Materials: protractor or Protractors (Copymaster M24)

Students draw a large quadrilateral and measure all the angles. They add the measures of the angles and compare their results with those of a classmate.

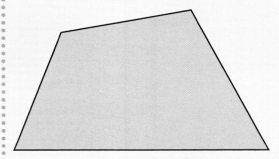

The total of the angle measures of each quadrilateral is 360°.

Challenge
for students seeking a challenge

`INDIVIDUALS`

Draw Angles

Materials: protractor or Protractors (Copymaster M24)

Students use a protractor to draw these four angles:

68°   52°   38°   112°

They cut out the angles and fit them together to show which two angles are complementary and which two are supplementary.

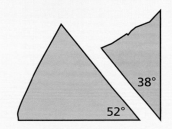

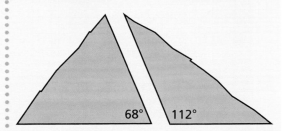

 Math Writing Prompt

Intervention

Draw a Picture

Draw a straight angle. Draw a line segment that makes a right angle near the center of the straight angle line segment. Use your drawing to explain why two right angles are supplementary angles.

 Math Writing Prompt

On Level

Summarize

Use symbols to describe all the straight geometric figures that contain two points, *A* and *B*.

 Math Writing Prompt

Challenge

Use Logic

Explain why an obtuse angle and an acute angle cannot be complementary. Explain why two acute angles cannot be supplementary.

③ Homework and Cumulative Review

B-1

Homework **Goal:** Additional Practice

✓ For homework, students draw and identify lines, rays, and angles.

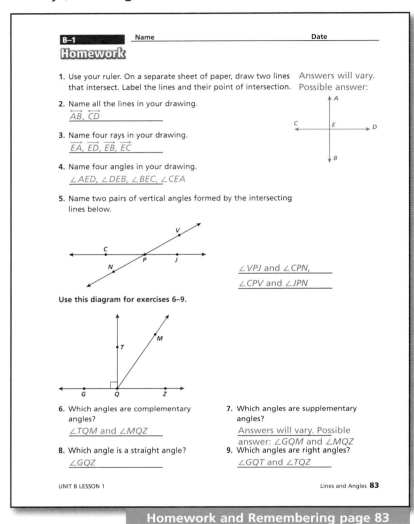

B-1 · Name · Date

Homework

1. Use your ruler. On a separate sheet of paper, draw two lines that intersect. Label the lines and their point of intersection. *Answers will vary. Possible answer:*

2. Name all the lines in your drawing.
   $\overleftrightarrow{AB}, \overleftrightarrow{CD}$

3. Name four rays in your drawing.
   $\overrightarrow{EA}, \overrightarrow{ED}, \overrightarrow{EB}, \overrightarrow{EC}$

4. Name four angles in your drawing.
   $\angle AED, \angle DEB, \angle BEC, \angle CEA$

5. Name two pairs of vertical angles formed by the intersecting lines below.

   $\angle VPJ$ and $\angle CPN$,
   $\angle CPV$ and $\angle JPN$

Use this diagram for exercises 6–9.

6. Which angles are complementary angles?
   $\angle TQM$ and $\angle MQZ$

7. Which angles are supplementary angles?
   Answers will vary. Possible answer: $\angle GQM$ and $\angle MQZ$

8. Which angle is a straight angle?
   $\angle GQZ$

9. Which angles are right angles?
   $\angle GQT$ and $\angle TQZ$

UNIT B LESSON 1 · Lines and Angles **83**

Homework and Remembering page 83

B-1

Remembering **Goal:** Cumulative Review

This Remembering activity is appropriate anytime after today's lesson.

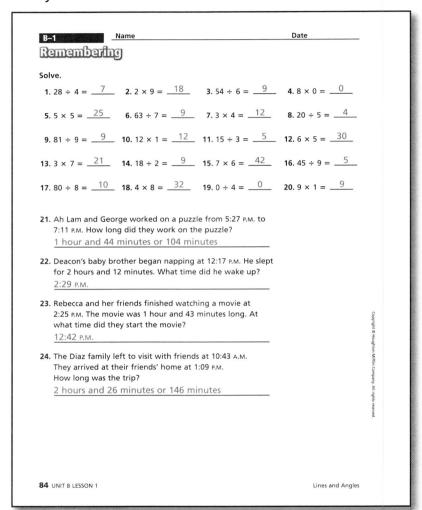

B-1 · Name · Date

Remembering

Solve.

1. $28 \div 4 = \underline{7}$ 2. $2 \times 9 = \underline{18}$ 3. $54 \div 6 = \underline{9}$ 4. $8 \times 0 = \underline{0}$

5. $5 \times 5 = \underline{25}$ 6. $63 \div 7 = \underline{9}$ 7. $3 \times 4 = \underline{12}$ 8. $20 \div 5 = \underline{4}$

9. $81 \div 9 = \underline{9}$ 10. $12 \times 1 = \underline{12}$ 11. $15 \div 3 = \underline{5}$ 12. $6 \times 5 = \underline{30}$

13. $3 \times 7 = \underline{21}$ 14. $18 \div 2 = \underline{9}$ 15. $7 \times 6 = \underline{42}$ 16. $45 \div 9 = \underline{5}$

17. $80 \div 8 = \underline{10}$ 18. $4 \times 8 = \underline{32}$ 19. $0 \div 4 = \underline{0}$ 20. $9 \times 1 = \underline{9}$

21. Ah Lam and George worked on a puzzle from 5:27 P.M. to 7:11 P.M. How long did they work on the puzzle?
    1 hour and 44 minutes or 104 minutes

22. Deacon's baby brother began napping at 12:17 P.M. He slept for 2 hours and 12 minutes. What time did he wake up?
    2:29 P.M.

23. Rebecca and her friends finished watching a movie at 2:25 P.M. The movie was 1 hour and 43 minutes long. At what time did they start the movie?
    12:42 P.M.

24. The Diaz family left to visit with friends at 10:43 A.M. They arrived at their friends' home at 1:09 P.M. How long was the trip?
    2 hours and 26 minutes or 146 minutes

84 UNIT B LESSON 1 · Lines and Angles

Homework and Remembering page 84

Home and School Connection

Family Letter Have children take home the Family Letter on Student Activity Book page 159. This letter explains how the concepts of angles and measuring angles are developed in *Math Expressions*. It gives parents and guardians a better understanding of the learning that goes on in math class and creates a bridge between school and home. A Spanish translation of this letter is on the following page in the Student Activity Book.

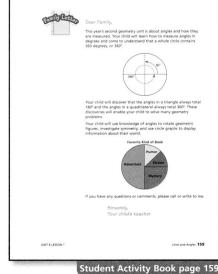

Student Activity Book page 159

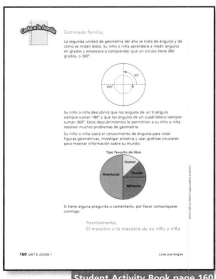

Student Activity Book page 160

Polygons and Angles

Lesson Objectives

- Discover the total measure of the interior angles of triangles and of quadrilaterals.

- Determine missing angle measures.

Vocabulary

angle
degree
proof

The Day at a Glance

Today's Goals	Materials	123 Math Talk
1 Teaching the Lesson **A1:** Cut and arrange angles to discover the total measure of the interior angles of a triangle. **A2:** Use a protractor to measure the total measure of the interior angles of a quadrilateral. **2 Extending the Lesson** ▶ Differentiated Instruction **3 Homework and Cumulative Review**	Student Activity Book pages 161–164 Rulers Scissors Protractors or Protractors (Copymaster M24) Math Journals Homework and Remembering pages 85–86	In today's activities, the students are involved in discussion as they ▶ measure the interior angles of triangles and quadrilaterals and generalize what they learn about the total measures

Teaching the Lesson

Interior Angles of a Triangle

 30 MINUTES

Goal: Cut and arrange angles to discover the total measure of the interior angles of a triangle.

Materials: Student Activity Book pages 161-162, rulers (1 per student), scissors

✔ **NCTM Standards:**
Measurement
Geometry
Reasoning and Proof

► **Measure Interior Angles of a Triangle**

WHOLE CLASS

Have students follow the directions for exercise 1.

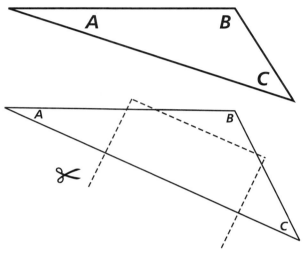

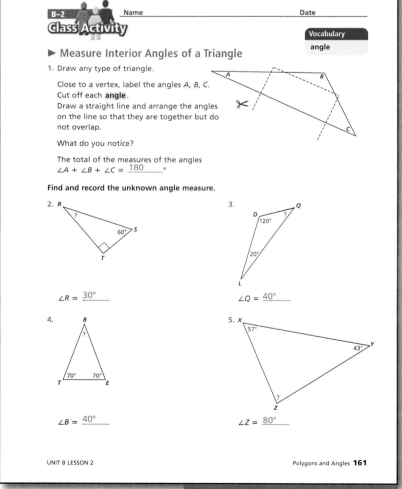

Now have students put the three angles together along a straight line (as shown).

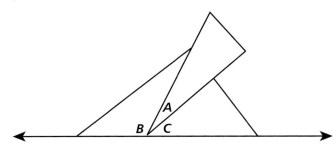

- The line represents a straight angle. What is the degree measure of a straight angle? 180°

- What is the total of the three angle measures of your triangle? 180°

Have students share their triangle proofs with other students and work together to create the generalization that the total of the angle measures of any triangle is 180°.

Find Unknown Angles Without Measuring To complete exercises 2–5, students must subtract the known angle measures, or the total of the known angle measures, from 180°.

Use Solve and Discuss for exercises 6–9. Ask students to suggest reasons why their predictions might be off by a degree or two, depending on the accuracy of their measurements.

Discuss the isosceles and equilateral triangles in exercises 10 and 11.

- What is the total measure of the two unknown angles in exercise 10? 180° − 110° = 70°

- If the two angles are the same size, what do you do to find the measure of each angle? Divide 70° by 2 to get 35°.

- What is the total measure of the three unknown angles in exercise 11? 180°

- If the three angles are the same size, what do you do to find the measure of each angle? Divide 180° by 3 to get 60°.

Interior Angles of a Quadrilateral

🕐 **30 MINUTES**

Goal: Use a protractor to measure the total measure of the interior angles of a quadrilateral.

Materials: Student Activity Book pages 163-164, protractors or Protractors (Copymaster M24)

✔ **NCTM Standards:**
Measurement
Geometry
Reasoning and Proof

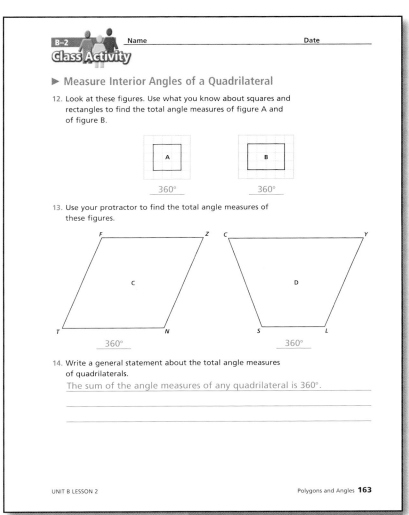

Student Activity Book page 163

Activity continued ▶

Activity 2

▶ Measure Interior Angles of a Quadrilateral WHOLE CLASS

Ask students to look at figures A and B in exercise 12.

● Without using a protractor, how can you determine the measure of each angle? The grid shows that each figure is made up of four right angles.

● What is the total of the measures of the angles of these rectangles? 4 × 90° = 360°

Have students use their protractors to determine the angle measures, and the total of the angle measures, of figures C and D in exercise 13. After they have completed and compared their measures, students work together to create a generalization about the total of the angle measures of any quadrilateral: The total of the angle measures of any quadrilateral is 360°.

✓ Ongoing Assessment

Ask students to draw any quadrilateral and to cut it into two pieces from one corner to the opposite corner.

▶ What two figures did you make?

▶ How does knowing that the total of the angle measures in a triangle is 180° tell you the total angle measures in a quadrilateral?

Find Unknown Angles Without Measuring One way students can determine the missing angle measures in exercises 15–20 is by adding the given measures and subtracting that total from 360°. For exercise 17, students should note that three angle measures are given; two are 90°.

Angles in a Full Turn Have students make a rectangle and cut off the angles as described in exercise 21.

● What happens when you put all the angles together? They fit together around a point and leave no gaps.

● How does this compare to the full angle around a circular protractor? There are 360° in the quadrilateral, around the protractor, and around the point.

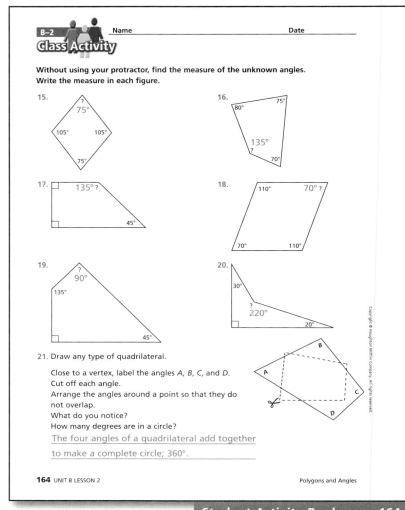

Student Activity Book page 164

② Extending the Lesson

Intervention
for students having difficulty

| PAIRS |

Draw Triangles

Materials: rulers (1 per student), protractor or Protractors (Copymaster M24) (1 per student)

Students use a ruler to draw three triangles. They measure and label two angles in each triangle. Then they trade triangles with a partner, who calculates the measure of the third angle in each triangle.

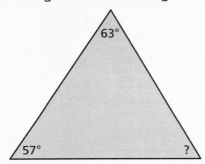

On Level
for students having success

| PAIRS |

Draw a Picture

Materials: ruler

Pose the following problem:

A quadrilateral has exactly one right angle. Two of its other angles are congruent. The fourth angle measures 60°.

Students sketch what the quadrilateral might look like and label the angle measures.

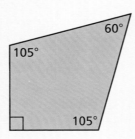

Challenge
for students seeking a challenge

| PAIRS |

Estimate Angles

Materials: protractor or Protractors (Copymaster M24)

Students play a game of estimating angles. Each player draws a large quadrilateral on a sheet of paper and trades with a partner. The partner writes an estimate of each of the four angles in the quadrilateral.

The players trade papers again and measure the angles. They find the difference between the estimates and the measured angles, and add the four differences.

The player with the smallest difference wins.

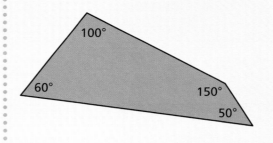

 Math Writing Prompt

Intervention
Straight Angles
In a right triangle, what is the total of the measures of the non-right angles? What is another name for this pair of angles?

 Math Writing Prompt

On Level
Use Logic
Explain why a triangle can never have more than one right angle.

 Math Writing Prompt

Challenge
Investigate Math
If you know the measure of two angles in a parallelogram, you can always find the measures of the other two angles without measuring. Explain why.

③ Homework and Cumulative Review

Homework **Goal:** Additional Practice

✔ Include students' work for page 85 as part of their portfolios.

Remembering **Goal:** Cumulative Review

This Remembering activity is appropriate anytime after today's lesson.

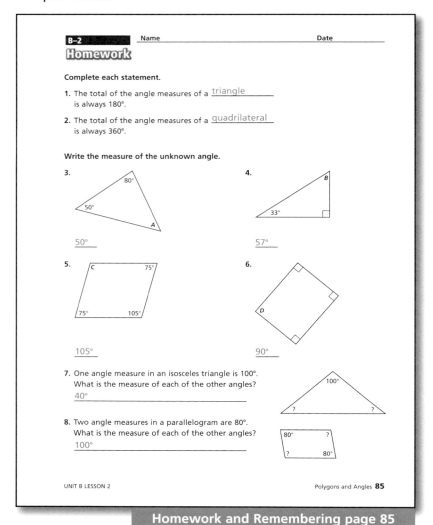

B–2   Name _____   Date _____

Homework

Complete each statement.

1. The total of the angle measures of a <u>triangle</u> is always 180°.

2. The total of the angle measures of a <u>quadrilateral</u> is always 360°.

Write the measure of the unknown angle.

3.   <u>50°</u>

4.   <u>57°</u>

5.   <u>105°</u>

6.   <u>90°</u>

7. One angle measure in an isosceles triangle is 100°. What is the measure of each of the other angles?
<u>40°</u>

8. Two angle measures in a parallelogram are 80°. What is the measure of each of the other angles?
<u>100°</u>

UNIT B LESSON 2   Polygons and Angles **85**

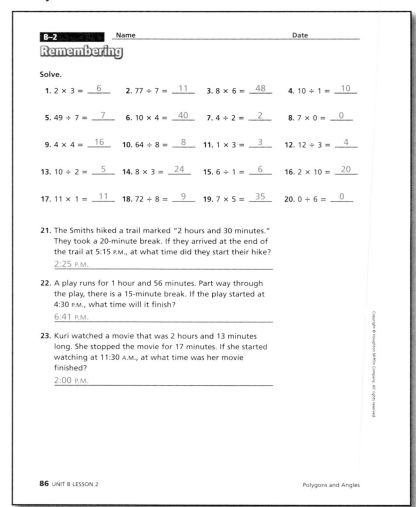

B–2   Name _____   Date _____

Remembering

Solve.

1. $2 \times 3 =$ <u>6</u>   2. $77 \div 7 =$ <u>11</u>   3. $8 \times 6 =$ <u>48</u>   4. $10 \div 1 =$ <u>10</u>

5. $49 \div 7 =$ <u>7</u>   6. $10 \times 4 =$ <u>40</u>   7. $4 \div 2 =$ <u>2</u>   8. $7 \times 0 =$ <u>0</u>

9. $4 \times 4 =$ <u>16</u>   10. $64 \div 8 =$ <u>8</u>   11. $1 \times 3 =$ <u>3</u>   12. $12 \div 3 =$ <u>4</u>

13. $10 \div 2 =$ <u>5</u>   14. $8 \times 3 =$ <u>24</u>   15. $6 \div 1 =$ <u>6</u>   16. $2 \times 10 =$ <u>20</u>

17. $11 \times 1 =$ <u>11</u>   18. $72 \div 8 =$ <u>9</u>   19. $7 \times 5 =$ <u>35</u>   20. $0 \div 6 =$ <u>0</u>

21. The Smiths hiked a trail marked "2 hours and 30 minutes." They took a 20-minute break. If they arrived at the end of the trail at 5:15 P.M., at what time did they start their hike?
<u>2:25 P.M.</u>

22. A play runs for 1 hour and 56 minutes. Part way through the play, there is a 15-minute break. If the play started at 4:30 P.M., what time will it finish?
<u>6:41 P.M.</u>

23. Kuri watched a movie that was 2 hours and 13 minutes long. She stopped the movie for 17 minutes. If she started watching at 11:30 A.M., at what time was her movie finished?
<u>2:00 P.M.</u>

86 UNIT B LESSON 2   Polygons and Angles

Homework and Remembering page 85

Homework and Remembering page 86

Home or School Activity

 Art Connection

Mathematics and Art Have students make a design using quadrilaterals and triangles. Encourage students to use figures that fit together to create a pleasing design.

Compare and Contrast Polygons

Vocabulary

polygon
congruent
isosceles triangle
equilateral triangle
scalene triangle
acute triangle
obtuse triangle
right triangle
right trapezoid

Lesson Objectives

● Identify congruent polygons.

● Sort and classify polygons.

The Day at a Glance

Today's Goals	Materials	123 Math Talk

1 Teaching the Lesson
A1: Identify congruent polygons.
A2: Define, describe, sort, and classify polygons.
 	
2 Extending the Lesson
▶ Differentiated Instruction
 	
3 Homework and Cumulative Review
	Student Activity Book
	  pages 165–168
	
	dot paper or MathBoard
	  materials
	
	Scissors
	
	Centimeter-Dot Paper
	  (Copymaster M25)
	
	Math Journals
	
	Homework and
	  Remembering pages 87–88
		In today's activities, the students are involved in discussion as they
		
		▶ explore ways to test the congruence of polygons
		
		▶ identify polygons and describe their characteristics
		
		▶ talk about sorting rules for classifying polygons based on sides and angles

Teaching the Lesson

Congruent Polygons

🕐 **20 MINUTES**

Goal: Identify congruent polygons.

Materials: Student Activity Book page 165, dot paper or MathBoard material

✔ **NCTM Standard:**
Geometry

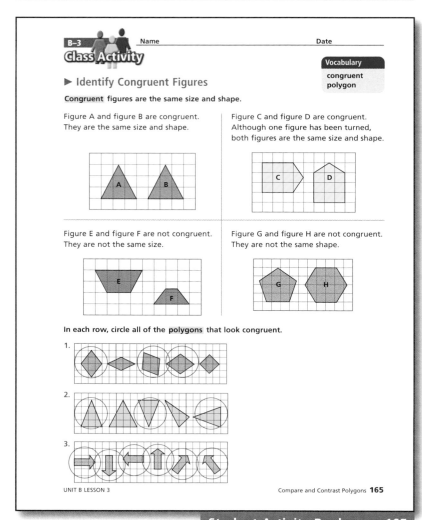

Student Activity Book page 165

▶ Identify Congruent Figures WHOLE CLASS

Introduce the word *polygon*, a figure with many sides. Discuss the examples of congruence and noncongruence at the top of Student Activity Book page 165 (figures A–H). Ask students to give reasons why the pairs of figures do or do not appear to be congruent.

● **How can tracing one of the figures help you?** If the tracing fits exactly over the other figure, then the figures must be the same size and shape, or congruent.

● **How might the grid help you?** If some squares or parts of squares inside each figure don't match up, then the figures can't be congruent.

● **How did you know figures E and F weren't congruent?** Figure F looks smaller. It is smaller because there are fewer squares inside it.

● **How did you know figures G and H weren't congruent?** Figure H has more sides, so a tracing of it won't fit over figure G.

Have students complete exercises 1–3. If they have difficulty, they can count squares or use a tracing.

Teaching Note

Mathematical Notation You may wish to introduce the symbols that are used to represent congruency. Using these symbols (tick marks) helps students keep track of equal measures and determine congruency.

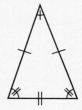 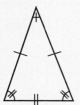

✔ Ongoing Assessment

Have students draw two congruent triangles on dot paper or their MathBoard. Then ask them to draw a third triangle that is not congruent to the other triangles.

Classify Polygons

 40 MINUTES

Goal: Define, describe, sort, and classify polygons.

Materials: Student Activity Book pages 166–168, scissors

 NCTM Standard:
Geometry

▶ Identify Polygons WHOLE CLASS

Have students cut along the vertical and horizontal dotted lines. Students should not cut out the actual figures within each square.

Explain to students that they should compare and contrast the characteristics of the polygons as you discuss each one as a class. If students need help, the student glossary at the end of the unit includes all of the polygons.

Remind students of the names of different figures and have them pick out the correct examples of each.

- Isosceles triangles have two congruent sides. Which figures are isosceles triangles? figures A, L, N, Q

- Equilateral triangles have all sides congruent. Which triangle is equilateral? figure W

- Scalene triangles have no congruent sides. Which figures are scalene triangles? figures F, S, V

- Which quadrilaterals are parallelograms? figures B, C, D, E, G, H, I, R

- Which parallelograms are also rhombuses? figures B, E, R

- Which quadrilaterals are rectangles? figures B, D, G, I, R

- Which rectangles are also squares? figures B, G, R

- Regular polygons have all sides and all angles congruent. Which polygons are regular? figures B, G, J, O, R, T, W

- Which polygons are pentagons? figures J, M

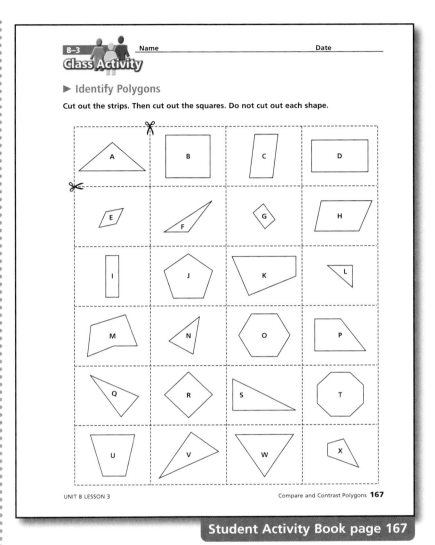

Student Activity Book page 167

- Which is a hexagon? figure O an octagon? figure T

- Which figures are trapezoids? figures P, U

- Isosceles figures have two equal sides. Which figure is an isosceles trapezoid? figure U

- Acute triangles have all angles less than 90°. Which triangles are acute? figures A, N, Q, W

- Obtuse triangles have one angle greater than 90°. Which triangle is obtuse? figure F

- Right triangles have one angle equal to 90°. Which triangles are right triangles? figure L, S, V

- Right trapezoids have one angle equal to 90°. Which figure is a right trapezoid? figure P

Activity continued ▶

Compare and Contrast Polygons **313**

Activity 2

Classify Polygons

Have students use what they've learned to label the backs of the figures.

A, N, Q: isosceles triangle, acute triangle

B, G, R: quadrilateral, parallelogram, rectangle, rhombus, square

C, H: quadrilateral, parallelogram

D, I: quadrilateral, parallelogram, rectangle

E: quadrilateral, rhombus

F: scalene triangle, obtuse triangle

G: quadrilateral, rectangle, square

J: regular pentagon

K, X: quadrilateral

L: right triangle, isosceles triangle

M: pentagon

O: regular hexagon

P: right trapezoid

S, V: scalene triangle, right triangle

T: regular octagon

U: isosceles trapezoid

W: equilateral triangle, acute triangle

▶ Sort and Classify Polygons WHOLE CLASS

Invite students to classify the polygons they have named by sorting them into different groups. As they work, encourage the students to use math vocabulary to describe the characteristics of the different groups. The students may use all of the polygons or only some of them.

Robbie: I sorted "quadrilaterals" and "not quadrilaterals." Figures B, C, D, E, G, H, I, K, P, R, U, and X are quadrilaterals. Figures A, F, J, L, M, N, O, Q, S, T, V, and W are not quadrilaterals.

Teresa: I sorted "right triangles" and "nonright triangles." Figures L, S, and V are right triangles. Figures A, F, N, Q, and W are nonright triangles.

Another way to sort is by sides: are all or some of the sides parallel, perpendicular, or both? This sorting rule will lead students to discover that some polygons have both parallel and perpendicular sides. You can use the Venn diagram on Student Activity Book page 166 to demonstrate how to sort the figures by type of side.

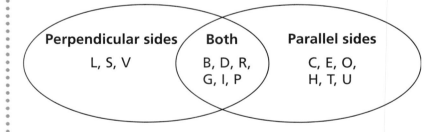

Perpendicular sides: L, S, V

Both: B, D, R, G, I, P

Parallel sides: C, E, O, H, T, U

② Extending the Lesson

Intervention
for students having difficulty

PAIRS

Congruent Rectangles

Materials: Centimeter-Dot Paper (Copymaster M25)

Students draw a rectangle on dot paper. They draw another rectangle congruent to the first one, but turned 90°. Have students explain how to check that the two rectangles are congruent.

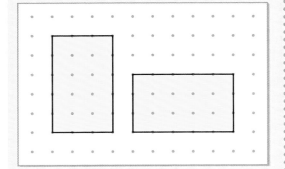

On Level
for students having success

PAIRS

Draw Triangles

Materials: Centimeter-Dot Paper (Copymaster M25)

The measures of the sides of a triangle are 3 cm, 4 cm, and 5 cm. The angles measure 30°, 60°, and 90°.

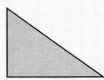

On dot paper, students draw a triangle congruent to the given triangle. They then draw another triangle, with the same angle measures, that is not congruent to the first triangle.

Challenge
for students seeking a challenge

INDIVIDUALS

Tiling

Copies of any parallelogram can be used to tile a floor without overlapping or leaving gaps.

Display a regular pentagon and a regular hexagon.

Regular pentagon   **Regular hexagon**

 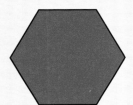

Students predict which of the two figures can be used to tile a floor without overlapping or leaving gaps, and they find a way to test their prediction.

 Math Writing Prompt

Intervention

Squares
Are all squares congruent to each other? Explain your answer.

 Math Writing Prompt

On Level

Impossible Triangles
Can one angle of a right triangle be obtuse? Why or why not? Can an obtuse triangle have two congruent angles? Why or why not?

 Math Writing Prompt

Challenge

Investigate Math
What is another name for a regular triangle? for a regular quadrilateral?

# ③ Homework and Cumulative Review

✓ For homework, students identify and draw congruent figures.

This Remembering activity is appropriate anytime after today's lesson.

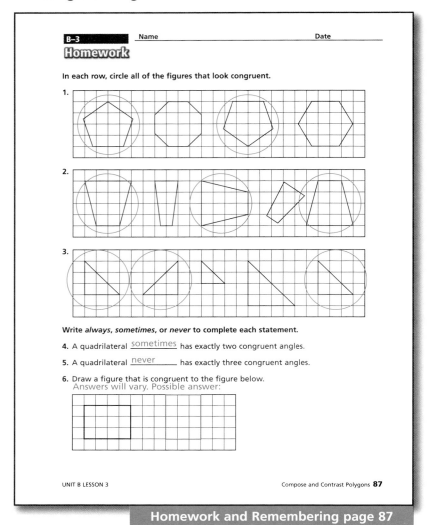

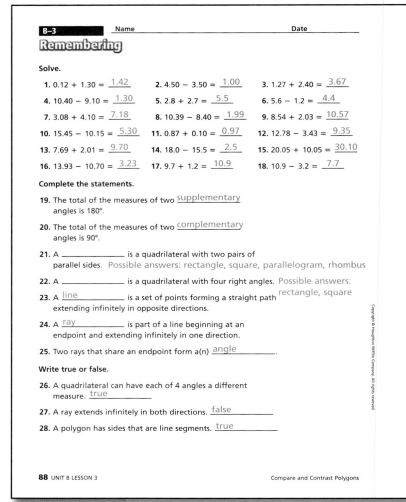

Homework and Remembering page 87

Homework and Remembering page 88

Home or School Activity

Language Arts Connection

Names for Polygons
Polygons are named with prefixes that tell the number of sides they have. *Tri* means "three," *quad* means "four," *penta* means "five," *hexa* means "six," and *octa* means "eight."

A decameter is ten meters. What name would you give a ten-sided polygon? If *dodeca* means "twelve," what is the name of a twelve-sided polygon? How many sides do you think a heptagon or a nonagon have?

MINI UNIT B

LESSON 4

Circles and Angles

Lesson Objectives

- **Identify angles of a circle.**
- **Identify turns about the center of a circle.**
- **Determine the position of an object after a turn or a series of turns.**

The Day at a Glance

Today's Goals	Materials	Math Talk

1 Teaching the Lesson
A1: Discuss and draw various angles of a circle.
A2: Model turns of a circle.
 	
2 Extending the Lesson
▶ Differentiated Instruction
 	
3 Homework and Cumulative Review
	Student Activity Book
	  pages 169–172
	Rulers
	Protractors or Protractors
	  (Copymaster M24)
	Scissors
	Math Journals
	Homework and
	  Remembering pages 89–90
		In today's activities, the students are involved in discussion as they
		
		▶ draw, measure, and calculate angles inside a circle
		
		▶ turn figures 90°, 180°, and 270° about a point

1 Teaching the Lesson

Interior Angles of a Circle

 30 MINUTES

Goal: Discuss and draw various angles of a circle.

Materials: Student Activity Book pages 169–170, rulers (1 per student), protractors or Protractors (Copymaster M24) (1 per student)

 NCTM Standards:
Geometry
Measurement

▶ Measure Angles in a Circle [WHOLE CLASS]

Students should be familiar with acute, right, obtuse, and straight angles. Invite students to share ideas about how to remember the names of various angles.

● An acute angle has a measure that is greater than 0° and less than 90°.

● A right angle has a measure of exactly 90°.

● An obtuse angle has a measure that is greater than 90° and less than 180°.

● A straight angle has a measure of exactly 180°.

Students do not need to have mastery of a reflex angle, but a discussion of this angle helps students recognize that the total angle measure of a circle is 360°.

● A reflex angle has a measure that is greater than 180° and less than 360°.

● A circle has a measure of 360°.

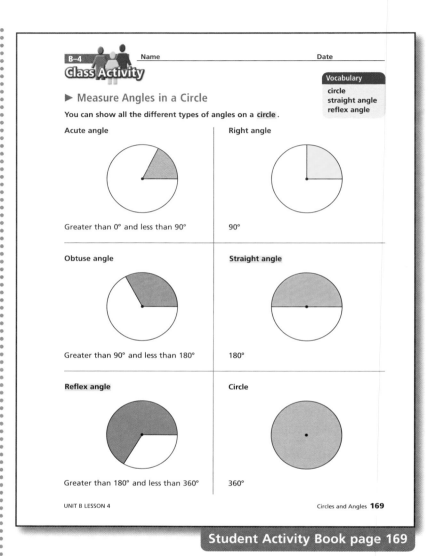

Student Activity Book page 169

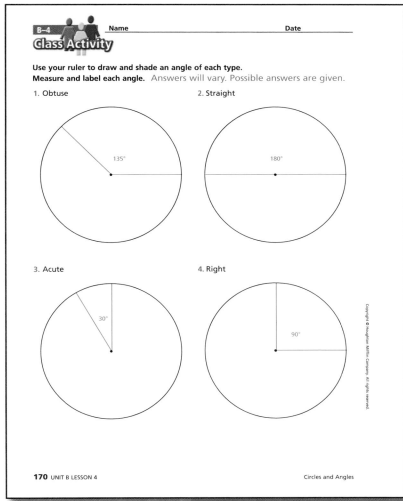

Student Activity Book page 170

Ask students to complete exercises 1–4 by drawing a new example of each angle, including an obtuse angle and an acute angle with measures different from those of the examples.

● Why will your new straight angles and right angles have the same measures as the examples? because all straight angles are 180° and all right angles are 90°

● How can you make your straight angles and right angles different from the examples? by drawing them in a different position

▶ Find Missing Angles INDIVIDUALS

Ask the students to measure (using a protractor) and label their acute and obtuse angles. They may have to extend the arms of the angles to measure them.

● The unshaded angle in your obtuse and acute angle figures is a reflex angle. How can you find the size of the reflex angle in each exercise without measuring? The whole circle is 360°, so subtract the measure of the shaded angle from 360.

Differentiated Instruction

Advanced Learners Since students have learned about complementary and supplementary angles, you may choose to introduce the idea that two angles are conjugate (or explementary) angles if their sum is 360°; either angle is the conjugate or explement of the other.

Challenge students to make a list of different ways that conjugate angles can be combined to make a circle. For example:

two straight angles

one acute angle and one reflex angle

one right angle and one reflex angle

one obtuse angle and one reflex angle

✔ Ongoing Assessment

Have students draw an acute angle on grid paper or dot paper. Ask them to measure their acute angle and label the measure of the reflex angle without actually measuring it. Have them repeat the procedure beginning with an obtuse angle.

Circles and Angles **319**

① Teaching the Lesson (continued)

Activity 2

Turns of a Circle

 30 MINUTES

Goal: Model turns of a circle.

Materials: Student Activity Book pages 171–172 (1 per pair)

 NCTM Standard:
Geometry

▶ Model Turns of a Circle WHOLE CLASS

Have students look at the circles on Student Activity Book page 171. Help them make the connection that the fractions $\frac{1}{4}$, $\frac{1}{2}$, $\frac{3}{4}$, and $\frac{4}{4}$ (or 1 whole) represent the different turns.

Ask volunteers to demonstrate how to turn an object, or their body, clockwise (in the direction that the hands of a clock move) and counter-clockwise (opposite to the direction that the hands of a clock move).

Have students look at the circle at the top of Student Activity Book page 172 and to name the direction of movement that is represented by the arrows of the circle (counter-clockwise). Repeat for the other circles.

Students work in pairs to turn a sheet of paper clockwise 90°, 180°, 270°, and 360°; then repeat the activity making counter-clockwise turns.

Use Solve and Discuss for exercises 5–8.

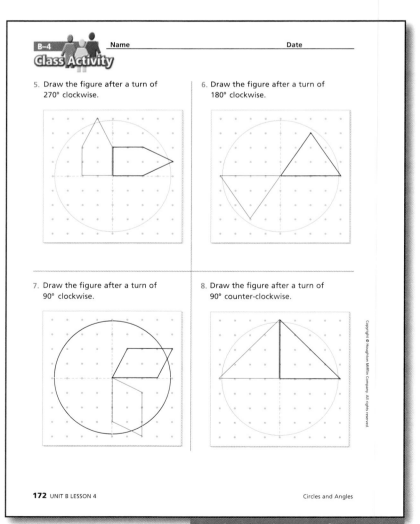

② Extending the Lesson

Intervention
for students having difficulty

PAIRS

Use a Right Angle

Materials: scissors

Have students trace a figure of their choice. They draw a right angle on the tracing and cut the paper along the edges of the right angle. Students use the whole paper to show quarter, half, and three-quarter turns of the figure.

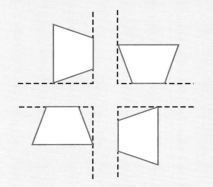

On Level
for students having success

PAIRS

Angles on a Clock

Students look at a clock and name a time when the hands form each of the following angles:

a right angle

an obtuse angle

an acute angle

a straight angle

a reflex angle

Challenge
for students seeking a challenge

INDIVIDUALS

Measure the Time

Students give the angle measure, in degrees, of clock hands that show the following times:

1 o'clock

5 o'clock

7 o'clock

11 o'clock

30° or 330°, 150° or 210°, 210° or 150°, 330° or 30°

 Math Writing Prompt

Intervention

Circle Angles

If one angle drawn from the center of a circle measures 130°, what is the measure of the other angle that is formed? Explain how you know.

 Math Writing Prompt

On Level

Explain Your Thinking

Why does a 90° turn counter-clockwise have the same effect as a 270° turn clockwise? Describe another pair of turns that have the same effect.

 Math Writing Prompt

Challenge

Turn Letters

Which upper-case letters stay the same after a reflection?

③ Homework and Cumulative Review

Homework **Goal:** Additional Practice

✓ Include students' work for page 89 as part of their portfolios.

Remembering **Goal:** Cumulative Review

This Remembering activity is appropriate anytime after today's lesson.

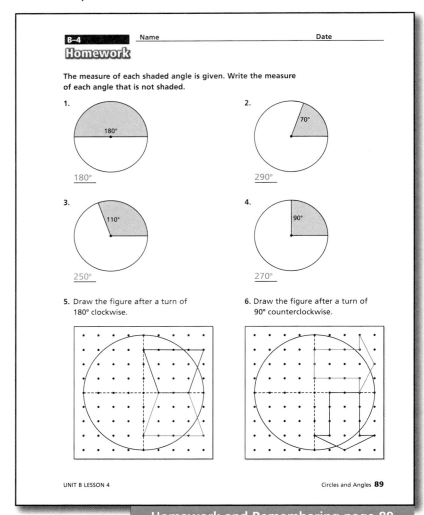

B-4
Homework

Name _____ Date _____

The measure of each shaded angle is given. Write the measure of each angle that is not shaded.

1. 180°   →   180°

2. 70°   →   290°

3. 110°   →   250°

4. 90°   →   270°

5. Draw the figure after a turn of 180° clockwise.

6. Draw the figure after a turn of 90° counterclockwise.

UNIT B LESSON 4   Circles and Angles **89**

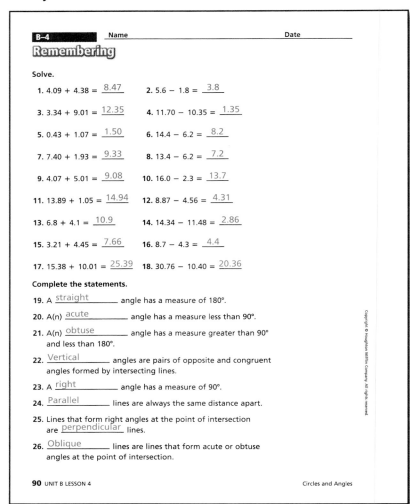

B-4
Remembering

Name _____ Date _____

Solve.

1. 4.09 + 4.38 = _8.47_
2. 5.6 − 1.8 = _3.8_
3. 3.34 + 9.01 = _12.35_
4. 11.70 − 10.35 = _1.35_
5. 0.43 + 1.07 = _1.50_
6. 14.4 − 6.2 = _8.2_
7. 7.40 + 1.93 = _9.33_
8. 13.4 − 6.2 = _7.2_
9. 4.07 + 5.01 = _9.08_
10. 16.0 − 2.3 = _13.7_
11. 13.89 + 1.05 = _14.94_
12. 8.87 − 4.56 = _4.31_
13. 6.8 + 4.1 = _10.9_
14. 14.34 − 11.48 = _2.86_
15. 3.21 + 4.45 = _7.66_
16. 8.7 − 4.3 = _4.4_
17. 15.38 + 10.01 = _25.39_
18. 30.76 − 10.40 = _20.36_

Complete the statements.

19. A _straight_ angle has a measure of 180°.
20. A(n) _acute_ angle has a measure less than 90°.
21. A(n) _obtuse_ angle has a measure greater than 90° and less than 180°.
22. _Vertical_ angles are pairs of opposite and congruent angles formed by intersecting lines.
23. A _right_ angle has a measure of 90°.
24. _Parallel_ lines are always the same distance apart.
25. Lines that form right angles at the point of intersection are _perpendicular_ lines.
26. _Oblique_ lines are lines that form acute or obtuse angles at the point of intersection.

90 UNIT B LESSON 4   Circles and Angles

Homework and Remembering page 89

Homework and Remembering page 90

Home or School Activity

 Science Connection

Rotations in Our World Earth rotates a full 360° every 24 hours. Ask students to describe other examples of rotations in astronomy or other examples of rotations in general science.

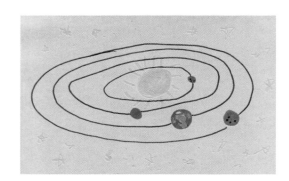

Symmetry

Lesson Objectives

- Recognize line symmetry and rotational symmetry.
- Determine the position of an object after a turn or a series of turns.

The Day at a Glance

Today's Goals	Materials	123 Math Talk
1 **Teaching the Lesson** **A1:** Review line symmetry and draw lines of symmetry on various figures. **A2:** Discover rotational symmetry in a variety of figures. **2** **Extending the Lesson** ▸ Differentiated Instruction **3** **Homework and Cumulative Review**	Student Activity Book pages 173–176 Rectangular sheet of unlined paper Scissors Centimeter-Dot Paper (Copymaster M25) Math Journals Homework and Remembering pages 91–92	In today's activities, the students are involved in discussion as they ▸ identify and describe the lines of symmetry in given figures ▸ test figures for rotational symmetry

Teaching the Lesson

Line Symmetry

 20 MINUTES

Goal: Review line symmetry and draw lines of symmetry on various figures.

Materials: Student Activity Book page 173, rectangular sheet of unlined paper (1 per student)

✔ **NCTM Standard:**
Geometry

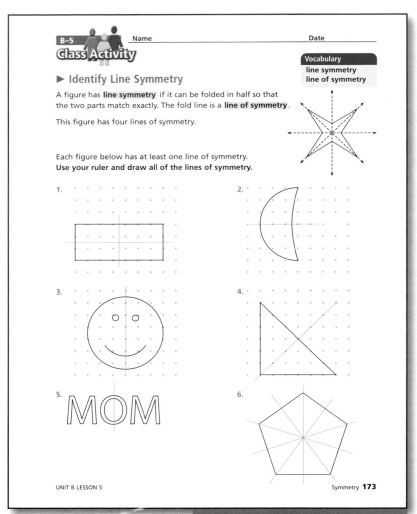

Student Activity Book page 173

► **Identify Line Symmetry** WHOLE CLASS

Some students may already know about line symmetry and lines of symmetry. Invite them to be student leaders as the class reviews these concepts.

Write on the board the words *line symmetry* and *line of symmetry*.

Have students discuss what they already know about symmetry. Lines of symmetry have exact mirror images on each side.

Discuss the figure at the top of Student Activity Book page 173. Give each student a rectangular sheet (longer in one dimension than in the other) of unlined paper. Invite students to fold the paper in different ways.

● How many lines of symmetry does the paper rectangle have? two

Ask students to draw the lines of symmetry on the rectangle in exercise 1. Next, focus on the figures in exercises 2 and 3. Discuss the idea that figures may have many, few, or no lines of symmetry.

● How can the dot grid help you discover a line of symmetry? The dots match up on either side of the line.

Talk about exercise 4.

● How is the figure in exercise 4 different from the others? There is no line of symmetry either straight up and down the figure or straight across it.

● Does it have any lines of symmetry? There is a line of symmetry that goes from the bottom left corner to the middle of the opposite side.

Define Line Symmetry Students draw at least two different figures with line symmetry. They draw the line(s) of symmetry for each figure. Invite them to define the terms *line symmetry* and *line of symmetry* in their own words.

Rotational Symmetry

 40 MINUTES

Goal: Discover rotational symmetry in a variety of figures.

Materials: unlined sheet of paper, scissors, Student Activity Book pages 174–176

 NCTM Standard:
Geometry

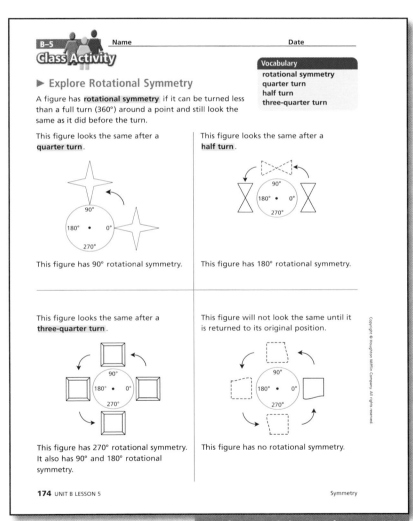

Student Activity Book page 174

Differentiated Instruction

Extra Help Students who have difficulty visualizing a rotation can trace and cut out each figure, then rotate the figures about a fixed point at the center.

▶ Explore Rotational Symmetry

WHOLE CLASS

An exploration of rotational symmetry enables students to consolidate their understanding of angles, turns, and symmetry. Discuss the four turns shown at the top of Student Activity Book page 174 and help students make the connection that a fraction having a denominator of four ($\frac{1}{4}$, $\frac{2}{4}$ or $\frac{1}{2}$, $\frac{3}{4}$, and $\frac{4}{4}$ or 1) can be used to represent the turns.

A figure has rotational symmetry if it can be turned less than a full turn (360°) around a point and still look the same as it did before the turn.

Invite students to fold a sheet of paper in half and cut it along the fold line.

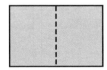

On one sheet of paper, have students draw a figure that they think has 90° (quarter turn) rotational symmetry. Students can turn their drawings to verify their predictions. Next, on the other sheet of paper, invite them to draw a figure that they think has 180° (half turn) rotational symmetry. Again, have them verify their predictions. Encourage volunteers to share their drawings and predictions with their classmates.

After discussing all of the examples of turns on Student Activity Book page 174, have students look again at the first figure.

● **What generalization can you make about a figure that has 90° rotational symmetry?** Any figure having 90° rotational symmetry also has 180° and 270° rotational symmetry.

✓ Ongoing Assessment

Have students explain how to tell whether a figure has rotational symmetry. Then ask them to describe a design or logo that has rotational symmetry.

Activity continued ▶

Activity 2 OPTIONAL

Use Solve and Discuss for exercises 7–12.

● Does the triangle in exercise 12 have 90°, 180°, or 270° symmetry? No. It doesn't look exactly the same after those turns.

● Does it have another kind of rotational symmetry? Yes. It looks the same after a one-third turn.

Some students may discover what that means in terms of the rotation angle. (120°)

Have students complete exercises 13–15. Discuss exercise 13.

● Can a figure have line symmetry but not rotational symmetry? Yes. The figure in exercise 10 has only line symmetry.

● Can a figure have rotational symmetry but not line symmetry? Yes. The figure in exercise 11 has only rotational symmetry.

✋ Alternate Approach

Turn About the Center A figure has rotational symmetry if you can turn it about its center and it fits exactly on itself in less than one full turn. You can describe a figure with rotational symmetry in two ways: either by its rotation angle or by its degree of rotational symmetry. The regular pentagon fits on itself five times in one full turn. Its degree of rotational symmetry is 5. The number of times a figure fits on itself after one full turn is its degree of rotational symmetry.

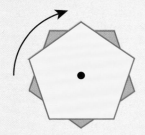

Ask students: What is the degree of rotational symmetry of each figure in exercises 7–12?

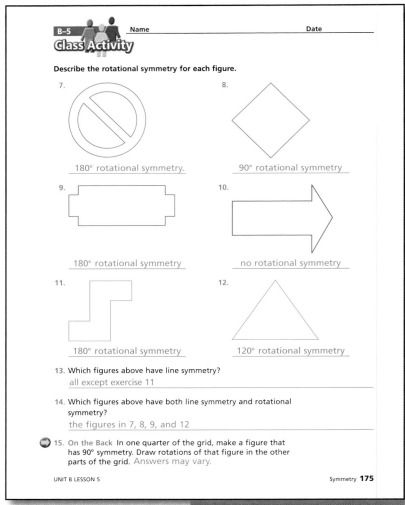

Student Activity Book page 175

Teaching Note

Math Background No figure has only 270° rotational symmetry. To help students understand why, invite them to think about the first occurrence of symmetry in a figure that has rotational symmetry. For example, a figure that has 180° rotational symmetry needs another 180° degrees to return to its original position. The total of the turns (180° + 180°) is 360°.

If the first occurrence of rotational symmetry in a figure is 270°, the figure would need another 270° to return to its original position. The total of the turns (270° + 270°) is greater than 360°.

You can generalize this fact as follows: The first time a figure has rotational symmetry can never be greater than 180° because no number greater than 180 can be a factor of 360, the degree measure of a circle. The greatest factor of any number is always less than or equal to that number divided by 2.

② Extending the Lesson

Activities for Individualizing

Intervention
for students having difficulty

PAIRS

The Other Half

Materials: Centimeter-Dot Paper (Copymaster M25)

Students draw half of a figure on dot paper or grid paper and exchange their work with a partner. The partner draws the other half to make a whole figure with line symmetry.

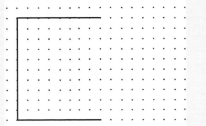

On Level
for students having success

PAIRS

Symmetry Drawing

Students draw two figures: one that has line symmetry but not rotational symmetry and one that has only rotational symmetry.

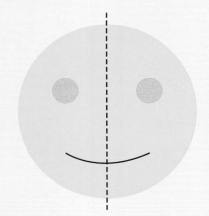

Challenge
for students seeking a challenge

INDIVIDUALS

Regular Polygons

Students investigate the symmetry of regular polygons and explain how line symmetry and rotational symmetry are related to the number of sides.

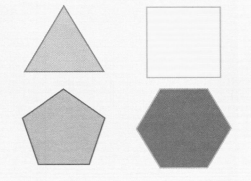

An n-sided regular polygon has n lines of symmetry. Its degree of rotational symmetry is also n; its angle of rotational symmetry is $360° \div n$.

 Math Writing Prompt

Intervention

Explain Your Thinking
Draw half of a figure in your Math Journal. Explain how to draw the other half so that the whole figure has line symmetry.

 Math Writing Prompt

On Level

Sort and Classify
Describe the following quadrilaterals by line symmetry and rotational symmetry: trapezoid, isosceles trapezoid, parallelogram, rhombus, rectangle, square.

 Math Writing Prompt

Challenge

Investigate Math
How many lines of symmetry can a figure have? How many times can a figure turn and still look exactly the same? Explain your answers.

③ Homework and Cumulative Review

Homework **Goal:** Additional Practice

✓ For homework, students draw a figure with at least one line of symmetry and identify line symmetry and rotational symmetry in letters of the alphabet.

Remembering **Goal:** Cumulative Review

This Remembering activity is appropriate anytime after today's lesson.

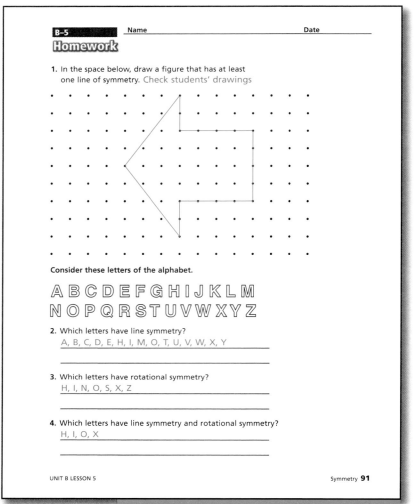

B–5 Name _____ Date _____
Homework

1. In the space below, draw a figure that has at least one line of symmetry. Check students' drawings

Consider these letters of the alphabet.

A B C D E F G H I J K L M
N O P Q R S T U V W X Y Z

2. Which letters have line symmetry?
   A, B, C, D, E, H, I, M, O, T, U, V, W, X, Y

3. Which letters have rotational symmetry?
   H, I, N, O, S, X, Z

4. Which letters have line symmetry and rotational symmetry?
   H, I, O, X

UNIT B LESSON 5   Symmetry **91**

Homework and Remembering page 91

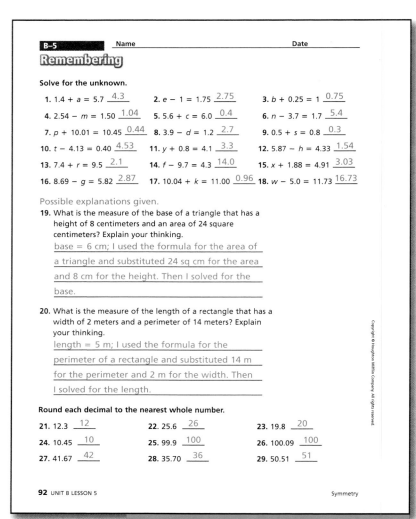

B–5 Name _____ Date _____
Remembering

Solve for the unknown.

1. $1.4 + a = 5.7$ __4.3__
2. $e - 1 = 1.75$ __2.75__
3. $b + 0.25 = 1$ __0.75__
4. $2.54 - m = 1.50$ __1.04__
5. $5.6 + c = 6.0$ __0.4__
6. $n - 3.7 = 1.7$ __5.4__
7. $p + 10.01 = 10.45$ __0.44__
8. $3.9 - d = 1.2$ __2.7__
9. $0.5 + s = 0.8$ __0.3__
10. $t - 4.13 = 0.40$ __4.53__
11. $y + 0.8 = 4.1$ __3.3__
12. $5.87 - h = 4.33$ __1.54__
13. $7.4 + r = 9.5$ __2.1__
14. $f - 9.7 = 4.3$ __14.0__
15. $x + 1.88 = 4.91$ __3.03__
16. $8.69 - g = 5.82$ __2.87__
17. $10.04 + k = 11.00$ __0.96__
18. $w - 5.0 = 11.73$ __16.73__

Possible explanations given.
19. What is the measure of the base of a triangle that has a height of 8 centimeters and an area of 24 square centimeters? Explain your thinking.
    base = 6 cm; I used the formula for the area of a triangle and substituted 24 sq cm for the area and 8 cm for the height. Then I solved for the base.

20. What is the measure of the length of a rectangle that has a width of 2 meters and a perimeter of 14 meters? Explain your thinking.
    length = 5 m; I used the formula for the perimeter of a rectangle and substituted 14 m for the perimeter and 2 m for the width. Then I solved for the length.

Round each decimal to the nearest whole number.

21. 12.3 __12__
22. 25.6 __26__
23. 19.8 __20__
24. 10.45 __10__
25. 99.9 __100__
26. 100.09 __100__
27. 41.67 __42__
28. 35.70 __36__
29. 50.51 __51__

92 UNIT B LESSON 5   Symmetry

Homework and Remembering page 92

Home or School Activity

🔬 Science Connection

Symmetry in Nature Have students look for and list examples of symmetry they see in nature. Encourage students to bring in examples for the class to discuss.

Circle Graphs

Lesson Objectives

- Read a circle graph, solve problems using a circle graph, and write questions about a circle graph.

- Display the same data in different ways.

- Determine angle measures to make a circle graph.

Vocabulary
circle graph
angle
area

The Day at a Glance

Today's Goals	Materials	123 Math Talk
1 Teaching the Lesson A1: Read a circle graph. A2: Use data to make a circle graph. A3: Display data different ways. **2 Extending the Lesson** ▶ Differentiated Instruction **3 Homework and Cumulative Review**	Student Activity Book pages 177–178 Rulers Protractor or Protractors (Copymaster M24) Math Journals Homework and Remembering pages 93–94	In today's activities, the students are involved in discussion as they ▶ read circle graphs and pose questions about the graphs ▶ learn how to partition a circle graph for a set of data ▶ talk about ways to solve problems about circle graphs

① Teaching the Lesson

Activity 1

Solve Problems Using a Circle Graph

 15 MINUTES

Goal: Read a circle graph.

Materials: Student Activity Book page 177

 NCTM Standards:
Geometry
Data Analysis

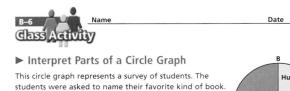

B-6 Name _____ Date _____

Class Activity

▶ **Interpret Parts of a Circle Graph**

This circle graph represents a survey of students. The students were asked to name their favorite kind of book.

Use the graph to answer the questions.

1. What kind of book was named twice as often as a humor book?
   mystery book

2. What kind of book was named half as often as an adventure book?
   mystery book

3. Is the number of students who chose either mystery or humor books more or less than the number of students who chose adventure books? Explain how you know.
   Answers will vary. Possible explanation: Since
   humor, fiction, or mystery choices equal adventure,
   mystery and humor, the number of students who
   chose mystery or humor is less than the number
   who chose adventure.

4. For this survey, 125 students named fiction books as their favorite kind of book. How many students named mystery books as their favorite kind of book?
   250 students

5. How many students were surveyed? Explain how you know.
   1,000; explanations may vary. Possible answer:
   Since 125 students named fiction as their favorite
   and they are $\frac{1}{8}$ of the sample, then
   8 × 125 students were surveyed.

UNIT B LESSON 6   Circle Graphs **177**

Student Activity Book page 177

▶ **Interpret Parts of a Circle Graph**

WHOLE CLASS

Direct the students' attention to the circle graph on page 177.

Ask what the graph represents. The results of a survey where students named their favorite kind of book. Point out that a circle graph shows data that emphasizes the relationships of the parts to the whole.

Discuss the relationship of each section to the whole circle. Encourage students to use the vocabulary and concepts from the previous days. If necessary, reinforce the idea that the entire graph represents one whole, or 1. Help students understand how the sections relate to each other.

● Use what you know about angles, degrees, and fractions to explain how adventure books relate to the whole circle. Line segment BE is a straight angle. It is 180°. Since the circle has 360°, Adventure represents 180° or one half of the circle.

● How do mystery books relate to the whole? Line segment AD and line segment AE form a right angle. A right angle is 90°. A circle has four 90° angles, so the section for mystery books is one fourth of the circle.

● How do the humor and adventure sections relate to each other? They appear to be the same size.

● How can we tell for sure? We can measure them. We can trace one and place it over the other.

330 UNIT B LESSON 6

Use Questions on the Student Page As students answer the questions, they should begin to relate each section of the circle to a number of students that are represented by that section. Students should generalize that the greater the area of a section, the greater the amount of data the section represents, and vice versa.

Be sure that students compare the areas of the humor and mystery sections, and recognize that the area of the mystery section is approximately twice the area of the fiction section and that the area of the humor section is approximately one-half the area of the mystery section.

You may want to invite those who answered exercise 5 correctly to demonstrate different ways of finding the answer.

Have students pose and solve a few more questions about the graph.

Make a Circle Graph

 20 MINUTES

Goal: Use data to make a circle graph.

Materials: rulers, protractors or Protractors (Copymaster M24), Student Activity Book page 178

 NCTM Standards:
Geometry
Measurement

▶ Plan and Make a Graph INDIVIDUALS

Discuss the data table and the marked circle on Student Activity Book page 178. One way to determine the degree measure of a section of the circle is to use a protractor. Another way is to use arithmetic: since there are 360° in a circle and there are 36 sections on the given circle, each section represents 360 ÷ 36 or 10°.

To determine the number of sections to use for each number of visitors, students first need to recognize that 180 visitors altogether visited the library that day. Therefore, each visitor represents 360 ÷ 180 or 2° of the circle.

Students may want to use a variety of colors or cross-hatchings, or design their own method of differentiating the various sections from each other. Remind students that their graph is not complete without a name and labels.

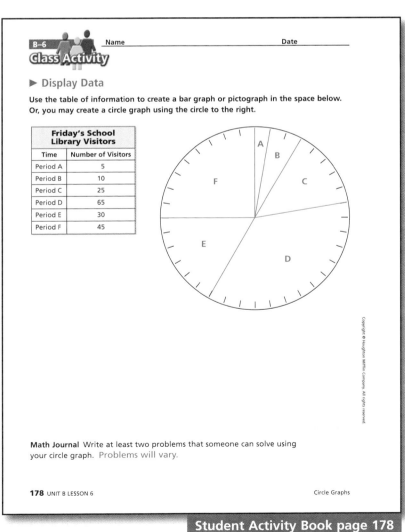

Student Activity Book page 178

Activity 3

Display the Same Data Different Ways

 25 MINUTES

Goal: Display data different ways.

Materials: Student Activity Book page 178

✔ **NCTM Standards:**
Data Analysis
Measurement

▶ Display Data

Discuss different ways to display the data from the table on Student Activity Book page 178.

Friday's School Library Visitors	
Time	Number of Visitors
Period A	5
Period B	10
Period C	25
Period D	65
Period E	30
Period F	45

Students might suggest displaying the data on a bar graph or on a pictograph that uses an icon, such as a book or a stick figure, to represent 5.

Invite students to choose a way and to display the data.

Ask each student to describe the way he or she displayed the data, and if the way is unique, invite them to share it with the class. Then have students compare and contrast the different ways and give reasons why one or more of the ways are clearer, or not clearer, than others. For example:

● Circle graphs emphasize visual comparisons of parts to the whole.

● Bar graphs emphasize both number and comparisons of the parts to each other.

● Pictographs emphasize visual comparisons of the parts to each other.

Write Problems Have students write problems that can be solved using their graphs. Discuss as many problems as time allows.

✔ Ongoing Assessment

▶ Ask questions like the following:

If a circle graph is divided into 3 equal sections, what do you know about the data? The 3 sets of data represent the same amount.

If you have data from 72 students, how will you start to make a circle graph? Divide 360° by 72 to find the number of degrees for each student's data.

Why are a name and labels important? They tell what the graph is about.

② Extending the Lesson

Differentiated Instruction
Activities for Individualizing

Intervention
for students having difficulty

PAIRS

Make a Graph

Ask students to work together to make a graph of the following data.

Bell Peppers For Sale

90 red peppers

90 yellow peppers

90 green peppers

90 orange peppers

Bell Peppers for Sale

On Level
for students having success

PAIRS

Graph Data

Tell students a farmer has 360 apples for sale. There are Jonathan, Macintosh, and Granny Smith apples. Students decide how many of each kind there are, make a table of the data, and then make a graph that shows the apples for sale.

Apples for Sale

Granny Smith   90

Macintosh   180

Jonathan   90

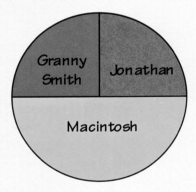

Challenge
for students seeking a challenge

INDIVIDUALS

Use Data to Make a Graph

Students use the numbers 60, 120, and 180 to create a data set. Then students make a circle graph for that data.

Favorite Colors

Red   60

Green   120

Blue   180

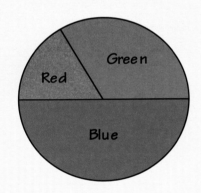

 Math Writing Prompt

Intervention

Write a Question

Find a graph in your math book or a magazine. Write a question that someone can answer using the graph.

 Math Writing Prompt

On Level

How to Make a Circle Graph

Write the steps for making a circle graph to help someone who missed this lesson.

Math Writing Prompt

Challenge

Ask a Question

Think of a good survey question. Ask 12 people the question and make a data table of your results. Then write the directions for making a circle graph from the data table.

③ Homework and Cumulative Review

B–6

Homework **Goal:** Additional Practice

✓ You can quickly review this homework to assess how well students understand how to make and use circle graphs.

B–6

Remembering **Goal:** Cumulative Review

This Remembering activity is appropriate anytime after today's lesson.

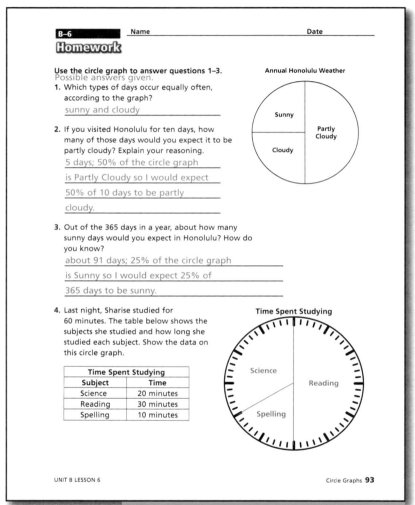

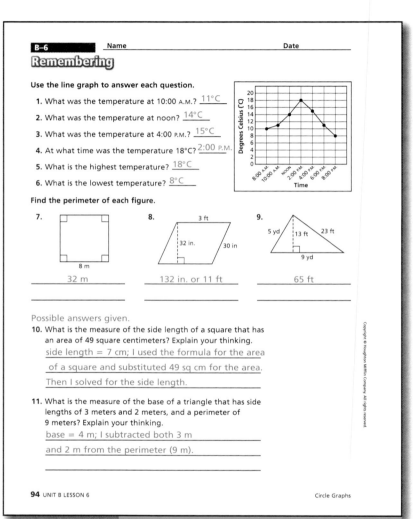

Home or School Activity

Social Studies Connection

Graphs in the Media Have students collect graphs from newspapers, magazines, and the Internet. Students should tell whether they think each graph clearly shows the data and helps the reader to understand the message or story that goes with the graph. Students should compare line graphs, bar graphs, and circle graphs, and decide which is easiest to understand.

I think bar graphs are the easiest to read because the scale helps you read each bar.

Circumference

Lesson Objectives

- Define and estimate circumference.
- Round lengths in millimeters to the nearest whole centimeter.
- Collect, record, and look for patterns in data.

Vocabulary
circumference
radius
diameter
pi

The Day at a Glance

Today's Goals	Materials	123 Math Talk
1 Teaching the Lesson **A1:** Discover the relationship shared by the diameter and the circumference of a circle. **A2:** Estimate the circumference of a circle by using 3 as an approximation for π. **2 Extending the Lesson** ▶ Differentiated Instruction **3 Homework and Cumulative Review**	Rulers Cans of various sizes String Student Activity Book pages 179–180 Strip of paper Scissors Circular object Math Journals Homework and Remembering pages 95–96	In today's activities, the students are involved in discussion as they ▶ identify, describe, and find a pattern in the relationship between diameter and circumference ▶ relate radius to diameter and use both measurements to estimate the circumference of a circle

Teaching the Lesson

Explore Circumference

 30 MINUTES

Goal: Discover the relationship shared by the diameter and the circumference of a circle.

Materials: rulers (1 per small group of students), cans of various sizes (1 per small group of students), string, Student Activity Book page 179

✔ **NCTM Standards:**
Measurement
Geometry
Reasoning and Proof

► Experiment With Circumference

SMALL GROUPS

Draw this picture on the board and discuss the terms *radius*, *diameter*, and *circumference* of a circle.

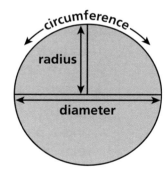

Make sure students understand that the terms *perimeter* and *circumference* represent the idea of "distance around."

● **How can you remember which word is used for circles and which is used for polygons?** You can use the starting sounds: perimeter for polygons, circumference for circles.

Give each small group of students one can and one sheet of paper. Have students record the type of can they have and draw a diagonal from one corner of the paper to the other. Students mark one end of the diagonal *Start*.

Have students place their can at the *Start* position and mark the diameter, the length across the can, on the diagonal.

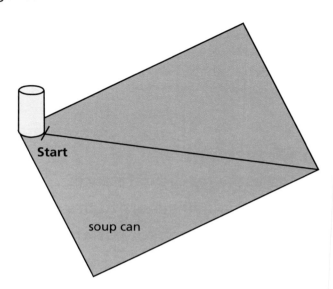

Next, have them make a mark on the top of the can. They place the can at *Start* and roll it one complete revolution, marking on the diagonal where it stops. This mark shows the circumference of the can.

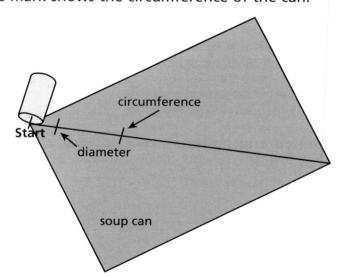

 Alternate Approach

Use String Students can mark the diameter and circumference of the can on a piece of string. They then measure each distance with a ruler.

Have students use a ruler to measure, in millimeters, the marks on their sheet of paper. Create a table on the board and invite students to compile and display their data. As a class, discuss the patterns in the table. For a sample of student dialogue, see Math Talk in Action. If necessary, direct students' attention to the "nearest cm" columns.

Student Activity Book page 179

Draw students' attention to Student Activity Book page 179. Have them work in small groups to complete the first exercise using the class data from the board.

Invite students to discuss and generalize the relationship between the diameter and the circumference of the can. Students should discover that there is a pattern for all the can measurements.

● About how many times as long as the diameter is the circumference? about three times

If they are having difficulty, students can fold the paper to discover that the distance around is about three times as long as the diameter.

 Math Talk in Action

What patterns do you see in your measurements?

Olivia: The circumference of my can is three times the diameter.

Is there another way to say that?

Olivia: You could say the diameter is one third of the circumference.

Correct. Do you all have the same pattern for your can measurements?

Anil: Almost. The circumference of my can is about 17 cm and the diameter is about 6 cm. 3 × 6 is 18. 17 isn't exactly three times 6, but it's close.

That's good. The circumference of a circle is close to three times the diameter. Where is it easiest to see this in the table?

Félix: In the "nearest cm" columns. The numbers are smaller so they're easier to multiply or divide in your head.

That's true. The rounded circumference can also be exactly three times the rounded diameter.

 Ongoing Assessment

As students complete exercises 1–4, check that they are measuring accurately and converting millimeters to centimeters correctly.

Teaching Note

Watch For! In the next activity, some students might confuse diameter and radius in their calculations. For example, they might estimate the circumference by multiplying the radius, instead of the diameter, by 3.

Activity 2

Estimate Circumference

 30 MINUTES

Goal: Estimate the circumference of a circle by using 3 as an approximation for π.

Materials: Student Activity Book page 180

 NCTM Standards:
Measurement
Geometry
Reasoning and Proof

▶ Estimate Circumference Using Diameter WHOLE CLASS

Sketch a circle on the board. Invite volunteers, one at a time, to go to the board, draw a diameter on the circle, and assign it an estimated length. Each time, challenge the rest of the class to estimate the circumference of the circle. Repeat, beginning with a circumference and challenging students to estimate the diameter.

▶ Estimate Circumference Using Radius
WHOLE CLASS

Draw several circles and mark the radius and diameter on each. Discuss how the measures relate to circumference:

● **How do the lengths of a diameter and a radius of a circle compare?** The length of a diameter is twice the length of a radius and the length of a radius is one half the length of a diameter.

● **What do you have to do to a radius before you can use it to find the circumference of a circle?** multiply it by 2

● **How can you find the diameter if you know the circumference?** divide by 3

● **After you find the diameter, what do you need to do to get the radius?** divide your answer by 2

Use the circles on the board. Have volunteers assign a radius and challenge the students to find the circumference; then have volunteers assign a circumference and challenge the students to find the radius.

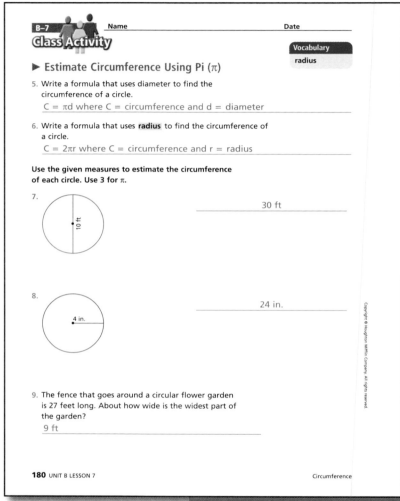

▶ Estimate Circumference Using Pi (π)
SMALL GROUPS

Explain that the relationship shared by circumference and diameter is called *pi* (π). Write the symbol on the board. Tell students that they will use 3 to represent π.

Have the students complete the exercises using C for circumference, 3 for π, d for diameter, and r for radius.

Teaching Note

Language and Vocabulary Pi (π) is a constant ratio of the diameter of a circle to its circumference. Pi is an irrational number. It cannot be written as a fraction or as a repeating or terminating decimal. Pi is approximately 3.14 or $\frac{22}{7}$. A less precise estimate of circumference is obtained when 3 is used for π.

② Extending the Lesson

Intervention
for students having difficulty

PAIRS

Circle Fences

Materials: strip of paper, scissors, ruler

Students draw a large circle on a sheet of paper and mark the diameter. They work together to cut a strip of paper three times as long as the diameter and wrap it around the circle like a fence to see that it fits, more or less.

Students then measure the strip of paper with a ruler and divide by three to find the diameter. They can measure the diameter with a ruler to check their calculation.

Possible answer:

The strip is 35 cm long; 35 ÷ 3 is almost 12, so the diameter is about 12 cm.

On Level
for students having success

PAIRS

Calculate and Compare

Materials: two cans of different sizes, string, ruler

One partner traces the bottom of one can onto paper, measures the diameter, and estimates the circumference.

The other partner uses string and a ruler to measure the circumference of the same can and then finds the diameter.

After comparing answers, the partners reverse roles and repeat the exercise with the other can.

In each case, the circumference should be about three times the diameter.

Challenge
for students seeking a challenge

INDIVIDUALS

Polygons and Circles

Materials: circular object, ruler

Students trace a circle three times onto a piece of paper. They place three equally spaced dots around one of the circles and connect them with lines.

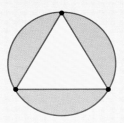

They repeat using four dots and five dots on the other two circles.

Students identify the polygon inside each circle and estimate the perimeter of the polygon and circumference of the circle. Students explain how the perimeter compares to the circumference as they use more dots.

 Math Writing Prompt

Intervention

Understand Circumference
Explain how to use the diameter of a circle to find the circumference of that circle.

 Math Writing Prompt

On Level

You Decide
You are checking your work and find two measurements for a circle are $r = 4$ cm and $C = 12$ cm. Is this correct? Explain how you know.

 Math Writing Prompt

Challenge

Explore Formulas
Is $C \div 6$ a formula that you can use to find the radius of a circle? Explain why or why not.

③ Homework and Cumulative Review

✓ Include students' work for page 95 as part of their portfolios.

This Remembering activity is appropriate anytime after today's lesson.

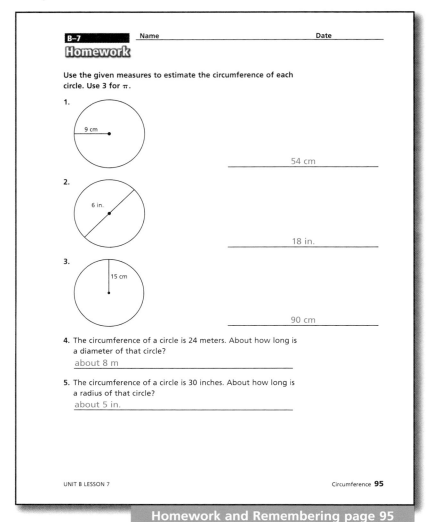

B–7 Name _____ Date _____
Homework

Use the given measures to estimate the circumference of each circle. Use 3 for π.

1.
9 cm

54 cm

2.
6 in.

18 in.

3.
15 cm

90 cm

4. The circumference of a circle is 24 meters. About how long is a diameter of that circle?
about 8 m

5. The circumference of a circle is 30 inches. About how long is a radius of that circle?
about 5 in.

UNIT B LESSON 7   Circumference **95**

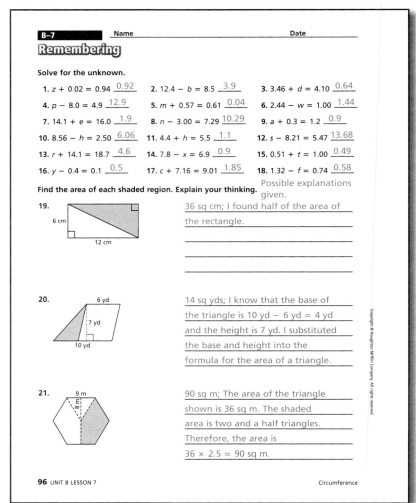

B–7 Name _____ Date _____
Remembering

Solve for the unknown.

1. $z + 0.02 = 0.94$ __0.92__ 2. $12.4 - b = 8.5$ __3.9__ 3. $3.46 + d = 4.10$ __0.64__
4. $p - 8.0 = 4.9$ __12.9__ 5. $m + 0.57 = 0.61$ __0.04__ 6. $2.44 - w = 1.00$ __1.44__
7. $14.1 + e = 16.0$ __1.9__ 8. $n - 3.00 = 7.29$ __10.29__ 9. $a + 0.3 = 1.2$ __0.9__
10. $8.56 - h = 2.50$ __6.06__ 11. $4.4 + h = 5.5$ __1.1__ 12. $s - 8.21 = 5.47$ __13.68__
13. $r + 14.1 = 18.7$ __4.6__ 14. $7.8 - x = 6.9$ __0.9__ 15. $0.51 + t = 1.00$ __0.49__
16. $y - 0.4 = 0.1$ __0.5__ 17. $c + 7.16 = 9.01$ __1.85__ 18. $1.32 - f = 0.74$ __0.58__

Find the area of each shaded region. Explain your thinking.   Possible explanations given.

19.
6 cm
12 cm

36 sq cm; I found half of the area of the rectangle.

20.
6 yd
7 yd
10 yd

14 sq yds; I know that the base of the triangle is 10 yd − 6 yd = 4 yd and the height is 7 yd. I substituted the base and height into the formula for the area of a triangle.

21.
9 m
E
8 m

90 sq m; The area of the triangle shown is 36 sq m. The shaded area is two and a half triangles. Therefore, the area is $36 \times 2.5 = 90$ sq m.

96 UNIT B LESSON 7   Circumference

Home or School Activity

 Literature Connection

Math and Literature Read the book *Sir Cumference and the Dragon of Pi* by Cindy Neuschwander (Charlesbridge Publishing, 1999). Encourage discussion of how the story relates to what students have learned about pi during math class.

Unit Review and Test

Lesson Objective

● **Assess student progress on unit objectives.**

The Day at a Glance

Today's Goals	Materials
1 Assessing the Unit ▶ Assess student progress on unit objectives. ▶ Use activities from unit lessons to reteach content. **2 Extending the Assessment** ▶ Use remediation for common errors. There is no homework assignment on a test day.	Unit B Test, Student Activity Book pages 181–182 Unit B Test, Form A or B, Assessment Guide (optional) Unit B Performance Assessment, Assessment Guide (optional)

 Class Management

Review and Test Day You may want to choose a quiet game or other activity (reading a book or working on homework for another subject) for students who finish early.

Assessing the Unit

Assess Unit Objectives

45 MINUTES (more if schedule permits)

Goal: Assess student progress on unit objectives.

Materials: Student Activity Book pages 181–182; Assessment Guide (optional)

▶ Review and Assessment

If your students are ready for assessment on the unit objectives, you may use either the test on the Student Activity Book pages or one of the forms of the Unit B Test in the Assessment Guide to assess student progress.

If you feel that students need some review first, you may use the test on the Student Activity Book pages as a review of unit content, and then use one of the forms of the Unit B Test in the Assessment Guide to assess student progress.

To assign a numerical score for all of these test forms, use 10 points for each question.

You may also choose to use the Unit B Performance Assessment. Scoring for that assessment can be found in its rubric in the Assessment Guide.

▶ Reteaching Resources

The chart lists the test items, the unit objectives they cover, and the lesson activities in which the objective is covered in this unit. You may revisit these activities with students who do not show mastery of the objectives.

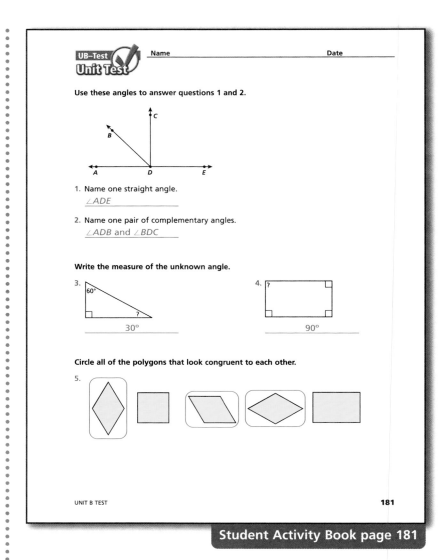

Student Activity Book page 181

Unit Test Items	Unit Objectives Tested	Activities to Use for Reteaching
1–2	**B.1** Identify and measure angles.	Lesson 1, Activity 1
3–4	**B.2** Find the measure of an unknown angle in a polygon.	Lesson 1, Activity 2 Lesson 2, Activity 2
5	**B.3** Identify congruent figures.	Lesson 3, Activity 1

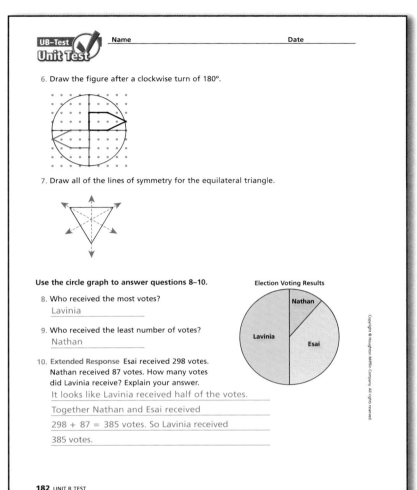

Student Activity Book page182

Unit Test Items	Unit Objectives Tested	Activities to Use for Reteaching
6	**B.4** Identify the position of an object after it has been turned.	Lesson 4, Activity 2
7	**B.5** Identify lines of symmetry.	Lesson 5, Activity 1
8–10	**B.6** Solve problems using a circle graph.	Lesson 6, Activity 1

▶ Assessment Resources

Free Response Tests
Unit B Test, Student Activity Book pages 181–182
Unit B Test, Form A, Assessment Guide

Extended Response Item
The last item in the Student Activity Book test and in the Form A test will require an extended response as an answer.

Multiple Choice Test
Unit B Test, Form B, Assessment Guide

Performance Assessment
Unit B Performance Assessment, Assessment Guide
Unit B Performance Assessment Rubric, Assessment Guide

▶ Portfolio Assessment

Teacher-selected Items for Student Portfolios:

- Homework, Lesson 2, 4, 7
- Class Activity work, Lessons 3, 6

Student-selected Items for Student Portfolios:

- Favorite Home or School Activity
- Best Writing Prompt

② Extending the Assessment

Unit Objective B.1
Identify and measure angles.

Common Error: Misidentifies Complementary and Supplementary Angles

Some students may confuse complementary angles and supplementary angles.

Remediation Point out to these students that "s" is the first letter of *straight* and *supplementary,* and that supplementary angles form straight lines, or angles of 180°. The word *complementary* does not begin with "s" and complementary angles do not form straight lines.

Unit Objective B.2
Find the measure of an unknown angle in a polygon.

Common Error: Confuses Sums of Angles of Polygons

Students may have difficulty remembering that the sum of the angles in a triangle is 180° and the sum of the angles in a rectangle is 360°.

Remediation Encourage these students to remember that a triangle has fewer angles than a rectangle, so the sum of its angles is less.

Unit Objective B.3
Identify congruent figures.

Common Error: Determines Congruence Incorrectly

Some students may have difficulty determining the congruence, or lack of congruence, of two figures.

Remediation Encourage these students to use tracing paper or a ruler to help make their decisions.

Unit Objective B.4
Identify the position of an object after it has been turned.

Common Error: Doesn't Connect Degree Measures to Fractional Turns

Some students may have difficulty recognizing that 90°, 180°, 270°, and 360° turns represent a one-quarter turn, a one-half turn, a three-quarter turn, and a full turn, respectively.

Remediation To help students make these connections, provide them with circles divided into fourths. Have them use their protractors to determine the angle measure of each quarter. Then ask students to label those measures and parts using appropriate fractions.

Unit Objective B.5
Identify lines of symmetry.

Common Error: Identifies Too Few Lines of Symmetry

Students may identify some, but not all, of the lines of symmetry of a figure. For example, in a square, they may recognize the vertical and horizontal lines of symmetry, but not the lines of symmetry along the diagonals.

Remediation Encourage these students to orient the figure in different ways (upside-down, sideways, etc.) to help them identify all of the lines of symmetry.

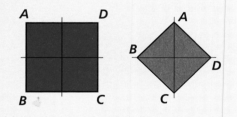

Unit Objective B.6
Solve problems using a circle graph.

Common Error: Misreads the Graph

Students may misinterpret the graph.

Remediation Have students reread and check their answers before submitting their tests. Remind them that the size of each section is related to the number it represents, so the largest section indicates the greatest number and the smallest section indicates the least number.

Fraction Concepts

UNIT 3 BUILDS on the conceptual understanding of fractions that students have developed in previous grades. Activities help students develop strategies to add and subtract like and unlike fractions, and to work with equivalent fractions. Students use a variety of representations in this unit to help them gain fluency with manipulating proper and improper fractions and mixed numbers. Students are expected to apply their understanding and skills with adding and subtracting fractions to numeric calculations and to real-world, problem-solving situations.

UNIT 3 CONTENTS

Unit 3 Assessment

✓ Unit Goals Tested	Unit Test Items	Lessons
3.1 Add and subtract fractions and mixed numbers with like and unlike denominators.	1–4	1, 7, 8, 15–17
3.2 Write and compare fractions and mixed numbers.	5–6	2, 6, 9
3.3 Relate fractions and wholes.	7	4, 5
3.4 Find equivalent fractions.	8	11–13
3.5 Express the probability of an event as a fraction.	9	14
3.6 Solve problems involving fractions.	10	1, 3–5, 8–10, 14, 16

Formal Assessment

Open or Free Response Tests

- Quick Quizzes (Assessment Guide)
- Unit Review and Test (Student Activity Book pages 221–222, Teacher's Guide pages 475–478)
- Unit 3 Test Form A (Assessment Guide)
- Unit 3 Open Response Test (Test Generator)
- Test Bank Items for Unit 3 (Test Generator)

Multiple-Choice Tests

- Unit 3 Test Form B (Assessment Guide)
- Unit 3 Multiple-Choice Test (Test Generator)
- Test Bank Items for Unit 3 (Test Generator)

Performance Tasks

- Unit 3 Performance Assessment (Assessment Guide)
- Unit 3 Performance Assessment (Test Generator)

Informal Assessment

Ongoing Assessment

- In every Teacher's Guide lesson

Performance Assessment

- Class discussions
- Small-group work
- Quick Practice (in every lesson)
- Individual work on teacher-selected tasks

Portfolios

- See Unit 3 Review and Test for suggestions for selecting items for portfolios.
- Some Homework pages are noted as suitable for portfolio inclusion.

Review Opportunities

Homework and Remembering

- Homework pages provide review of recently taught topics.
- Remembering pages provide cumulative review.

Teacher's Guide

- Unit Review and Test (page 475)

Teacher's Resource Book

- Problem Bank

Test Generator CD-ROM

- Test Bank items can be used to create custom review sheets.

Planning Unit 3 Unit Pacing: 20–24 days

Lesson Title	Lesson Resources	Materials and Manipulatives	
		Math Expressions	**Other**
1 Build With Unit Fractions	Family Letter Student Activity Book pages 183–186 Homework and Remembering pages 97–98	MathBoard materials	Identical small items in 2 colors, grid paper, Math Journals
2 Compare Fractions	Student Activity Book pages 187–188 Homework and Remembering pages 99–100	MathBoard materials, Fraction Bars (Copymaster M26)	Colored pencils, grid paper, scissors, Math Journals
3 Subtract Fractions	Student Activity Book pages 189–190 Homework and Remembering pages 101–102		Index cards, Math Journals
4 Fractional Addends of One	Student Activity Book pages 191–192 Homework and Remembering pages 103–104	MathBoard materials, Unknown Addend Cards (Copymaster M27)	Identical small items in 2 colors, Math Journals
5 Relate Fractions and Wholes	Student Activity Book pages 193–194 Homework and Remembering pages 105–106 **Quick Quiz 1**	MathBoard materials, Pattern Blocks (Copymaster M28) (optional)	Pattern blocks (optional), masking tape, chapter books, Math Journals
6 Fractions Greater Than One	Homework and Remembering pages 107–108		Greeting cards or photos for cutting, index cards, Math Journals
7 Add Fractions Greater Than One (Like Denominators)	Student Activity Book pages 195–196 Homework and Remembering pages 109–110	MathBoard materials, Fraction Bars (Copymaster M26), Fraction Cards (Copymaster M29), and Fraction Circles (Copymaster M30)	Scissors, envelopes, Math Journals
8 Subtract Mixed Numbers (Like Denominators)	Student Activity Book pages 197–198 Homework and Remembering pages 111–112	MathBoard materials, Fraction Bars (Copymaster M26), Fraction Cards (Copymaster M29)	Scissors, envelopes, Math Journals
9 Comparison Situations	Student Activity Book pages 199–200 Homework and Remembering pages 113–114		Inch rulers, play money, Math Journals
10 Mixed Practice With Like Fractions	Student Activity Book pages 201–202 Homework and Remembering pages 115–116 **Quick Quiz 2**		Math Journals
11 Discover Equivalent Fractions	Student Activity Book pages 203–206 Homework and Remembering pages 117–118	Equivalent Fractions (Copymaster M31), Fraction Match-Up Cards (Copymaster M32)	Rulers, scissors, Math Journals
12 Equivalent Fractions and Multipliers	Student Activity Book pages 207–208 Homework and Remembering pages 119–120	Tens and Hundreds Grids (Copymaster M33)	Clock with a second hand or minute timer, Math Journals
13 Solve Equivalence Problems	Student Activity Book pages 209–210 Homework and Remembering pages 121–122	MathBoard materials	Index cards, Math Journals
14 Probability and Equivalent Fractions	Student Activity Book pages 211–214 Homework and Remembering pages 123–124	Spinner (Copymaster M34)	Paper clips, coins, Math Journals
15 Add and Subtract Unlike Fractions	Student Activity Book pages 215–216 Homework and Remembering pages 125–126	MathBoard materials, Fraction Circles (Copymaster M30)	Math Journals
16 Solve With Unlike Mixed Numbers	Student Activity Book pages 217–218 Homework and Remembering pages 127–128		Dimes and pennies, Math Journals
17 Practice With Unlike Mixed Numbers	Student Activity Book pages 219–220 Homework and Remembering pages 129–130 **Quick Quiz 3**		Index cards, grid paper, rulers, colored pencils, Math Journals
✓ Unit 3 Review and Test	Student Activity Book pages 221–222 Assessment Guide		

Unit 3 Teaching Resources

Differentiated Instruction

Reaching All Learners

Advanced Learners
Lesson 5, page 379

English Learners
Lesson 1, page 346   Lesson 9, page 406
Lesson 3, page 366   Lesson 14, page 444

Extra Help
Lesson 2, page 360   Lesson 8, page 398
Lesson 7, page 391   Lesson 9, page 402
Lesson 7, page 392   Lesson 11, page 422
Lesson 8, page 396   Lesson 15, page 457

Special Needs
Lesson 1, page 347
Lesson 6, page 385
Lesson 11, page 417

Individualizing Instruction

Activities
• Intervention (in every lesson)
• On Level (in every lesson)
• Challenge (in every lesson)

Math Writing Prompts
• Intervention (in every lesson)
• On Level (in every lesson)
• Challenge (in every lesson)

Cross-Curricular Links • Home or School Activities

 Math Connections
Measuring (Lesson 2, page 362)
Add Fractions to Find Perimeter
(Lesson 7, page 394)

 Real-World Connections
Printable Area (Lesson 3, page 368)
Fractions and Mixed Numbers in Use (Lesson 8, page 400)
Money (Lesson 13, page 440)
Birthdays (Lesson 14, page 450)
Plan a Feast (Lesson 16, page 468)

 Science Connections
Our Solar System (Lesson 4, page 374)
Compare Animal Size (Lesson 9, page 408)

 Art Connection
Sierpinski Carpet (Lesson 5, page 382)

 Social Studies Connections
Television Viewing (Lesson 6, page 388)
Ancient Egyptian Fractions (Lesson 15, page 460)

 Language Arts Connection
Media Advertisements (Lesson 10, page 414)

 Literature Connection
Write About It (Lesson 11, page 424)

 Sports Connections
Fractions in Baseball (Lesson 12, page 432)
Shots Made (Lesson 17, page 474)

Teaching Unit 3

Putting Research into Practice for Unit 3

From Our Curriculum Research Project: Math Talk Is Important

A significant part of the collaborative classroom culture in *Math Expressions* is the frequent exchange of problem-solving strategies, or math talk. The benefits of math talk are multiple. Describing one's methods to another person can clarify one's own thinking as well as clarify the matter for others. Another person's approach can supply a new perspective, and frequent exposure to different approaches tends to engender flexible thinking. Math talk creates opportunities to understand errors and permits teachers to assess students' understanding on an ongoing basis. It encourages students to develop their language skills, both in math and in everyday English. Finally, math talk enables students to become active helpers and questioners, creating student-to-student talk that stimulates engagement and community.

From Current Research: Models of Fractions

During grades 3–5, students should build their understanding of fractions as parts of a whole and as division. They will need to see and explore a variety of models of fractions, focusing primarily on familiar fractions such as halves, thirds, fourths, fifths, sixths, eighths, and tenths. By using an area model in which part of a region is shaded, students can see how fractions are related to a unit whole, compare fractional parts of a whole, and find equivalent fractions. They should develop strategies for ordering and comparing fractions, often using benchmarks such as $\frac{1}{2}$ and 1. For example, fifth graders can compare fractions such as $\frac{2}{5}$ and $\frac{5}{8}$ by comparing each with $\frac{1}{2}$; one is a little less than $\frac{1}{2}$, and the other is a little more. By using parallel number lines, each showing a unit fraction and its multiples (see fig. 5.1), students can see fractions as numbers, note their relationship to 1, and see relationships among fractions, including equivalence. They should also begin to understand that between any two fractions, there is always another fraction.

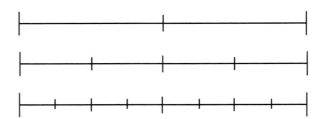

Fig. 5.1. Parallel number lines with unit fractions and their multiples

National Council of Teachers of Mathematics. *Principles and Standards for School Mathematics.* Reston: NCTM, 2000. 149.

Other Useful References: Fractions

Kilpatrick, Jeremy, Jane Swafford, Bradford Findell, eds. *Adding It Up: Helping Children Learn Mathematics.* Mathematics Learning Study Committee, National Research Council. Washington: NAP, 2001 (especially Chapter 7: Developing Proficiency with Other Numbers).

Mack, Nancy K. "Connecting to Develop Computational Fluency with Fractions." *Teaching Children Mathematics* 11.4 (Nov. 2004): 226–232.

National Council of Teachers of Mathematics. *Making Sense of Fractions, Ratios, and Proportions* (2002 Yearbook). Ed. Bonnie Litwiller. Reston: NCTM, 2002.

National Council of Teachers of Mathematics. *Principles and Standards for School Mathematics* (Number and Operations Standard for Grades 3–5). Reston: NCTM, 2000.

Reys, Barbara J., Rita Barger, Maxim Bruckheimer, Barbara Dougherty, Jack Hope, Linda Lembke, Zvia Markovits, Andy Parnas, Sue Reehm, Ruthi Sturdevant, and Marianne Weber. *Developing Number Sense in the Middle Grades: Addenda Series, Grades 5–8.* Curriculum and Evaluation Standards Addenda Series. Reston: NCTM, 1991. 28–33.

Wu, H. Chapter 2: *Fractions.* Draft, June 20, 2001. Revised Sept. 3, 2002. <http://math.berkeley.edu/~wu/EMI2a.pdf>

Math Background

Build Models of Fractions

Build with Fraction Chains

We focus on unit fractions first, or fractions that represent just one piece of the whole, such as $\frac{1}{3}$ or $\frac{1}{5}$. Students build the whole with unit fractions arranged in a fraction chain. Activities with fraction chains help to stabilize the denominator in students' minds. They also help everyone link fractional notation with the number of pieces that make up the whole.

A Basic Fraction Chain:

$\frac{1}{3} + \frac{1}{3} + \frac{1}{3} = \frac{3}{3} = 1$

Gradually this understanding of unit fractions is extended as students build more complex fractions. Here, non-unit fractions are emerging.

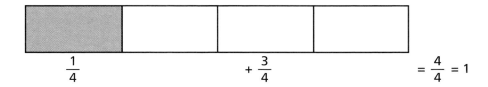

$\frac{1}{4} \qquad + \frac{3}{4} \qquad = \frac{4}{4} = 1$

This model also helps students see the fractional addends of 1: the two fractions that together form one whole. Knowing these addends is extremely useful in finding out how many more need to be added to get one whole. (For example, "I ran $\frac{4}{5}$ of the distance. What fraction of the distance do I still have to run?")

Fraction chains are also useful for helping students visualize fractional subtraction. The subtraction chain below is a solution to the problem: $\frac{6}{7} - \frac{2}{7}$. Again, this kind of representation establishes the denominator as a fixed number.

$$\cancel{\frac{1}{7}} + \cancel{\frac{1}{7}} + \frac{1}{7} + \frac{1}{7} + \frac{1}{7} + \frac{1}{7}$$

When students encounter subtraction in the context of comparison situations (Who has more? How much more?), they can identify the larger fraction and the difference with the help of fraction chains, as shown below.

Katie $\quad \frac{1}{8} + \frac{1}{8}$

Otto $\quad \frac{1}{8} + \frac{1}{8} + \boxed{\frac{1}{8} + \frac{1}{8} + \frac{1}{8}}$

Use the MathBoard

Length Models

As a result of building wholes from unit fractions, students catch on rather quickly to the use of length models, which allow them to see the cumulative total of unit fractions. The MathBoards feature a collection of length models called fraction bars, which are used to introduce all fractional operations. Students provide the labels.

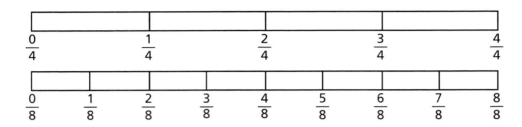

Fraction bars have some advantages over circular fraction models (such as pizza or pie). Fraction bars give students a strong visual sense of the relative size of fractions. They set the stage for concepts that will come later in the unit, such as equivalence. (Note that the two fraction bars above show several equivalent fractions.) Students can also produce fraction bars themselves, a feature that allows students to become more actively involved in exploring fractions.

Number Lines

When the class is ready for mixed numbers, calibrated lines not only help students understand addition and subtraction with mixed numbers, but also help them see some important relationships. This number line makes it clear that $\frac{5}{3}$ is the same as $1\frac{2}{3}$.

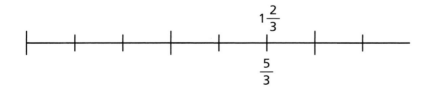

Problem Solving

A Variety of Strategies

Throughout the unit, problem-solving situations are introduced to help students develop strategies to work with fractions. Students are often asked to choose a strategy to solve a problem, and then to share it with the class. Other students are invited to ask questions about the strategy and to share their own strategies. By exposing students to several strategies to solve the same problem, you are doing two very important things:

1. You are reinforcing the idea that there are often many correct ways to arrive at a solution, and many ways to communicate mathematical ideas.

2. You are allowing students to learn in the way that makes the most sense to them. Different people learn new ideas in different ways. For example, some people may need to look at a diagram to visualize a problem situation, while others will understand it best from seeing an equation.

Each representation reveals a different way of thinking about the problem. Giving attention to the different methods as well as to the different representations will help students see the power of viewing a problem from different perspectives. Observing how different students select and use representations also gives the teacher assessment information about what aspects of the problem they notice and how they reason about the patterns and regularities revealed in their representations.

Principles and Standards for School Mathematics. National Council of Teachers of Mathematics. Reston: NCTM, 2000. 208.

In this unit you are trying to move students gradually toward using equations to represent problems involving fractions, because that strategy will become more useful to them as they work to solve more complicated problems. Fraction bars, fraction chains, and other representations, however, can also be part of valid and effective problem-solving strategies. Especially near the beginning of the unit, exposure to many representations and strategies can help students develop a more thorough understanding of what fractions mean. This solid conceptual understanding will help them develop, use, and remember algorithms to add, subtract, multiply, and divide fractions.

Frequent opportunities to share strategies will deepen students' understanding of fractions. Opportunities to share and discuss their own strategies in an open, accepting environment will also improve students' abilities to communicate mathematically.

Fluency Days

Fluency Days provide students with in-class opportunities to assess themselves on basic multiplications and divisions. Students will monitor their own learning through the use of hands-on materials and quick activities that were first introduced in Grade 5 Unit 1. A lesson reference is included for a more detailed description of each activity. Copymasters of all necessary materials are located in the Teacher's Resource Book. If your students need more practice to build fluency, include a Fluency Day in your teaching plan for this unit or use one or more of these activities throughout the school year.

Diagnostic Quizzes (See Unit 1 Lesson 10)

These quizzes help students determine which multiplications and divisions they "automatically" know and which they still need to study. Distribute copies of the multiplication quiz, division quiz, or both to the class. Allow only 3 minutes for students to complete each quiz. Encourage students to work out any unfinished or missed problems in class and to take home their quizzes for further practice.

Division Cards (See Unit 1 Lesson 10)

Students may practice with these cards individually or with a partner. Students first stack their cards so that the slanted corners line up on the right. Then, one student reads the problem, solves the problem mentally, and turns the card over to check his or her answer. Students then sort their Division Cards into *Fast, Slow,* and *Don't Know* piles. They practice the *Slow* and *Don't Know* piles.

Games

The Factor Field (Unit 1 Lesson 10) – Students practice their divisions by reading each division problem on their Division Cards and then placing the card on the *Factor Field* game board section that corresponds to the answer.

Factor the Footprints (Unit 1 Lesson 14) – Students practice finding factors with a partner by naming all the possible factor pairs they can find for each number they follow along the *Factor the Footprints* game board path.

Target Practice (See Unit 1 Lesson 3)

The Target is used together with students' multiplication tables. It may be used either independently or with an in-class practice partner. The shaded overlay with the transparent L-shape and Target circle can be moved to any product. The ends of the L show the factors, and the Target shows the product. Covering the product provides multiplication practice while covering one end of the L provides division practice.

Scrambled Multiplication Tables (See Unit 1 Lesson 11)

These scrambled tables are multiplication tables with the rows and columns moved around. Students complete the missing factors or products in each table.

Factor Puzzles (See Unit 1 Lesson 14)

Students use their knowledge of count-bys and multiplications to fill in the unknown section of the Factor Puzzle. Their answer is correct if the corresponding four cells on the Multiplication Table form a rectangle.

12	18
20	

Build Unit Fractions

Lesson Objectives

- Build other fractions from unit fractions.
- Add like fractions.
- Express information from pictures, stories, and data formats as fractions.

Vocabulary
unit fraction
non-unit fraction

The Day at a Glance

Today's Goals	Materials	Math Talk
Quick Practice Practice reading fractions. **① Teaching the Lesson** **A1:** Add unit fractions and non-unit fractions with the same denominators. **A2:** Apply knowledge of fractions to real-life situations. **② Extending the Lesson** ▶ Differentiated Instruction **③ Homework and Cumulative Review**	MathBoard materials Student Activity Book pages 183–186 Identical small items in 2 colors (counters, pattern blocks, plastic tags from bread) Grid paper Homework and Remembering pages 97–98 Math Journals Family Letter	In today's activities, the students are involved in discussion as they ▶ talk about unit fractions ▶ explain why fractions with the same numerator and denominator represent one whole ▶ use fractions to describe real-world situations ▶ describe fractions as equal parts of a whole

Quick Practice

🕐 **5 MINUTES**   **Goal:** Practice reading fractions.

Fraction Parade Send six students to the board and have them each write a fraction quickly. One at a time, each student gives an arm signal and the class says the fraction out loud. (Students should say the fraction name—"two-thirds," not "2 over 3.")

$\frac{2}{3}$ $\frac{1}{10}$

two-thirds   one-tenth

$\frac{1}{16}$ $\frac{1}{20}$

one-sixteenth   one-twentieth

Teaching the Lesson

Add Like Fractions

 25 MINUTES

Goal: Add unit fractions and non-unit fractions with the same denominators.

Materials: MathBoard materials

✔ **NCTM Standards:**
Number and Operations
Problem Solving

Differentiated Instruction

English Learners If students have trouble naming fractions, help them to see and describe the pattern. Except for halves and thirds, fractions are formed with the ending *th*: fourths, fifths, sixths, and so on. If necessary, write a few fractions with larger numbers in the denominator for the students to name.

▶ **Introduce Unit Fractions** | WHOLE CLASS |

Draw a large rectangle on the board and invite a student volunteer to divide it into fourths and to shade $\frac{1}{4}$ of it. Ask other students whether they can think of different ways to divide rectangles into fourths.

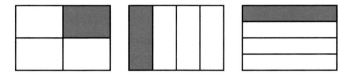

Write the fraction $\frac{1}{4}$ on the board next to the drawings. Explain that one-fourth is a *unit fraction* and explain what that means:

● A unit fraction is one equal part of a whole.

● The whole in this case has been divided into 4 equal parts, and we have shaded one of them.

Ask the students to name some other unit fractions. Answers will vary. Possible answers: $\frac{1}{3}, \frac{1}{5}, \frac{1}{16}$

Discuss unit fractions in relation to divisions of the whole.

● If we have four divisions of the whole, what is the unit fraction? $\frac{1}{4}$

● If we have five divisions of the whole, what is the unit fraction? $\frac{1}{5}$

● If we have three divisions of the whole, what is the unit fraction? $\frac{1}{3}$

● If we have *d* divisions of the whole, what is the unit fraction? $\frac{1}{d}$

Explain that $\frac{1}{d}$ is an algebraic way to show any unit fraction.

▶ Add Unit Fractions on the MathBoard ⟨WHOLE CLASS⟩

Distribute MathBoard materials. Begin by directing students' attention to the fraction bar that represents halves. Using the class MathBoard, show the students how to label each section with the appropriate unit fraction and then how to add them together to make $\frac{2}{2}$, or one whole.

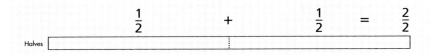

Ask students to do the same for thirds, fourths, and fifths.

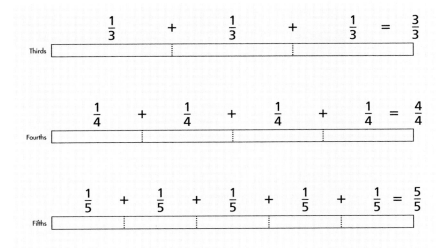

Discuss the meaning of $\frac{2}{2}$, $\frac{3}{3}$, $\frac{4}{4}$, and $\frac{5}{5}$.

- What do you have when the numerator and denominator are the same? one whole

- How do you know? There are a certain number of parts and we are using all of them.

Activity continued ▶

Teaching Note

Math Background

Length Models Fraction bars are length models. Length models have an advantage over the traditional circular models for fractions, such as pizzas or pies, because they can be constructed to be easily divided into equal parts. For example, a circle may be very difficult to divide into 7 equal parts, but a length model can be made 7 centimeters long and the centimeters can be marked easily.

Differentiated Instruction

Special Needs You can help visual learners understand the relationship of parts to a whole by having them fold a piece of paper in half and cut along the fold. Ask them to compare the two pieces for size, and to label each as $\frac{1}{2}$. Point out that the unit fraction $\frac{1}{2}$ means 1 of 2 equal pieces of the whole paper. Repeat for fourths and eighths by folding and cutting the halves into smaller, equal pieces.

Activity 1

Teaching Note

Watch For! A typical student error when finding the sum of fractions is to add not only the numerators, but also the denominators. For example, students might write $\frac{2}{5} + \frac{1}{5} = \frac{3}{10}$. Writing unit fraction chains helps students see that the bottom number stays the same:

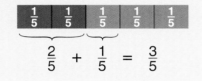

✓ Ongoing Assessment

Ask students:

▶ How can you tell what the unit fraction is?

▶ How can you build a non-unit fraction from unit fractions?

▶ How can you use unit fractions to add fractions with like denominators?

▶ Add Non-Unit Fractions on the MathBoard

WHOLE CLASS

Direct the students' attention to the fraction bar that shows sixths.

Give students the word problems below and ask everyone to solve them by circling fractions on the MathBoards. Ask them to write a fraction equation above the bar for each problem.

● Ellis is building a sidewalk with 6 equal parts. Yesterday he built $\frac{2}{6}$ of the sidewalk. Today he built $\frac{3}{6}$ of the sidewalk. What fraction of the sidewalk has Ellis built? $\frac{5}{6}$

● Glennette is also building a sidewalk with 6 equal parts. Yesterday she built 4 of the parts. Today she built only 1 part. What fraction of the sidewalk has Glennette built? $\frac{5}{6}$

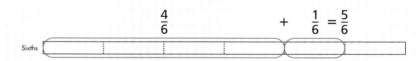

The first word problem states the fractions directly. The second word problem asks students to construct the fractions from the situation.

Discuss the fractions in the equations:

● Which fraction in the equations is a unit fraction? $\frac{1}{6}$

● Which fractions in the equations are not unit fractions? $\frac{2}{6}, \frac{3}{6}, \frac{4}{6}, \frac{5}{6}$

● How can you build these other fractions from the unit fraction $\frac{1}{6}$? by adding; $\frac{2}{6} = \frac{1}{6} + \frac{1}{6}, \frac{3}{6} = \frac{1}{6} + \frac{1}{6} + \frac{1}{6}$, and so on

Introduce the term *non-unit fraction* for fractions such as $\frac{2}{6}, \frac{3}{6}, \frac{4}{6}$, or $\frac{5}{6}$. Non-unit fractions are built by adding unit fractions. Ask students to name some other non-unit fractions. Answers will vary. Possible answers: $\frac{3}{16}, \frac{2}{7}, \frac{4}{5}$

Invite students to invent more sidewalk problems using sevenths, then eighths, ninths, and tenths. Ask a student volunteer to work at the board while the rest of the students solve the problems at their seats. Be sure students write an equation for each problem that is presented.

▶ Add Fractions Without Fraction Bars WHOLE CLASS

Ask students to turn their MathBoards over to the blank side. Present the following addition equations and ask everyone to complete them without using the fraction bars.

$$\frac{3}{8} + \frac{2}{8} =$$

$$\frac{2}{5} + \frac{3}{5} =$$

$$\frac{4}{9} + \frac{2}{9} + \frac{1}{9} =$$

Discuss the results.

● Which part of each fraction did not change when you added the fractions? the bottom numeral, or denominator

● How do you find the top numeral, or numerator, for the total? Add the numerators of the given fractions to get the numerator for the sum.

● Did any of these fractions add to one whole? yes; the second pair

Teaching Note

What to Expect from Students
Some students may be confused about equivalent fractions when talking about unit and non-unit fractions. For example, the non-unit fraction $\frac{2}{4}$ is equivalent to the unit fraction $\frac{1}{2}$. A fraction is a unit fraction if it describes one of the equal parts only (as $\frac{1}{2}$ does). It is not necessary to discuss this if students do not bring it up on their own.

Class Management

If students need more practice adding fractions with like denominators without using fraction bars, have them work in pairs or small groups to create and solve more addition questions. Encourage them to share and discuss their answers.

Teaching the Lesson (continued)

Activity 2

Fractions in Context

 25 MINUTES

Goal: Apply knowledge of fractions to real-life situations.

Materials: MathBoard materials; Student Activity Book pages 183–184

✔ **NCTM Standards:**
Number and Operations
Connection

Teaching Note

Watch For! Some students might confuse the "other" part with the whole. For example, they might say that E makes up $\frac{1}{4}$ of "Emily" because there is one E and there are four other letters. If so, ask them to find the total number of letters first and emphasize that this number is the whole.

▶ **Observe Fractions in the Classroom** [WHOLE CLASS]

Have the students discuss some fractional amounts that relate to the classroom. It is important to emphasize that students need to find the total, or whole, first. Some examples include:

● How many people are in the classroom? possible answer: 26

● How many people in the classroom are teachers? possible answer: 1

● What fraction of all the people in the room are teachers? $\frac{1}{26}$

● What fraction of all the people in the room are students? How do you know? $\frac{25}{26}$, because the whole has 26 equal parts and 25 of them are students

Write one or two students' names on the board. (For example, Emily and Waneta.)

● What fraction of Emily's name is the letter E? How do you know? $\frac{1}{5}$, because there are 5 letters altogether and one of them is an E.

● What fraction of Waneta's name is the letter A? How do you know? $\frac{2}{6}$, because there are 6 letters altogether and 2 of them are the letter A.

● What fraction of my fingers have a ring? possible answer: $\frac{1}{10}$.

● What fraction of the class is wearing blue today? Answers will vary.

If time permits, invite students to think of other fractions they can observe in the room.

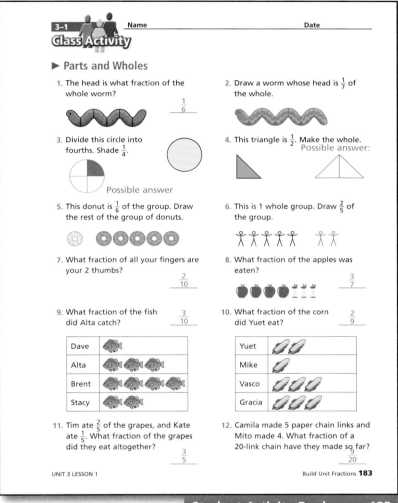

Student Activity Book page 183

Student Activity Book page 183

Teaching Note

Math Background The best way to divide the circle into fourths in exercise 3 is to draw the lines through the center. Otherwise it is very difficult to split the circle into equal parts. If necessary, remind students that the word *fourths* means four *equal* parts.

Teaching Note

What to Expect from Students There are several correct answers for exercise 4. Because the triangle is scalene, there are six possible geometric wholes; each side can be matched to its corresponding side by reflecting or rotating the triangle.

Students may also show the whole as two separate triangles.

▶ Parts and Wholes WHOLE CLASS

To emphasize that a unit fraction is one *equal* part of a whole, draw this figure on the class board. Discuss the fraction of the circle that is shaded.

● **Does the shaded section show $\frac{1}{3}$? Why or why not?**
No. Three of the shaded sections won't completely fill the circle.

● **Why might someone think that it shows $\frac{1}{3}$?** There are 3 sections and 1 section is shaded, but the sections aren't the same size.

● **What fraction does the shaded section show? Why?** The shaded section shows $\frac{1}{4}$ because the circle can be divided into 4 parts that are the exact size of the shaded section.

Have students look at Student Activity Book page 183. Read and discuss the exercises as a class. When a drawing is required, send several volunteers to the board while the others draw on the back of their MathBoard or on a sheet of paper.

Activity continued ▶

Teaching the Lesson (continued)

Activity 2

Class Management

If the students understand the material well, they can complete the activity in pairs or small groups. Exercise 20 may still require a class discussion.

Teaching Note

Fluency During this unit, it is important that students maintain and improve their knowledge of basic multiplication and division. You will find suggestions for games and practice at the end of the Unit 3 Overview.

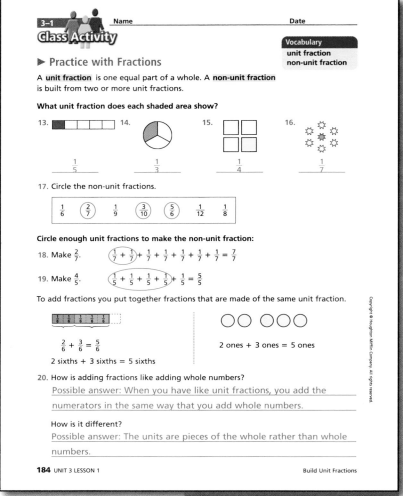

Student Activity Book page 184

▶ Practice With Fractions WHOLE CLASS

Discuss the definitions and exercises on Student Activity Book page 184.

Discuss the last question in more detail. Emphasize that in math we always add like to like—tens to tens, ones to ones, sixths to sixths. If we added 2 tens and 3 ones, we would not get 5 of *anything* because the units are not the same. This rule applies to fractions, too. We add only *like* unit fractions. Adding fractions is different from adding whole numbers only because the units are pieces of the whole rather than whole numbers.

② Extending the Lesson

Differentiated Instruction Activities for Individualizing

Intervention
for students having difficulty

PAIRS

Create a Whole

Materials: identical small items in 2 colors (counters, pattern blocks, plastic tags from bread)

One student chooses a quantity of identical items of the same color. A partner chooses a quantity of the same item in the other color. Pairs put their items together. They name the unit fraction and the fraction of the whole that each color represents.

The unit fraction is $\frac{1}{7}$. $\frac{3}{7}$ of the tags are blue and $\frac{4}{7}$ of the tags are pink.

On Level
for students having success

PAIRS

Divide the Whole

Materials: grid paper

Students take turns drawing a rectangle on the grid paper. Together, they investigate different ways to divide the rectangle evenly, using the grid. Students write the corresponding unit fraction and then add the fractions together to make one whole.

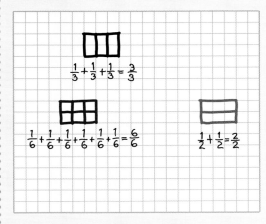

$\frac{1}{3} + \frac{1}{3} + \frac{1}{3} = \frac{3}{3}$

$\frac{1}{6} + \frac{1}{6} + \frac{1}{6} + \frac{1}{6} + \frac{1}{6} + \frac{1}{6} = \frac{6}{6}$

$\frac{1}{2} + \frac{1}{2} = \frac{2}{2}$

Challenge
for students seeking a challenge

INDIVIDUALS

Describe with Fractions

Students think of a topic to investigate, such as favorite color. They survey at least 10 of their classmates and create a pictograph to represent the data. Then they summarize the results with fractional statements.

Favorite Color

$\frac{3}{10}$ of the people prefer red, $\frac{2}{10}$ prefer yellow, $\frac{4}{10}$ prefer blue, and $\frac{1}{10}$ prefer green.

 Math Writing Prompt

Intervention

Draw a Picture
Draw a picture to show that $\frac{5}{5}$ is the same as one whole. Write an addition equation with unit fractions to go with your picture.

 Math Writing Prompt

On Level

Analyze
You are checking your friend's homework and find this:
$\frac{5}{8} + \frac{1}{8} = \frac{6}{16}$.
Write a note to your friend explaining the error and how to fix it.

 Math Writing Prompt

Challenge

Write a Problem
Write a word problem about your favorite sport, using fractions. Solve the word problem.

③ Homework and Cumulative Review

✓ For homework, students practice adding unit fractions.

This Remembering activity is appropriate anytime after today's lesson.

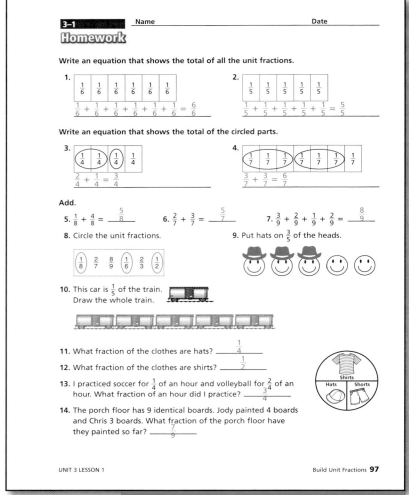

Homework and Remembering page 97

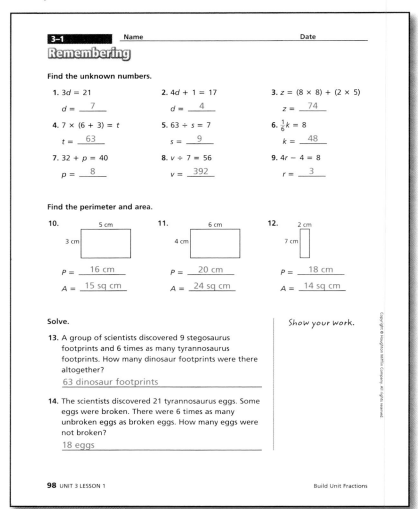

Homework and Remembering page 98

Home and School Connection

Family Letter Have students take home the Family Letter on Student Activity Book page 185. This letter explains how the concept of fractions is developed in *Math Expressions*. It gives parents and guardians a better understanding of the learning that goes on in math class and creates a bridge between school and home. A Spanish translation of this letter is on the following page in the Student Activity Book.

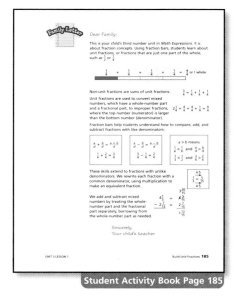

Student Activity Book Page 185

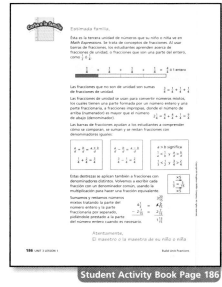

Student Activity Book Page 186

UNIT 3
LESSON 2

Compare Fractions

Lesson Objectives

- Compare unit fractions and fractions with the same denominator.
- Express and refine comparative concepts.
- Apply greater than (>) and less than (<) notation.

Vocabulary

numerator
denominator

The Day at a Glance

Today's Goals	Materials	Math Talk
Quick Practice Practice reading fractions.	Student Activity Book pages 187–188	In today's activities, the students are involved in discussion as they
1 Teaching the Lesson **A1:** Compare common fractions using fraction bars and apply findings to other fractions. **A2:** Compare fractions on the number line and express ideas about comparative fraction size.	MathBoard materials Colored pencils Grid paper Fraction Bars (Copymaster M26)	▶ compare fractions ▶ summarize the general rules about comparing fractions
2 Extending the Lesson ▶ Going Further: Fractions and Inequalities ▶ Differentiated Instruction	Homework and Remembering pages 99–100	
3 Homework and Cumulative Review	Math Journals	

Quick Practice

⏱ **5 MINUTES**   **Goal:** Practice reading fractions.

Unit Fraction Parade Send six students to the board and have them each write a unit fraction. In turn, each student gives an arm signal and the class says each fraction out loud. Everyone checks to make sure all answers are unit fractions.

① Teaching the Lesson

Visualize With Fraction Bars

 25 MINUTES

Goal: Compare common fractions using fraction bars and apply findings to other fractions.

Materials: Student Activity Book page 187

 NCTM Standard:
Number and Operations

Teaching Note

Watch For! Some students might be confused by the use of the greater than (>) and less than (<) signs. Tell them that the names of these signs come from how they are read. Emphasize that either sign can be correct for a given pair of numbers; the order the numbers are in determines which sign should be used. For example, both of the following are correct:

- $\frac{1}{6} > \frac{1}{8}$ "$\frac{1}{6}$ is greater than $\frac{1}{8}$"
- $\frac{1}{8} < \frac{1}{6}$ "$\frac{1}{8}$ is less than $\frac{1}{6}$"

To help students remember the proper usage, tell them that the wide end of the symbol is nearer to the greater number.

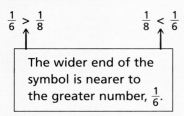

The wider end of the symbol is nearer to the greater number, $\frac{1}{6}$.

▶ Review Comparison Signs (< >) [WHOLE CLASS]

Begin by asking students which number is greater, $\frac{1}{2}$ or $\frac{1}{3}$. Then ask a volunteer to draw fraction bars to show that the answer $\frac{1}{2}$ is correct.

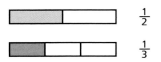

Discuss the drawing.

- How can you tell from the drawing that $\frac{1}{2}$ is greater than $\frac{1}{3}$? The shaded half is larger than the shaded third. You can see it easily because the bars are aligned.

- What has to be true about the fraction bars in order to compare the fractions? They have to be the same size to show the same whole.

- Why might the idea that $\frac{1}{2}$ is greater than $\frac{1}{3}$ be confusing? Because 3 is greater than 2, some people might expect the fraction with a denominator of 3 to be greater than the fraction with a denominator of 2.

On the board, write the mathematical notation that shows which fraction is greater.

$$\frac{1}{2} > \frac{1}{3} \qquad\qquad \frac{1}{3} < \frac{1}{2}$$

Review this notation with the class.

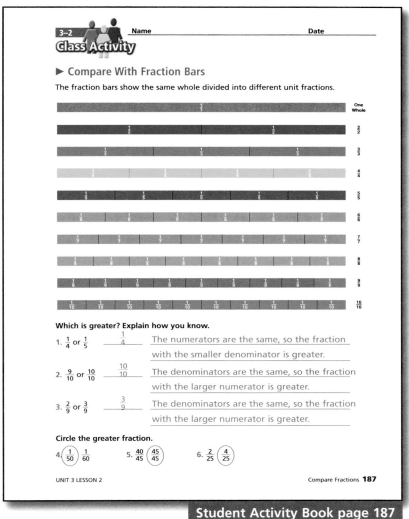

Student Activity Book page 187

▶ **Compare With Fraction Bars** WHOLE CLASS

Have the students turn to Student Activity Book page 187. Discuss the fractions to the right of the fraction bars. If necessary, remind students that when the numerator and denominator are the same, the fraction is the same as the whole, or 1.

Ask the students to complete the exercises. In exercises 4, 5, and 6, students will find that the fraction bars are not directly helpful. Instead, they must recognize these general principles:

● The larger the number of pieces in a whole, the smaller each piece must be. When the numerators are the same, the greater fraction has the smaller denominator.

● When comparing fractions with like denominators, the pieces are all the same size. The greater fraction has the greater numerator, or number of pieces.

Activity 2

Visualize With Number Lines

 25 MINUTES

Goal: Compare fractions on the number line and express ideas about comparative fraction size.

Materials: MathBoard materials

 NCTM Standard:
Number and Operations

Teaching Note

Watch For! Fractions on number lines are difficult for many students to understand. Students may think that the fraction is the line marked by the label rather than the part of the number line from 0 to that label. Be sure everyone understands that the labels show the total number of unit fractions so far $\frac{n}{d}$. is the sum of n of the unit fractions $\frac{1}{d}$:

$$\underbrace{\frac{n}{d} = \frac{1}{d} + \frac{1}{d} + \ldots + \frac{1}{d} + \frac{1}{d}}_{n \text{ addends}}$$

 Class Management

If you do not have a class MathBoard, create an overhead transparency by tracing the appropriate fraction bars on a student MathBoard. Alternatively, use a yardstick and chalk to draw a fraction bar on the board, thus reinforcing the ruler analogy. For convenience, use a 36-inch length for thirds, fourths, and sixths. Mark the divisions as follows:

• every 12 inches for thirds

• every 9 inches for fourths

• every 6 inches for sixths

Separately, use a 35-inch length for fifths, marking the divisions 7 inches apart.

▶ **Construct Number Lines** WHOLE CLASS

Distribute the MathBoard materials. Ask students to write unit fractions centered above the fraction bar that shows thirds. On the class MathBoard, label the fraction bar as a *number line*. As you label each third, write a plus sign between the unit fractions above to show that you are recording the total of the thirds so far.

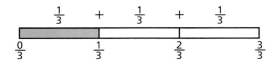

Point out that a number line is like a ruler. We label the endpoints of the number line rather than the spaces. A number line adds as it goes, as does a ruler, and the labels show the total length so far. For example, $\frac{2}{3}$ is the total of $\frac{1}{3} + \frac{1}{3}$ and $\frac{3}{3}$ is the total of $\frac{1}{3} + \frac{1}{3} + \frac{1}{3}$.

In a similar way, have the students label the fraction bars that show fourths, fifths, and sixths as number lines.

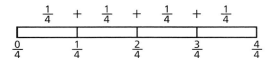

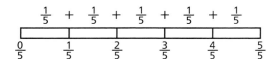

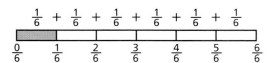

Ask everyone to shade $\frac{1}{6}$ of the appropriate number line. Then ask them to shade $\frac{2}{6}$, followed by $\frac{3}{6}$.

▶ Compare Fractions on the Number Line WHOLE CLASS

Allow the class ample opportunity to practice comparing fractions using the number lines they created. Ask a volunteer to go to the board as the class recorder. Students take turns selecting two fractions either from the same number line or from two different number lines. The class discusses which fraction is greater and why. The class recorder writes the inequality on the board.

▶ Summarize the Big Ideas WHOLE CLASS

Have the class discuss the main ideas about comparing fractions. Let students initiate the discussion and encourage them to use the terms *numerator* and *denominator* whenever possible. Ask questions and elicit examples to ensure all topics are covered:

- If two fractions are unit fractions, which one is greater? The one with the smaller denominator is greater, for example, $\frac{1}{3}$ is greater than $\frac{1}{7}$.

- Why is this true? Because a smaller denominator means the whole has been divided into fewer parts, and so each part is larger.

- Unit fractions all have the same numerator. What is it? 1; for example, $\frac{1}{2}$ and $\frac{1}{4}$

- If two fractions have the same numerator—2, for example— which fraction is greater? The one with the smaller denominator is greater. These fractions are built from unit fractions; for example, $\frac{2}{5}$ is greater than $\frac{2}{9}$.

- If two fractions have the same denominator, which one is greater? The one with the greater numerator is the greater fraction. We are taking more pieces of the same size; for example, $\frac{7}{8}$ is greater than $\frac{3}{8}$.

- What if two fractions have a numerator and denominator that are the same, such as $\frac{4}{4}$ or $\frac{8}{8}$? Which fraction is greater? They are the same size. They are both equal to one whole.

Teaching Note

Math Background Comparing fractions using number lines is very similar to comparing them using fraction bars. The left sides of the number lines, representing 0, are aligned. Because the labels on the number lines tell the distance from 0, the fraction that is farther to the right is greater. Labeling cumulatively in this way eliminates the need to shade the portion from 0 up to a fraction.

Teaching Note

Memory Aid Students may find it useful to think of the <u>n</u>umerator as the <u>n</u>umber of pieces and the <u>d</u>enominator as the <u>d</u>ivisions of the whole. (The <u>d</u>enominator is also the number that is <u>d</u>own while the numerator is <u>n</u>ot.)

$$\frac{\text{numerator} \atop \text{number of pieces} \longrightarrow}{\text{denominator} \atop \text{divisions}}\begin{array}{l} n \\ \\ d \end{array}$$

② Extending the Lesson

Going Further: Fractions and Inequalities

Goal: Write inequality signs to compare fractions.

Materials: colored pencils, Student Activity Book page 188

✔ **NCTM Standards:**
Number and Operations
Representation

▶ Compare Unequal Fractions [INDIVIDUALS]

Read and discuss the instructions with the class. Be sure students know that they need to shade new parts of the bars for each pair of fractions. In order for the activity to be successful, they must also follow the trail in order. This will guarantee that useful space is left on the fraction bars to allow for the remaining comparisons. If possible, students should use a different color at each step so that they can easily make visual comparisons.

As students complete the activity, they will encounter choices of sections to shade. Any option is acceptable, providing the sections can be compared vertically. For example, this shading lets you compare $\frac{1}{2}$ to $\frac{2}{3}$:

$\frac{1}{2}$		$\frac{1}{2}$	
$\frac{1}{3}$	$\frac{1}{3}$		$\frac{1}{3}$

This shading does not:

$\frac{1}{2}$		$\frac{1}{2}$	
$\frac{1}{3}$		$\frac{1}{3}$	$\frac{1}{3}$

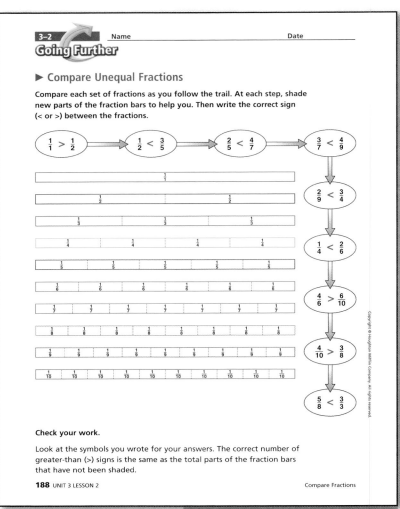

Differentiated Instruction

Extra Help Students who have difficulty with inequality signs may find it helpful to work with a partner. Encourage them to shade very lightly initially. Any mistakes with > or < will likely be evident when they find the fraction of greater-than signs while checking their work. (It is possible, however, to make errors and still have the correct fraction of greater-than signs.) If necessary, students can repeat the activity, reshading more heavily.

Intervention
for students having difficulty

PAIRS

Compare Unit Fractions

Materials: grid paper

Each student chooses a different denominator from 2 to 10. Students then draw a rectangle on grid paper with the length, in number of squares, equal to one of the denominators chosen and the width equal to the other. This rectangle represents the whole. Students shade one row or column to show a unit fraction with the denominator they chose.

Partners compare the number of squares in each shaded section to see which fraction is greater.

$\frac{1}{3} > \frac{1}{4}$

On Level
for students having success

PAIRS

Comparing Game

Materials: MathBoard materials or Fraction Bars (Copymaster M26)

Each player secretly writes a fraction that can be compared using the available fractions bars. They then show their fractions.

- If the fractions are identical, no one scores a point.
- If the fractions have like numerators or denominators, the player with the greater fraction scores a point.
- If the fractions do not have like numerators or denominators, the player with the lesser fraction scores a point.

10 points is a winning score.

Jon	Stefanie	point to:
$\frac{2}{3}$	$\frac{6}{7}$	Jon
$\frac{3}{4}$	$\frac{3}{8}$	Jon
$\frac{2}{6}$	$\frac{3}{6}$	Stefanie

Challenge
for students seeking a challenge

PAIRS

Inequalities in Real Life

To park at a downtown parking lot costs $0.50 for every $\frac{1}{4}$ hour or less. Students write inequalities using <, >, ≤, or ≥ to show how many hours they might have parked if they paid a given amount of money, for example, $2.50, $5.00, or $6.00. One partner names an amount and the other records the inequality. Then partners reverse roles.

t = time parked
For $2.50, $1 < t \le 1\frac{1}{4}$
For $5.00, $2\frac{1}{4} < t \le 2\frac{1}{2}$
For $6.00, $2\frac{3}{4} < t \le 3$

 Math Writing Prompt

Intervention

In Your Own Words

Explain how to tell the greater fraction when the denominators are the same. Use $\frac{6}{10}$ and $\frac{4}{10}$ as an example.

 Math Writing Prompt

On Level

Compare and Contrast

How are fraction bars and number lines alike? How are they different? How do you compare fractions using each of them?

 Math Writing Prompt

Challenge

Guess and Test

To show that $\frac{2}{9} < \frac{3}{6}$, compare both to a fraction that shares a numerator with one and a denominator with the other:

- $\frac{2}{9} < \frac{3}{9} < \frac{3}{6}$ • $\frac{2}{9} < \frac{2}{6} < \frac{3}{6}$.

Will this method work for any two fractions? Give examples.

 # Homework and Cumulative Review

3-2
Homework **Goal:** Additional Practice

✓ For homework, students compare fractions.

3-2
Remembering **Goal:** Cumulative Review

This Remembering activity is appropriate anytime after today's lesson.

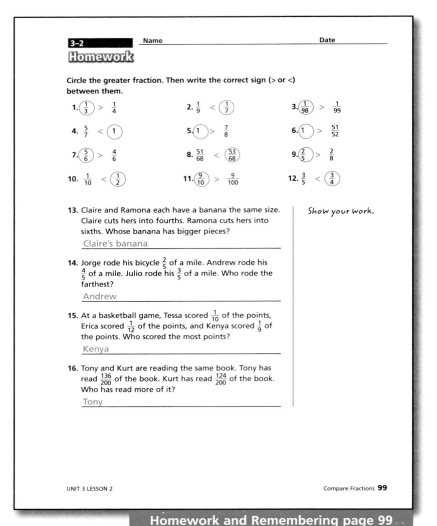

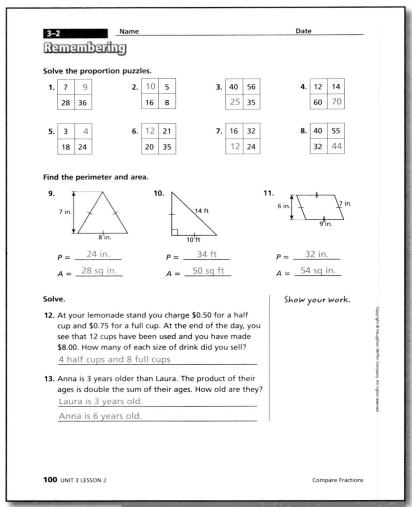

Homework and Remembering page 99

Homework and Remembering page 100

Home or School Activity

 Math Connection

Measuring Carpenters, tailors, and others often measure small items using fractions of an inch. Have students assemble a collection of items less than one inch long and measure them as acccurately as possible using a ruler. They can order the items by length and list the measurements from smallest to greatest.

Object	Length in inches
Letter A	$\frac{5}{16}$
Thumbtack	$\frac{3}{8}$
Macaroni	$\frac{7}{8}$

Subtract Fractions

Lesson Objectives

- **Subtract like fractions and mixed numbers.**
- **Understand simple algebraic notation for fractions.**
- **Solve problems with algebraic notation.**

The Day at a Glance

Today's Goals	Materials	123 Math Talk
Quick Practice Practice writing and comparing fractions.	Student Activity Book pages 189–190	In today's activities, the students are involved in discussion as they
1 Teaching the Lesson **A1:** Solve word problems that involve simple subtraction of like fractions. **A2:** Use simple algebraic notation to express an unknown numerator (*n*) or denominator (*d*).	Index cards Homework and Remembering pages 101–102 Math Journals	▶ share strategies for solving subtraction problems involving fractions ▶ review the terms *numerator* and *denominator*
2 Extending the Lesson ▶ Differentiated Instruction		▶ use Solve and Discuss for fraction word problems
3 Homework and Cumulative Review		

Quick Practice

 5 MINUTES   **Goal:** Practice writing and comparing fractions.

Small Fraction Parade: Begin by writing the fraction $\frac{1}{2}$ on the board. Send six students to the board. The first student writes a unit fraction smaller than $\frac{1}{2}$. The next student writes a unit fraction smaller than the one just written. Continue in this way until each student has had a turn.

$$\frac{1}{2} \quad \frac{1}{6} \quad \frac{1}{10} \quad \frac{1}{12} \quad \frac{1}{20} \quad \frac{1}{40} \quad \frac{1}{96}$$

Have the class say each fraction aloud after it is written. Have the class check to be sure each fraction is smaller than the previous one.

① Teaching the Lesson

Subtract Like Fractions

 20 MINUTES

Goal: Solve word problems that involve simple subtraction of like fractions.

 NCTM Standards:
Number and Operations
Problem Solving

Teaching Note

What to Expect from Students

Some students may make a drawing to solve the problem. Others will be able to subtract the two fractions in their current form.

$$\frac{5}{8} - \frac{3}{8} = \frac{2}{8}$$

Others might make a chain of five unit fractions (with or without the corresponding fraction bar) and cross out three of them to show what is really happening.

$$\cancel{\frac{1}{8}} + \cancel{\frac{1}{8}} + \cancel{\frac{1}{8}} + \frac{1}{8} + \frac{1}{8}$$

Be sure to show students this method if none of the students demonstrate it. This will help clarify the process for everyone.

▶ Explore Methods of Subtraction WHOLE CLASS

Send several volunteers to the board to work while the other students work at their seats. Ask them to solve the following word problem, using any method:

- We had $\frac{5}{8}$ of a pizza. Then we ate $\frac{3}{8}$ of it. How much pizza is left? $\frac{2}{8}$

Have students share and discuss their methods with the class. Then ask students to solve this problem using numerical methods:

- If $\frac{6}{7}$ of the class was in school and $\frac{2}{7}$ of the class went to the library, what fraction of the class is left? $\frac{4}{7}$

$$\frac{6}{7} - \frac{2}{7} = \frac{4}{7} \quad or \quad \cancel{\frac{1}{7}} + \cancel{\frac{1}{7}} + \frac{1}{7} + \frac{1}{7} + \frac{1}{7} + \frac{1}{7}$$

Encourage those who made a subtraction drawing the first time to now write chains of unit fractions (without the corresponding fraction bar).

Invite several students to contribute subtraction word problems of their own for everyone to solve.

▶ Subtract a Fraction From One Whole WHOLE CLASS

Again, have several students work at the board. Present this problem:

- A herd of zebras is traveling north. Suddenly, $\frac{2}{5}$ of the herd turns around and heads south. What fraction of the zebras is still traveling north? $\frac{3}{5}$

$$\frac{5}{5} - \frac{2}{5} = \frac{3}{5} \quad or \quad \cancel{\frac{1}{5}} + \cancel{\frac{1}{5}} + \frac{1}{5} + \frac{1}{5} + \frac{1}{5}$$

This problem is slightly more challenging because the first number, 1, is not stated explicitly nor is it given in fractional terms. Some students may be able to use mental math. Others will want to write the one whole as a fraction before they proceed.

Activity 2

Algebraic Notation

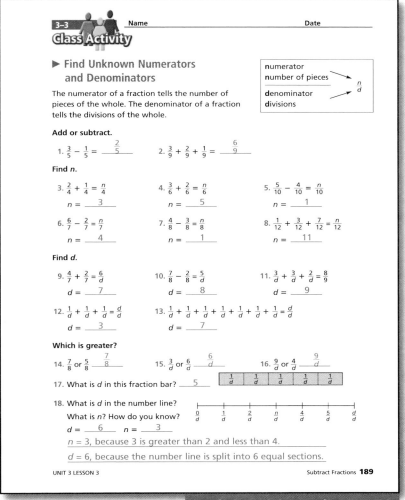

▶ Find Unknown Numerators and Denominators

The numerator of a fraction tells the number of pieces of the whole. The denominator of a fraction tells the divisions of the whole.

numerator
number of pieces

denominator
divisions

$\dfrac{n}{d}$

Add or subtract.

1. $\dfrac{3}{5} - \dfrac{1}{5} = \dfrac{2}{5}$

2. $\dfrac{3}{9} + \dfrac{2}{9} + \dfrac{1}{9} = \dfrac{6}{9}$

Find n.

3. $\dfrac{2}{4} + \dfrac{1}{4} = \dfrac{n}{4}$
   $n = 3$

4. $\dfrac{3}{6} + \dfrac{2}{6} = \dfrac{n}{6}$
   $n = 5$

5. $\dfrac{5}{10} - \dfrac{4}{10} = \dfrac{n}{10}$
   $n = 1$

6. $\dfrac{6}{7} - \dfrac{2}{7} = \dfrac{n}{7}$
   $n = 4$

7. $\dfrac{4}{8} - \dfrac{3}{8} = \dfrac{n}{8}$
   $n = 1$

8. $\dfrac{1}{12} + \dfrac{3}{12} + \dfrac{7}{12} = \dfrac{n}{12}$
   $n = 11$

Find d.

9. $\dfrac{4}{7} + \dfrac{2}{7} = \dfrac{6}{d}$
   $d = 7$

10. $\dfrac{7}{8} - \dfrac{2}{8} = \dfrac{5}{d}$
    $d = 8$

11. $\dfrac{3}{d} + \dfrac{3}{d} + \dfrac{2}{d} = \dfrac{8}{9}$
    $d = 9$

12. $\dfrac{1}{d} + \dfrac{1}{d} + \dfrac{1}{d} = \dfrac{d}{d}$
    $d = 3$

13. $\dfrac{1}{d} + \dfrac{1}{d} + \dfrac{1}{d} + \dfrac{1}{d} + \dfrac{1}{d} + \dfrac{1}{d} + \dfrac{1}{d} = \dfrac{d}{d}$
    $d = 7$

Which is greater?

14. $\dfrac{7}{8}$ or $\dfrac{5}{8}$ $\dfrac{7}{8}$

15. $\dfrac{3}{d}$ or $\dfrac{6}{d}$ $\dfrac{6}{d}$

16. $\dfrac{9}{d}$ or $\dfrac{4}{d}$ $\dfrac{9}{d}$

17. What is d in this fraction bar? 5

18. What is d in the number line?
    What is n? How do you know?

    $d = 6$ $n = 3$
    $n = 3$, because 3 is greater than 2 and less than 4.
    $d = 6$, because the number line is split into 6 equal sections.

⏱ **30 MINUTES**

Goal: Use simple algebraic notation to express an unknown numerator (n) or denominator (d).

Materials: Student Activity Book pages 189–190

✔ **NCTM Standards:**
Number and Operations
Algebra

✔ Ongoing Assessment

Help students verbalize their understanding by asking them such questions as:

▶ How did you find n?

▶ What part of the fraction doesn't change when you add or subtract? How did that help you find d?

▶ If the denominators were given to you and the numerators were both n, would you be able to compare the fractions?

▶ Find Unknown Numerators and Denominators

WHOLE GROUPS

Review the terms *numerator* and *denominator*.

● **What part is the numerator? the denominator?** the top number; the bottom number

● **What do the numbers mean?** The numerator is the number of pieces and the denominator tells the divisions of the whole.

Explain that we can use the letters n and d to show an unknown numerator or denominator: $\dfrac{n}{d}$. When we know that the numerator and denominator are the same number, we can write $\dfrac{d}{d}$. Have students complete exercises 1–18 on Student Activity Book page 189.

Activity continued ▶

Activity 2

Differentiated Instruction

English Learners The problems in Real-World Fractions are also well suited to the Student Pairs method. This will give English learners more practice saying and hearing fractions.

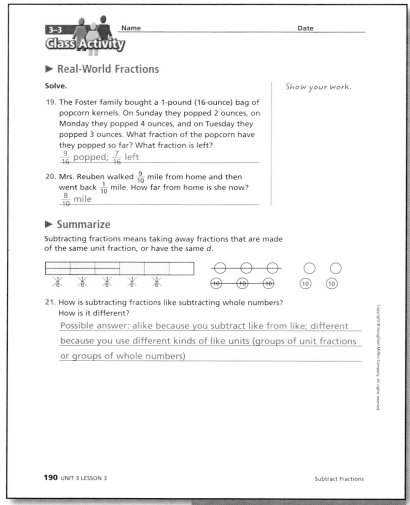

Student Activity Book page 190

▶ Real-World Fractions WHOLE CLASS

Use Solve and Discuss for these word problems. If you feel students are ready, invite them to share their work through a class discussion.

▶ Summarize WHOLE CLASS

Have students discuss subtracting fractions. Comparing the subtraction of fractions to the subtraction of whole numbers helps students see that the two concepts are not as different as they first appear. In both cases, we subtract like from like. The only difference is the kind of like units (groups of unit fractions or groups of whole numbers).

② Extending the Lesson

Intervention
for students having difficulty

PAIRS

Fraction Subtractions

Materials: 10 index cards each showing $\frac{1}{10}$

Partners begin by creating a subtraction equation whose answer is $\frac{1}{10}$.

One partner lays out any number of the index cards and writes the corresponding fraction. The other partner removes enough of the cards to leave $\frac{1}{10}$ and finishes writing the equation.

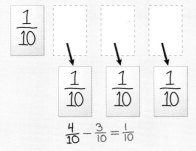

$$\frac{4}{10} - \frac{3}{10} = \frac{1}{10}$$

Repeat for all possible answers $\frac{n}{10}$.

On Level
for students having success

PAIRS

Fraction Puzzles

Each student creates and solves a fraction addition or subtraction question. They create a fraction puzzle by rewriting it on a separate sheet and replacing some numbers with n or d, as appropriate. Students exchange questions and try to solve for the unknown.

For these examples, the puzzles could be $\frac{4}{d} - \frac{1}{d} = \frac{3}{5}$ and $\frac{n}{12} + \frac{n}{12} = \frac{6}{12}$.

Challenge
for students seeking a challenge

INDIVIDUALS

Solve the Problem

Pose this question to the students:

What fraction when added to $\frac{1}{12}$ and to itself twice has a sum of $\frac{10}{12}$?

Students write an equation that corresponds to the question. They find a solution to the problem using any method and explain their thinking.

$$\frac{n}{d} + \frac{1}{12} + \frac{n}{d} + \frac{n}{d} = \frac{10}{12}$$

$$\frac{3}{12} + \frac{1}{12} + \frac{3}{12} + \frac{3}{12} = \frac{10}{12}$$

 Math Writing Prompt

Intervention

Draw a Picture

Draw a picture with a fraction bar that shows how to subtract fractions with like denominators. Use $\frac{5}{8} - \frac{2}{8}$ as an example.

 Math Writing Prompt

On Level

Investigate Math

Describe some real-life fraction subtraction situations that might occur while preparing and serving a meal.

 Math Writing Prompt

Challenge

Explain Your Thinking

Your goal is to exercise for 4 hours this week. If you know the number of minutes you exercised on Monday and Tuesday, how do you find the fraction of your goal left to complete?

 **Homework and Cumulative Review**

3-3
Homework **Goal:** Additional Practice

✔ Include students' work for page 101 as part of their portfolios.

3-3
Remembering **Goal:** Cumulative Review

This Remembering activity is appropriate anytime after today's lesson.

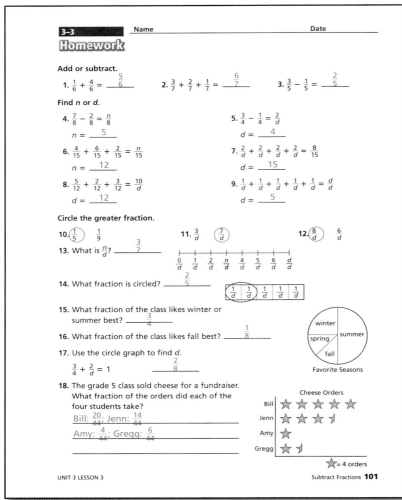

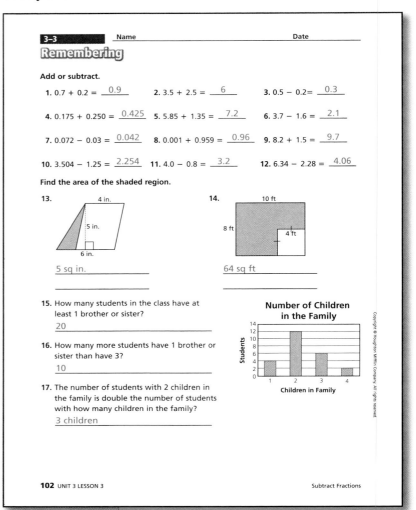

Homework and Remembering page 101

Homework and Remembering page 102

Home or School Activity

 Real-World Connection

Printable Area The pages of books have margins around the edges where there is no print. Have students measure the dimensions of a full page from a book and also the dimensions of the rectangular portion containing print. Then have them calculate the fraction of the page that the margins take up.

Fractional Addends of One

Lesson Objectives

- Practice adding and subtracting fractions with like denominators.
- Build fractions from unit fractions and identify how many more it will take to make one whole.

Vocabulary
addend
sum

The Day at a Glance

Today's Goals	Materials	Math Talk
Quick Practice Practice writing and comparing fractions.	MathBoard materials	In today's activities, the students are involved in discussion as they
1 Teaching the Lesson A1: Review like fractions and generate fraction partners. A2: Solve problems that involve like fractions and fraction partners.	Student Activity Book pages 191–192 Identical small items in 2 colors (counters, pattern blocks, plastic tags from bread)	▶ find fraction partners ▶ describe how to find unknown addends
2 Extending the Lesson ▶ Differentiated Instruction	Unknown Addend Cards (Copymaster M27)	
3 Homework and Cumulative Review	Homework and Remembering pages 103–104 Math Journals	

Quick Practice

 5 MINUTES   **Goal:** Practice writing and comparing fractions.

Small Fraction Parade: Begin by writing the fraction $\frac{1}{2}$ on the board. Send six students to the board. The first student writes a unit fraction smaller than $\frac{1}{2}$. The next student writes a unit fraction smaller than the one just written. Continue in this way. Have the class say the fractions as one student points to them in order. At the end, ask someone to explain why the last fraction is smaller than $\frac{1}{2}$.

1 Teaching the Lesson

Fractional Addends

 25 MINUTES

Goal: Review like fractions and generate fraction partners.

Materials: MathBoard materials

 NCTM Standard:
Number and Operations

The Learning Classroom

Building Concepts Once students have demonstrated a solid understanding of the idea behind fraction partners, or addends that total 1, allow them to write the equations without shading the fraction bar. Students who are struggling should continue with the shading until they are comfortable with the concept.

▶ **Find Embedded Fourths and Sixths** WHOLE CLASS

Distribute the MathBoards and direct students' attention to the fraction bar that shows fourths.

Ask the students how many fourths there are in one whole. Have everyone write, above the fraction bar, the equation that shows how the unit fractions add up to $\frac{4}{4}$, or one whole. Demonstrate on the class MathBoard.

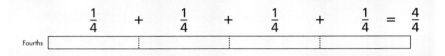

Tell the students that you want to find all the pairs of fractions, or fraction partners, that add to $\frac{4}{4}$. Have them shade the first section of the fraction bar and write the corresponding equation to the right.

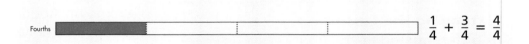

Elicit the other equations from the students. They should shade one more section of the fraction bar each time and then generate the other fraction partners.

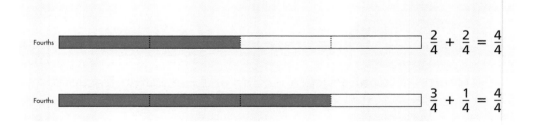

Have students independently repeat the activity using the fraction bar that shows sixths. Invite a volunteer to work on the class MathBoard.

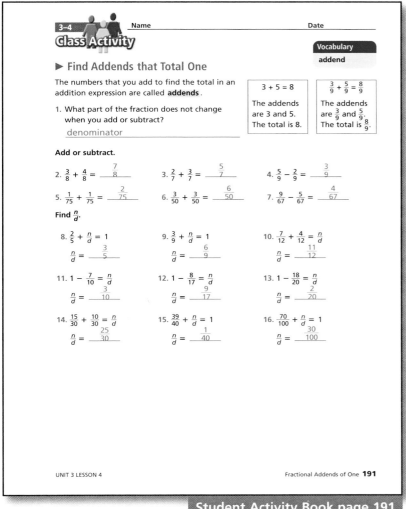

Student Activity Book page 191

▶ Find Addends that Total One [SMALL GROUPS]

Discuss the terms *addend* and *sum* with the class. Explain that when an entire fraction is unknown, not just the numerator or denominator, we can show the unknown fraction as $\frac{n}{d}$. Write these equations on the board and ask students to identify whether an addend or the total is missing:

- $\frac{4}{6} + \frac{n}{d} = 1$ addend
- $\frac{n}{d} + \frac{1}{8} = 1$ addend
- $\frac{1}{16} + \frac{3}{16} = \frac{n}{d}$ total

Ask the class to find $\frac{n}{d}$ in these equations:

- $\frac{n}{d} + \frac{1}{6} = 1$ $\frac{n}{d} = \frac{5}{6}$
- $1 - \frac{1}{6} = \frac{n}{d}$ $\frac{n}{d} = \frac{5}{6}$

Point out that the answers are the same and that students can think of unknown addend questions as subtraction questions. Students work in small groups or in pairs to complete the exercises.

Alternate Approach

MathBoards To help students understand visually that unknown addend questions are equivalent to subtraction questions, have students shade $\frac{1}{6}$ of the appropriate fraction bar and write the sum of unit fractions that give one whole above the bar.

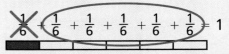

Subtracting involves crossing out the shaded sixth and seeing what is left. Finding the unknown addend involves looking at the unshaded sixths, which amounts to the same thing.

Teaching Note

Language and Vocabulary An addend is also known as a *summand*. In a subtraction expression, the corresponding terms are *minuend* (which derives from the Latin word for "diminish") and *subtrahend* (which derives from the Latin word for "subtract"). More commonly known is the term *difference*, which is the result of a subtraction.

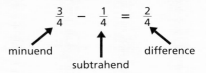

$$\frac{3}{4} - \frac{1}{4} = \frac{2}{4}$$

minuend   subtrahend   difference

Teaching the Lesson (continued)

Activity 2

Unknown Addends and Real-Life Applications

 25 MINUTES

Goal: Solve problems that involve like fractions and fraction partners.

Materials: Student Activity Book page 192

 NCTM Standards:
Number and Operations
Problem Solving

Ongoing Assessment

Visit the groups and ensure that students understand the idea of addends in the context of the problems. Ask questions such as:

► How many seventeenths are in one whole?

► How many more seventeenths are needed to make one whole?

► How can you write that as an equation?

Student Activity Book page 192

► Unknown Addends in Real Life SMALL GROUPS

Have students read question 17 on Student Activity Book page 192 and draw an arrow to the woman's location on the sidewalk. Discuss the problem.

● How did you figure out where to draw the arrow? By counting 8 parts of the sidewalk.

● Should the arrow be at the beginning, the middle, or the end of the eighth part? Why? at the end; if it isn't at the end, she hasn't walked the full 8 parts yet.

● How far does she have to go to reach the end? 2 more parts

● How can you say that as a fraction? $\frac{2}{10}$

● How can you find the answer without the picture? You can figure out what you have to add to $\frac{8}{10}$ to get $\frac{10}{10}$, or one whole.

Read exercise 18. Ask students to draw an arrow to the man's location on the sidewalk. Have students work in small groups to complete the page.

② Extending the Lesson

Differentiated Instruction — Activities for Individualizing

Intervention
for students having difficulty

`PAIRS`

Fraction Partner Practice

Materials: identical small items in 2 colors (counters, pattern blocks, plastic tags from bread)

Students take turns thinking of a fraction. Together, using the items to help them, they figure out its fraction partner and write the equation.

The fraction partner for $\frac{4}{7}$ is $\frac{3}{7}$; the equation is $\frac{4}{7} + \frac{3}{7} = 1$.

On Level
for students having success

`PAIRS`

Matching Game

Materials: Unknown Addend Cards (Copymaster M27)

Cards are laid out face down. Students take turns flipping over a pair of cards. If one card shows an equation and the other shows the correct unknown addend for the equation, the player keeps the pair. Otherwise the cards are turned face down again.

$$\frac{1}{5} + \frac{n}{d} = 1 \qquad \frac{4}{5}$$

When there are no cards left to flip over, the player with the most cards wins.

Challenge
for students seeking a challenge

`INDIVIDUALS`

Write a Word Problem

Students create a word problem that corresponds to this equation:

$$\frac{10}{60} + \frac{n}{d} = \frac{45}{60}$$

Students solve the problem.

Justine has to practice piano for 45 minutes every day. In the morning she practiced for 10 minutes. What fraction of an hour does she have left to practice? $\frac{35}{60}$

 Math Writing Prompt

Intervention

In Your Own Words

Explain the terms *addend* and *fraction partner*. Use examples to illustrate.

 Math Writing Prompt

On Level

Summarize

How is an unknown addend problem the same as a subtraction question?

 Math Writing Prompt

Challenge

Explain Your Thinking

Explain two different ways to find the unknown addend in $\frac{4}{7} + \frac{n}{d} = \frac{6}{7}$.

③ Homework and Cumulative Review

3-4 Homework **Goal:** Additional Practice

Homework **Goal:** Additional Practice

 For homework, students continue doing operations with fractions.

Remembering **Goal:** Cumulative Review

This Remembering activity is appropriate anytime after today's lesson.

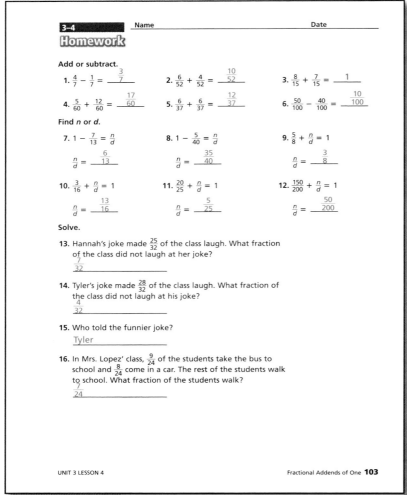

Homework and Remembering page 103

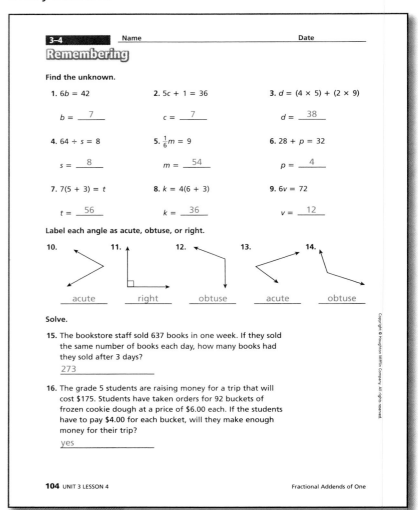

Homework and Remembering page 104

Home or School Activity

 Science Connection

Our Solar System The table shows the distances of the planets from the Sun in millions of kilometers. Have students read from the chart how far light from the Sun travels to get to Pluto. Using that distance as the denominator, have them write, as a fraction, the distance sunlight travels to each other planet.

For example: Distance to Earth $= \frac{150}{5,906}$

Have students pose and solve a problem like this one using a fraction: Once sunlight reaches the Earth, how much farther does it have to travel to get to Pluto? $\frac{5,756}{5,906}$

Planet	Distance from Sun
Mercury	58
Venus	108
Earth	150
Mars	228
Jupiter	778
Saturn	1,427
Uranus	2,869
Neptune	4,498
Pluto	5,906

374 UNIT 3 LESSON 4

UNIT 3

LESSON

5

Relate Fractions and Wholes

Lesson Objectives

- **Understand that the size of a fraction depends on the size of the whole.**

- **Solve and explain open-ended word problems that relate fractions and wholes.**

The Day at a Glance

Today's Goals	Materials	123 Math Talk
Quick Practice Practice finding fraction partners.	Student Activity Book pages 193–194	In today's activities, the students are involved in discussion as they
❶ **Teaching the Lesson** A1: Explore how fractional parts change as the whole changes. A2: Represent the changing whole and observe what happens to the fraction.	Pattern blocks or Pattern Blocks (Copymaster M28) (optional) Masking tape MathBoard materials	▶ discover that fractions are relative to the whole ▶ solve problems with changing wholes
❷ **Extending the Lesson** ▶ Differentiated Instruction	Chapter books Homework and Remembering pages 105–106	▶ describe fractions of changing wholes
❸ **Homework and Cumulative Review**	Math Journals	

Quick Practice

 5 MINUTES **Goal:** Practice finding fraction partners.

How Many More to One? Invite six students to the board and ask them to stand in pairs. The first person in each pair writes a fraction that is not a unit fraction and also writes a plus sign. The other member of the pair writes the addend that will make a total of 1, followed by "= 1." When everyone is done, ask the class to check each pair to see if it adds up to one whole.

Do these fractions add to one whole? $\frac{2}{8} + \frac{6}{8} = 1$

Together, the whole class reads the equation: "Two eighths plus six eighths equals one whole."

Teaching the Lesson

Change the Whole

 25 MINUTES

Goal: Explore how fractional parts change as the whole changes.

Materials: Student Activity Book pages 193–194; pattern blocks or Pattern Blocks (Copymaster M28) (optional); masking tape (optional); MathBoard materials (optional)

✔ **NCTM Standard:**
Number and Operations

✔ Ongoing Assessment

Make sure students understand the general concept of the size of a fraction being relative to the size of the whole. Ask questions such as:

▶ What fraction of the name Elizabeth is vowels?

▶ If we shorten that to Beth, what is the fraction?

▶ What if we shorten it to Liza?

If possible, use variations of a student's name when asking the questions.

▶ Discover that Fractions Are Relative to the Whole WHOLE CLASS

Invite one student to step to the front of the room to represent a fraction.

What fraction of the group of students at the front of the class is the student? $\frac{1}{1}$, or one whole

Ask three more students to come to the front and form a group of four.

● What fraction of the group is the first student now? $\frac{1}{4}$

Have one more student come to the front, forming a group of five.

● What fraction of the group is the student now? $\frac{1}{5}$

● The person did not change. Why does the person represent a different fraction? The size of the group changed.

● If the first student were in a group of 25 people, what fraction would he or she represent? $\frac{1}{25}$

Explain that the same part, in this case the student, is a different fraction of different wholes.

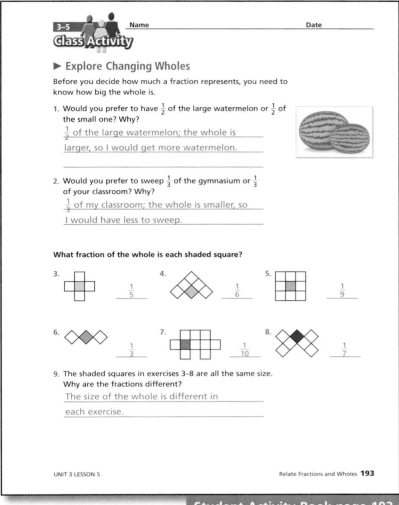

Student Activity Book page 193

The Student Activity Book page 193 contains:

3–5 Class Activity Name _____ Date _____

▶ **Explore Changing Wholes**

Before you decide how much a fraction represents, you need to know how big the whole is.

1. Would you prefer to have $\frac{1}{2}$ of the large watermelon or $\frac{1}{2}$ of the small one? Why?
   $\frac{1}{2}$ of the large watermelon; the whole is
   larger, so I would get more watermelon.

2. Would you prefer to sweep $\frac{1}{3}$ of the gymnasium or $\frac{1}{3}$ of your classroom? Why?
   $\frac{1}{3}$ of my classroom; the whole is smaller, so
   I would have less to sweep.

What fraction of the whole is each shaded square?

3. $\frac{1}{5}$ 4. $\frac{1}{6}$ 5. $\frac{1}{9}$

6. $\frac{1}{3}$ 7. $\frac{1}{10}$ 8. $\frac{1}{7}$

9. The shaded squares in exercises 3–8 are all the same size. Why are the fractions different?
   The size of the whole is different in
   each exercise.

UNIT 3 LESSON 5   Relate Fractions and Wholes **193**

Class Management

Students, kinesthetic learners in particular, may find it helpful to use pattern blocks to complete exercises 3-8.

▶ Explore Changing Wholes [PAIRS]

Discuss questions 1 and 2 on Student Activity Book page 193 with the class. Emphasize that the amount that a fraction represents depends on the size of the whole. Ask students to think of other real objects or scenarios that show this. Possible examples include:

- eating $\frac{1}{2}$ of a cherry or $\frac{1}{2}$ of an apple
- walking $\frac{1}{3}$ of a block or $\frac{1}{3}$ of a mile
- having $\frac{1}{4}$ of a dollar or $\frac{1}{4}$ of a million dollars in the bank

Students work in pairs to complete the exercises.

Activity continued ▶

❶ Teaching the Lesson (continued)

Activity 1

Teaching Note

Math Background It may seem obvious to your students that the size of the fraction depends on the size of the whole. They know that half a cherry is not the same size as half a watermelon and that a fourth of an inch is not the same as a fourth of a yard. But many real-world fraction errors stem from students' failure to take this property of fractions into account. The problems in the Student Activity Book should help students understand this concept.

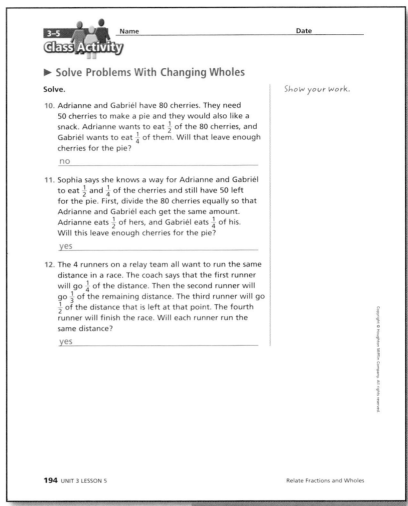

3–5
Class Activity

Name _____ Date _____

▶ Solve Problems With Changing Wholes

Solve.   *Show your work.*

10. Adrianne and Gabriél have 80 cherries. They need 50 cherries to make a pie and they would also like a snack. Adrianne wants to eat $\frac{1}{2}$ of the 80 cherries, and Gabriél wants to eat $\frac{1}{4}$ of them. Will that leave enough cherries for the pie?

    no

11. Sophia says she knows a way for Adrianne and Gabriél to eat $\frac{1}{2}$ and $\frac{1}{4}$ of the cherries and still have 50 left for the pie. First, divide the 80 cherries equally so that Adrianne and Gabriél each get the same amount. Adrianne eats $\frac{1}{2}$ of hers, and Gabriél eats $\frac{1}{4}$ of his. Will this leave enough cherries for the pie?

    yes

12. The 4 runners on a relay team all want to run the same distance in a race. The coach says that the first runner will go $\frac{1}{4}$ of the distance. Then the second runner will go $\frac{1}{3}$ of the remaining distance. The third runner will go $\frac{1}{2}$ of the distance that is left at that point. The fourth runner will finish the race. Will each runner run the same distance?

    yes

194 UNIT 3 LESSON 5   Relate Fractions and Wholes

Student Activity Book page 194

▶ Solve Problems With Changing Wholes ⟨WHOLE CLASS⟩

Use Solve and Discuss for problems 10 and 11. Ask questions to help students see the big picture:

● **Why does Sophia's plan work?** It involves making the whole smaller.

● **What happens to the amount a fraction represents when the whole gets smaller?** It gets smaller, too.

● **How can you see this in the number of cherries that Adrianne and Gabriél have for a snack?** Originally Adrianne wanted 40 cherries. With Sophia's plan she gets 20. Gabriél wanted 20 at first, and now he gets 10.

Approaching Problem 12 This problem is more challenging. Choose an approach that suits your students.

- Divide the class into groups. Give students time to think about the problem and to discuss strategies. Then ask volunteers to go to the board and to explain how they solved the problem.

- Act out a scenario: Invite four students to the front of the room to be the relay team. Have another pair of students measure a 4-yard length to represent the length of the race and mark the beginning and end with masking tape. Involve the rest of the class by asking questions such as how far a runner should move to represent his or her fraction of the race.

- Lead the class through the solution using the MathBoard materials. Begin with the fraction bar for fourths and shade $\frac{1}{4}$. Ask what the whole is for the remaining part of the race at each step.

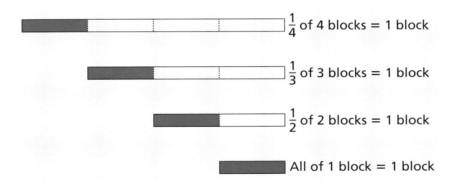

$\frac{1}{4}$ of 4 blocks = 1 block

$\frac{1}{3}$ of 3 blocks = 1 block

$\frac{1}{2}$ of 2 blocks = 1 block

All of 1 block = 1 block

The important thing for students to recognize is that the whole keeps changing. The different fractions are the same-size piece because they are each part of a different-size whole.

Differentiated Instruction

Advanced Learners Pose this version of a famous problem that illustrates the concept of the size of a fraction being relative to the size of the whole:

A flea is on the carpet and spies a dog across the room. It manages to jump halfway to the dog, but it starts to feel tired. The next jump takes it halfway to the dog again, as does each jump after that. Will the flea ever reach the dog?

In theory, the answer is "No" because no jump ever takes the flea all the way to the dog. Each half is smaller than the one before. (In practice, the flea will be so close at some point that it can bite the dog anyway.)

Activity 2

Parts and Wholes Using MathBoards

 25 MINUTES

Goal: Represent the changing whole and observe what happens to the fraction.

Materials: MathBoard materials

✔ **NCTM Standards:**
Number and Operations
Problem Solving

The Learning Classroom

Helping Community This activity is well suited to the Student Pairs approach, particularly in a class with diverse abilities. Everyone benefits when you match students who are having difficulty with students who are having success.

 **Quick Quiz**

See Assessment Guide for Unit 3 Quick Quiz 1.

▶ **Construct Parts and Wholes** [WHOLE CLASS]

Distribute the MathBoard materials. Direct students' attention to the tenths fraction bar. Ask students to represent the following problems on their MathBoards.

A train has 10 cars. The first car is painted, and the rest are not. (Have everyone shade the first car.) What fraction of the train is painted? $\frac{1}{10}$

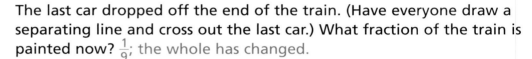

The last car dropped off the end of the train. (Have everyone draw a separating line and cross out the last car.) What fraction of the train is painted now? $\frac{1}{9}$; the whole has changed.

When the train returned to the station, another car got painted. (Have everyone shade a second car.) What fraction of the train is painted now? $\frac{2}{9}$

Then the last 2 cars were taken off the train. (Have everyone draw a new separating line and cross out the last 2 cars.) What fraction of the train is painted now? $\frac{2}{7}$

Today the fifth car was painted. (Have everyone color the fifth car.) What fraction of the train is painted now? $\frac{3}{7}$

If time permits, invite students to create other train stories using a different fraction bar on the MathBoard.

② Extending the Lesson

Intervention
for students having difficulty

PAIRS

Name That Fraction

Materials: pattern blocks of the same shape; masking tape

Mark 1 pattern block with a small piece of masking tape. Students take turns creating a small tessellation by adding other identically shaped pattern blocks. When they have finished the tessellation, they decide what fraction of the whole the marked pattern block represents.

The pattern block is $\frac{1}{5}$ of the tessellation.

On Level
for students having success

PAIRS

Compare Halves

Materials: chapter books (1 per pair)

Partners figure out the number of pages in half of each chapter in a chapter book, and then graph the results on a bar graph or pictograph.

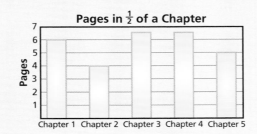

Pages in $\frac{1}{2}$ of a Chapter

For books with many chapters, students may select a few chapters to graph.

Challenge
for students seeking a challenge

PAIRS

Create the Whole

Each student draws a figure and states whether it is $\frac{1}{2}$ or $\frac{1}{3}$ of a whole. Partners finish each other's drawings to complete the whole.

$\frac{1}{3}$

Students repeat with other fractions, including non-unit fractions.

 Math Writing Prompt

Intervention

Explain Your Thinking
Explain how two different fractions can describe the same amount. Use pictures and words in your explanation.

 Math Writing Prompt

On Level

Solve the Puzzle
Two students walked to school. One was very wet when they arrived while the other was quite dry. One student said, "It started to rain when I was halfway here and I didn't have an umbrella or raincoat." The other student said, "That's exactly what happened to me!" How can this be true?

 Math Writing Prompt

Challenge

Create Your Own
Work backwards to create a word problem that uses different fractions to represent the same amount. Check that your problem works by solving it.

 **Homework and Cumulative Review**

Homework **Goal:** Additional Practice

✔ For homework, students relate fractions and wholes.

Remembering **Goal:** Cumulative Review

This Remembering activity is appropriate anytime after today's lesson.

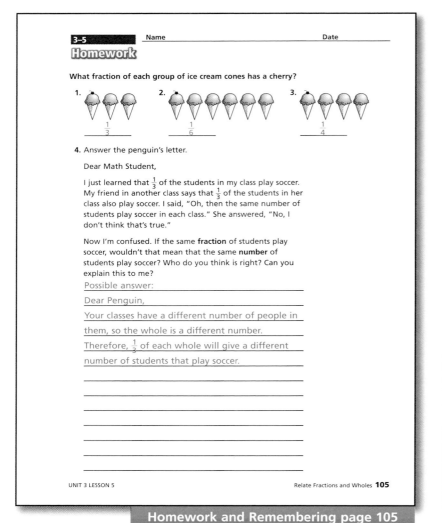

Homework and Remembering page 105

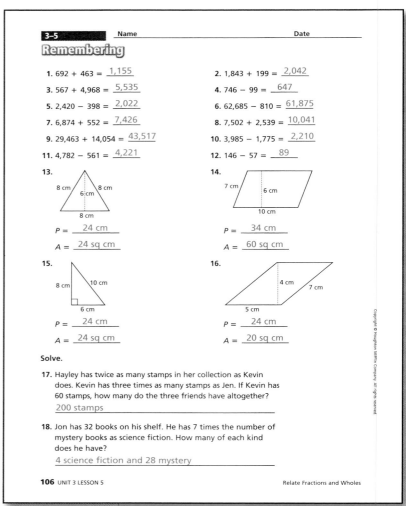

Homework and Remembering page 106

Home or School Activity

 Art Connection

Sierpinski Carpet Fractal patterns occur in nature, but many artists create fractal patterns simply for their beauty. If you enlarge one section of a fractal pattern, it looks the same as the whole. The Sierpinski carpet is an example of a fractal pattern made of decreasing ninths.

Students can make their own Sierpinski carpet. On grid paper, have them draw a square that measures 27 squares by 27 squares. Have them divide the whole square into ninths and then color the center square, as shown. Students can then divide each uncolored ninth into ninths and color the center square of each one, and so on. If you use larger grid paper or a computer, you can continue this pattern several more times. Students can also experiment with different colors.

382 UNIT 3 LESSON 5

Fractions Greater Than One

Lesson Objectives

- Represent improper fractions and mixed numbers.
- Convert between improper fractions and mixed numbers.
- Apply the terms *improper fraction* and *mixed number*.

Vocabulary
improper fraction
mixed number

The Day at a Glance

Today's Goals	Materials	Math Talk
Quick Practice Recognize fractions that add to one.	Greeting cards or photos for cutting	In today's activities, the students are involved in discussion as they
1 Teaching the Lesson **A1:** Represent improper fractions and mixed numbers numerically and with drawings. **A2:** Explore ways to convert between mixed numbers and improper fractions.	Index cards labeled 2 to 10 Homework and Remembering pages 107–108 Math Journals	► express mixed numbers and improper fractions ► change mixed numbers to improper fractions
2 Extending the Lesson ► Differentiated Instruction		► change improper fractions to mixed numbers
3 Homework and Cumulative Review		

Quick Practice

🕐 **5 MINUTES**   **Goal:** Recognize fractions that add to one.

How Many More to One? Invite six students to the board and ask them to stand in pairs. The first person in each pair writes a fraction that is not a unit fraction. The other member of the pair writes the addend that will make the fraction equal one. When they are done, ask the class to check that each pair of fractions equals one.

$$\frac{2}{8} \qquad \frac{6}{8}$$

Do these fractions add up to 1?

① Teaching the Lesson

Improper Fractions and Mixed Numbers

 20 MINUTES

Goal: Represent improper fractions and mixed numbers numerically and with drawings.

Materials: greeting cards or photos for cutting, Math Journals

 NCTM Standards:
Numbers and Operations
Representation

Teaching Note

Math Background In later lessons, students will add and subtract mixed numbers by separating the whole number part and the fractional part. Taking the time now to demonstrate that a mixed number represents the total of a whole number and a fraction will help students to separate the parts later.

▶ **Introduce Fractions Greater Than One** | WHOLE CLASS |

Write this chain of fractions on the board:

$$\frac{1}{4} + \frac{1}{4} + \frac{1}{4} + \frac{1}{4} + \frac{1}{4}$$

Ask students for the total and add "$= \frac{5}{4}$" to the chain. Introduce the term *improper fraction*. Discuss its meaning with the class and explain that it is acceptable to write a fraction in this way.

● An improper fraction has a numerator that is greater than or equal to the denominator.

Invite several students to represent and explain this fraction on the board. There are a variety of ways they can show this. Be sure they demonstrate that the fraction is more than one whole.

     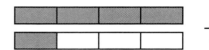

Go back to the original chain of unit fractions. Group the fractions to show that there is one whole ($\frac{4}{4}$) and $\frac{1}{4}$ more. Write the mixed number and elicit its meaning from the students.

$$\boxed{\frac{1}{4} + \frac{1}{4} + \frac{1}{4} + \frac{1}{4}} + \frac{1}{4} = 1\frac{1}{4}$$

Then present, on the board, another chain of unit fractions that totals more than one whole, for example, $\frac{1}{3} + \frac{1}{3} + \frac{1}{3} + \frac{1}{3} + \frac{1}{3}$.

Ask students to express the fraction chain as a mixed number.

● Can we make one whole? yes

● How many more thirds do we have? 2

Why do you think $1\frac{2}{3}$ is called a mixed number? It is a mixture of a whole number and a fractional part.

Be sure the class understands that $1\frac{2}{3}$ is pronounced "one **and** two thirds" and that it means the same thing as $1 + \frac{2}{3}$. To reinforce this point, ask students to write mixed numbers for the following:

$1 + \frac{1}{6}$ $2 + \frac{7}{8}$ $9 + \frac{2}{3}$

$5 + \frac{7}{10}$ $4 + \frac{11}{12}$ $20 + \frac{1}{5}$

▶ See Fractions With Several Wholes WHOLE CLASS

Draw this configuration on the board.

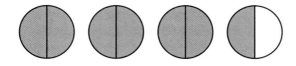

Ask the students to express the shaded parts as a mixed number and as an improper fraction. $3\frac{1}{2}$; $\frac{7}{2}$

▶ Build Mixed Numbers From Unit Fractions

WHOLE CLASS

Ask students to draw a chain of unit fractions that contains several wholes. They can choose any unit fraction they want. Send several students to the board to work while the others work in their Math Journals.

Ask students to write the improper fraction next to the chain and then to circle the individual wholes and write the mixed number. Students at their seats can trade papers to see and check each other's examples.

Example

$$\boxed{\frac{1}{3} + \frac{1}{3} + \frac{1}{3}} + \boxed{\frac{1}{3} + \frac{1}{3} + \frac{1}{3}} + \frac{1}{3} + \frac{1}{3} = \frac{8}{3} = 2\frac{2}{3}$$

Send another group of students to the board and repeat the activity. Encourage students to build larger mixed numbers with 3, 4, or 5 as the whole number. Repeat the activity if you think your students would benefit from the practice.

Differentiated Instruction

Special Needs Kinesthetic learners may benefit from arranging fractions of an object into wholes. Bring in several greeting cards or photos cut into quarters. Give each student 7 quarters (including 4 from one card and 3 from another) and ask each student to arrange the pieces into wholes.

• How many cards do you have?

• How many whole cards?

• How many part cards?

Students fit the pieces together to make one entire picture and see the three parts that are left over. They can now build $1\frac{3}{4}$.

✓ Ongoing Assessment

Ask students to tell you what they are thinking as they get ready to change a chain of fractions to a mixed number.

Activity 2

Conversions

 30 MINUTES

Goal: Explore ways to convert between mixed numbers and improper fractions.

 NCTM Standards:
Numbers and Operations
Reasoning and Proof
Communication

Teaching Note

What to Expect from Students
One approach to changing mixed numbers to improper fractions is to draw a picture and count the total number of parts. Try to move students into numeric methods.

• There are 4 fourths in 1 whole, so there must be 8 fourths in 2 wholes. Take these 8 fourths and add 3 extra fourths. The improper fraction is $\frac{11}{4}$.

Be sure students understand this line of reasoning before you proceed. Many students may need to "unbuild" the fraction: $2\frac{3}{4} = \frac{4}{4} + \frac{4}{4} + \frac{3}{4} = \frac{11}{4}$

A few students may want to use long division to change $\frac{9}{4}$ to a mixed number. Help them to see that the main answer will be the whole number (2 groups of 4 fourths) and that the remainder will be the numerator of the fractional part (1 group of 3 fourths left).

$$\begin{array}{r} 2\frac{3}{4} \\ 4\overline{)11} \\ \underline{8} \\ 3 \end{array}$$

▶ Change Mixed Numbers to Improper Fractions

WHOLE CLASS

Write this mixed number on the board and ask students to change it to an improper fraction.

$$2\frac{3}{4}$$

Send several volunteers to the board while the other students work at their seats. Invite students at the board to explain their results. Other students can ask questions or help to clarify.

Give students several more mixed numbers to change to improper fractions. This time ask them all to use numeric methods and to write out any steps they need. Again, invite several volunteers to work at the board while the others work at their seats.

$$3\frac{2}{5} \qquad \left(\frac{17}{5}\right) \qquad\qquad 2\frac{3}{8} \qquad \left(\frac{19}{8}\right)$$

▶ Change Improper Fractions to Mixed Numbers

WHOLE CLASS

Write the improper fraction $\frac{9}{4}$ on the board and ask students to change it to a mixed number. Send several volunteers to the board while the others work at their seats. Invite the students at the board to explain their results. Encourage other students to contribute to the explanations or to ask questions.

Give the class a few more improper fractions to change to mixed numbers. Send several volunteers to the board to work. Ask students to use numeric methods and to write out any steps they need. Students who are struggling should be encouraged to use the "unbuilding" method described in the teaching note, which will help them to see the relationship between the parts and the whole.

$$\frac{10}{7} \qquad \frac{12}{5} \qquad \frac{8}{3} \qquad\qquad \left(1\frac{3}{7},\ 2\frac{2}{5},\ 2\frac{2}{3}\right)$$

② Extending the Lesson

Intervention
for students having difficulty

PAIRS

Equivalent Quantities

Each student writes an improper fraction and a mixed number with the same denominator. Partners exchange papers and write "=" if the fractions are equivalent and "≠" if the fractions do not represent the same number. Partners discuss their answers to reach an agreement on each one.

$$\frac{5}{3} \neq 2\frac{1}{3}$$

They aren't equal because $\frac{5}{3}$ is less than 2 and $2\frac{1}{3}$ is greater than 2.

On Level
for students having success

PAIRS

Write Improper Fractions as Mixed Numbers

Materials: index cards labeled 2 to 10 (1 set per pair)

Players take turns flipping over two cards and making an improper fraction.

The player writes an equivalent mixed number and scores one point if correct. The other player can challenge incorrect answers.

Challenge
for students seeking a challenge

PAIRS

Build a Fraction

Using any numbers from 0 to 9, but using each number once only, students complete the equation.

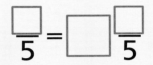

Challenge them to complete the equation in as many ways as they can, using each numeral only once in each equation. Pairs can also complete other similar equations that they create themselves.

 Math Writing Prompt

Intervention

Explain Your Thinking
Explain what the fraction $\frac{9}{2}$ means. Is $\frac{9}{2}$ greater than or less than 2? Explain how you decided.

 Math Writing Prompt

On Level

In Your Own Words
Is $\frac{13}{5}$ greater than or less than $2\frac{4}{5}$? Explain how you decided.

 Math Writing Prompt

Challenge

Create Your Own
Write a problem that can be answered by writing a mixed number as an improper fraction. Provide the answer for your problem.

③ Homework and Cumulative Review

 **Homework** **Goal:** Additional Practice

✓ Include students' work for page 107 as part of their portfolios.

 **Remembering** **Goal:** Cumulative Review

This Remembering activity is appropriate anytime after today's lesson.

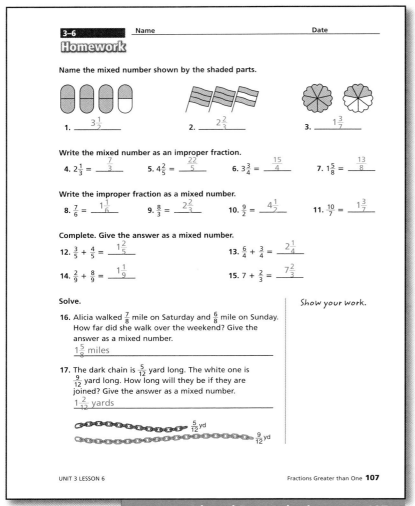

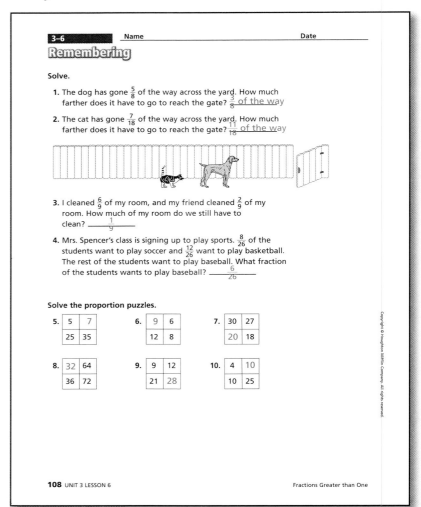

Home or School Activity

 Social Studies Connection

Television Viewing Many groups are interested in knowing how much television we watch. Results are often gathered by surveys and used to develop programs, sell advertising time, and encourage healthy habits.

Have students keep track of every quarter hour of television they watch each day. At the end of the week they can make a fraction chain and write a mixed number to show how many hours of television they watched that week. Students can also graph their results.

Day	Number of Quarter Hours Watched
Sunday	卌 ‖
Monday	‖
Tuesday	
Wednesday	

Add Fractions Greater Than One (Like Denominators)

Lesson Objectives

- Add mixed numbers, applying quick methods when appropriate.
- Read and represent mixed numbers on calibrated lines and rulers.

Vocabulary
mixed number

The Day at a Glance

Today's Goals	Materials	Math Talk
Quick Practice Change fractions to mixed numbers.	Student Activity Book pages 195–196	In today's activities, the students are involved in discussion as they
1 Teaching the Lesson **A1:** Explore ways to add mixed numbers and learn to represent mixed numbers on a number line. **A2:** Develop useful solution strategies for adding mixed numbers.	Fraction Bars (Copymaster M26) Fraction Cards (Copymaster M29) Scissors Envelopes	▶ compare strategies to add mixed numbers
2 Extending the Lesson ▶ Differentiated Instruction	Fraction Circles (Copymaster M30)	
3 Homework and Cumulative Review	Homework and Remembering pages 109–110 Math Journals	

Quick Practice

🕐 **5 MINUTES** **Goal:** Change fractions to mixed numbers.

Improper Fraction Parade: Invite six students to the board and ask them to stand in pairs. The first person in each pair writes an improper fraction that only contains numbers less than 10. The other member of the pair writes the corresponding mixed number or whole number. When pairs are finished, ask the class to check each mixed number to see if it is correct.

Invite the class to read aloud each number together. Nine fourths equals two and one fourth.

$$\frac{9}{4} \quad 2\frac{1}{4}$$

Do these fractions show the same amount?

1 Teaching the Lesson

Explore Solution Methods

25 MINUTES

Goal: Explore ways to add mixed numbers and learn to represent mixed numbers on a number line.

Materials: Student Activity Book page 195, Fraction Bars (Copymaster M26)

 NCTM Standards:
Number and Operations
Problem Solving
Communication

Teaching Note

What to Expect from Students A few students may use drawings or number lines to solve the problem. These approaches are fine for now.

Generally, a good method is to add whole numbers and fractions separately and then add the totals together.

Some students may convert the numbers to improper fractions before adding.

(The final step of the swimming problem can be expanded as shown here.)

$$\frac{5}{3} + \frac{5}{3} = \frac{10}{3} = 3\frac{1}{3}$$

$$\frac{10}{3} = \frac{3}{3} + \frac{3}{3} + \frac{3}{3} + \frac{1}{3} = 3\frac{1}{3}$$

Other students may set up the problem in a vertical format, and add whole numbers and fractions separately.

▶ Student-Generated Solutions WHOLE CLASS

Write this word problem on the board and ask students to solve it using a method of their choice. Invite several volunteers to work at the board. For now, allow students to work through the problem without your direction.

> Celso swam $1\frac{2}{3}$ lengths of the swimming pool this morning and $1\frac{2}{3}$ lengths of the pool this afternoon. How many lengths did he swim today?

Have students discuss their solution strategies. Before moving on, be sure students see several methods.

Discuss how adding mixed numbers is like adding money: you add together the dollars and you add together the quarters (the fourths).

$$1\frac{3}{4}$$
$$+ \ 2\frac{2}{4}$$
$$= 3\frac{5}{4} \ = \ 4\frac{1}{4}$$

▶ Represent and Add Mixed Numbers WHOLE CLASS

Number Lines and Rulers Refer students to Student Activity Book page 195 and have them look at the number line shown at the top of the page. The number line shows units divided into thirds. Many students are used to seeing fraction number lines with a total of only one whole, so this is a slight variation.

● The first finger points to $4\frac{2}{3}$. How much more to 5? $\frac{1}{3}$

● The second finger points to $9\frac{1}{3}$. How much more to 12? $2\frac{2}{3}$

Ask students to complete exercises 1–11 on their own; provide assistance as necessary. In exercises 3 and 4, students need to recognize that the first two improper fractions convert to exact whole numbers (4 and 10). In exercise 5, $\frac{31}{3}$ is just $\frac{1}{3}$ more than 10, or $10\frac{1}{3}$.

In exercise 6, the best way to add the two mixed numbers on the number line is to add the two whole numbers first (4 + 1) and then to add the two fractional parts ($\frac{1}{3} + \frac{1}{3}$).

3–7 Class Activity

Name ____ Date ____

Vocabulary
mixed number

► Represent and Add Mixed Numbers

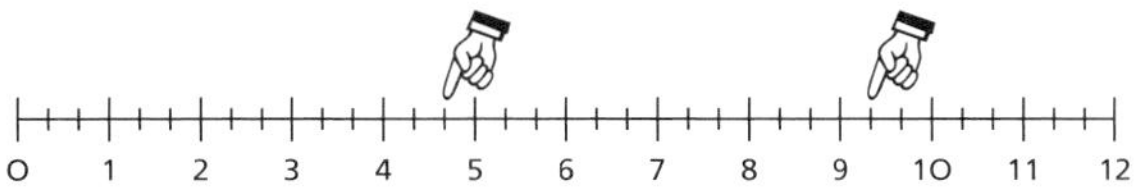

1. What fractional parts are shown on the number line?
   thirds
2. What **mixed numbers** do the fingers show?
   $4\frac{2}{3}$; $9\frac{1}{3}$
3. Where is $\frac{12}{3}$ on the number line?
   at 4
4. Where is $\frac{30}{3}$?
   at 10
5. Where is $\frac{31}{3}$?
   1 mark to the right of 10
6. How can you add $4\frac{1}{3} + 1\frac{1}{3}$ on the number line?
   Find $4\frac{1}{3}$ on the number line and move $1\frac{1}{3}$ to the right.

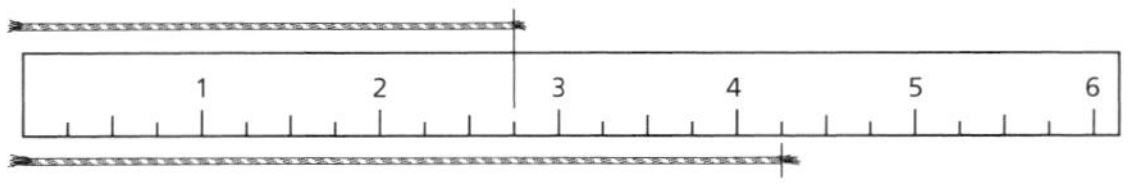

7. What fractional parts are shown on the inch ruler?
   quarters
8. How long is each string? $2\frac{3}{4}$ in.; $4\frac{1}{4}$ in.
9. If you place the strings end to end, how long are they?
   7 in.

Complete these equations.

10. $9\frac{5}{12} + 3\frac{1}{12} = 12\frac{6}{12}$
11. $7\frac{1}{8} + 2\frac{5}{8} = 9\frac{6}{8}$

UNIT 3 LESSON 7 — Add Fractions Greater Than One (Like Denominators) 195

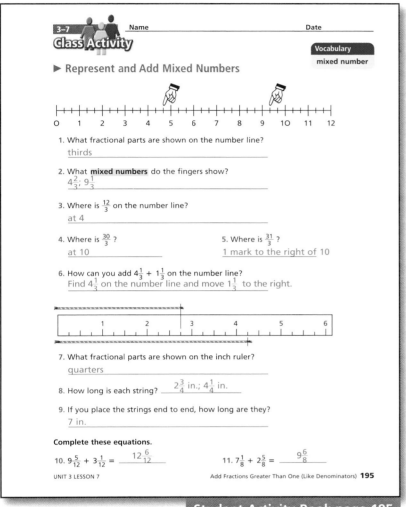

Student Activity Book page 195

For exercise 8, the string on top of the ruler is $2\frac{3}{4}$ inches long and the string below the ruler is $4\frac{1}{4}$ inches long. Remind students to include units in their answers.

In exercise 9, some students may see that $\frac{3}{4}$ and $\frac{1}{4}$ add to 1 whole.

If not, point this out. A drawing may be helpful. Recognizing the addends of 1 is a useful strategy when adding mixed numbers.

Solve Without Number Lines Ask students to complete exercises 10 and 11. Invite several volunteers to work at the board. These exercises deal with larger whole numbers, so students may find it difficult to make drawings or to convert to improper fractions. At this point, students should see the value of adding whole numbers and fractions separately. Writing the equation vertically will help some students keep the wholes and the fractional parts separate.

Differentiated Instruction

Extra Help Some students may find the fraction bars on Copymaster M26 useful when adding or subtracting mixed numbers. Have these students cut out the bars and use them to represent each mixed number to add, to trade parts for a whole as needed, and to represent the total of the mixed numbers.

Ongoing Assessment

Observe students as they complete exercises 10 and 11. Do they write equations that show the whole numbers separate from the fractional parts? Do they first draw diagrams and then write equations to match the diagrams?

Activity 2

Applications and Practice

25 MINUTES

Goal: Develop useful solution strategies for adding mixed numbers.

Materials: Student Activity Book page 196, Fraction Cards (Copymaster M29), scissors, envelopes (1 per pair), Fraction Bars (Copymaster M26)

NCTM Standards:
Number and Operations
Reasoning and Proof

Differentiated Instruction

Extra Help Distribute one copy of Copymaster M29 to each pair of students. Have students cut out the fraction cards and place both sets of one type of fraction (for example, eighths) in an envelope. They take turns selecting a fraction from the envelope and adding it to the previous total, until they have used all the fractions in the envelope. The initial total is 0.

Students who are still struggling with adding fractions can use the fraction bars on Copymaster M26 to help them, by trading for wholes.

3-7 Class Activity

Name ____________ Date ____________

▶ Add Mixed Numbers by Separating Them

The box shows the properties and definitions we can use to prove that $8\frac{1}{9} + 2\frac{4}{9} = (8 + 2) + \left(\frac{1}{9} + \frac{4}{9}\right)$.

Definition of a Mixed Number: $a\frac{n}{d} = a + \frac{n}{d}$
Commutative Property: $a + b = b + a$
Associative Property: $a + (b + c) = (a + b) + c$

Below is the math proof. Write the property or definition for each step.

12. $8\frac{1}{9} + 2\frac{4}{9} = \left(8 + \frac{1}{9}\right) + 2\frac{4}{9}$ Definition of a Mixed Number
13. $8\frac{1}{9} + 2\frac{4}{9} = 8 + \left(\frac{1}{9} + 2\frac{4}{9}\right)$ Associative Property
14. $8\frac{1}{9} + 2\frac{4}{9} = 8 + \left(\frac{1}{9} + \left(2 + \frac{4}{9}\right)\right)$ Definition of a Mixed Number
15. $8\frac{1}{9} + 2\frac{4}{9} = 8 + \left(\frac{1}{9} + \left(\frac{4}{9} + 2\right)\right)$ Commutative Property
16. $8\frac{1}{9} + 2\frac{4}{9} = 8 + \left(\left(\frac{1}{9} + \frac{4}{9}\right) + 2\right)$ Associative Property
17. $8\frac{1}{9} + 2\frac{4}{9} = 8 + \left(2 + \left(\frac{1}{9} + \frac{4}{9}\right)\right)$ Commutative Property
18. $8\frac{1}{9} + 2\frac{4}{9} = \left(8 + 2\right) + \left(\frac{1}{9} + \frac{4}{9}\right)$ Associative Property
19. Solve the addition problem. $10\frac{5}{9}$

Complete these equations. Circle those you can do in your head.

20. $4\frac{1}{9} + 2\frac{1}{9} = 6\frac{2}{9}$
21. $5\frac{3}{8} + 2\frac{2}{8} = 7\frac{5}{8}$
22. $1\frac{1}{6} + 3\frac{4}{6} = 4\frac{5}{6}$
23. $4\frac{1}{3} + 6\frac{1}{3} = 10\frac{2}{3}$
24. $2\frac{1}{4} + 2\frac{3}{4} = 5$
25. $3\frac{2}{7} + 2\frac{5}{7} = 6$
26. $3\frac{2}{3} + 1\frac{1}{3} = 5$
27. $1\frac{7}{8} + 5\frac{1}{8} = 7$

Write each total as a mixed number.

28. $1\frac{3}{5} + 2\frac{4}{5} = 4\frac{2}{5}$
29. $40\frac{6}{7} + 22\frac{5}{7} = 63\frac{4}{7}$

196 UNIT 3 LESSON 7 Add Fractions Greater Than One (Like Denominators)

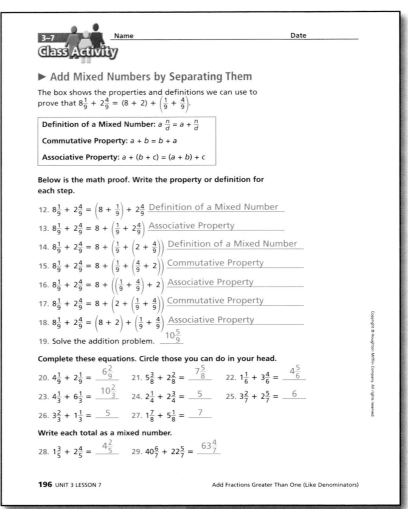

Student Activity Book page 196

▶ Add Mixed Numbers by Separating Them

WHOLE CLASS

Refer students to Student Activity Book page 196. The proof demonstrates why you can add fractions and whole numbers separately when adding mixed numbers together. Help students track the changes at each step and to find the definition or property that explains why you can make each of these changes. Together, work through exercises 12–19.

Note that students will not be expected to use formal proofs at any point in Grade 5. This example of a proof is only an initial exposure.

Discuss exercises 20–29 as a class. Students can complete exercises 20–23 using mental math. The total of the two fractions is less than 1. In exercises 24–27, each pair of fractions adds to 1.

In exercises 28 and 29, the two fractional parts add up to a number greater than 1. Here, students will see the importance of adding whole numbers and fractions separately.

② Extending the Lesson

Intervention
for students having difficulty

PAIRS

Add Fractions of Circles

Materials: Fraction Circles (Copymaster M30)

Working in pairs, one student names two mixed numbers with the same denominator. The other student uses Copymaster M30 to build the mixed numbers with parts of circles, trading parts for whole circles where possible, and then adds the two mixed numbers and tells the total. Partners can switch roles.

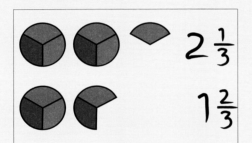

On Level
for students having success

PAIRS

Work Backward

Each student makes up a mixed number with the same denominator. Together, pairs then decide what they have to add to the smaller number to obtain the larger one. Once students agree on an answer, they can repeat the activity with new numbers.

$$12\tfrac{3}{8} + \underline{\hspace{1cm}} = 14\tfrac{7}{8}$$

Challenge
for students seeking a challenge

PAIRS

Add It Your Way

Explain how to play the game: Starting with "1," the first player adds between $\frac{1}{8}$ and $\frac{8}{8}$ and says the equation—for example, $1 + \frac{3}{8} = 1\frac{3}{8}$. Players then take turns adding any number of eighths between $\frac{1}{8}$ and $\frac{8}{8}$ to the total. For example, the second player says "$\frac{7}{8}$" and adds $1\frac{3}{8} + \frac{7}{8} = 2\frac{2}{8}$. The player who is able to make an equation that adds to 10 is the winner.

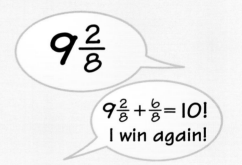

 Math Writing Prompt

Intervention

Draw a Picture
Draw a picture that you might use to show a younger student how to add two mixed numbers. Write what you would say to explain your picture.

 Math Writing Prompt

On Level

You Decide
Jonathan adds $4\frac{3}{10} + 3\frac{8}{10}$ and gets $7\frac{1}{10}$. Dalia gets $7\frac{11}{10}$ as her answer. Who is correct? Explain your thinking.

 Math Writing Prompt

Challenge

Write a Description
Describe an everyday situation when you might need to add mixed numbers. What are the numbers? How will you add them together?

③ Homework and Cumulative Review

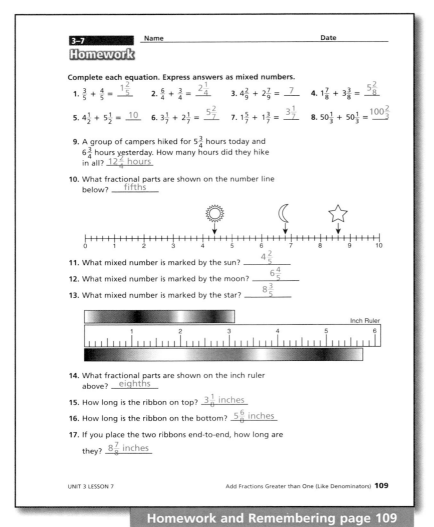

3–7 Homework **Goal:** Additional Practice

✔ On this Homework page, students solve equations and work with mixed numbers.

Homework and Remembering page 109

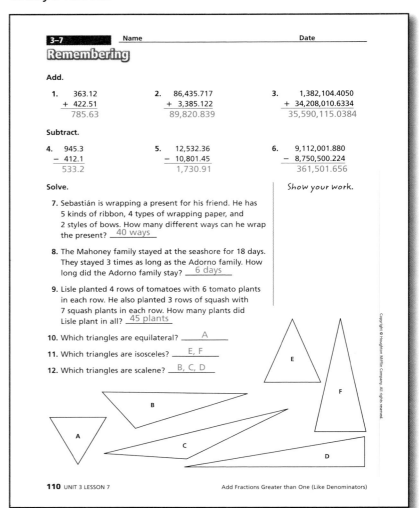

3–7 Remembering **Goal:** Cumulative Review

This Remembering activity is appropriate anytime after today's lesson.

Homework and Remembering page 110

Home or School Activity

Math-to-Math Connection

Add Fractions to Find Perimeter Measuring in the customary system often requires adding fractions. Have students draw a polygon, measure each side to the nearest $\frac{1}{8}$ inch, and calculate the perimeter of their polygon. Ask them to create a polygon with a perimeter as close as possible to 5 inches, 10 inches, or a measurement of their choice. Challenge them to create two different polygons with the same perimeter.

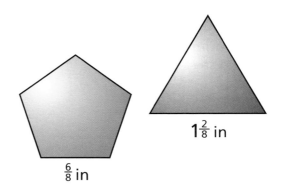

Subtract Mixed Numbers (Like Denominators)

Vocabulary
mixed number
ungroup
add on

Lesson Objectives

● Subtract mixed numbers with like denominators.

● Ungroup the first mixed number in a subtraction problem when necessary.

● Explain student-generated methods of subtraction to the class.

The Day at a Glance

Today's Goals	Materials	123 Math Talk
Quick Practice Change mixed numbers to improper fractions.	MathBoard materials	In today's activities, the students are involved in discussion as they
① **Teaching the Lesson** **A1:** Solve problems that involve subtraction of mixed numbers. **A2:** Practice ungrouping problems in real-world contexts.	Student Activity Book pages 197–198 Fraction Bars (Copymaster M26) Fraction Cards (Copymaster M29) Scissors	► share their self-generated methods of subtraction ► decide whether they need to ungroup a number in order to subtract
② **Extending the Lesson** ► Differentiated Instruction	Envelopes	
③ **Homework and Cumulative Review**	Homework and Remembering pages 111–112 Math Journals	

Quick Practice

 5 MINUTES **Goal:** Change mixed numbers to improper fractions.

Mixed Number Parade: Invite six students to the board and ask them to stand in pairs. The first student in each pair writes a mixed number that only contains numbers less than 10. The other student writes the corresponding improper fraction. When they are finished, ask the class to check each improper fraction to see if it is correct.

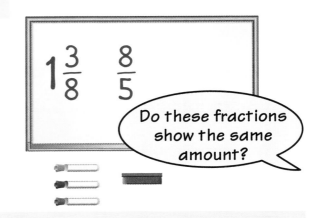

$$1\tfrac{3}{8} \quad \tfrac{8}{5}$$

Do these fractions show the same amount?

Teaching the Lesson

Subtraction With Mixed Numbers

 30 MINUTES

Goal: Solve problems that involve subtraction of mixed numbers.

Materials: MathBoard materials, Fraction Bars (Copymaster M26), scissors

✔ **NCTM Standards:**
Number and Operations
Communication
Representation

Differentiated Instruction

Extra Help Some students may find the fraction bars on Copymaster M26 useful when adding and subtracting. Have students cut out the bars and use them to represent the fractions with which they are working. For example, to represent $\frac{3}{8}$ they can fold back some of the eighths bars so they do not show. When students need to regroup a fraction in order to subtract from it, they can trade a whole for the equivalent set of parts.

Expanded Notation

$$7\frac{1}{5} = 6 + \frac{5}{5} + \frac{1}{5} = 6\frac{6}{5}$$
$$\underline{\qquad\qquad - 2\frac{4}{5}}$$
$$4\frac{2}{5}$$

Ungroup

$$6\frac{6}{5}$$
$$\cancel{7}\cancel{\frac{1}{5}}$$
$$\underline{- 2\frac{4}{5}}$$
$$4\frac{2}{5}$$

▶ **Perform Simple Subtraction** WHOLE CLASS

Read aloud this word problem and ask students to solve it.

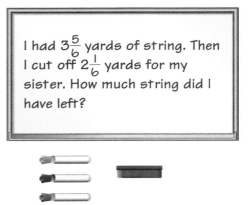

I had $3\frac{5}{6}$ yards of string. Then I cut off $2\frac{1}{6}$ yards for my sister. How much string did I have left?

Invite several students to work at the board. Many students will be able to solve this problem mentally; others may choose to use their MathBoards. You might remind those students who are struggling that they can subtract the whole numbers and the fractions separately.

When students are finished, invite them to show how they solved the problem. If students had difficulty, provide them with another problem of this type, such as $4\frac{7}{8} - 2\frac{3}{8}$.

▶ **Subtraction With Ungrouping** WHOLE CLASS

Write this equation on the board and have students complete it. Again, invite several volunteers to work at the board.

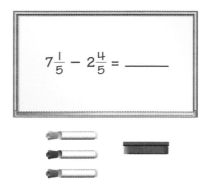

$$7\frac{1}{5} - 2\frac{4}{5} = \underline{\qquad}$$

There are many effective methods for solving problems like this one.

Ungroup Students may find it helpful to ungroup the first mixed number in some way. There are many ways to do this; eventually, the choice becomes a matter of personal preference. The ungrouping methods shown at the left are recommended for struggling students who are looking for guidance.

Add On Some students may add on from the smaller mixed number to the larger.

$$2\frac{4}{5} \quad \text{to } 3 \quad \text{to } 7 \quad \text{to } 7\frac{1}{5}$$

$$\frac{1}{5} \qquad 4 \qquad \frac{1}{5} = 4\frac{2}{5}$$

Use Improper Fractions Students may try to convert both numbers to improper fractions before subtracting: $\frac{36}{5} - \frac{14}{5} = \frac{22}{5}$, or $4\frac{2}{5}$. As it does with addition, this method can become cumbersome.

Ask several students to demonstrate the method they used. Encourage students to share a variety of methods to provide exposure to different approaches. As students share their ideas, try to validate any method that reflects understanding. Invite students to ask questions and to help each other explain their approaches.

When a volunteer shows one of the ungrouping methods, ask the class how the subtraction of mixed numbers is like the subtraction of greater numbers (for example, 243 − 158). As students respond, they should demonstrate an understanding that to subtract mixed numbers, you can ungroup a whole. So, to subtract 243 − 158, you can ungroup a ten to subtract 8 from 13 ones.

Present students with several other problems of this type to solve; invite volunteers to share their methods. Two examples are at the right.

▶ Decide What to Do WHOLE CLASS

Invite several students to the board. Have each of them quickly write down two or three subtraction problems with mixed numbers. The problems can be easy or difficult.

Point to each problem and have the class respond by saying "ungroup" or "do not ungroup," depending on whether the first number needs to be changed to solve the problem. Have a volunteer explain how to decide. If necessary, repeat this activity until students respond quickly and confidently.

$$2\frac{2}{7} - 1\frac{4}{7} \quad \overset{\text{Ungroup!}}{} \qquad\qquad 28\frac{7}{9} - 13\frac{5}{9} \quad \overset{\text{Do not ungroup!}}{}$$

If no students write problems with large mixed numbers, like the second problem above, provide one or two of these problems yourself.

Teaching Note

Watch For! Some students may try to subtract the smaller fractional part from the larger fractional part even when this involves "going the wrong way." Encourage these students to use the vertical format. It resembles the ungrouping they already know in multi-digit subtraction.

Incorrect	Correct
$8\frac{3}{5}$	$8\frac{3}{5}$
$-1\frac{4}{5}$	$-1\frac{4}{5}$
$7\frac{1}{5}$	$6\frac{4}{5}$

$$5\frac{3}{5} - 1\frac{4}{5} \quad 6\frac{2}{9} - 2\frac{7}{9}$$

Teaching the Lesson (continued)

Subtraction Practice

 25 MINUTES

Goal: Practice ungrouping problems in real-world contexts.

Materials: Student Activity Book pages 197–198, Fraction Cards (Copymaster M29) (1 copy per pair), scissors, envelopes

✓ **NCTM Standards:**
Number and Operations
Representation

Differentiated Instruction

Extra Help Distribute one copy of Copymaster M29 to each pair of students. Have pairs cut out the fraction cards and place both sets of one type of fraction in an envelope. One partner selects a fraction from the envelope and subtracts the number from 42. Pairs continue to take turns choosing a fraction and subtracting it from the most recent answer. Students will need to regroup in order to perform some subtractions.

Ongoing Assessment

Throughout this lesson, as students subtract mixed numbers, observe whether they are ungrouping the first number only when necessary. Also check that they are not simply subtracting the smaller fractional part from the larger fractional part.

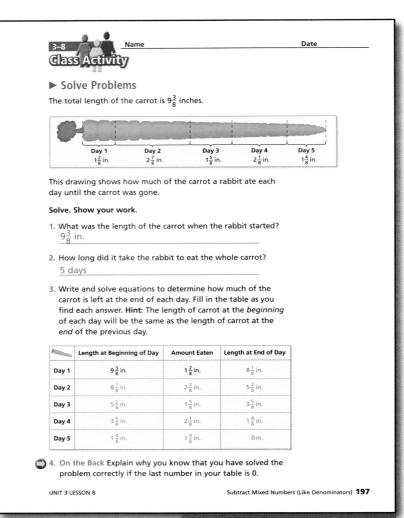

Student Activity Book page 197

► Solve Problems INDIVIDUALS

Refer students to Student Activity Book page 197. Ensure that they understand the problem situation before having them work independently to complete the page. If time permits, invite students to share their explanations for exercise 3.

② Extending the Lesson

Intervention
for students having difficulty

PAIRS

Write Fractions in Different Ways

Working in pairs, one student writes a mixed number. The other student rewrites the mixed number in as many ways as he or she can. Pairs then switch roles. Encourage students to ask each other for explanations, as necessary.

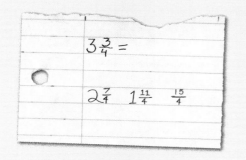

On Level
for students having success

PAIRS

Representations for Subtraction

In pairs, students show as many ways as possible to complete the following subtraction: $2\frac{3}{10} - 1\frac{7}{10}$. For example, they might use regrouping and subtracting, drawing fraction bars, or converting to improper fractions or decimals.

When they cannot think of any other methods, they can compare strategies with another pair of students.

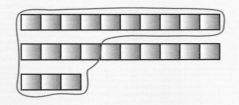

Challenge
for students seeking a challenge

INDIVIDUALS

Double the Recipe

Students look for recipes that include fractions and mixed numbers as part of the ingredient measures. They might look for cookbooks at home or in the school library.

For each recipe, students show how to use what they know to write a recipe for twice as much as the original. If necessary, point out that to double a recipe, you can add the amount in the first recipe to itself.

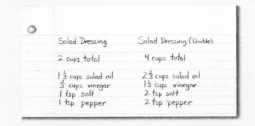

 Math Writing Prompt

Intervention

Explain Your Thinking
Describe how to change $3\frac{1}{8}$ to an improper fraction. Explain each step.

 Math Writing Prompt

On Level

Solve a Problem
Alejandro is making muffins. He needs $3\frac{3}{4}$ cups of flour, but has only $1\frac{1}{4}$ cups. How much flour must he borrow from his neighbor? Explain two ways to find the answer.

 Math Writing Prompt

Challenge

Summarize
Explain why $6\frac{7}{8} - 2\frac{5}{8}$ is the same as $(6 - 2) + (\frac{7}{8} - \frac{5}{8})$.

③ Homework and Cumulative Review

3–8
Homework **Goal:** Additional Practice

✓ On this Homework page, students solve problems involving subtraction with mixed numbers.

3–8
Remembering **Goal:** Cumulative Review

This Remembering activity is appropriate anytime after today's lesson.

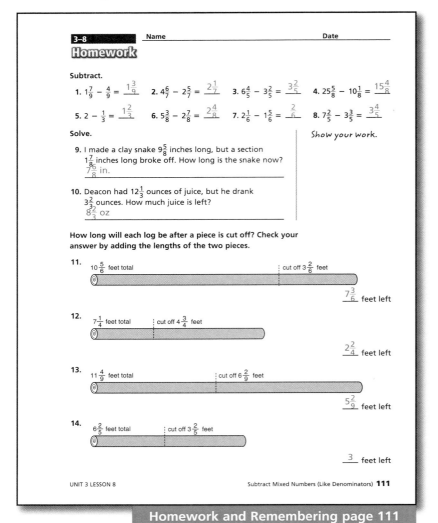

3–8 Name _____ Date _____
Homework

Subtract.

1. $1\frac{7}{9} - \frac{4}{9} = 1\frac{3}{9}$ 2. $4\frac{6}{7} - 2\frac{5}{7} = 2\frac{1}{7}$ 3. $6\frac{4}{5} - 3\frac{2}{5} = 3\frac{2}{5}$ 4. $25\frac{5}{8} - 10\frac{1}{8} = 15\frac{4}{8}$

5. $2 - \frac{1}{3} = 1\frac{2}{3}$ 6. $5\frac{3}{8} - 2\frac{7}{8} = 2\frac{4}{8}$ 7. $2\frac{1}{6} - 1\frac{5}{6} = \frac{2}{6}$ 8. $7\frac{2}{5} - 3\frac{3}{5} = 3\frac{4}{5}$

Solve.   *Show your work.*

9. I made a clay snake $9\frac{5}{8}$ inches long, but a section $1\frac{7}{8}$ inches long broke off. How long is the snake now?
   $7\frac{6}{8}$ in.

10. Deacon had $12\frac{1}{3}$ ounces of juice, but he drank $3\frac{2}{3}$ ounces. How much juice is left?
    $8\frac{2}{3}$ oz

How long will each log be after a piece is cut off? Check your answer by adding the lengths of the two pieces.

11. $10\frac{5}{6}$ feet total   cut off $3\frac{2}{6}$ feet
    $7\frac{3}{6}$ feet left

12. $7\frac{1}{4}$ feet total   cut off $4\frac{3}{4}$ feet
    $2\frac{2}{4}$ feet left

13. $11\frac{4}{9}$ feet total   cut off $6\frac{2}{9}$ feet
    $5\frac{2}{9}$ feet left

14. $6\frac{2}{5}$ feet total   cut off $3\frac{2}{5}$ feet
    3 feet left

UNIT 3 LESSON 8   Subtract Mixed Numbers (Like Denominators) **111**

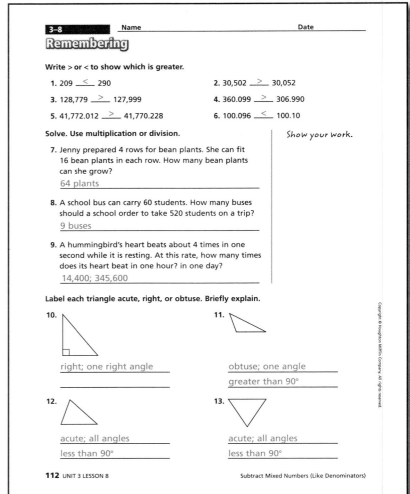

3–8 Name _____ Date _____
Remembering

Write > or < to show which is greater.

1. 209 _<_ 290   2. 30,502 _>_ 30,052

3. 128,779 _>_ 127,999   4. 360.099 _>_ 306.990

5. 41,772.012 _>_ 41,770.228   6. 100.096 _<_ 100.10

Solve. Use multiplication or division.   *Show your work.*

7. Jenny prepared 4 rows for bean plants. She can fit 16 bean plants in each row. How many bean plants can she grow?
   64 plants

8. A school bus can carry 60 students. How many buses should a school order to take 520 students on a trip?
   9 buses

9. A hummingbird's heart beats about 4 times in one second while it is resting. At this rate, how many times does its heart beat in one hour? in one day?
   14,400; 345,600

Label each triangle acute, right, or obtuse. Briefly explain.

10.   11.
   right; one right angle   obtuse; one angle
                                greater than 90°

12.   13.
   acute; all angles   acute; all angles
   less than 90°   less than 90°

112 UNIT 3 LESSON 8   Subtract Mixed Numbers (Like Denominators)

Homework and Remembering page 111   Homework and Remembering page 112

Home or School Activity

Real-World Connection

Fractions and Mixed Numbers in Use Ask students to interview parents, guardians, and other adults they know to learn how they use fractions and mixed numbers in their everyday lives. They will likely find that the most common use is found in measuring: a cook preparing a recipe, a pharmacist preparing a prescription, a carpenter measuring lumber, or a machinist determining the depth of a hole.

Invite students to share their findings with the class or prepare a bulletin board with the most interesting discoveries.

Comparison Situations

Lesson Objectives

- Compare the sizes of two like fractions or mixed numbers and use subtraction to determine the exact difference.
- Construct a chart of comparative measurements.

Vocabulary
mixed number
subtract
add on

The Day at a Glance

Today's Goals	Materials	Math Talk
Quick Practice Compare fractions using > and <. **1 Teaching the Lesson** **A1:** Compare fractions and find the difference. **A2:** Solve problems that involve subtraction of mixed numbers. **A3:** Take real measurements of hands or feet and make comparisons. **2 Extending the Lesson** ▸ Going Further: Solve Problems with Mixed Numbers ▸ Differentiated Instruction **3 Homework and Cumulative Review**	Student Activity Book pages 199–200 Inch rulers Play money Homework and Remembering pages 113–114 Math Journals	In today's activities, the students are involved in discussion as they ▸ evaluate various strategies to compare fractions ▸ compare the results of adding on and subtracting to compare fractions

---

Quick Practice

🕐 **5 MINUTES**   **Goal:** Compare fractions using > and <.

Which Fraction Is Less? Invite six pairs of students to the board. The first student in each pair writes a fraction. The other student then writes a different fraction with the same denominator.

Next, invite one student from each pair to remain at the board and to point to each set of fractions, asking "Which is less?" The class responds by pointing and the student at the board writes > or < between the fractions. Have the whole class read aloud the inequality.

Five twelfths is less than nine twelfths.

$$\frac{5}{12} < \frac{9}{12}$$

Which is less?

1 Teaching the Lesson

Compare Fractions

 15 MINUTES

Goal: Compare fractions and find the difference.

✔ **NCTM Standards:**
Number and Operations
Communication
Representation

Differentiated Instruction

Extra Help If students are struggling to see why they can use subtraction to solve comparison problems, give them an analogous situation with whole numbers. This will help make relationships more apparent.

For example, Katie has 7 melons. Otto has 5 melons.

▶ Who has more? Katie

▶ How many more? 2 more

▶ How did you find this answer?
I subtracted 5 from 7.

Students can also solve comparisons like this by adding on to the smaller number to make the larger number. They can use this strategy with fractions, too. It is especially effective with fractions that are less than 1.

▶ Solve Simple Comparisons With Like Fractions

WHOLE CLASS

Write the following word problem on the board and invite students to solve it and share their strategies.

> Katie has $\frac{2}{8}$ of a melon. Otto has $\frac{5}{8}$ of the same melon. Who has more? How much more?

Students must first see that Otto has more melon. They then need to determine that they can find out how much more by subtracting or by adding on. Some students may find this obvious; others may need to work with chains of unit fractions to see that Otto has $\frac{3}{8}$ more melon.

Katie $\quad \frac{1}{8} \; + \; \frac{1}{8}$

Otto $\quad \frac{1}{8} \; + \; \frac{1}{8} \; \left(+ \; \frac{1}{8} \; + \; \frac{1}{8} \; + \; \frac{1}{8} \right)$

Next, ask

● Who has less melon? How much less? Katie; $\frac{3}{8}$ less

Help students realize that the answer to a "how much less?" question is always the same as the answer to a "how much more?" question. Use fraction chains to illustrate this concept.

Give students this word problem to solve using a method of their choice. Invite volunteers to share and explain their strategies.

> My black shoelace is $\frac{7}{12}$ of a yard long. My white shoelace is $\frac{9}{12}$ of a yard long. Which shoelace is shorter? How much shorter?

The two main numerical models will be variations of the following:
$\frac{7}{12} + \frac{n}{d} = \frac{9}{12}$ and $\frac{9}{12} - \frac{7}{12} = \frac{n}{d}$.

Compare With Mixed Numbers

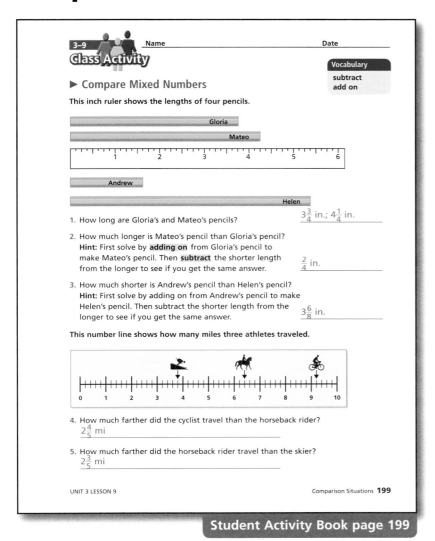

Student Activity Book page 199

⏱ **20 MINUTES**

Goal: Solve problems that involve subtraction of mixed numbers.

Materials: Student Activity Book page 199

✔ **NCTM Standards:**
Number and Operations
Problem Solving
Representation

▶ Compare Mixed Numbers WHOLE CLASS

Refer students to Student Activity Book page 199 and work together to complete exercises 1–5. For all of these exercises, emphasize that a mixed number is a whole number plus a fractional part. For example, $3\frac{4}{5}$ is three wholes plus four fifths.

Compare Mixed Numbers Using a Number Line As students complete exercises 1–5, remind them to find the difference first by adding on and then to check their answer using subtraction. This process will help students realize why they can solve comparisons by subtracting or by adding on.

Activity continued ▶

Activity 2

Teaching Note

What to Expect from Students
Students may use one or more of these strategies to find the differences in exercises 4 and 5.

Count the Marks Students can count the individual marks between two athletes on the number line and then convert the improper fraction to a mixed number. For example, the cyclist traveled $\frac{14}{5}$ miles, or $2\frac{4}{5}$ miles, farther than the horseback rider.

Add On Students can start with the smaller number, add on to the next whole, add on the number of complete wholes, and then add on the remaining fraction.

Subtract Students can subtract the two mixed numbers by ungrouping the larger number as they did in Lesson 8.

The first ruler on Student Activity Book page 199 is divided into fourths. Mateo's pencil is $4\frac{1}{4}$ inches and Gloria's is $3\frac{3}{4}$ inches. From $3\frac{3}{4}$ to 4 is $\frac{1}{4}$ and it is $\frac{1}{4}$ more to $4\frac{1}{4}$, so Mateo's pencil is $\frac{2}{4}$ (or $\frac{1}{2}$) inches longer than Gloria's.

The second ruler on this page is divided into eighths. The difference between Andrew's pencil and Helen's pencil is much greater than the difference between Mateo's pencil and Gloria's pencil.

Ask students to suggest a quicker way to add on, without counting every mark.

Andrew's pencil is $1\frac{5}{8}$ inches long. Helen's pencil is $5\frac{3}{8}$ inches long.

Add on: Subtract:

$$4\frac{11}{8}$$
$$\not{5}\frac{\not{3}}{\not{8}}$$
$$-1\frac{5}{8}$$
$$\overline{3\frac{6}{8}}$$

From $1\frac{5}{8}$ to 2 to 5 to $5\frac{3}{8}$

$\frac{3}{8}$ 3 $\frac{3}{8}$ = $3\frac{6}{8}$

Reinforce for students that they can use adding on to solve any fraction subtraction problem. Ask students to try this subtraction: $5\frac{2}{7} - 2\frac{6}{7}$.

From $2\frac{6}{7}$ to 3 to $5\frac{2}{7}$

$\frac{1}{7}$ $2\frac{2}{7}$ = $2\frac{3}{7}$

Compare Mixed Numbers Using Other Methods Have students look at the number line at the bottom of Student Activity Book page 199, and ask them what fractional parts are shown. fifths

Encourage students to use any method of their choice to complete exercises 4 and 5. Invite students to share and explain the different methods they used.

Real-World Comparisons

▶ Make a Measurement Table WHOLE CLASS

Invite three students of different heights to the front of the classroom. Measure the hand or foot of each student to the nearest eighth of an inch and complete a table on the board.

Length of Hand

Samantha	6 7/8 inches
Pedro	7 5/8 inches
Robby	6 1/8 inches

Next, ask students to make several comparisons using the information in the table.

- Who has the longest hand? Pedro Who has the shortest hand? Robby

- How much shorter is Samantha's hand than Pedro's? $\frac{3}{4}$ inches

- How much longer is Pedro's hand than Robby's? $1\frac{1}{2}$ inches

If time permits, repeat the activity with a new group of students. Alternatively, you might have students work in groups of three to measure their own hands or feet and subtract to compare measurements.

 20 MINUTES

Goal: Take real measurements of hands or feet and make comparisons.

Materials: inch rulers (1 per student)

 NCTM Standards:
Number and Operations
Measurement

 Ongoing Assessment

Watch students as they subtract to compare mixed numbers. Do they subtract accurately, even when the numbers begin with different whole numbers (for example $7\frac{3}{8}$ and $6\frac{5}{8}$)?

Going Further: Solve Problems With Mixed Numbers

Goal: Add and subtract mixed numbers to solve problems.

Materials: Student Activity Book page 200

✓ **NCTM Standards:**
Number and Operations
Problem Solving

▶ Solve Problems SMALL GROUPS

Refer students to the word problems on Student Activity Book page 200. Working in small groups, have students select one of the four word problems and do the following:

- restate the problem in their own words to ensure everyone understands it

- agree on a strategy to solve the problem; they may suggest strategies such as adding, subtracting, drawing a diagram, or working backward

Invite each group to explain to the rest of the class how they would solve their problem. Encourage other students to ask questions to be sure they understand the strategies.

Next, ask groups to solve all four problems using the suggested strategies or others of their choice.

When students have solved all four problems, discuss solutions as a class.

- What was your solution to problem 3?

- How can you check that the answer is correct?

- What might you do differently next time?

- Did anyone solve this problem in a different way?

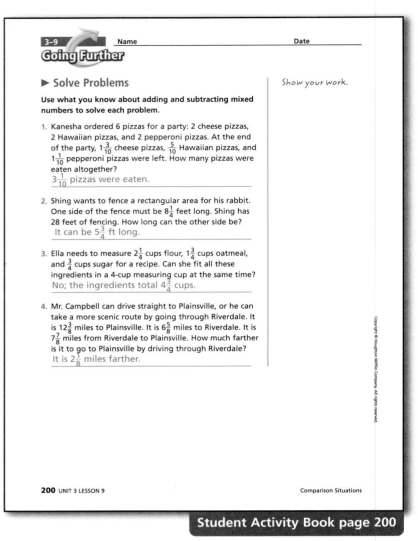

Student Activity Book page 200

Differentiated Instruction

English Learners Working in small groups offers an opportunity for fluent English speakers to help English learners with the language in the word problems. You might select one group member to explain any unclear language to those group members who do not understand.

Intervention
for students having difficulty

PAIRS

Benchmark Numbers

Materials: play money (dimes, quarters, nickels)

Working in pairs, students select a coin or a small group of coins and use what they know about fractions to complete a table with decimal and fraction equivalents. Provide them with the column headings shown in the table below. Encourage them to include common decimals like 0.10, 0.25, 0.50, and 0.75.

On Level
for students having success

PAIRS

Fractions on a Number Line

Each partner writes five fractions between 0 and 3 on a sheet of paper. Partners exchange sheets of paper, draw a number line from 0 to 3, and place the fractions on the number line. Partners can check each other's work.

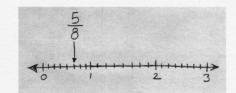

Challenge
for students seeking a challenge

PAIRS

Fractions and Decimals on a Number Line

Each partner writes three fractions and three decimals between 0 and 3 on a sheet of paper. Partners exchange sheets of paper, draw a number line from 0 to 3, and place the fractions and decimals on the number line. Partners can check each other's work.

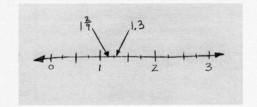

✎ Math Writing Prompt

Intervention

You Decide
Your uncle offers to give you $0.60 if you give him $\frac{1}{2}$ of a dollar in return. Should you make the trade? Explain why or why not.

✎ Math Writing Prompt

On Level

In Your Own Words
Your brother doesn't believe that $1\frac{1}{8}$ is closer to $\frac{7}{8}$ than it is to $1\frac{7}{8}$. What might you say, write, or draw to convince him?

✎ Math Writing Prompt

Challenge

Investigate Math
How can you determine if $1\frac{7}{8}$ is closer to $2\frac{1}{8}$ or to 1.6?

③ Homework and Cumulative Review

Homework **Goal:** Additional Practice

✓ Include students' work for page 113 as part of their portfolios.

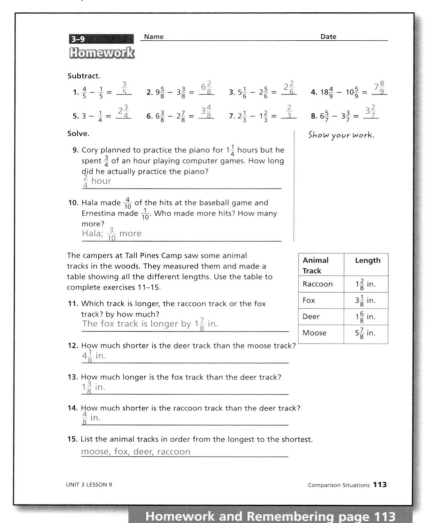

3–9

Homework

Name _____ Date _____

Subtract.

1. $\frac{4}{5} - \frac{1}{5} = \frac{3}{5}$ 2. $9\frac{5}{8} - 3\frac{3}{8} = 6\frac{2}{8}$ 3. $5\frac{1}{6} - 2\frac{5}{6} = 2\frac{2}{6}$ 4. $18\frac{4}{9} - 10\frac{5}{9} = 7\frac{8}{9}$

5. $3 - \frac{1}{4} = 2\frac{3}{4}$ 6. $6\frac{3}{8} - 2\frac{7}{8} = 3\frac{4}{8}$ 7. $2\frac{1}{3} - 1\frac{2}{3} = \frac{2}{3}$ 8. $6\frac{5}{7} - 3\frac{3}{7} = 3\frac{2}{7}$

Solve.   *Show your work.*

9. Cory planned to practice the piano for $1\frac{1}{4}$ hours but he spent $\frac{3}{4}$ of an hour playing computer games. How long did he actually practice the piano?
$\frac{2}{4}$ hour

10. Hala made $\frac{4}{10}$ of the hits at the baseball game and Ernestina made $\frac{1}{10}$. Who made more hits? How many more?
Hala; $\frac{3}{10}$ more

The campers at Tall Pines Camp saw some animal tracks in the woods. They measured them and made a table showing all the different lengths. Use the table to complete exercises 11–15.

Animal Track	Length
Raccoon	$1\frac{2}{8}$ in.
Fox	$3\frac{1}{8}$ in.
Deer	$1\frac{6}{8}$ in.
Moose	$5\frac{7}{8}$ in.

11. Which track is longer, the raccoon track or the fox track? by how much?
The fox track is longer by $1\frac{7}{8}$ in.

12. How much shorter is the deer track than the moose track?
$4\frac{1}{8}$ in.

13. How much longer is the fox track than the deer track?
$1\frac{3}{8}$ in.

14. How much shorter is the raccoon track than the deer track?
$\frac{4}{8}$ in.

15. List the animal tracks in order from the longest to the shortest.
moose, fox, deer, raccoon

UNIT 3 LESSON 9   Comparison Situations **113**

Homework and Remembering page 113

Remembering **Goal:** Cumulative Review

This Remembering activity is appropriate anytime after today's lesson.

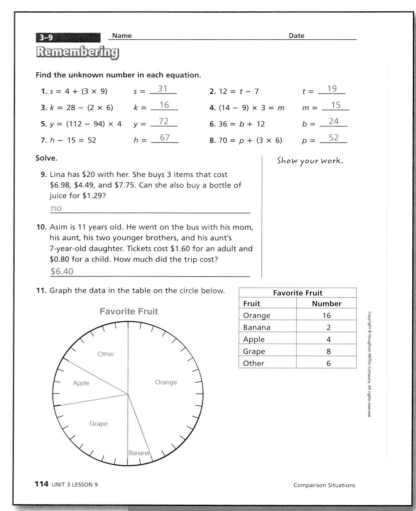

3–9

Remembering

Name _____ Date _____

Find the unknown number in each equation.

1. $s = 4 + (3 \times 9)$ $s = 31$ 2. $12 = t - 7$ $t = 19$

3. $k = 28 - (2 \times 6)$ $k = 16$ 4. $(14 - 9) \times 3 = m$ $m = 15$

5. $y = (112 - 94) \times 4$ $y = 72$ 6. $36 = b + 12$ $b = 24$

7. $h - 15 = 52$ $h = 67$ 8. $70 = p + (3 \times 6)$ $p = 52$

Solve.   *Show your work.*

9. Lina has $20 with her. She buys 3 items that cost $6.98, $4.49, and $7.75. Can she also buy a bottle of juice for $1.29?
no

10. Asim is 11 years old. He went on the bus with his mom, his aunt, his two younger brothers, and his aunt's 7-year-old daughter. Tickets cost $1.60 for an adult and $0.80 for a child. How much did the trip cost?
$6.40

11. Graph the data in the table on the circle below.

Favorite Fruit	
Fruit	Number
Orange	16
Banana	2
Apple	4
Grape	8
Other	6

Favorite Fruit

Other

Apple   Orange

Grape

Banana

114 UNIT 3 LESSON 9   Comparison Situations

Homework and Remembering page 114

Home or School Activity

 Science Connection

Compare Animal Size Guidebooks to insects, birds, and other animals often include the length of the animal in inches as a mixed number.

Have students find a guidebook at home, at school, at a library, or on the Internet. Ask them to record the length of several interesting animals using mixed numbers, and to create a word problem that involves comparing animals' sizes.

Monarch Butterfly
$3\frac{3}{8}$ to $4\frac{7}{8}$ inches

Mixed Practice With Like Fractions

Lesson Objectives

- Consolidate understanding of addition and subtraction with like fractions.
- Express the main concept of adding and subtracting like fractions.

The Day at a Glance

Today's Goals	Materials	Math Talk
Quick Practice Compare fractions using > and <.	Student Activity Book pages 201–202	In today's activities, the students are involved in discussion as they
1 Teaching the Lesson **A1:** Discuss a word problem presented by the Puzzled Penguin. **A2:** Present and solve fraction word problems.	Homework and Remembering pages 115–116 Math Journals	▶ identify and correct an error in a subtraction problem
2 Extending the Lesson ▶ Differentiated Instruction		▶ explain and compare solutions to problems using like fractions
3 Homework and Cumulative Review		

Quick Practice

⏱ **5 MINUTES**   **Goal:** Compare fractions using > and <.

Which Fraction Is Less? Invite six pairs of students to the board. The first student in each pair writes a fraction. The other student then writes a different fraction with the same denominator.

Next, invite one student from each pair to remain at the board and to point to each set of fractions, asking "Which is less?" The class responds by pointing and the student at the board writes > or < between the fractions. Then have the whole class read aloud the inequality. Seven tenths is greater than three tenths.

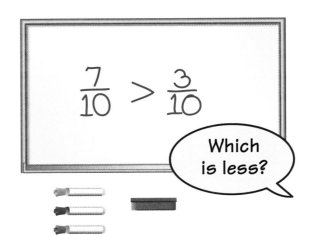

$$\frac{7}{10} > \frac{3}{10}$$

Which is less?

① Teaching the Lesson

Activity 1

The Puzzled Penguin

 20 MINUTES

Goal: Discuss a word problem presented by the Puzzled Penguin.

Materials: Student Activity page 201

 NCTM Standards:
Number and Operations
Problem Solving
Communication

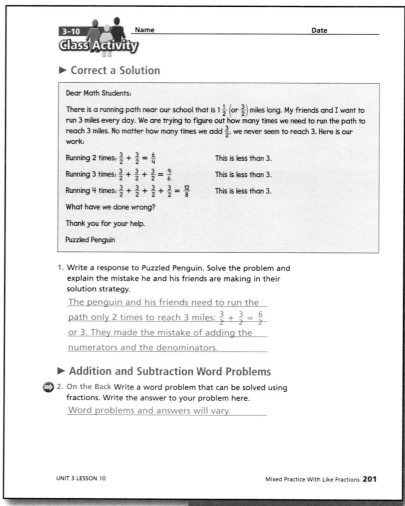

Student Activity Book page 201

▶ **Correct a Solution** WHOLE CLASS

Explain that the class received a letter from the Puzzled Penguin. Refer students to Student Activity Book page 201.

Give students several minutes to think about how they might respond to the letter. Then discuss their ideas as a class.

It is most important that students recognize that the Puzzled Penguin and his friends added both the numerators and the denominators of the fractions; they should have added only the numerators. To emphasize this point, you can pose this problem to the class:

● Suppose the Puzzled Penguin ran 3 miles (or $\frac{24}{8}$ miles) one day but his friend ran $\frac{1}{8}$ mile more. How can the Penguin calculate how far his friend ran? Add $\frac{1}{8}$ to $\frac{24}{8}$.

- Should the Penguin add the numerator and the denominator?
No; $\frac{24}{8} + \frac{1}{8}$ is not equal to $\frac{25}{16}$. $\frac{25}{16} = 1\frac{9}{16}$, which is less than 3.

- How can the Penguin use addition to find out how far his friend ran?
He can add the numerators, but not the denominators:
$\frac{24}{8} + \frac{1}{8} = \frac{25}{8}$, or $3\frac{1}{8}$.

- Does the answer $3\frac{1}{8}$ seem reasonable? Yes; $\frac{1}{8}$ is a small amount, so the answer should be a little more than 3. $3\frac{1}{8}$ is a little more than 3.

Invite students to complete exercise 1 and to compare their responses to the Puzzled Penguin with a partner.

▶ Choose the Correct Answer WHOLE CLASS

Write these three equations on the board. Tell students that one of them is correct and the other two are incorrect.

$$1.\ 7\tfrac{1}{8} - 5\tfrac{3}{8} \overset{?}{=} 2\tfrac{2}{8}$$
$$2.\ 7\tfrac{1}{8} - 5\tfrac{3}{8} \overset{?}{=} 1\tfrac{6}{8}$$
$$3.\ 7\tfrac{1}{8} - 5\tfrac{3}{8} \overset{?}{=} 2\tfrac{6}{8}$$

Working in pairs, allow students several minutes to determine which equation is correct and to identify the errors that caused the incorrect answers in the other two equations. Invite pairs to share their ideas and encourage questions from classmates. Students should realize that:

- equation 1 is incorrect. The person who completed the equation subtracted 5 from 7, but also subtracted $\frac{1}{8}$ from $\frac{3}{8}$; he or she should have subtracted $\frac{3}{8}$ from $\frac{1}{8}$.

- equation 2 is correct.

- equation 3 is incorrect. The person who completed it took apart 7 to create more eighths from which to subtract $\frac{3}{8}$, but he or she forgot to subtract 5 from 6 instead of from 7.

Activity 2

Student-Generated Problems

 30 MINUTES

Goal: Present and solve fraction word problems.

Materials: Student Activity Book page 201

 NCTM Standards:
Number and Operations
Problem Solving
Communication

 Class Management

To ensure balanced practice, you might ask certain students to write subtraction problems and others to write addition problems.

The Learning Classroom

Math Talk When students have completed their solutions at the board, invite the class to discuss the solutions and to suggest possible ways to improve them. If students are hesitant to make suggestions, ask questions to promote a discussion of what might need to be changed and why.

 Quick Quiz

See Assessment Guide for Unit 3 Quick Quiz 2.

▶ **Addition and Subtraction Word Problems**

WHOLE CLASS

Refer students to exercise 2 on Student Activity Book page 201 and have them write a word problem that can be solved using fractions. Invite one student at a time to read aloud his or her problem, and to ask the rest of the class to solve it. Encourage students to discuss their solutions; have several students work at the board.

If any students present problems that include fractions with unlike denominators, ask them to make an adjustment.

● You are asking us to add fourths and fifths. Which shall we use?

② Extending the Lesson

Differentiated Instruction Activities for Individualizing

Intervention
for students having difficulty

INDIVIDUALS

Work Backward

Write an equation involving adding or subtracting mixed numbers on the board. For example,

$$3\tfrac{2}{5} - 1\tfrac{3}{5} = \underline{\qquad}$$

Students work backward to write a word problem that can be solved using the equation. When they are finished, they can gather in a small group and share their problems.

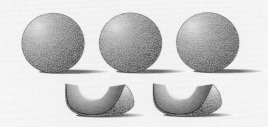

On Level
for students having success

INDIVIDUALS

Complete the Square

Draw this square on the board and fill in the black numbers as shown. Explain to students that each horizontal, vertical, and diagonal row must add to 6. Students copy the square on a sheet of paper and use what they know about adding and subtracting mixed numbers to complete it.

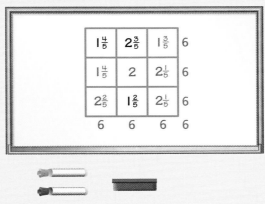

Challenge
for students seeking a challenge

PAIRS

Build a Square

Working in pairs, students arrange these mixed numbers in a 3-by-3 array so that every horizontal, vertical, and diagonal row adds to 9.

$$2\tfrac{4}{9}, 2\tfrac{5}{9}, 2\tfrac{6}{9}, 2\tfrac{8}{9}, 3, 3\tfrac{1}{9}, 3\tfrac{3}{9}, 3\tfrac{4}{9}, 3\tfrac{5}{9}$$

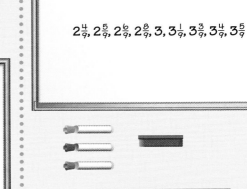

$3\tfrac{1}{9}$	$2\tfrac{4}{9}$	$3\tfrac{4}{9}$
$3\tfrac{3}{9}$	3	$2\tfrac{6}{9}$
$2\tfrac{5}{9}$	$3\tfrac{5}{9}$	$2\tfrac{8}{9}$

 Math Writing Prompt

Intervention

In Your Own Words
Look at a word problem you solved in this lesson. How did you determine that your solution was correct?

 Math Writing Prompt

On Level

Explain Your Thinking
Explain how you decided which numbers should go in which squares in the "Complete the Square" activity.

 Math Writing Prompt

Challenge

Solve a Problem
On the first day, a squirrel ate $\tfrac{1}{5}$ of a pile of nuts. On the second day, she ate $\tfrac{1}{5}$ of the remaining nuts. On the third day, she ate $\tfrac{1}{5}$ of the remaining nuts, and so on. On what day will she finish the nuts? Explain.

③ Homework and Cumulative Review

Goal: Additional Practice

✔ On this Homework page, students solve problems involving the addition and subtraction of like fractions.

Goal: Cumulative Review

This Remembering activity is appropriate anytime after today's lesson.

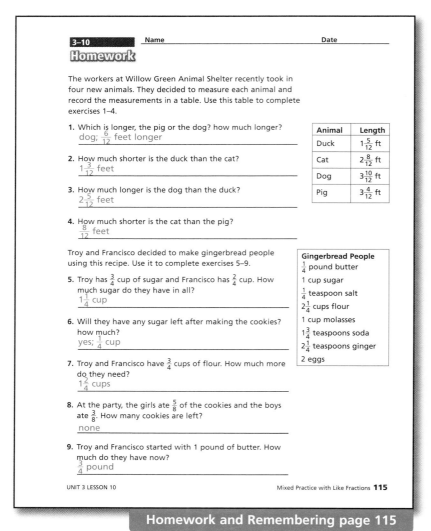

3–10 Name _____ Date _____

Homework

The workers at Willow Green Animal Shelter recently took in four new animals. They decided to measure each animal and record the measurements in a table. Use this table to complete exercises 1–4.

1. Which is longer, the pig or the dog? how much longer?
   dog; $\frac{6}{12}$ feet longer

2. How much shorter is the duck than the cat?
   $1\frac{3}{12}$ feet

3. How much longer is the dog than the duck?
   $2\frac{5}{12}$ feet

4. How much shorter is the cat than the pig?
   $\frac{8}{12}$ feet

Animal	Length
Duck	$1\frac{5}{12}$ ft
Cat	$2\frac{8}{12}$ ft
Dog	$3\frac{10}{12}$ ft
Pig	$3\frac{4}{12}$ ft

Troy and Francisco decided to make gingerbread people using this recipe. Use it to complete exercises 5–9.

5. Troy has $\frac{3}{4}$ cup of sugar and Francisco has $\frac{2}{4}$ cup. How much sugar do they have in all?
   $1\frac{1}{4}$ cup

6. Will they have any sugar left after making the cookies? how much?
   yes; $\frac{1}{4}$ cup

7. Troy and Francisco have $\frac{3}{4}$ cups of flour. How much more do they need?
   $1\frac{2}{4}$ cups

8. At the party, the girls ate $\frac{5}{8}$ of the cookies and the boys ate $\frac{3}{8}$. How many cookies are left?
   none

9. Troy and Francisco started with 1 pound of butter. How much do they have now?
   $\frac{3}{4}$ pound

Gingerbread People
$\frac{1}{4}$ pound butter
1 cup sugar
$\frac{1}{4}$ teaspoon salt
$2\frac{1}{4}$ cups flour
1 cup molasses
$1\frac{3}{4}$ teaspoons soda
$2\frac{1}{4}$ teaspoons ginger
2 eggs

UNIT 3 LESSON 10   Mixed Practice with Like Fractions **115**

Homework and Remembering page 115

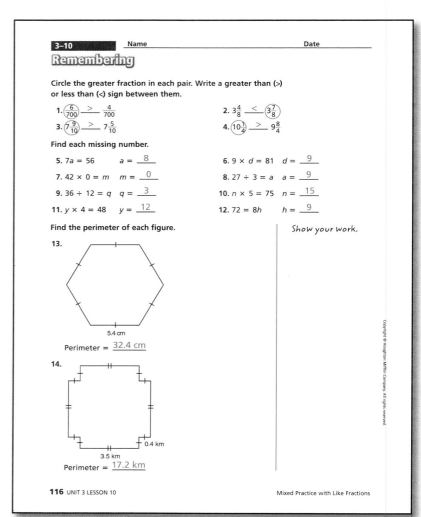

3–10 Name _____ Date _____

Remembering

Circle the greater fraction in each pair. Write a greater than (>) or less than (<) sign between them.

1. $\frac{6}{700}$ **>** $\frac{4}{700}$

2. $3\frac{4}{8}$ **<** $3\frac{7}{8}$

3. $7\frac{9}{10}$ **>** $7\frac{5}{10}$

4. $10\frac{1}{4}$ **>** $9\frac{8}{4}$

Find each missing number.

5. $7a = 56$ $a = 8$

6. $9 \times d = 81$ $d = 9$

7. $42 \times 0 = m$ $m = 0$

8. $27 \div 3 = a$ $a = 9$

9. $36 \div 12 = q$ $q = 3$

10. $n \times 5 = 75$ $n = 15$

11. $y \times 4 = 48$ $y = 12$

12. $72 = 8h$ $h = 9$

Find the perimeter of each figure.   *Show your work.*

13.

5.4 cm
Perimeter = 32.4 cm

14.

0.4 km
3.5 km
Perimeter = 17.2 km

116 UNIT 3 LESSON 10   Mixed Practice with Like Fractions

Homework and Remembering page 116

Home or School Activity

 Language Arts Connection

Media Advertisements Ask students to look for advertisements in newspapers or magazines. Have them estimate how many pages of advertising there are in one section of a newspaper or a group of pages in a magazine, to the nearest eighth of a page. They can add and subtract to compare the amount of advertising in different sections or in different publications.

Discover Equivalent Fractions

Lesson Objectives

- Generate and explain simple equivalent fractions.
- Understand and apply the terms *equivalent fraction* and *simplify*.

Vocabulary
equivalent
  fractions
multiplier
simplify
unsimplify

The Day at a Glance

Today's Goals	Materials	Math Talk
Quick Practice Recognize when to ungroup mixed numbers to solve a subtraction problem.	Student Activity Book pages 203–206	In today's activities, the students are involved in discussion as they
1 Teaching the Lesson **A1:** Generate equivalent fractions and discuss the multipliers. **A2:** Use a number line to create and visualize equivalent fractions.	Equivalent Fractions (Copymaster M31) Rulers Fraction Match-Up Cards (Copymaster M32)	► make chains of equivalent fractions ► show equivalent fractions on a number line
2 Extending the Lesson ► Differentiated Instruction	Scissors Math Journals	
3 Homework and Cumulative Review	Homework and Remembering pages 117–118	

Quick Practice

5 MINUTES   **Goal:** Recognize when to ungroup mixed numbers to solve a subtraction problem.

Ungroup Invite six students to the board to write a subtraction problem involving mixed numbers; they should leave the problem unsolved. Ask one student to remain at the board and to point to each problem while the class responds, "ungroup" or "do not ungroup," depending on whether the first number needs to be changed to solve the problem. (See Lesson 8.)

① Teaching the Lesson

Explore Equivalence

 25 MINUTES

Goal: Generate equivalent fractions and discuss the multipliers.

 NCTM Standards:
Number and Operations
Reasoning and Proof
Representation

▶ Generate Equivalent Halves [WHOLE CLASS]

Write the fraction $\frac{1}{2}$ on the board. Ask students to suggest as many fractions as they can that are equivalent to one half. Create a long fraction equation on the board and write fractions in the order in which students generate them. Leave the fraction chain on the board.

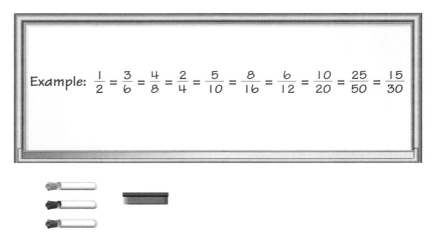

Example: $\frac{1}{2} = \frac{3}{6} = \frac{4}{8} = \frac{2}{4} = \frac{5}{10} = \frac{8}{16} = \frac{6}{12} = \frac{10}{20} = \frac{25}{50} = \frac{15}{30}$

Invite several volunteers to the board to demonstrate that one half is equal to one of the other fractions in the chain. Typically, the easiest way to do this is with a drawing.

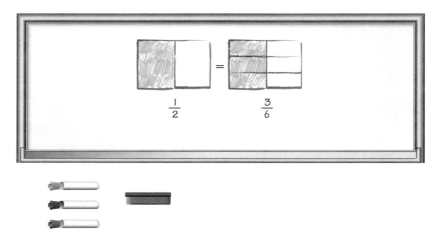

$\frac{1}{2}$ = $\frac{3}{6}$

▶ Understand Equivalence [WHOLE CLASS]

Point out that all the fractions on the board are equivalent fractions. Define equivalent fractions as those that are the same sized part of a whole.

Explain that we can divide a whole into more and more equal parts and that we can make one half by taking the correct number of parts. Present some examples and ask students to find one half.

- If I divide a cake into 20 equal parts, how many parts will it take to make $\frac{1}{2}$? 10 parts

- If I divide the same cake into 100 equal parts, how many parts will it take to make $\frac{1}{2}$? 50 parts

Write these two fractions on the board.

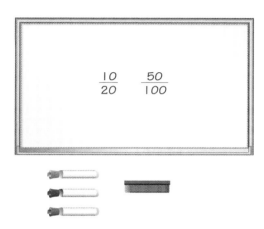

- Would you say that $\frac{10}{20}$ and $\frac{50}{100}$ are equivalent fractions? Yes; they are both the same as $\frac{1}{2}$.

▶ Introduce the Multiplier WHOLE CLASS

Have students turn their attention to the fraction chain on the board. Ask whether there is any way to tell if two fractions are equivalent without drawing a picture. Students may notice that when the numerator and denominator are multiplied by the same number, the result is an equivalent fraction. Have the class give examples from the fraction chain and tell what the multiplier is.

- We started out with $\frac{1}{2}$. What did we do to get $\frac{3}{6}$? We multiplied the numerator and the denominator by 3.

- How can you get $\frac{4}{8}$? You can multiply the numerator and the denominator by 4.

At this point, you might invite students to name a different unit fraction, such as $\frac{1}{3}$ or $\frac{1}{4}$. Choose volunteers to name fractions equivalent to the unit fraction named and to draw a picture to show that each fraction is equivalent.

Ask students whether they think they can find fractions equivalent to any unit fraction by multiplying the numerator and the denominator by the same number. If there is disagreement, lead a discussion and encourage students to explain their reasoning.

Activity continued ▶

Special Needs Have students who learn best by being active draw a line down the center of a sheet of paper to represent $\frac{1}{2}$. They fold the paper once vertically and unfold it, so that the paper is divided in fourths. Ask students how many fourths are in each half.

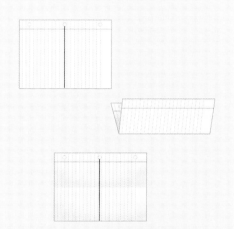

Students should see that each half contains two fourths. Repeat the activity by folding the paper again into eighths.

Activity 2

Equivalent Fractions on the Number Line

 30 MINUTES

Goal: Use a number line to create and visualize equivalent fractions.

Materials: Student Activity Book pages 203–206

✔ **NCTM Standards:**
Number and Operations
Reasoning and Proof
Representation

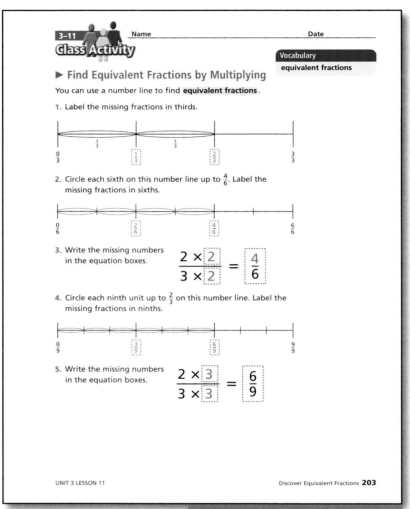

Student Activity Book page 203

▶ Find Equivalent Fractions by Multiplying WHOLE CLASS

Refer students to exercise 1 on Student Activity Book page 203. Explain that they will be finding equivalent fractions for $\frac{2}{3}$.

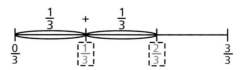

Begin by asking students to fill in the empty boxes in the number line. Explain that this is the simplest way to write the fractions $\frac{1}{3}$ and $\frac{2}{3}$. Elicit from students the total of the circled thirds: $\frac{1}{3} + \frac{1}{3} = \frac{2}{3}$.

Direct students' attention to the number line in exercise 2, which shows sixths. Ask students to label all fractions shown on the line. The fractions that belong in the empty boxes are equivalent to $\frac{1}{3}$ and $\frac{2}{3}$.

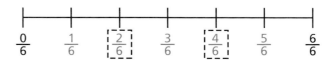

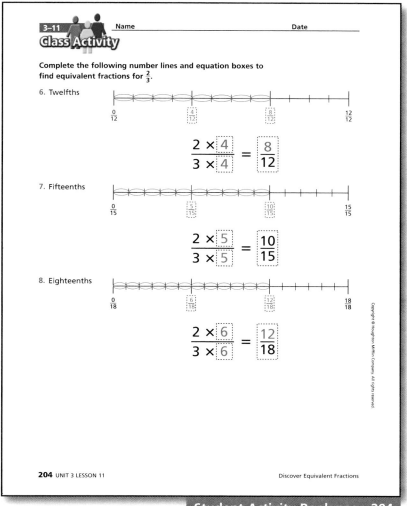

204 UNIT 3 LESSON 11   Discover Equivalent Fractions

Student Activity Book page 204

Next, have students circle enough sixths to make $\frac{1}{3}$ and $\frac{2}{3}$. Then, ask them to write the total above each part: $\frac{2}{6} + \frac{2}{6} = \frac{4}{6}$.

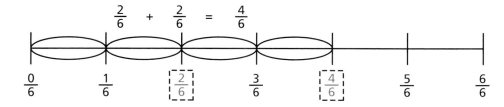

Use questions to encourage students to share their observations about the numbers on the line.

● How many sixths does it take to make $\frac{1}{3}$? 2 sixths

● How many sixths does it take to make $\frac{2}{3}$? 4 sixths

● How can $\frac{4}{6}$ be equal to $\frac{2}{3}$ when $\frac{4}{6}$ has bigger numbers than $\frac{2}{3}$? $\frac{4}{6}$ has twice as many pieces as $\frac{2}{3}$, but each piece is only half as big.

Activity continued ▶

Discover Equivalent Fractions **419**

Activity 2

Have students look at the equation box in exercise 3. Ask them to identify the multiplier and to write it in both stacked boxes. The multiplier tells how many times each third was split to make sixths. Have students supply the equivalent fraction produced by this multiplier.

$$\frac{2 \times \boxed{2}}{3 \times \boxed{2}} = \boxed{\frac{4}{6}}$$

Repeat the process for ninths by completing exercises 4 and 5 together.

Then have students cover the page to the right of $\frac{1}{3}$, $\frac{2}{6}$, and $\frac{3}{9}$ on their number lines. Discuss these equivalencies and how they made them.

● Into how many equal parts is $\frac{1}{3}$ split to make sixths? 2 equal parts

● Into how many equal parts is $\frac{1}{3}$ split to make ninths? 3 equal parts

Continue in this way until students have completed exercises 6–8 and generated all of the multipliers and equivalent fractions. They do not need to label every fraction on each number line; they can simply fill in the empty boxes.

As you proceed, emphasize repeatedly the inverse relationship between the size of the pieces and the size of the numbers in the numerator (n) and the denominator (d): the greater the number in the denominator, the smaller the pieces. Be sure to have students connect the multipliers with the number of equal splits of $\frac{1}{3}$ in n and d. As you work through the exercises, both n and d will have 2, 3, 4, 5, and 6 times as many parts as the original simple fraction. For eighteenths, there are 6 times as many parts, but each part is only $\frac{1}{6}$ the original size.

Ask students to cover the page to the right of $\frac{4}{12}$, $\frac{5}{15}$, and $\frac{6}{8}$.

● Into how many equal parts is $\frac{1}{3}$ split to make twelfths?
4 equal parts

● Into how many equal parts is $\frac{1}{3}$ split to make fifteenths?
5 equal parts

● Into how many equal parts is $\frac{1}{3}$ split to make eighteenths?
6 equal parts

Write this sentence on the board and have students tell you how to complete it. After students reach an agreement, have a volunteer write the missing word.

For smaller unit fractions, it takes <u>more</u> units to make $\frac{2}{3}$. (more or fewer)

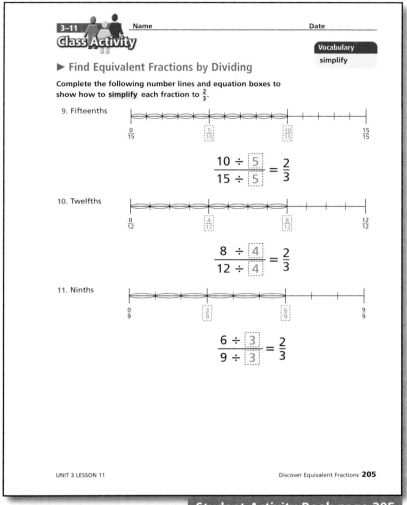

▶ Find Equivalent Fractions by Dividing [WHOLE CLASS]

Ask students to look at the answer ($\frac{12}{18}$) in the last equation on Student Activity Book page 204.

● How can you change $\frac{12}{18}$ back to $\frac{2}{3}$? Divide the numerator and denominator by 6.

Introduce the term *simplify:* to produce an equivalent fraction with lesser numerator and denominator. Have students complete exercises 9–11. Then have them cover the whole page to the right of $\frac{1}{3}$.

● How many fifteenths are grouped together to make $\frac{1}{3}$? 5

● So, how can you find the number of thirds in $\frac{10}{15}$? Divide 10 by 5.

● How many twelfths are grouped together to make $\frac{1}{3}$? 4

● How can you find the number of thirds in $\frac{8}{12}$? Divide 8 by 4.

● How many ninths are grouped together to make $\frac{1}{3}$? 3

● How can you find the number of thirds in $\frac{6}{9}$? Divide 6 by 3.

Activity continued ▶

Teaching Note

Math Background Some math programs use the term *reduce* rather than *simplify*. The word *reduce*, however, can imply to students that the amount is actually getting smaller. Your students should be aware of this alternate term because they may see it in other contexts, including some standardized math tests.

✓ Ongoing Assessment

Remind students that there are two ways to make equivalent fractions: simplify and unsimplify. Ask students how to simplify and unsimplify a given fraction.

▶ $\frac{4}{8}$ can be simplified to $\frac{1}{2}$. Explain what you need to do to simplify a fraction.

▶ $\frac{1}{2}$ can be unsimplified to $\frac{3}{6}$. Explain what you need to do to unsimplify a fraction.

① Teaching the Lesson (continued)

Activity 2

Differentiated Instruction

Extra Help If students are having difficulty, they can circle each fractional part of the number line and count the parts up to the equivalent fractions they are trying to find.

The Learning Classroom

Building Concepts Ask students to summarize what they have learned about how to make a new fraction that is equivalent to a given fraction. They should recognize that you can always multiply the numerator and denominator by the same whole number to make an equivalent fraction. Discuss when it is possible to divide the numerator and denominator by the same whole number to simplify a fraction.

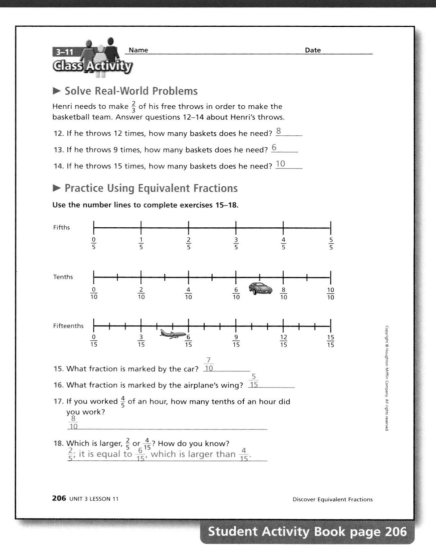

Student Activity Book page 206

Write this sentence on the board and have students tell you how to complete it:

For larger unit fractions; it takes <u>fewer</u> units to make $\frac{2}{3}$. (more or fewer)

▶ Solve Real-World Problems PAIRS

Use Solve and Discuss for problems 12–14 on Student Activity Book page 206. Remind students to refer to the number lines on the previous pages and discuss how to use them to solve the problem.

▶ Practice Using Equivalent Fractions INDIVIDUALS

Refer students to Student Activity Book page 206 and ask them to complete exercises 15–18.

Intervention
for students having difficulty

INDIVIDUALS

Find Equivalent Fractions

Materials: Equivalent Fractions (Copymaster M31), rulers

Using a ruler, students line up fractions on Copymaster M31 and write all of the equivalent fractions they can find for each vertical row that has more than one fraction.

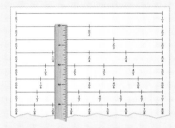

$\frac{1}{4}$ and $\frac{2}{8}$ are equivalent.

On Level
for students having success

PAIRS

Fraction Match-Up

Materials: Fraction Match-Up Cards (Copymaster M32) (1 copy per pair), scissors

In pairs, students cut out the cards from Copymaster M32 and play a match-up game.

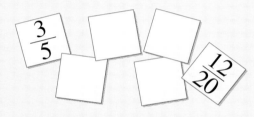

One player turns over two cards. If the cards show equivalent fractions, the player keeps the cards and takes another turn. If the cards do not match, the player returns them face down and his or her partner takes a turn. The first player to collect five pairs of matching cards wins.

Challenge
for students seeking a challenge

PAIRS

Compare Fractions

Materials: Equivalent Fractions (Copymaster M31) (1 copy per pair), rulers (1 per pair)

One student writes two fractions using a denominator between 2 and 12. The other student then predicts which of the two fractions is greater, or if they are equivalent.

Together, they check the prediction using the chart on Copymaster M31 by lining up the greater fraction (according to the prediction) with a ruler. If the other fraction is less, it will appear to the left of the ruler.

This example shows that $\frac{1}{4}$ is greater than $\frac{1}{5}$, less than $\frac{2}{7}$, and equivalent to $\frac{2}{8}$.

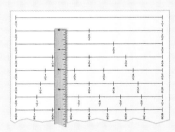

 Math Writing Prompt

Intervention

Show Your Thinking
Use a diagram to explain why the fractions $\frac{2}{5}$ and $\frac{4}{10}$ are equivalent.

 Math Writing Prompt

On Level

Use Reasoning
Write three equivalent fractions. Identify the simplest fraction and explain why it is the simplest.

 Math Writing Prompt

Challenge

Explain Your Thinking
Use equivalent fractions to explain why 25 cm is the same length as $\frac{1}{4}$ m.

③ Homework and Cumulative Review

✓ Include students' work for page 117 as part of their portfolios.

This Remembering activity is appropriate anytime after today's lesson.

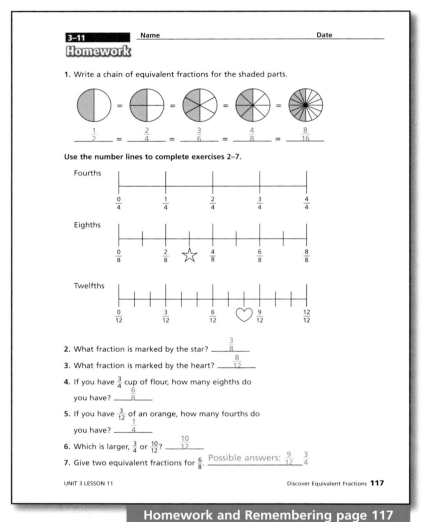

3-11 Homework   Name   Date

1. Write a chain of equivalent fractions for the shaded parts.

$$\frac{1}{2} = \frac{2}{4} = \frac{3}{6} = \frac{4}{8} = \frac{8}{16}$$

Use the number lines to complete exercises 2–7.

Fourths
$$\frac{0}{4} \quad \frac{1}{4} \quad \frac{2}{4} \quad \frac{3}{4} \quad \frac{4}{4}$$

Eighths
$$\frac{0}{8} \quad \frac{2}{8} \quad ☆ \quad \frac{4}{8} \quad \frac{6}{8} \quad \frac{8}{8}$$

Twelfths
$$\frac{0}{12} \quad \frac{3}{12} \quad \frac{6}{12} \quad ♡ \quad \frac{9}{12} \quad \frac{12}{12}$$

2. What fraction is marked by the star? $\frac{3}{8}$

3. What fraction is marked by the heart? $\frac{8}{12}$

4. If you have $\frac{3}{4}$ cup of flour, how many eighths do you have? $\frac{6}{8}$

5. If you have $\frac{3}{12}$ of an orange, how many fourths do you have? $\frac{1}{4}$

6. Which is larger, $\frac{3}{4}$ or $\frac{10}{12}$? $\frac{10}{12}$

7. Give two equivalent fractions for $\frac{6}{8}$. Possible answers: $\frac{9}{12}$ $\frac{3}{4}$

UNIT 3 LESSON 11   Discover Equivalent Fractions **117**

Homework and Remembering page 117

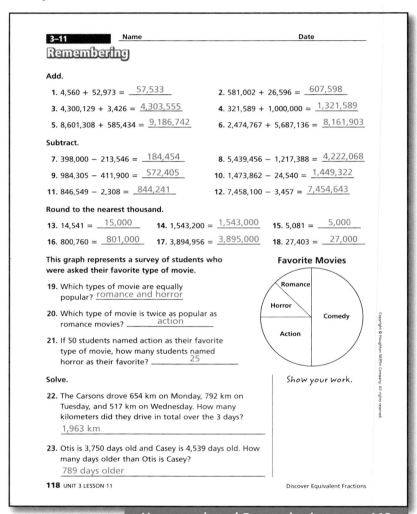

3-11 Remembering   Name   Date

Add.

1. 4,560 + 52,973 = 57,533
2. 581,002 + 26,596 = 607,598
3. 4,300,129 + 3,426 = 4,303,555
4. 321,589 + 1,000,000 = 1,321,589
5. 8,601,308 + 585,434 = 9,186,742
6. 2,474,767 + 5,687,136 = 8,161,903

Subtract.

7. 398,000 − 213,546 = 184,454
8. 5,439,456 − 1,217,388 = 4,222,068
9. 984,305 − 411,900 = 572,405
10. 1,473,862 − 24,540 = 1,449,322
11. 846,549 − 2,308 = 844,241
12. 7,458,100 − 3,457 = 7,454,643

Round to the nearest thousand.

13. 14,541 = 15,000
14. 1,543,200 = 1,543,000
15. 5,081 = 5,000
16. 800,760 = 801,000
17. 3,894,956 = 3,895,000
18. 27,403 = 27,000

This graph represents a survey of students who were asked their favorite type of movie.

19. Which types of movie are equally popular? romance and horror

20. Which type of movie is twice as popular as romance movies? action

21. If 50 students named action as their favorite type of movie, how many students named horror as their favorite? 25

Favorite Movies

Romance
Horror
Comedy
Action

Solve.

22. The Carsons drove 654 km on Monday, 792 km on Tuesday, and 517 km on Wednesday. How many kilometers did they drive in total over the 3 days? 1,963 km

23. Otis is 3,750 days old and Casey is 4,539 days old. How many days older than Otis is Casey? 789 days older

Show your work.

118 UNIT 3 LESSON 11   Discover Equivalent Fractions

Homework and Remembering page 118

Home or School Activity

 Literature Connection

Write About It Have students read the book *Gator Pie* by Louise Mathews (Sundance Publishing, 1995). Ask them to write about how the story is related to the topic of equivalent fractions.

Equivalent Fractions and Multipliers

Vocabulary

multiplication
 table
multiplier
simplify
unsimplify

Lesson Objectives

- Understand the role of the multiplier in equivalent fractions.
- Simplify and unsimplify common fractions.

The Day at a Glance

Today's Goals	Materials	Math Talk
Quick Practice Recognize when to ungroup mixed numbers to solve a subtraction problem.	Student Activity Book pages 207–208	In today's activities, students are involved in discussion as they
1 Teaching the Lesson **A1:** Discuss how equivalent fractions relate to the multiplication table. **A2:** Find equivalent fractions.	Tens and Hundreds Grids (Copymaster M33) Clock with a second hand or minute timer	▶ use fraction bars and rows of multiplication tables to generate equivalent fractions
2 Extending the Lesson ▶ Differentiated Instruction	Math Journals	▶ solve problems involving equivalent fractions
3 Homework and Cumulative Review	Homework and Remembering pages 119–120	

Quick Practice

🕐 5 MINUTES **Goal:** Recognize when to ungroup mixed numbers to solve a subtraction problem.

Ungroup Invite six students to the board to write a subtraction problem involving mixed numbers; they should leave the problem unsolved. Ask one student to remain at the board and point to each problem while the class responds, "ungroup" or "do not ungroup," depending on whether the first number needs to be changed to solve the problem. (See Lesson 8.)

Teaching the Lesson

Explore Equivalence

 35 MINUTES

Goal: Discuss how equivalent fractions relate to the multiplication table.

Materials: Student Activity Book pages 207–208

NCTM Standards:
Number and Operations
Reasoning and Proof
Problem Solving

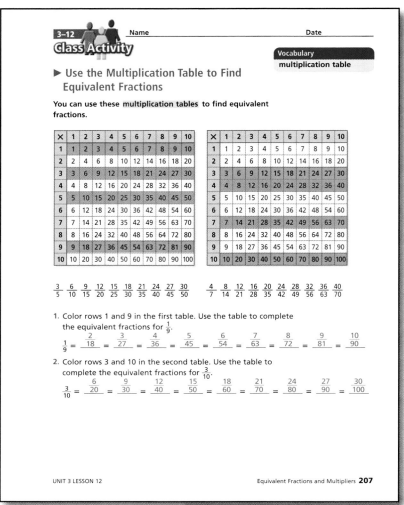

Student Activity Book page 207

▶ Use the Multiplication Table to Find Equivalent Fractions WHOLE CLASS

Write the fraction $\frac{3}{5}$ on the board. Ask students to suggest as many equivalent fractions as they can. It is fine if they are able to come up with only a few suggestions.

Refer students to Student Activity Book page 207.

● What do you see at the top of the page? multiplication tables

● What does row 3 in each table show? multiples of 3

● What does row 5 in each table show? multiples of 5

Tell students to think of the numbers in row 3 as numerators and the numbers in row 5 as denominators.

● Why is $\frac{3}{5}$ equivalent to $\frac{6}{10}$? Both the numerator and denominator of $\frac{3}{5}$ have been multiplied by 2.

Draw students' attention to the shaded section at the bottom of the first table.

- The first fraction, $\frac{3}{5}$, is the simplest fraction. Why can't we write it with smaller numbers for the numerator and denominator? You can't divide both numbers by the same number to make them smaller.

- What are the multipliers for the fractions, as you look across the row? 2, 3, 4, 5, 6, 7, 8, 9, 10

- Write the multiplier below each fraction. Where do you see the multipliers in the table? in the top row

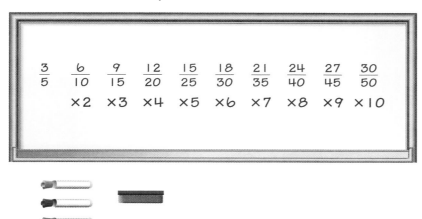

$$\frac{3}{5} \quad \frac{6}{10} \quad \frac{9}{15} \quad \frac{12}{20} \quad \frac{15}{25} \quad \frac{18}{30} \quad \frac{21}{35} \quad \frac{24}{40} \quad \frac{27}{45} \quad \frac{30}{50}$$
$$\times 2 \quad \times 3 \quad \times 4 \quad \times 5 \quad \times 6 \quad \times 7 \quad \times 8 \quad \times 9 \quad \times 10$$

▶ Simplify and Unsimplify WHOLE CLASS

Encourage students to consult this chain of fractions as you discuss simplifying and unsimplifying. Relate the fractions to the columns in the first multiplication table on Student Activity Book page 207.

- How can you change $\frac{3}{5}$ to $\frac{18}{30}$? Multiply the numerator and denominator by 6.

- How can you simplify $\frac{18}{30}$? Divide the numerator and denominator by 6.

- How can you change $\frac{3}{5}$ to $\frac{27}{45}$? Multiply the numerator and denominator by 9.

- How can you simplify $\frac{27}{45}$? Divide the numerator and denominator by 9.

Remind students that when they divide the numerator and denominator to make them smaller, they are simplifying the fraction to make larger-unit fractions. Multiplying the numerator and denominator *un*simplifies the fraction by making smaller unit fractions. The two fractions still represent the same number; they are still the same part of the whole. This is why we call them *equivalent fractions.*

Activity continued ▶

The Learning Classroom

Math Talk Having students pose questions for their classmates and lead discussions, after you have modeled a similar process, is a good way to help them take ownership of the learning that goes on in the classroom.

▶ Find Numerators and Denominators WHOLE CLASS

Have students look at the second multiplication table on Student Activity Book page 207. Ask them to write the multiplier below each fraction and to relate this multiplier to the column in the multiplication table.

Ask questions related to simplifying and unsimplifying the fractions. Also have students find fractions with specific numerators and denominators, such as the examples shown here.

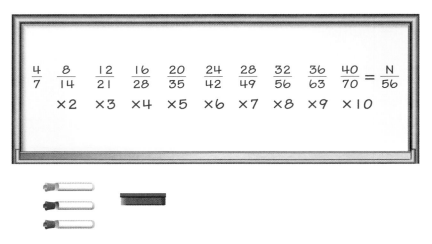

$$\frac{4}{7} \quad \frac{8}{14} \quad \frac{12}{21} \quad \frac{16}{28} \quad \frac{20}{35} \quad \frac{24}{42} \quad \frac{28}{49} \quad \frac{32}{56} \quad \frac{36}{63} \quad \frac{40}{70} = \frac{N}{56}$$

$$\times 2 \quad \times 3 \quad \times 4 \quad \times 5 \quad \times 6 \quad \times 7 \quad \times 8 \quad \times 9 \quad \times 10$$

- What is the simplest way to express this fraction? $\frac{4}{7}$

- If I need a fraction equivalent to $\frac{4}{7}$ with a denominator of 56, what will the numerator be? 32

- How did you get 32? Since you multiplied the denominator by 8, you have to multiply the numerator by 8.

- If I need a fraction equivalent to $\frac{4}{7}$ with a numerator of 24, what will the denominator be? 42

$$\frac{4}{7} = \frac{24}{d}$$

- How did you get 42? Since you multiplied the numerator by 6, you have to multiply the denominator by 6.

Invite students to make up similar questions for their classmates to answer. For each question, encourage students to explain how they found the unknown number.

Have students complete exercises 1 and 2 on their own or in pairs.

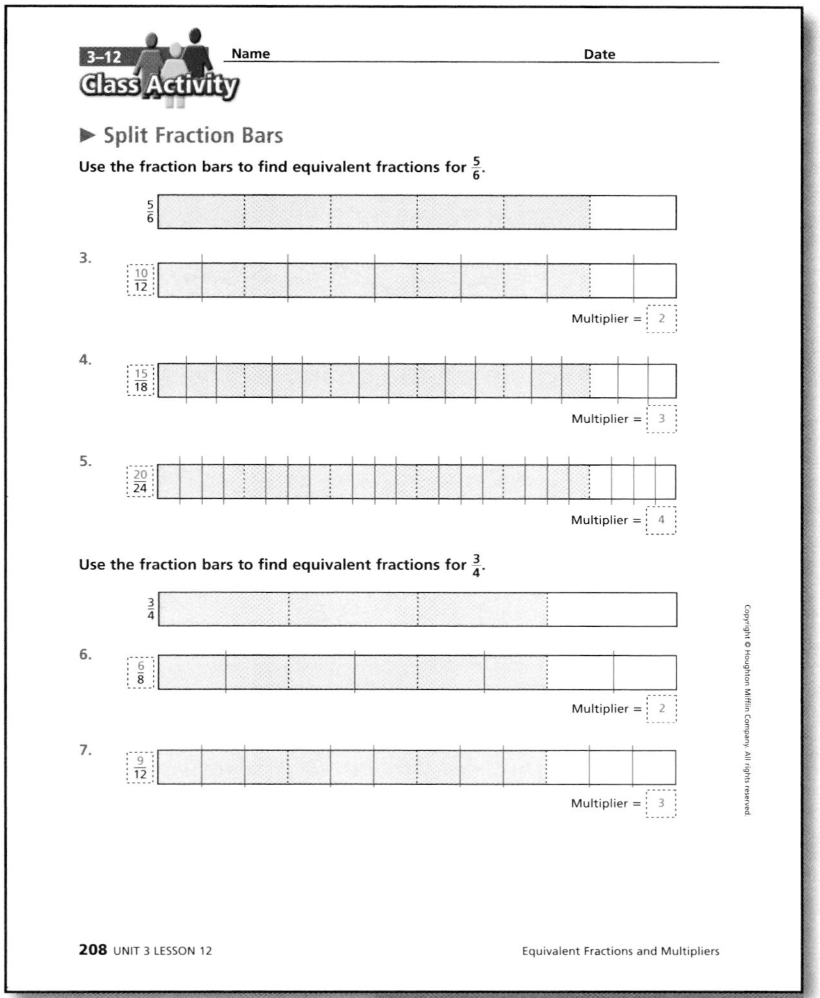

3–12 Class Activity Name Date

► Split Fraction Bars

Use the fraction bars to find equivalent fractions for $\frac{5}{6}$.

$\frac{5}{6}$

3. $\frac{10}{12}$ Multiplier = 2

4. $\frac{15}{18}$ Multiplier = 3

5. $\frac{20}{24}$ Multiplier = 4

Use the fraction bars to find equivalent fractions for $\frac{3}{4}$.

$\frac{3}{4}$

6. $\frac{6}{8}$ Multiplier = 2

7. $\frac{9}{12}$ Multiplier = 3

208 UNIT 3 LESSON 12 Equivalent Fractions and Multipliers

Student Activity Book page 208

► Split Fraction Bars INDIVIDUALS

Refer students to Student Activity Book page 208 and draw their attention to the fraction bars for $\frac{5}{6}$. Ask students how they can modify the bar to show twelfths. You can split each sixth in 2 parts.

Next, ask them how they can modify the bar to show eighteenths and twenty-fourths. You can split each sixth in 3 parts for eighteenths and 4 parts for twenty-fourths.

Ask students to split the bars as described and complete exercises 3–5. Invite a volunteer to demonstrate the first series of splits on the classroom MathBoard.

When students are finished, have them split the fraction bars and find the equivalent fractions in exercises 6 and 7.

Activity 2

Equivalence Chains

 20 MINUTES

Goal: Find equivalent fractions.

Materials: Math Journals

 NCTM Standards:
Number and Operations
Reasoning and Proof

 Ongoing Assessment

Choose an unsimplified fraction, such as $\frac{10}{12}$, and ask students to make equivalent fractions with given multipliers or divisors.

▶ Write a simpler fraction using 2 as a divisor.

▶ Write an equivalent fraction using 3 as a multiplier.

▶ Generate Equivalent Fractions WHOLE CLASS

Write the fraction $\frac{3}{8}$ on the board and leave room to the right for a row of equivalent fractions. Invite nine volunteers to line up at the board. Each student writes the next equivalent fraction in the series and places the multiplier below. Ask the rest of the class to write the same fraction chain in their Math Journals or on a sheet of paper, working ahead if possible. When the chain is complete, have students check it to make sure it is correct. Leave the fraction chain on the board for the next activity.

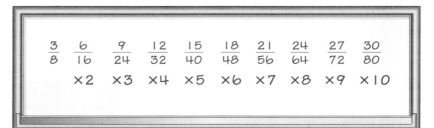

▶ Share a Giant Pizza WHOLE CLASS

Ask a girl and a boy to go to the board and to circle a fraction in the chain, except the first or the last. Above their fractions, have them label the letter *B* for boy and *G* for girl.

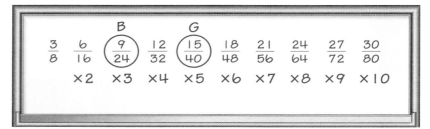

Have students pretend that these fractions represent slices of the same-sized giant pizza. Ask these questions.

● What does each denominator represent? the total number of slices

● What does each numerator represent? the number of slices that the boy or girl gets

● Who gets more slices? girl larger slices? boy

● Who gets a larger amount, the girl or the boy? Why? They get the same amount because both fractions are equivalent to $\frac{3}{8}$.

● What does the boy's multiplier mean? He has 3 times as many slices as the $\frac{3}{8}$ of a pizza. Each slice is only $\frac{1}{3}$ as large.

● What does the girl's multiplier mean? She has 5 times as many slices as the $\frac{3}{8}$ of a pizza. Each slice is only $\frac{1}{5}$ as large.

If time permits, have students generate another chain of equivalent fractions and repeat the activity.

② Extending the Lesson

Differentiated Instruction | Activities for Individualizing

Intervention
for students having difficulty

`INDIVIDUALS`

Decimals and Fractions

Materials: Tens and Hundreds Grids (Copymaster M33)

Students shade parts of each grid on Copymaster M33. They then write a fraction and a decimal for the shaded part of the whole grid.

 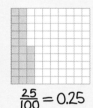

$$\frac{2}{10} = 0.2 \qquad \frac{25}{100} = 0.25$$

On Level
for students having success

`PAIRS`

Equivalent Fractions

Each student writes an improper fraction and an equivalent fraction using a multiplier. Pairs then trade fractions and rewrite both as mixed numbers.

$$\frac{13}{5} = \frac{26}{10}$$

$$2\frac{3}{5} = 2\frac{6}{10}$$

Challenge
for students seeking a challenge

`PAIRS`

Equivalent Forms

Materials: clock with a second hand or minute timer

Each student writes a whole number, a fraction with a denominator of 10, and a fraction with a denominator of 100.

Pairs trade papers and write each number in as many equivalent ways as possible in one minute.

Students score 2 points for the first new form of each fraction and 1 point for each additional form.

$$3 = 3.0 = \frac{3}{1}$$

$$\frac{5}{10} = 0.5 = \frac{1}{2} = \frac{50}{100}$$

$$\frac{75}{100} = 0.75 = \frac{15}{20} = \frac{150}{200}$$

11 points ✓

 Math Writing Prompt

Intervention

Explain Your Thinking
Write a fraction with a denominator of 100. Use an example to explain what the numerator and denominator might mean.

 Math Writing Prompt

On Level

You Decide
Floyd used 2 as a multiplier to change $1\frac{2}{3}$ to $2\frac{4}{6}$. Are his fractions equivalent? Explain why or why not.

 Math Writing Prompt

Challenge

Investigate Math
Explain how to use whole numbers 2, 3, 4, 5, and so on as divisors to test whether you can simplify a fraction. Can you simplify the fraction $\frac{35}{91}$?

③ Homework and Cumulative Review

3–12

Homework **Goal:** Additional Practice

✔ On this Homework page, students practice writing equivalent fractions.

3–12

Remembering **Goal:** Cumulative Review

This Remembering activity is appropriate anytime after today's lesson.

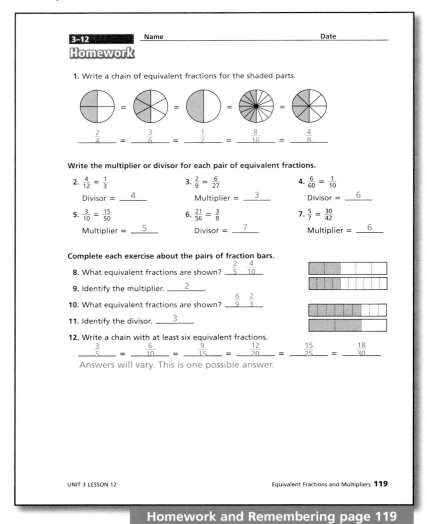

3–12 Name _____ Date _____
Homework

1. Write a chain of equivalent fractions for the shaded parts.

$\frac{2}{4}$ = $\frac{3}{6}$ = $\frac{1}{2}$ = $\frac{8}{16}$ = $\frac{4}{8}$

Write the multiplier or divisor for each pair of equivalent fractions.

2. $\frac{4}{12} = \frac{1}{3}$ 3. $\frac{2}{9} = \frac{6}{27}$ 4. $\frac{6}{60} = \frac{1}{10}$
Divisor = __4__   Multiplier = __3__   Divisor = __6__

5. $\frac{3}{10} = \frac{15}{50}$ 6. $\frac{21}{56} = \frac{3}{8}$ 7. $\frac{5}{7} = \frac{30}{42}$
Multiplier = __5__   Divisor = __7__   Multiplier = __6__

Complete each exercise about the pairs of fraction bars.

8. What equivalent fractions are shown? $\frac{2}{5}$ $\frac{4}{10}$

9. Identify the multiplier. __2__

10. What equivalent fractions are shown? $\frac{6}{9}$ $\frac{2}{3}$

11. Identify the divisor. __3__

12. Write a chain with at least six equivalent fractions.
$\frac{3}{5}$ = $\frac{6}{10}$ = $\frac{9}{15}$ = $\frac{12}{20}$ = $\frac{15}{25}$ = $\frac{18}{30}$
Answers will vary. This is one possible answer.

UNIT 3 LESSON 12   Equivalent Fractions and Multipliers **119**

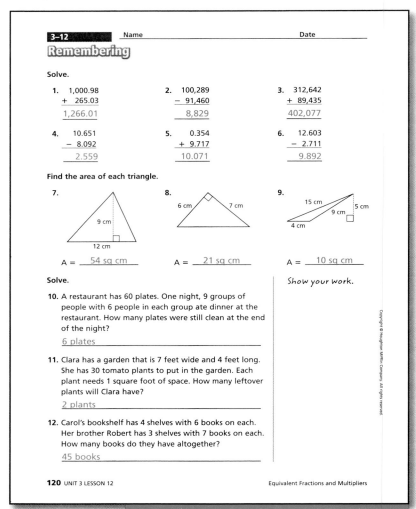

3–12 Name _____ Date _____
Remembering

Solve.

1. 1,000.98
  + 265.03
  ‾‾‾‾‾‾‾‾
  1,266.01

2. 100,289
  − 91,460
  ‾‾‾‾‾‾‾‾
  8,829

3. 312,642
  + 89,435
  ‾‾‾‾‾‾‾‾
  402,077

4. 10.651
  − 8.092
  ‾‾‾‾‾‾‾
  2.559

5. 0.354
  + 9.717
  ‾‾‾‾‾‾‾
  10.071

6. 12.603
  − 2.711
  ‾‾‾‾‾‾‾
  9.892

Find the area of each triangle.

7. 9 cm, 12 cm
A = __54 sq cm__

8. 6 cm, 7 cm
A = __21 sq cm__

9. 15 cm, 9 cm, 4 cm, 5 cm
A = __10 sq cm__

Solve.   *Show your work.*

10. A restaurant has 60 plates. One night, 9 groups of people with 6 people in each group ate dinner at the restaurant. How many plates were still clean at the end of the night?
__6 plates__

11. Clara has a garden that is 7 feet wide and 4 feet long. She has 30 tomato plants to put in the garden. Each plant needs 1 square foot of space. How many leftover plants will Clara have?
__2 plants__

12. Carol's bookshelf has 4 shelves with 6 books on each. Her brother Robert has 3 shelves with 7 books on each. How many books do they have altogether?
__45 books__

120 UNIT 3 LESSON 12   Equivalent Fractions and Multipliers

Homework and Remembering page 119   Homework and Remembering page 120

Home or School Activity

Sports Connection

Fractions in Baseball Have students write an improper fraction for $5\frac{2}{3}$ and have them consider this question: In baseball, how many outs has a pitcher made after $5\frac{2}{3}$ innings?

Have students describe what each part of the fraction means in their response. Then challenge them to think of other fractions used in baseball or a sport of their choice.

Solve Equivalence Problems

Lesson Objective

- Generate and simplify fractions in real-world contexts.

Vocabulary
equivalent
simplify
unsimplify

The Day at a Glance

Today's Goals	Materials	Math Talk
Quick Practice Generate equivalent fractions.	Homework page 119	In today's activities, the students are involved in discussion as they
1 Teaching the Lesson **A1:** Generate an out-of-order equivalent-fraction chain and compare equivalent fractions. **A2:** Find unknown numerators and denominators of equivalent fractions. **A3:** Generate and simplify fractions in real-world contexts.	Student Activity Book pages 209–210 MathBoard materials Numbered index cards 2 through 10 Math Journals Homework and Remembering pages 121–122	▶ explain equivalent fractions ▶ describe how to find a missing part of two equivalent fractions ▶ explore applications of fractions
2 Extending the Lesson ▶ Going Further: Greatest Common Factor ▶ Differentiated Instruction		
3 Homework and Cumulative Review		

Quick Practice

🕐 **5 MINUTES** **Goal:** Generate equivalent fractions.

Equivalent Fraction Parade: Write the fraction $\frac{1}{4}$ on the board. Invite six students to the board. Taking turns, each student writes a fraction equivalent to $\frac{1}{4}$, being careful not to write one that is already on the board. As each fraction appears, the writer turns and gives a signal. The class says the fraction out loud and tells the multiplier that made that fraction from $\frac{1}{4}$. Fractions do not have to be in any particular order; for example,

$$\frac{1}{4} \quad \frac{3}{12} \quad \frac{2}{8} \quad \frac{5}{20}$$

At the end, the class reads the list together. "One fourth equals three twelfths equals two eighths," and so on.

Teaching the Lesson

Practice With Equivalence

 15 MINUTES

Goal: Generate an out-of-order equivalent-fraction chain and compare equivalent fractions.

Materials: Homework page 119

✔ **NCTM Standards:**
Number and Operations
Reasoning and Proof

▶ The Pizza Activity WHOLE CLASS

Ask a boy and a girl to go to the board and to write a chain of equivalent fractions, using exercise 12 from yesterday's homework page. This time the fractions should be written out of order. Ask each student to circle one fraction and to write *B* for *boy* and *G* for *girl* above the one he or she chose.

$$\frac{3}{8} \quad \overset{B}{\left(\frac{9}{24}\right)} \quad \frac{18}{48} \quad \overset{G}{\left(\frac{15}{40}\right)} \quad \frac{6}{16} \quad \frac{12}{32}$$

For each pair of fractions, ask the class these questions. Answers will vary; these answers are based on the example above.

● Who gets more slices, the girl or the boy? the girl

● Who gets larger slices, the girl or the boy? the boy

● Who gets a larger amount, the girl or the boy? Why? They get the same amount; there are more of the smaller slices and fewer of the larger slices; both fractions are equivalent to $\frac{3}{8}$.

● How do you know their two fractions are equivalent? because both fractions are also equivalent to $\frac{3}{8}$

Erase the circles and have another boy and girl circle and label two different fractions. Repeat the activity emphasizing that the person with more slices has smaller slices. The total amount continues to be equal. If time permits, have students generate another chain of equivalent fractions and repeat the activity.

Activity 2

Equivalence With Unknown Parts

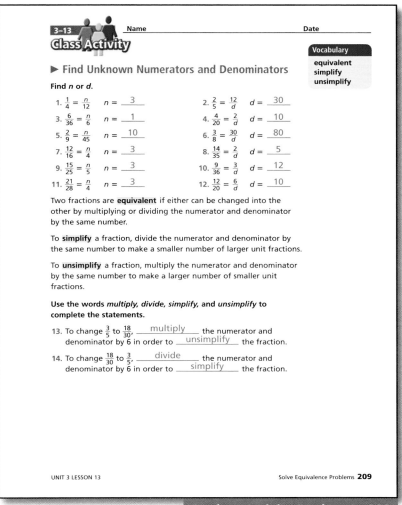

Student Activity Book page 209

 25 MINUTES

Goal: Find unknown numerators and denominators of equivalent fractions.

Materials: Math Journals, Homework page 119, Student Activity Book page 209

 NCTM Standards:
Number and Operations
Reasoning and Proof

The Learning Classroom

Helping Community Invite a few volunteers to work at the board and to discuss how they found the answer.

▶ Find Unknown Numerators and Denominators

WHOLE CLASS

Before beginning this activity, check students' understanding of exercises 2–7 on Homework page 119. They need to understand that the new equivalent fraction comes from multiplying or dividing both the numerator and denominator of the first fraction by the same number.

Write these two fractions on the board. Explain that n is an unknown numerator.

$$\frac{5}{8} = \frac{n}{24}$$

Have everyone write a value for n in their journals. Discuss the answer as a class.

● What if we wanted to change $\frac{5}{8}$ to a fraction with 24 as the denominator? What would the multiplier be? Why? 3; because you have to multiply 8 by 3 to get 24

Activity continued ▶

① Teaching the Lesson (continued)

Activity 2

Teaching Note

What to Expect from Students
Students will need to apply their knowledge of multipliers and divisors in order to solve these problems. Some extra notations may be helpful. Students may simply write the multiplier or divisor above the problem, or use arrows to help them track what they are doing. Encourage students to share their different approaches. Some students may be able to solve the problems without any special notation.

Unsimplify

$$\overset{\times 3}{\frac{5}{8}} = \frac{n}{24} \qquad \frac{5}{8} \overset{\times 3}{=} \frac{n}{24} \qquad \frac{5 \times 3}{8 \times 3} = \frac{15}{24}$$

Simplify

$$\overset{\div 4}{\frac{20}{32}} = \frac{n}{8} \qquad \frac{20}{32} \overset{\div 4}{=} \frac{n}{8} \qquad \frac{20 \div 4}{32 \div 4} = \frac{5}{8}$$

● What would you multiply the numerator, 5, by to get an equivalent fraction. Why? 3; the multiplier of the denominator was 3, so the multiplier of the numerator also has to be 3.

$$\frac{5}{8} = \frac{15}{24}$$

Repeat the activity using an example with a missing denominator.

$$\frac{9}{12} = \frac{3}{d}$$

● We want to change $\frac{9}{12}$ to a fraction with 3 as the numerator. What will the divisor be? Why? 3; because you divide 9 by 3 to get 3

● What will you divide the denominator, 12, by to get an equivalent fraction? Why? 3; the divisor of the numerator was 3, so the divisor of the denominator also has to be 3.

Give the class some more equivalence problems to solve. Send several students to work on each problem at the board and to explain their methods.

$$\frac{3}{5} = \frac{n}{40}\ 24 \qquad \frac{7}{8} = \frac{28}{d}\ 32 \qquad \frac{20}{32} = \frac{n}{8}\ 5 \qquad \frac{3}{4} = \frac{21}{d}\ 28$$

$$\frac{10}{15} = \frac{2}{d}\ 3 \qquad \frac{42}{49} = \frac{n}{7}\ 6 \qquad \frac{18}{81} = \frac{n}{9}\ 2 \qquad \frac{63}{90} = \frac{7}{d}\ 10$$

Have students complete exercises 1–14 on Student Activity Book page 209.

Activity 3

Applications

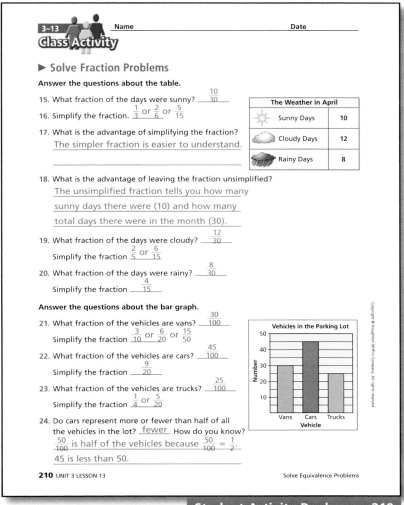

Student Activity Book page 210

▶ Solve Fraction Problems [INDIVIDUALS]

Together, discuss the definitions and exercises 13 and 14 on Student Activity Book page 209. Then have students apply these concepts by answering the questions about the chart and graph on the next page.

In exercises 15–20, students will need to find the total number of days in the month (30) before they can generate any fractions.

For exercises 21–24, students will need to find the total number of vehicles (100) first. In problem 24, 45 vehicles is less than half. Students may recognize quickly that 50 is half of 100, or they may have to compare $\frac{45}{100}$ to $\frac{50}{100}$.

 15 MINUTES

Goal: Generate and simplify fractions in real-world contexts.

Materials: Student Activity Book pages 209–210

 NCTM Standards:
Number and Operations
Problem Solving

 Ongoing Assessment

Ask students to explain different ways to change the same fraction.

▶ Explain how you can simplify the fraction $\frac{6}{9}$.

▶ Show how to unsimplify the fraction $\frac{6}{9}$.

▶ What do you know about the two new fractions?

② Extending the Lesson

Going Further: Greatest Common Factor

> **Goal:** Find the greatest common factor (GCF) of two numbers.
>
> ✔ **NCTM Standards:**
> Number and Operations
> Reasoning and Proof

▶ Review Factors and Prime Numbers

WHOLE CLASS

Review the meaning of factors and prime numbers as taught in Unit 1, Lesson 4 (Going Further).

● **What is a factor of a number?** Possible answers: a (whole) number that you can multiply by another (whole) number to get the original number; a (whole) number that divides evenly into a (whole) number

● **Name two factors of 28.** Possible answers: 4 and 7

● **Are there any other factors?** yes; possible answers: 2 and 14

Write "factors of 28" on the board and list all the factors named so far. If the students haven't mentioned 1 and 28, ask these questions.

● **What number is a factor of every whole number?** 1

● **Why is that so?** because any number multiplied by 1 gives you that original number

● **What other factors can we list for 28? Why?** 1 and 28; 1 × 28 = 28

Write 1 and 28 on the board. Ask the students what they know about prime numbers.

● **What is a prime number?** a number whose only factors are 1 and the number itself

● **Which factors of 28 are prime numbers?** 2 and 7

Tell the students that these are called the *prime factors* of 28.

Find the Greatest Common Factor Repeat the activity for the number 42; list all the factors of 42 on the board.

● **What factors are in both factor lists for 28 and 42?** 1, 2, 7, and 14

● **What is the greatest number in both lists?** 14

Tell students that 1, 2, 7, and 14 are called *common factors* of 28 and 42, and that 14 is called the *greatest common factor* (GCF).

List other pairs of numbers on the board, such as 12 and 15, 24 and 20, 33 and 66, and so on. Use Solve and Discuss to have students find the GCF of each pair of numbers.

> **Teaching Note**
>
> **Math Background** The definition of a prime number says that the number must have exactly two distinct factors. Since 1 has only one whole-number factor (itself), it is not considered a prime number.

Intervention
for students having difficulty
`PAIRS`

Use Fraction Strips

Materials: MathBoard materials

Students draw a vertical line through the center of the fraction strips on the MathBoard to create two halves. They name the denominator for each strip that has a center line that aligns with one half. Then they count the parts of each strip to the left of the center line and use that number as the numerator to create an equivalent fraction.

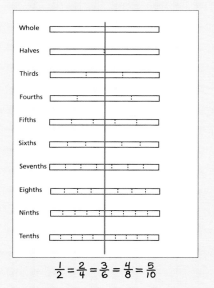

On Level
for students having success
`PAIRS`

Simpler Fractions

Materials: numbered index cards 2 through 10

Each student turns over two cards and makes a proper fraction with the cards. They write an equivalent fraction, either simplified or unsimplified. If they cannot simplify the fraction, they must unsimplify it.

$$\frac{2}{8} = \frac{1}{4} \qquad \frac{3}{7} = \frac{6}{14}$$

Students score 2 points for a simplified fraction, 1 point for an unsimplified fraction, and 0 points for an incorrect answer, if the opponent correctly challenges the answer. The opponent loses 2 points for an incorrect challenge. The first to score 10 points wins the game.

Challenge
for students seeking a challenge
`INDIVIDUALS`

Brain Teaser

Materials: numbered index cards 2 through 10

Students use eight of the cards to make two pairs of equivalent fractions and then they tell which card is left over.

$$\frac{4}{5} = \frac{8}{10}$$

$$\frac{2}{3} = \frac{6}{9}$$

 Math Writing Prompt

Intervention

Draw a Picture
Use a picture to explain why $\frac{3}{4}$ is equivalent to $\frac{6}{8}$.

 Math Writing Prompt

On Level

Look for a Pattern
Give an example of an ordered chain of equivalent fractions. Explain the number pattern shown by the denominators.

 Math Writing Prompt

Challenge

Explain Your Thinking
Explain why you can always unsimplify a fraction, but it is often impossible to simplify it.

 **Homework and Cumulative Review**

Homework **Goal:** Additional Practice

✓ Include students' work for page 121 as part of their portfolios.

Remembering **Goal:** Cumulative Review

This Remembering activity is appropriate anytime after today's lesson.

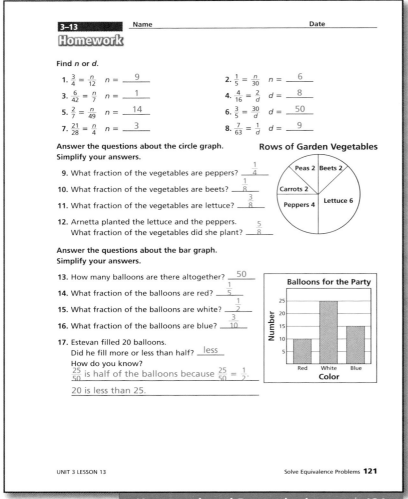

3–13 Homework | Name _____ Date _____

Find n or d.

1. $\frac{3}{4} = \frac{n}{12}$ $n = \underline{9}$
2. $\frac{1}{5} = \frac{n}{30}$ $n = \underline{6}$
3. $\frac{6}{42} = \frac{n}{7}$ $n = \underline{1}$
4. $\frac{4}{16} = \frac{2}{d}$ $d = \underline{8}$
5. $\frac{2}{7} = \frac{n}{49}$ $n = \underline{14}$
6. $\frac{3}{5} = \frac{30}{d}$ $d = \underline{50}$
7. $\frac{21}{28} = \frac{n}{4}$ $n = \underline{3}$
8. $\frac{7}{63} = \frac{1}{d}$ $d = \underline{9}$

Answer the questions about the circle graph. Simplify your answers.

Rows of Garden Vegetables

Peas 2 | Beets 2 | Carrots 2 | Peppers 4 | Lettuce 6

9. What fraction of the vegetables are peppers? $\frac{1}{4}$
10. What fraction of the vegetables are beets? $\frac{1}{8}$
11. What fraction of the vegetables are lettuce? $\frac{3}{8}$
12. Arnetta planted the lettuce and the peppers. What fraction of the vegetables did she plant? $\frac{5}{8}$

Answer the questions about the bar graph. Simplify your answers.

13. How many balloons are there altogether? $\underline{50}$
14. What fraction of the balloons are red? $\frac{1}{5}$
15. What fraction of the balloons are white? $\frac{1}{2}$
16. What fraction of the balloons are blue? $\frac{3}{10}$
17. Estevan filled 20 balloons. Did he fill more or less than half? $\underline{less}$
How do you know?
$\frac{25}{50}$ is half of the balloons because $\frac{25}{50} = \frac{1}{2}$.
20 is less than 25.

Balloons for the Party

Number: Red, White, Blue — Color

UNIT 3 LESSON 13 — Solve Equivalence Problems **121**

Homework and Remembering page 121

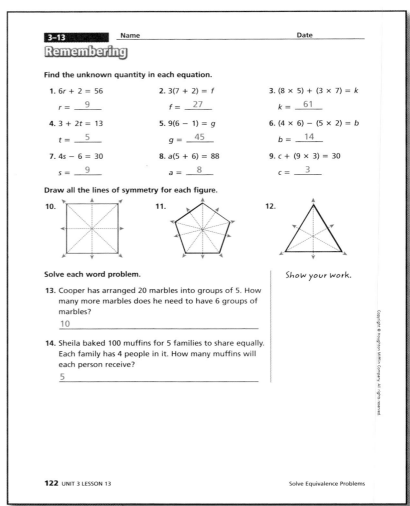

3–13 Remembering | Name _____ Date _____

Find the unknown quantity in each equation.

1. $6r + 2 = 56$
   $r = \underline{9}$
2. $3(7 + 2) = f$
   $f = \underline{27}$
3. $(8 \times 5) + (3 \times 7) = k$
   $k = \underline{61}$
4. $3 + 2t = 13$
   $t = \underline{5}$
5. $9(6 - 1) = g$
   $g = \underline{45}$
6. $(4 \times 6) - (5 \times 2) = b$
   $b = \underline{14}$
7. $4s - 6 = 30$
   $s = \underline{9}$
8. $a(5 + 6) = 88$
   $a = \underline{8}$
9. $c + (9 \times 3) = 30$
   $c = \underline{3}$

Draw all the lines of symmetry for each figure.

10. 11. 12.

Solve each word problem. *Show your work.*

13. Cooper has arranged 20 marbles into groups of 5. How many more marbles does he need to have 6 groups of marbles?
    $\underline{10}$

14. Sheila baked 100 muffins for 5 families to share equally. Each family has 4 people in it. How many muffins will each person receive?
    $\underline{5}$

122 UNIT 3 LESSON 13 — Solve Equivalence Problems

Homework and Remembering page 122

Home or School Activity

 Real-World Connection

Money Using 100 as the denominator, students write equivalent fractions for common coins: a half-dollar, a quarter, and a dime (tenth of a dollar). Students use an equivalent fraction with a numerator of 1 to show what fraction of a dollar is represented by a nickel.

$$\frac{1}{2} = \frac{n}{100} \qquad \frac{1}{4} = \frac{n}{100} \qquad \frac{1}{10} = \frac{n}{100} \qquad \frac{5}{100} = \frac{1}{d}$$

UNIT 3
LESSON
14

Probability and Equivalent Fractions

Lesson Objectives
- Apply the language of probability.
- Solve probability situations by finding fractional equivalents.

Vocabulary
probability

The Day at a Glance

Today's Goals	Materials	Math Talk
Quick Practice Generate equivalent fractions.	Student Activity Book pages 211–214	In today's activities, the students are involved in discussion as they
1 Teaching the Lesson A1: Use probability terminology to describe a simple probability situation. A2: Discuss situations involving probability.	Spinner (Copymaster M34) Pencil and paper clip Coins	▶ use probability language to determine which color marble they will draw from a box
2 Extending the Lesson ▶ Going Further: Line Plots ▶ Differentiated Instruction	Math Journals Homework and Remembering pages 123–124	▶ describe probability situations using fractions
3 Homework and Cumulative Review		▶ solve and discuss probability problems

Quick Practice

⏱ **5 MINUTES**   **Goal:** Generate equivalent fractions.

Equivalent Fraction Parade: Write the fraction $\frac{1}{6}$ on the board. Invite six students to the board. Taking turns, each student writes a fraction equivalent to $\frac{1}{6}$, being careful not to write one that is already on the board. As each fraction appears, the writer turns and gives a signal. The class says the fraction out loud and tells the multiplier that made that fraction from $\frac{1}{6}$. Fractions do not have to be in any particular order; for example,

$$\frac{1}{6} \qquad \frac{3}{18} \qquad \frac{4}{24} \qquad \frac{2}{12}$$

At the end, the class reads the list together. "One sixth equals three eighteenths equals four twenty-fourths," and so on.

Teaching the Lesson

The Language of Probability (Marbles and Spinners)

 20 MINUTES

Goal: Use probability terminology to describe a simple probability situation.

Materials: Student Activity Book page 211

✔ **NCTM Standards:**
Data Analysis and Probability
Number and Operations
Reasoning and Proof

Teaching Note

Language and Vocabulary
Probability is sometimes called *chance*. Chance is a term often used to refer to something that happens unpredictably, such as a chance event. Probability is the mathematical science of measuring and estimating predictability. The mathematical probability of an event may also be referred to informally as the chance or chances of the event happening.

▶ **Use the Language of Probability** WHOLE CLASS

Begin by drawing on the board the two figures that follow. The figures represent marbles in a box. Use the first figure to demonstrate the meanings of *more likely* and *less likely.*

Use the second figure to demonstrate the meaning of *equally likely.* If these terms are used in a clear context, students will catch on quickly. No formal definitions should be needed.

● Look at the first box of marbles. If I reach in and take out a marble without looking, am I more likely to get a white one or a black one? Why? a white one; there are more white ones in the box

● Which color am I less likely to choose? Why? black; only 1 black marble and 3 white ones

● Suppose I had 99 white marbles and 1 black marble in the box. What is likely to happen when I draw a marble from the box? What is unlikely to happen? drawing a white one; drawing a black one

● Look at the second box of marbles. If I reach in and take out a marble without looking, am I more likely to draw a white one or a black one? neither is more likely

● How could you describe the likelihood of drawing white or black? equally likely

Draw another box that has all white marbles.

Tell the students that sometimes the likelihood of an event can be described by the words *certain* or *impossible.*

● Suppose I had no black marbles in the box. What is certain to happen when I draw a marble from the box? drawing a white one

● What is impossible when I draw a marble from the box? drawing a black one

Have students complete exercises 1–5 on Student Activity Book page 211. Discuss any questions that arise.

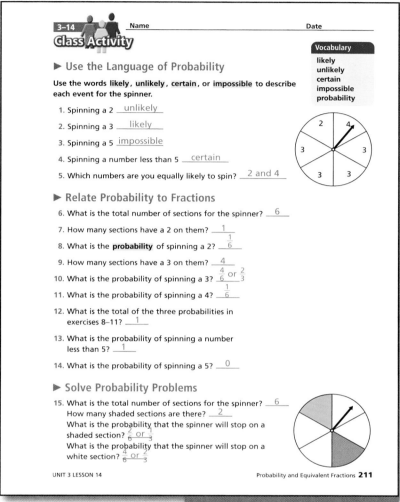

Student Activity Book page 211

▶ Relate Probability to Fractions WHOLE CLASS

Explain to the class what is meant by probability, a mathematical way of stating the likelihood that an event will happen. Explain that it is often expressed as a fraction, usually as simply as possible. When people talk about the likelihood of something happening, they are talking about probability.

There are four marbles altogether and two of them are white. The probability that I will get a white marble is 2 out of 4. This can be expressed as a fraction, $\frac{2}{4}$.

● Can you make this fraction any simpler? yes; $\frac{1}{2}$

Activity continued ▶

1 Teaching the Lesson (continued)

Activity 1

Differentiated Instruction

English Learners Have students make a list of the vocabulary associated with mathematical probabilities, or have them label a number line from 0 to 1 with the words.

0: impossible

Close to 0: unlikely or improbable

Close to 1: likely or probable

1: certain

Understand the Total Discuss the probabilities involved in the first box of marbles that you drew on the board and find the total. Do the same for the second box that you drew on the board. Elicit from students that the total of all fractions in a probability situation will always be one whole.

- Look at the first box of marbles again. What is the probability that I will get a black marble? 1 out of 4, or $\frac{1}{4}$

- What is the probability of drawing a white marble? 3 out of 4, or $\frac{3}{4}$

- What is the total of $\frac{1}{4}$ and $\frac{3}{4}$? $\frac{4}{4}$, or one whole

Ask the same questions about the second box.

- What is the probability of drawing a white marble? $\frac{1}{2}$

- What is the probability of drawing a black marble? $\frac{1}{2}$

- What is the total of $\frac{1}{2}$ and $\frac{1}{2}$? $\frac{2}{2}$, or one whole

- What do you think is the total of all the probabilities in any situation? 1

Ask about the third box that you drew.

How many marbles are there altogether? 4

- How many white marbles are there? 4

- What is the probability of drawing a white marble? $\frac{4}{4}$, or 1

- What is the probability of something that is certain? 1

- How many black marbles are there in the box? 0

- What is the probability of drawing a black marble? $\frac{0}{4}$, or 0

- What is the probability of something that is impossible? 0

Have students complete exercises 6–14. Discuss any questions that arise.

Probability Situations

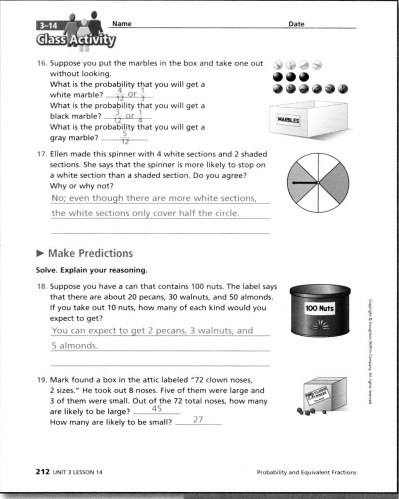

Student Activity Book page 212

▶ Solve Probability Problems WHOLE CLASS

Use Solve and Discuss as students complete problems 15–17 on *Student Activity* Book pages 211–212.

Emphasize to students that they should begin every probability problem by finding the total number of possibilities. It will not always be as obvious as it is in problem 15. In this case, there are six total possibilities, so 6 will be the denominator of the fractions. The probability of landing on a dark section is 2 out of 6, or $\frac{2}{6}$ or $\frac{1}{3}$. The probability of landing on a white section is 4 out of 6, or $\frac{4}{6}$ or $\frac{2}{3}$.

Have students add the fractions to see if they get one whole.

$$\frac{1}{3} + \frac{2}{3} = \frac{3}{3}$$

Activity continued ▶

35 MINUTES

Goal: Discuss situations involving probability.

Materials: Student Activity Book pages 211–212

✔ **NCTM Standards:**
Data Analysis and Probability
Number and Operations
Problem Solving

1 Teaching the Lesson (continued)

Activity 2

Teaching Note

Math Background Predicting results using probabilities is almost never exact. Polls and surveys always state a margin of error with the results. For example, a poll may state that it is accurate within four percentage points, 19 times out of 20, or 95% of the time. This means that $\frac{1}{20}$ of the time, it may be even less accurate. In problem 18, 2 pecans, 3 walnuts, and 5 almonds are likely to be chosen, but often the distribution will be slightly different. For situations like problem 19, the prediction will rarely be exact, but should be close most of the time.

Problem 16 has three variables but the procedure is the same. There are 12 possibilities. The probability of getting a white marble is 4 out of 12, or $\frac{4}{12}$ or $\frac{1}{3}$. The probability of getting a black marble is 3 out of 12, or $\frac{3}{12}$ or $\frac{1}{4}$. The probability of getting a gray marble is $\frac{5}{12}$. Ask students to add the three fractions to see if they get one whole. You might want to have several students try it at the board. They will need to use fractions with like denominators.

$$\frac{4}{12} + \frac{3}{12} + \frac{5}{12} = \frac{12}{12}$$

If students look closely at the spinner in problem 17, they will see that the sections are not all the same size. The four white sections are equal to the two shaded sections. If the lines were removed from the white sections, it would be easy to see that the spinner is divided into fourths. The probability of landing on a shaded section or a white section is exactly equal.

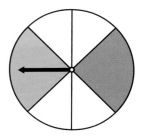

▶ Make Predictions [WHOLE CLASS]

Tell students that probabilities are used in real life to make predictions, such as in weather forecasting and taking polls for elections and other kinds of surveys. Discuss how to use probabilities for problem 18.

● What is the probability of choosing a pecan? $\frac{20}{100}$, or $\frac{1}{5}$

● What is the probability of choosing a walnut? $\frac{30}{100}$, or $\frac{3}{10}$

● What is the probability of choosing an almond? $\frac{50}{100}$, or $\frac{1}{2}$

● What do you expect to happen if you choose 10 nuts? How are they likely to be distributed? in the same fractions (proportions) as the whole can

Have them write equivalent fractions using a denominator of 10 to make their predictions.

Problem 19 is similar except that it starts with the sample and then generalizes to the whole. Tell students that this situation is like polls that take samples of people to make predictions about the whole population. In the sample, $\frac{5}{8}$ of the noses are large and $\frac{3}{8}$ are small. Equivalent fractions with a denominator of 72 are $\frac{45}{72}$ and $\frac{27}{72}$. Therefore, out of a total of 72 noses, 45 are likely to be large and 27 are likely to be small.

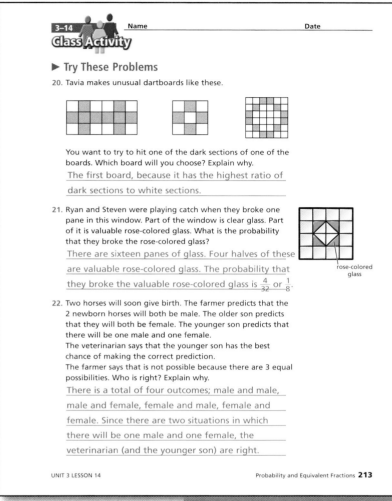

▶ Try These Problems PAIRS

Your students can consolidate their understanding of probabilities as fractions as they work with classmates to solve the problems on Student Activity Book page 213.

The probability of hitting the dark sections of the dartboards in problem 20 is $\frac{5}{9}$ for the first, $\frac{4}{9}$ for the second, and $\frac{1}{3}$ for the third, after the fractions are simplified. You are most likely to hit a dark section on the first dartboard.

The key to solving problem 21 is to realize that each triangular section of rose-colored glass is exactly one half of a square. Since there are four triangular sections, they are the equivalent of two squares out of a total of 16 squares. The probability of hitting the rose-colored glass, then, is $\frac{2}{16}$, or $\frac{1}{8}$.

In problem 22, the veterinarian is right. There are four equally likely possibilities. Students will see this if you make a chart of all the combinations.

The probability that there will be one male and one female is actually 2 out of 4.

Horse 1	Horse 2
Male	Male
Male	Female
Female	Male
Female	Female

Extending the Lesson

Going Further: Line Plots

Goal: Create a line plot from a frequency table.

Materials: Student Activity book page 214

✔ **NCTM Standards:**
Data Analysis and Probability
Number and Operations

▶ Read Data from a Line Plot INDIVIDUALS

Draw a number line on the board and label it from 1 to 31. Ask a student to come to the board and put an X over the day of the month of his or her birthday.

```
                                     x
1 2 3 4 5 6 7 8 9 10 11 12 13 14 15 16 17 18 19 20 21 22 23 24 25 26 27 28 29 30 31
```

The rest of the students call out their birthdays and the student at the board records each one on the number line, "stacking" the ones that occur more than once.

Tell the students that the completed number line is called a *line plot*. Ask questions about the final results.

● Which number is most frequent?

● Which number is least frequent?

● Why do you think 31 usually occurs less often on a line plot like this? Some months don't have 31 days.

● Should 30 occur less often than other numbers? maybe a little less because February has only 28 or 29 days

Have students complete the exercises on Student Activity Book page 214.

Discuss the students' answer to exercise 7.

● Is the probability of tossing a 12 based on this sample the real probability? Why or why not? No, because it is possible to toss a 12; it just has not happened in these 30 trials.

If time remains, students can survey their classmates and make a frequency table and a line plot of the results. Possible topics include number of pets or siblings or number of hours per day doing homework, reading, sleeping, or watching television.

Have students write conclusions about the data.

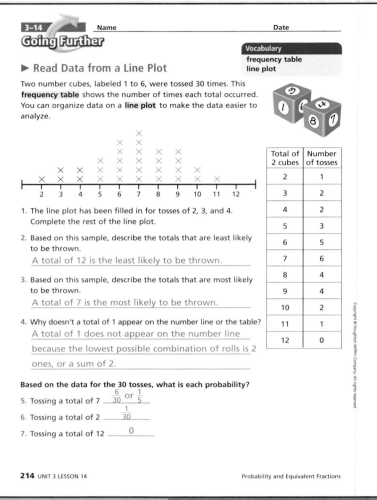

Student Activity Book page 214

Intervention
for students having difficulty

SMALL GROUPS

Make a Spinner

Materials: Spinner (Copymaster M34), pencil and paper clip

Students make a spinner from Copymaster M34.

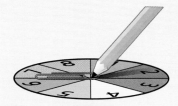

They identify the probability of spinning each number from 1 to 8 and of spinning an even number or an odd number. Then they predict what will happen if they spin the spinner 24 times. Students test their predictions and record their results.

On Level
for students having success

SMALL GROUPS

Scrabble™ Probabilities

Discuss the game of Scrabble™. There are 100 letter tiles in a Scrabble™ set. Tiles with vowels occur with the frequency shown below. Record the information on the board.

A – 9
E – 12
I – 9
O – 8
U – 4

Students identify the probability of picking each vowel and the probability of picking any vowel from the 100 letters. They compare the likelihood of picking each vowel from most likely to least likely. Which two are equally likely? Students discuss, in their groups, why there are varying numbers of each letter in the set of tiles (the letters in the English language appear with different frequencies).

Challenge
for students seeking a challenge

INDIVIDUALS

Tossing a Coin

Materials: 2 coins

Each student lists all the possible results that might happen when you toss two coins simultaneously: two heads, two tails, heads and tails. Students predict what will happen when they toss the same coin twice.

Students carry out the experiment 20 times and record the results.

HH
HT
TH
HT
HT
TT

 Math Writing Prompt

Intervention

Make Predictions
Describe what should happen if you toss a coin 100 times. Explain your thinking.

 Math Writing Prompt

On Level

Explain Your Thinking
How does knowing about probability help you to make predictions?

 Math Writing Prompt

Challenge

In Your Own Words
Explain why the results of an experiment are usually different from what you might predict based on probability.

③ Homework and Cumulative Review

3-14 Homework **Goal:** Additional Practice

✔ Include students' work for page 123 as part of their portfolios.

3-14 Remembering **Goal:** Cumulative Review

This Remembering activity is appropriate anytime after today's lesson.

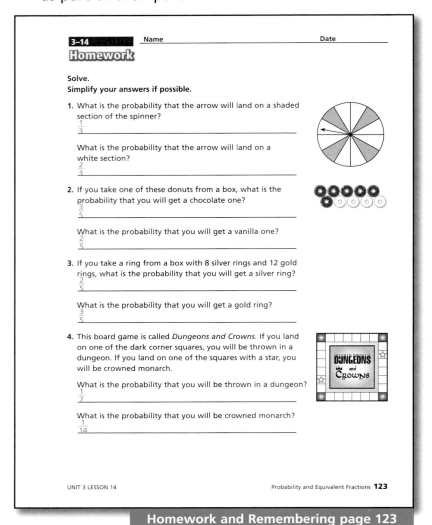

3-14 Homework Name ___ Date ___

Solve.
Simplify your answers if possible.

1. What is the probability that the arrow will land on a shaded section of the spinner?
   $\frac{1}{3}$

   What is the probability that the arrow will land on a white section?
   $\frac{2}{3}$

2. If you take one of these donuts from a box, what is the probability that you will get a chocolate one?
   $\frac{3}{5}$

   What is the probability that you will get a vanilla one?
   $\frac{2}{5}$

3. If you take a ring from a box with 8 silver rings and 12 gold rings, what is the probability that you will get a silver ring?
   $\frac{2}{5}$

   What is the probability that you will get a gold ring?
   $\frac{3}{5}$

4. This board game is called *Dungeons and Crowns*. If you land on one of the dark corner squares, you will be thrown in a dungeon. If you land on one of the squares with a star, you will be crowned monarch.

   What is the probability that you will be thrown in a dungeon?
   $\frac{1}{7}$

   What is the probability that you will be crowned monarch?
   $\frac{1}{14}$

UNIT 3 LESSON 14   Probability and Equivalent Fractions **123**

Homework and Remembering page 123

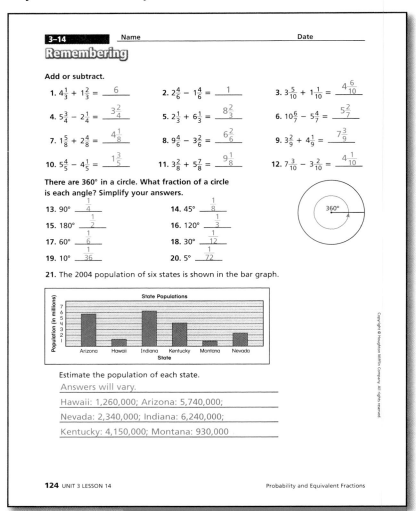

3-14 Remembering Name ___ Date ___

Add or subtract.

1. $4\frac{1}{3} + 1\frac{2}{3} =$ ___ 6
2. $2\frac{4}{6} - 1\frac{4}{6} =$ ___ 1
3. $3\frac{5}{10} + 1\frac{1}{10} =$ ___ $4\frac{6}{10}$
4. $5\frac{3}{4} - 2\frac{1}{4} =$ ___ $3\frac{2}{4}$
5. $2\frac{1}{3} + 6\frac{1}{3} =$ ___ $8\frac{2}{3}$
6. $10\frac{6}{7} - 5\frac{4}{7} =$ ___ $5\frac{2}{7}$
7. $1\frac{5}{8} + 2\frac{4}{8} =$ ___ $4\frac{1}{8}$
8. $9\frac{4}{6} - 3\frac{2}{6} =$ ___ $6\frac{2}{6}$
9. $3\frac{2}{9} + 4\frac{1}{9} =$ ___ $7\frac{3}{9}$
10. $5\frac{4}{5} - 4\frac{1}{5} =$ ___ $1\frac{3}{5}$
11. $3\frac{2}{8} + 5\frac{7}{8} =$ ___ $9\frac{1}{8}$
12. $7\frac{3}{10} - 3\frac{2}{10} =$ ___ $4\frac{1}{10}$

There are 360° in a circle. What fraction of a circle is each angle? Simplify your answers.

13. 90° ___ $\frac{1}{4}$
14. 45° ___ $\frac{1}{8}$
15. 180° ___ $\frac{1}{2}$
16. 120° ___ $\frac{1}{3}$
17. 60° ___ $\frac{1}{6}$
18. 30° ___ $\frac{1}{12}$
19. 10° ___ $\frac{1}{36}$
20. 5° ___ $\frac{1}{72}$

21. The 2004 population of six states is shown in the bar graph.

State Populations

(bar graph: Population (in millions) vs State — Arizona, Hawaii, Indiana, Kentucky, Montana, Nevada)

Estimate the population of each state.
Answers will vary.
Hawaii: 1,260,000; Arizona: 5,740,000;
Nevada: 2,340,000; Indiana: 6,240,000;
Kentucky: 4,150,000; Montana: 930,000

124 UNIT 3 LESSON 14   Probability and Equivalent Fractions

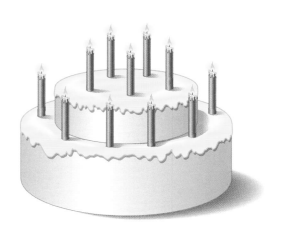

Homework and Remembering page 124

Home or School Activity

Real-World Connection

Birthdays In a group of 23 people, the probability is more than 1 out of 2 that two people will have the same birthday—both the same month and same day of the month. Ask the students to test this in the classroom to see if any two students have the same birthday.

Add and Subtract Unlike Fractions

Lesson Objectives

- Add and subtract fractions with unlike denominators.
- Apply the terms *common denominator* and *least common denominator.*

Vocabulary

common denominator
least common
   denominator

The Day at a Glance

Today's Goals	Materials	Math Talk
Quick Practice Create equivalent fractions. **1 Teaching the Lesson** **A1:** Using MathBoards, visualize how to find a common denominator when adding or subtracting unlike fractions. **A2:** Rename fractions and solve problems that involve adding and subtracting unlike fractions. **2 Extending the Lesson** ▶ Going Further: Change Fractions to Simplest Form ▶ Differentiated Instruction **3 Homework and Cumulative Review**	MathBoard materials Student Activity Book pages 215–216 Fraction Circles (Copymaster M30) Math Journals Homework and Remembering pages 125–126	In today's activities, the students are involved in discussion as they ▶ explain strategies to add and subtract unlike fractions ▶ choose a common denominator ▶ compare and discuss solutions to problems

Quick Practice

🕐 **5 MINUTES   Goal:** Create equivalent fractions.

Equivalent Fraction Parade: Begin by writing the fraction $\frac{2}{5}$ on the board. Invite six students to the board. Taking turns, each student writes a fraction equivalent to $\frac{2}{5}$, being careful not to write one that is already on the board. As each fraction appears, the writer turns and gives a signal. The class says the fraction out loud and tells the multiplier that made that fraction from $\frac{2}{5}$. Fractions do not have to be in any special order; for example,

$$\frac{2}{5} \qquad \frac{20}{50} \qquad \frac{12}{30} \qquad \frac{4}{10}$$

At the end, the class reads the list together. "Two fifths equals twenty fiftieths equals twelve thirtieths equals four tenths," and so on.

Teaching the Lesson

Rename Fractions

 25 MINUTES

Goal: Using MathBoards, visualize how to find a common denominator when adding or subtracting unlike fractions.

Materials: MathBoard materials

✔ **NCTM Standards:**
Number and Operations
Problem Solving
Representation
Communication

Teaching Note

Watch for! Some students may add numerators and denominators and write $\frac{1}{3} + \frac{1}{4} = \frac{2}{7}$. Look at $\frac{2}{7}$ on the MathBoard. $\frac{2}{7} < \frac{1}{3}$, so it can't be the total of $\frac{1}{3} + \frac{1}{4}$.

► Student-Generated Solutions [WHOLE CLASS]

Present the addition problem shown here. Invite several students to work at the board while the others work at their seats.

$$\frac{1}{2} + \frac{1}{3}$$

This is an opportunity to see what your students already know about renaming and adding fractions. If no one is able to solve the problem, go directly to activity **Rename Fractions to Add or Subtract.** If some students know about renaming, let them explain their solutions to the class. Ask a few probing questions to help clarify the process. Use the term *common denominator* frequently throughout the lesson.

● I see you changed $\frac{1}{2}$ to $\frac{3}{6}$ and $\frac{1}{3}$ to $\frac{2}{6}$. Why did you do that? Fractions need to have the same denominator before you can add them. They have to be made from the same unit fraction.

● Yes, we need to give them a common denominator. What made you choose 6 as the common denominator? Why not 4 or 5? 6 is a product of both 2 and 3.

► Rename Fractions to Add or Subtract [WHOLE CLASS]

Students use the fraction bars on their MathBoards to solve the two problems shown below. This activity helps students visualize how to split two wholes into same sized pieces before adding or subtracting.

Addition Problem: $\frac{1}{3} + \frac{1}{4}$

Have students circle $\frac{1}{3}$ on the thirds fraction bar and try to add $\frac{1}{4}$.

● Why can't you add $\frac{1}{4}$ easily?

You can't tell where $\frac{1}{4}$ is on the bar.

Have students circle $\frac{1}{4}$ on the fourths bar.

Make 1/3 and 1/4 on different bars.

Thirds

Fourths

Make twelfths on both bars.

Fourths

Thirds

● How can you divide both fourths and thirds into same sized pieces?
Split each third into 4 parts and split each fourth into 3 parts. That
gives us twelfths on both bars.

Have students split the thirds and fourths on their MathBoards into
twelfths. Explain that twelfths then become a common denominator so
that students can add the two fractions.

Ask,

● How many twelfths is $\frac{1}{4}$? 3 twelfths

Add 4/12 + 3/12.

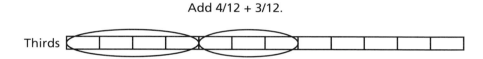

Thirds

Have students add $\frac{3}{12}$ to the $\frac{4}{12}$ already circled on the thirds fraction bar.

● What is the total of $\frac{1}{3} + \frac{1}{4}$? $\frac{7}{12}$

Subtraction Problem: $\frac{5}{6} - \frac{2}{3}$

Have students circle $\frac{5}{6}$ on the sixths fraction bar. Then challenge them:

● Try to subtract $\frac{2}{3}$. How can you do it without using the thirds fraction
bar? We can write the thirds as sixths: $\frac{1}{3} = \frac{2}{6}$ and $\frac{2}{3} = \frac{4}{6}$. Then we can
draw the sixths on the bar. The difference between $\frac{5}{6}$ and $\frac{2}{3}$ is $\frac{1}{6}$.

Make 5/6. How can you subtract 2/3?

Sixths

Change thirds into sixths and subtract.

Sixths

$$\frac{5}{6} - \frac{2}{3} = \frac{5}{6} - \frac{4}{6} = \frac{1}{6}$$

Teaching Note

Watch for! Some students may
subtract numerators and
denominators and write $\frac{5}{6} - \frac{2}{3} = \frac{3}{3}$.
But $\frac{3}{3} = 1$ and $1 > \frac{5}{6}$, so this can't
be correct.

Activity 2

Problems and Stories

 25 MINUTES

Goal: Rename fractions and solve problems that involve adding and subtracting unlike fractions.

Materials: Student Activity Book pages 215–216

 NCTM Standards:
Number and Operations
Problem Solving
Representation
Communication

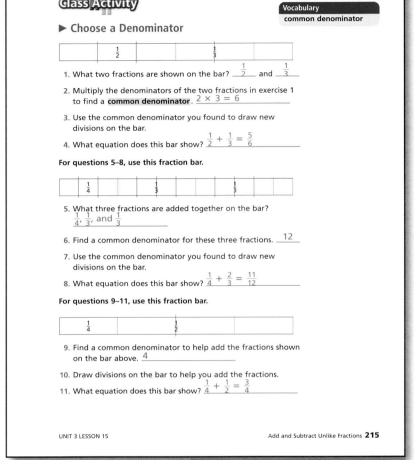

Student Activity Book page 215

Teaching Note

Watch For! Some students may add both numerators and denominators to get: $\frac{1}{2} + \frac{1}{3} = \frac{2}{5}$. Ask those students,

▶ Where is $\frac{2}{5}$ on the fraction bar?
before $\frac{1}{2}$

▶ Why can $\frac{2}{5}$ not be the correct answer? $\frac{1}{2} + \frac{1}{3}$ must be greater than $\frac{1}{2}$.

▶ Choose a Denominator WHOLE CLASS

Have students look at the fraction bar at the top of Student Activity Book page 215. Let students lead the discussion as much as possible.

The first bar shows $\frac{1}{2} + \frac{1}{3}$. Does it tell us what the total is called? No.

● How can we decide what to call the total? Divide the bar using a fraction that can rename halves and thirds.

● How can we find a fraction that does that? Multiply the two denominators: 2×3.

Have students complete exercises 1–4.

The second problem, $\frac{1}{4} + \frac{2}{3}$, is solved in a similar way. Ask students to explain how.

- What three fractions are added on the bar? $\frac{1}{4} + \frac{1}{3} + \frac{1}{3}$

- How can we find a common denominator? Multiply 4 by 3.

- What common denominator can we use? 12

Have students complete exercises 5–8. Invite one student to show and explain a solution on the board. Encourage other students to ask questions.

- What is the total of $\frac{1}{4} + \frac{1}{3} + \frac{1}{3}$? $\frac{11}{12}$

The third bar raises an important issue: Do we always have to rename both fractions? Have students work on exercises 9–11 individually, and then discuss their answers as a class.

- What common denominator did you use? Some will have used 4; some may have used 8.

Ask those students who used 4 as the common denominator,

- Why didn't you use 2 × 4 = 8? because there is less multiplying to do if you use 4

Explain that sometimes one denominator is a factor of the other denominator. In this case, 2 is a factor of 4. So we can just use 4 as our new common denominator:

$$\frac{1}{4} + \frac{2}{4} = \frac{3}{4}$$

- Which common denominator would you choose if you were adding $\frac{1}{25}$ and $\frac{1}{50}$? 50; 25 is one of its factors.

Point out that it is helpful to look for a small denominator that works.

Activity continued ▶

Teaching Note

What to Expect from Students

▶ It is not always necessary for students to find the least common denominator before solving a problem. Sometimes it is better to use the obvious multiple than to spend extra time trying to find the smallest multiple.

▶ At this point it is also acceptable for students to give an answer that has not been simplified. Although the Answer Key for today's homework gives the answer in simplest form, your students may give unsimplified answers.

Activity 2

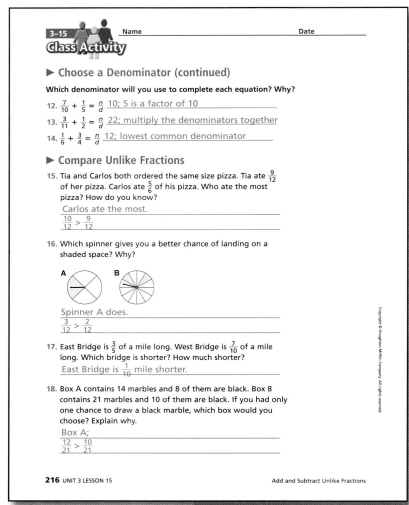

Student Activity Book page 216

Invite students to complete exercises 12–14 on Student Activity Book page 216. Discuss their responses as a class. Students do not have to solve the problems; simply focus on a strategy for finding a common denominator.

For many equations, there are many denominators that students can use. However, there is usually one that will provide them with the simplest route to completing the equation. After students share their responses and explain them to others as needed, highlight these principles.

- From exercise 12: students should first look to see if one denominator is a factor of the other when finding a common denominator.

- From exercise 13: students should realize that they can always find a common denominator by multiplying the two given denominators together. However, this may produce a large denominator that is hard to work with.

- From exercise 14: students may multiply the two denominators together, but there may be a smaller denominator that is easier to work with, in this case 12.

At this point, send one student to the board to complete exercise 14 using 12 as a common denominator and another to complete it using 24. Compare the answers.

- Are they the same? Yes; $\frac{11}{12}$ is equal to $\frac{22}{24}$ because we could multiply the numerator and the denominator by 2 to get $\frac{22}{24}$.

Introduce the term *least common denominator* (the smallest possible common denominator).

Write these equations on the board and ask students to tell what denominator they would choose in order to complete each equation. Invite input from other students.

$\frac{7}{16} + \frac{1}{4} = ?$ 16; 4 is a factor of 16.

$\frac{2}{9} + \frac{1}{6} = ?$ 18; Some students may multiply the two given denominators together to get 54 or recognize that 9 and 6 both go into 36. Using 54 as a common denominator would produce an awkward pair of fractions to work with.

$\frac{2}{3} - \frac{7}{12} = ?$ 12; 3 is a factor of 12.

▶ Compare Unlike Fractions WHOLE CLASS

Ask,

- Which is greater, 23 or 56? 56

- Which is greater, $\frac{2}{3}$ or $\frac{5}{6}$? What do we need to do before we decide? $\frac{5}{6}$; first we have to see them in the same countable units—sixths. One fraction ($\frac{2}{3}$) has 4 sixths and the other has 5 sixths.

Have students solve problems 15–18 on Student Activity Book page 216. Then discuss their strategies as a class.

- How did you compare the two fractions in each question? I changed them to like fractions.

- What common denominator did you use?

Have a student write an equation to compare the fractions on the board. Invite others to ask questions to clarify the solution.

In exercise 18, students must first use the total number of marbles in each box, to build fractions; then they must find a common denominator and compare the fractions.

Extending the Lesson

Going Further: Change Fractions to Simplest Form

Goal: Recognize when a simplified fraction is in simplest form.

✔ **NCTM Standards:**
Number and Operations
Reasoning and Proof

▶ Review Greatest Common Factor

WHOLE CLASS

Remind students of the meaning of greatest common factor (from Going Further, Lesson 13). The greatest common factor (GCF) of two numbers is the greatest number that divides evenly into both numbers.

- What are the factors of 12? 1, 2, 3, 4, 6, and 12

- What are the factors of 16? 1, 2, 4, 8, and 16

- What is the GCF of 12 and 16? 4

▶ Change Fractions to Simplest Form

WHOLE CLASS

Work together to simplify a fraction.

- Simplify the fraction $\frac{12}{16}$. $\frac{3}{4}$

- What divisor did you use to simplify $\frac{12}{16}$? 4

- Can you simplify your answer, $\frac{3}{4}$? No.

- What is the GCF of 12 and 16? 4

Tell students that $\frac{3}{4}$ is called the *simplest form* of the fraction.

The simplest form of a fraction is obtained when you use the GCF as the divisor.

Have students review the answers they have written for the lessons in this unit and change any that are not in simplest form to simplest form.

Class Management

Walk around the room and observe as students check their fractions for simplest form. Watch for students who do not divide by the greatest common factor.

- ▶ Is your new fraction in simplest form?
- ▶ By what number can you divide the numerator and the denominator?
- ▶ Did you divide by the greatest common factor?

Intervention

for students having difficulty

PAIRS

Add and Subtract With Fraction Circles

Materials: Fraction Circles (Copymaster M30)

Fraction circles are circles cut and color coded to show sixths, thirds, and other fractional parts. They provide a visual representation of fractions that is an alternative to bars or strips. Provide students with fraction circles and ask students to solve some addition and subtraction equations, for example, $1\frac{1}{6} + \frac{2}{3}$. Students show the equation using fraction circles, trade fractional parts so both fractions use the same pieces, then add or subtract.

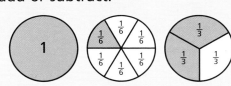

On Level

for students having success

PAIRS

Estimate Sums and Differences

Each pair draws a number line from 0 to 5, showing whole numbers and halves. Give each pair this list of equations.

$$4\frac{11}{12} - 3\frac{1}{8} = \; ? \qquad 3\frac{2}{7} + 1\frac{5}{8} = \; ?$$

$$\frac{4}{7} - \frac{1}{6} = \; ? \qquad 3\frac{11}{13} - 1\frac{5}{8} = \; ?$$

One student reads an equation aloud, and when both are ready, they point to the mark on their number line nearest to where the total or the difference will be. If they both point to the same spot, they go on to the next equation. If they do not, they discuss their strategies for estimating, then go on. Students can also make up their own equations to estimate. A useful strategy for estimating these sums and differences is to round each number to the nearest whole or half, then add or subtract.

Challenge

for students seeking a challenge

PAIRS

Simplify

Each partner writes an addition or subtraction equation with fractions. Partners exchange papers, complete each other's equations by adding or subtracting, and simplify their answer. The student who made up the equation then checks the work of his or her partner. Students receive one point for each equation completed correctly and simplified to lowest terms.

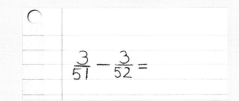

 Math Writing Prompt

Intervention

Explain Your Thinking

Explain why you can only add fractions that have the same denominator. Use an example to help you explain.

 Math Writing Prompt

On Level

Create a Problem

Write a real-life problem that can be solved by adding or subtracting fractions that have different denominators. Provide the solution to your problem.

 Math Writing Prompt

Challenge

In Your Own Words

Describe the steps you follow to find a useful common denominator. Use an example to help you explain.

 Homework and Cumulative Review

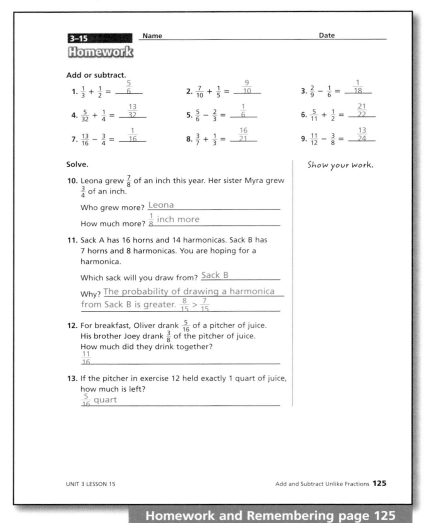

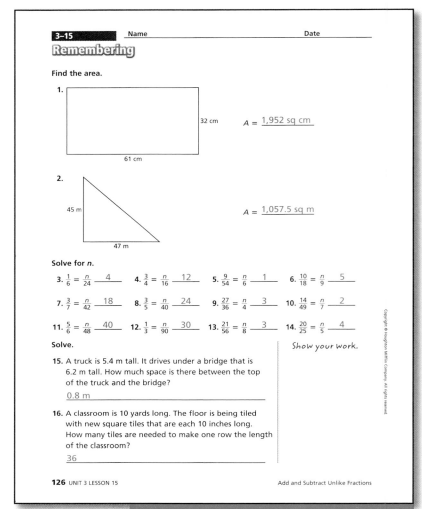

3-15 Homework **Goal:** Additional Practice

✓ Include students' work for page 125 as part of their portfolios.

3-15 Remembering **Goal:** Cumulative Review

This Remembering activity is appropriate anytime after today's lesson.

Homework and Remembering page 125

Homework and Remembering page 126

Home or School Activity

 Social Studies Connection

Ancient Egyptian Fractions In ancient Egypt, people used the fractions $\frac{2}{3}$ and $\frac{3}{4}$ but, other than that, only fractions with a numerator of 1 were used. To show $\frac{5}{6}$, ancient Egyptians would write $\frac{1}{2} + \frac{1}{3}$. Challenge students to write other fractions as the ancient Egyptians would have written them. If they wish, they can use the number symbols that appear in ancient Egyptian writing.

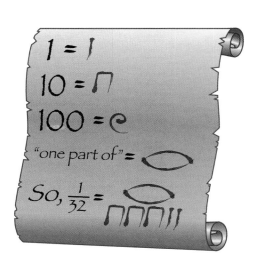

Solve With Unlike Mixed Numbers

Lesson Objectives

● Consolidate understanding of equivalent fractions and operations with unlike fractions.

● Express the main concept of equivalent fractions in writing and refine it through class discussion.

The Day at a Glance

Today's Goals	Materials	123 Math Talk
Quick Practice Practice finding common denominators.	Student Activity Book pages 217–218	In today's activities, the students are involved in discussion as they
1 Teaching the Lesson **A1:** Rename and ungroup to add and subtract mixed numbers. **A2:** Recognize common errors and solve word problems with mixed fractions.	Real or play dimes and pennies Math Journals Homework and Remembering pages 127–128	▶ use the Step-by-Step at the Board method to add and subtract mixed numbers ▶ work in groups to find strategies for solving a word problem
2 Extending the Lesson ▶ Going Further: Equations Involving Fractions ▶ Differentiated Instruction		▶ share their strategies with the class
3 Homework and Cumulative Review		

Quick Practice

 5 MINUTES   **Goal:** Practice finding common denominators.

Common Denominator Parade Invite six students to the board. Each student writes an addition problem with any two fractions. The only requirement is that no fraction can contain a number larger than 10. In turn, each person at the board points to his or her problem and says, "Name the least common denominator." At a signal, the class responds with the answer.

$$\frac{2}{3} + \frac{1}{9}$$

Teaching the Lesson

Rename and Ungroup

25 MINUTES

Goal: Rename and ungroup to add and subtract mixed numbers.

 NCTM Standard:
Number and Operations

Teaching Note

What to Expect from Students
Some students may solve these equations using methods such as crossing out. Encourage students to write mixed number equations that require renaming. They can track the renaming by writing the renamed fractions out to the side.

Ongoing Assessment

As students add and subtract, make sure they understand how to rename and ungroup, and why it is done. Ask questions such as:

► Why do we have to rename the fractions at this step?

► Why do we have to ungroup before we can subtract?

► How can we tell the answer is in its simplest form?

▶ **Rename and Ungroup to Solve** WHOLE CLASS

Give the class a few equations that require the renaming of fractions, such as these:

A.
$$2\frac{3}{8} = 2\frac{3}{8}$$
$$-1\frac{1}{4} = 1\frac{2}{8}$$
$$\overline{\quad 1\frac{1}{8}}$$

B.
$$4\frac{1}{5} = 4\frac{3}{15}$$
$$+2\frac{1}{3} = 2\frac{5}{15}$$
$$\overline{\quad 6\frac{8}{15}}$$

C.
$$7\frac{5}{6} = 7\frac{10}{12}$$
$$-3\frac{1}{4} = 3\frac{3}{12}$$
$$\overline{\quad 4\frac{7}{12}}$$

Invite several students to work at the board while the others work at their seats. Discuss various solution methods.

Your students now know how to perform renaming and ungrouping, but they might need practice doing them simultaneously. Use Solve and Discuss again, or Step-by-Step at the Board for these problems:

D.
$$3\frac{20}{15}$$
$$4\frac{1}{3} = \cancel{4}\frac{5}{15}$$
$$-2\frac{7}{15} = 2\frac{7}{15}$$
$$\overline{\quad 1\frac{13}{15}}$$

E.
$$6\frac{2}{3} = 6\frac{8}{12}$$
$$+4\frac{5}{12} = 4\frac{5}{12}$$
$$\overline{\quad 10\frac{13}{12} = 11\frac{1}{12}}$$

F.
$$8\frac{21}{18}$$
$$9\frac{1}{6} = \cancel{9}\frac{3}{18}$$
$$-5\frac{7}{18} = 5\frac{7}{18}$$
$$\overline{\quad 3\frac{14}{18} = 3\frac{7}{9}}$$

If you feel your students need more practice, give them a few more problems that require renaming, or ungrouping, or both. Here are a few examples:

G.
$$4\frac{14}{10}$$
$$5\frac{2}{5} = \cancel{5}\frac{4}{10}$$
$$-3\frac{7}{10} = 3\frac{7}{10}$$
$$\overline{\quad 1\frac{7}{10}}$$

H.
$$8\frac{2}{3} = 8\frac{6}{9}$$
$$+2\frac{4}{9} = 2\frac{4}{9}$$
$$\overline{\quad 10\frac{10}{9} = 11\frac{1}{9}}$$

I.
$$6\frac{27}{24}$$
$$7\frac{1}{8} = \cancel{7}\frac{3}{24}$$
$$-4\frac{5}{12} = 4\frac{10}{24}$$
$$\overline{\quad 2\frac{17}{24}}$$

 **Math Talk**

Let's solve question D using Step-by-Step at the board.

Eric: The first step is to rename the fractions so that they both have the same denominator. The denominators are 3 and 15. 3 is a factor of 15, so 15 is a common denominator. We can rename $\frac{1}{3}$ as $\frac{5}{15}$.

$$4\frac{1}{3} = 4\frac{5}{15}$$
$$-2\frac{7}{15} = 2\frac{7}{15}$$

Max: You can't subtract $\frac{7}{15}$ from $\frac{5}{15}$ because $\frac{5}{15}$ is smaller. I'll ungroup. The 4 becomes a 3 because I'm giving a 1 to the 15ths. One is the same as $\frac{15}{15}$. Adding $\frac{15}{15}$ to $\frac{5}{15}$, I get $\frac{20}{15}$.

$$3\frac{20}{15}$$
$$4\frac{1}{3} = 4\frac{5}{15}$$
$$-2\frac{7}{15} = 2\frac{7}{15}$$

Sara: Now we can subtract. First I'll subract the whole numbers: $3 - 2 = 1$. Then I'll subtract the fractions:

$$\frac{20}{15} - \frac{7}{15} = \frac{13}{15}.$$

$$3\frac{20}{15}$$
$$4\frac{1}{3} = 4\frac{5}{15}$$
$$-2\frac{7}{15} = 2\frac{7}{15}$$
$$1\frac{13}{15}$$

Can anyone think of one more step?

Vanya: The last step is to see if the answer can be simplified. $\frac{13}{15}$ can't be regrouped and 13 and 15 have no common factors. The answer in simplest form is $1\frac{13}{15}$.

Good.

Teaching Note

Watch For!
Make sure students realize that regrouping may be necessary *after* an addition or subtraction. For example, in question H the answer is regrouped to give a simplified answer.

$$10\frac{10}{9} = 11\frac{1}{9}$$

Although students know how to simplify, they may not always remember to do it.

Activity 2

Practice With Mixed Numbers

 20 MINUTES

Goal: Recognize common errors and solve word problems with mixed fractions.

Materials: Student Activity Book page 217

 NCTM Standards:
Number and Operations
Problem Solving

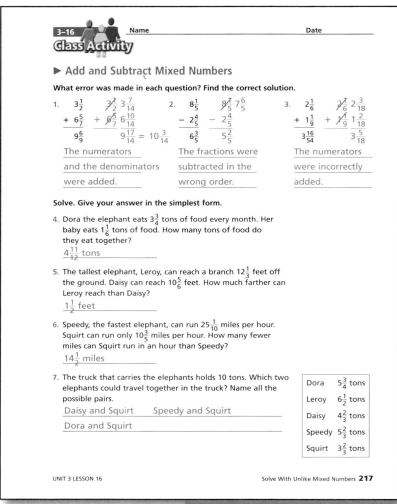

Student Activity Book page 217

Teaching Note

Watch For!

Exercise 3 shows the difficulty that may result from selecting a large common denominator. The problem solver could have used 18 for the new denominator, but instead used 54. The chance of error may be greater with larger numbers. Also, a smaller common denominator can sometimes make it unnecessary to simplify.

▶ Add and Subtract Mixed Numbers WHOLE CLASS

Direct students' attention to exercises 1–3 on Student Activity Book page 217. These show common errors that students need to be able to recognize. Give the class a minute to look over each problem before discussing it.

● In exercise 1, the denominators have been added as well as the numerators.

● Exercise 2 shows the "wrong-way" error that sometimes occurs with subtraction. Since $\frac{4}{5}$ cannot be subtracted from $\frac{1}{5}$, the problem solver reversed the order and subtracted $\frac{1}{5}$ from $\frac{4}{5}$. Remind the class that regrouping is needed instead.

● The error in exercise 3 is less obvious. The numerators have been added incorrectly after renaming.

If students cannot spot some of the errors, revisit the discussion after they have found the correct solutions.

Word Problems With Mixed Numbers

Use **Solve and Discuss** for word problems 4–6.

Approach word problem 7 strategically so that students don't add together every possible pair of numbers to see if the sum is 10 tons or less. Break the class into small groups and ask them to brainstorm for strategies to make solving the problem easier. Have each group share its ideas with the class.

One good approach is to start with the heaviest elephant and work to the lightest, or vice versa.

- To see that the heaviest elephant, Leroy, cannot travel with any of the other elephants, students can check that even the lightest elephant, Squirt, is too heavy to go with Leroy. They can then deduce that the others are too heavy as well.

- Other students might instead find the unknown addend in $6\frac{1}{2} + x = 10$ to see that no elephant over $3\frac{1}{2}$ tons can travel with Leroy.

Some groups may also think of rounding. For example, to see that Dora and Speedy cannot ride together, students can round down to see that their total is more than 10 tons. To see that Daisy and Squirt can ride together, students can round up.

② Extending the Lesson

Going Further: Equations Involving Fractions

Goal: Solve for an unknown in an equation.

Materials: Student Activity Book page 218

 NCTM Standards:
Number and Operations

▶ Solve Equations Involving Fractions PAIRS

Draw a fraction bar on the board and shade a little more than half of it. Tell the class that the whole for this fraction bar is $1\frac{7}{10}$ and the shaded part represents $\frac{9}{10}$.

Write the equation $\frac{9}{10} + x = 1\frac{7}{10}$ above the fraction bar.

$$\frac{9}{10} \qquad + \qquad x \qquad = \qquad 1\frac{7}{10}$$

Discuss methods to find the unknown addend.

● How can we find out what fraction x represents?
Use mental math; $\frac{9}{10} + \frac{1}{10}$ equals 1, then add another $\frac{7}{10}$ to get $1\frac{7}{10}$. So x is $\frac{1}{10} + \frac{7}{10} = \frac{8}{10}$, or $\frac{4}{5}$.

● Can we subtract to find x? Yes. $1\frac{7}{10} - \frac{9}{10}$ is the same as $\frac{17}{10} - \frac{9}{10} = \frac{8}{10}$, or $\frac{4}{5}$.

Cross out the $\frac{9}{10}$ on the board to illustrate that subtracting $\frac{9}{10}$ from $1\frac{7}{10}$ gives x.

Have students work in pairs to complete the activity. To avoid frustration, make sure their answers to exercises 1–6 are correct before they proceed.

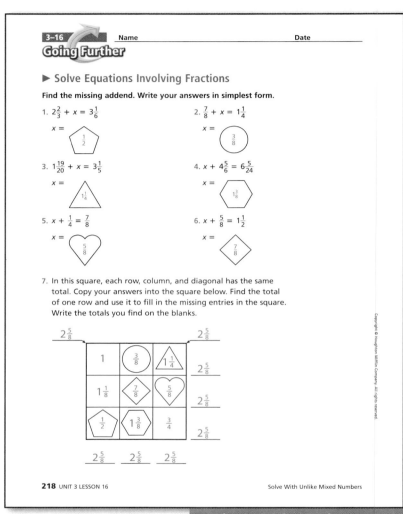

Student Activity Book page 218

📁 Class Management

Students will not need to find the sum of every row, column, and diagonal to complete the entries in the magic square, but they should be encouraged to do so anyway to check that each sum is the same. It will also give them extra practice adding fractions.

Teaching Note

Math Background Magic squares date back to around 2800 B.C. in Chinese literature with the magic square, *Loh-Shu*. Each number is represented by a symbol and the magic number is 15.

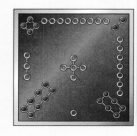

Intervention
for students having difficulty

PAIRS

Practice Regrouping

Materials: real or play dimes and pennies

Tell students that a dime represents one whole and a penny represent one tenth. Students use dimes and pennies to model these questions, and others if time allows:

$1\frac{2}{10} - \frac{8}{10}$ $3\frac{4}{10} - 2\frac{7}{10}$

$\frac{4}{10} + \frac{7}{10}$ $1\frac{5}{10} + 2\frac{6}{10}$

For the example shown, students replace the dime with 10 pennies to give 12 pennies altogether. Then they remove 8 of the pennies, leaving 4. They write $\frac{4}{10}$ for the answer.

 Math Writing Prompt

Intervention
Explain Your Thinking
Why do you sometimes have to rename fractions when you add or subtract? Use the example $\frac{3}{10} - \frac{1}{5}$ in your answer.

On Level
for students having success

PAIRS

Estimate Sums and Differences

Each student thinks of a mixed fraction.

They compare fractions to see which is larger. Then they estimate the sum and difference of the two numbers and verify by calculating.

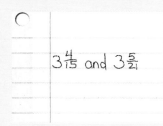

$3\frac{4}{15}$ and $3\frac{5}{21}$

 Math Writing Prompt

On Level
Investigate Mathematics
Tell why you need to regroup in some addition or subtraction questions and explain how to do it. Use an example to illustrate.

Challenge
for students seeking a challenge

INDIVIDUALS

Solve This!

Draw these figures on the board and tell students that they show the land a farmer owns:

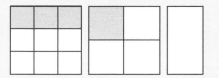

The shaded areas are not yet plowed. Students calculate the fraction of land that the farmer has already plowed.

One of various solutions that yield the correct answer:

$2\frac{1}{2} - \frac{3}{9} - \frac{1}{4}$

$= 2\frac{1}{2} - \frac{1}{3} - \frac{1}{4}$

$= 2\frac{6}{12} - \frac{4}{12} - \frac{3}{12}$

$= 2\frac{2}{12} - \frac{3}{12}$

$= 1\frac{14}{12} - \frac{3}{12}$

$= 1\frac{11}{12}$

 Math Writing Prompt

Challenge
Create and Solve
Write a word problem to go with $3\frac{1}{5} + 2\frac{3}{7} - \frac{3}{10}$, then solve it.

③ Homework and Cumulative Review

3–16

Homework **Goal:** Additional Practice

✓ Include students' work for page 127 as part of their portfolios.

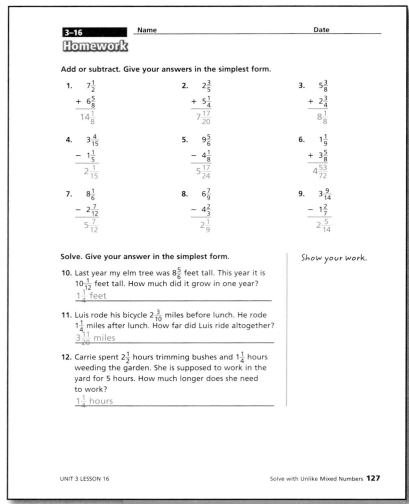

3–16 Name _____ Date _____

Homework

Add or subtract. Give your answers in the simplest form.

1. $7\frac{1}{2}$
   $+ 6\frac{5}{8}$
   $14\frac{1}{8}$

2. $2\frac{3}{5}$
   $+ 5\frac{1}{4}$
   $7\frac{17}{20}$

3. $5\frac{3}{8}$
   $+ 2\frac{3}{4}$
   $8\frac{1}{8}$

4. $3\frac{4}{15}$
   $- 1\frac{1}{5}$
   $2\frac{1}{15}$

5. $9\frac{5}{6}$
   $- 4\frac{1}{8}$
   $5\frac{17}{24}$

6. $1\frac{1}{9}$
   $+ 3\frac{5}{8}$
   $4\frac{53}{72}$

7. $8\frac{1}{6}$
   $- 2\frac{7}{12}$
   $5\frac{7}{12}$

8. $6\frac{7}{9}$
   $- 4\frac{2}{3}$
   $2\frac{1}{9}$

9. $3\frac{9}{14}$
   $- 1\frac{2}{7}$
   $2\frac{5}{14}$

Solve. Give your answer in the simplest form.

Show your work.

10. Last year my elm tree was $8\frac{5}{6}$ feet tall. This year it is $10\frac{1}{12}$ feet tall. How much did it grow in one year?
    $1\frac{1}{4}$ feet

11. Luis rode his bicycle $2\frac{3}{10}$ miles before lunch. He rode $1\frac{1}{4}$ miles after lunch. How far did Luis ride altogether?
    $3\frac{11}{20}$ miles

12. Carrie spent $2\frac{1}{2}$ hours trimming bushes and $1\frac{1}{4}$ hours weeding the garden. She is supposed to work in the yard for 5 hours. How much longer does she need to work?
    $1\frac{1}{4}$ hours

UNIT 3 LESSON 16   Solve with Unlike Mixed Numbers **127**

Homework and Remembering page 127

3–16

Remembering **Goal:** Cumulative Review

This Remembering activity is appropriate anytime after today's lesson.

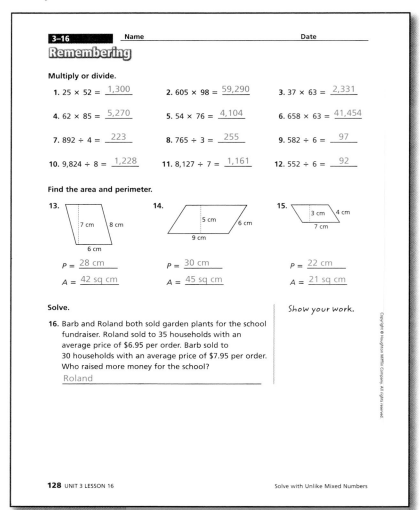

3–16 Name _____ Date _____

Remembering

Multiply or divide.

1. $25 \times 52 = $ 1,300
2. $605 \times 98 = $ 59,290
3. $37 \times 63 = $ 2,331
4. $62 \times 85 = $ 5,270
5. $54 \times 76 = $ 4,104
6. $658 \times 63 = $ 41,454
7. $892 \div 4 = $ 223
8. $765 \div 3 = $ 255
9. $582 \div 6 = $ 97
10. $9,824 \div 8 = $ 1,228
11. $8,127 \div 7 = $ 1,161
12. $552 \div 6 = $ 92

Find the area and perimeter.

13. 7 cm 8 cm
     6 cm

14. 5 cm 6 cm
     9 cm

15. 3 cm 4 cm
     7 cm

P = 28 cm
A = 42 sq cm

P = 30 cm
A = 45 sq cm

P = 22 cm
A = 21 sq cm

Solve.

Show your work.

16. Barb and Roland both sold garden plants for the school fundraiser. Roland sold to 35 households with an average price of $6.95 per order. Barb sold to 30 households with an average price of $7.95 per order. Who raised more money for the school?
    Roland

128 UNIT 3 LESSON 16   Solve with Unlike Mixed Numbers

Homework and Remembering page 128

Home or School Activity

 Real-World Connection

Plan a Feast

Have each student find a recipe for a dish to contribute to the feast. Make sure the recipe uses customary units of measurement. Have each student total the amount of dry ingredients and the amount of wet ingredients in their recipe, using cups. Keep track of the students' totals on a class chart. Then have everyone find the grand total, in cups, for each type of ingredient for the whole feast.

1 tablespoon = 3 teaspoons

$\frac{1}{4}$ cup = 4 tablespoons

Practice With Unlike Mixed Numbers

Lesson Objectives

● Consolidate understanding of equivalent fractions and operations with unlike fractions.

● Express the main concept of renaming and ungrouping fractions.

The Day at a Glance

Today's Goals	Materials	Math Talk
Quick Practice Determine common denominators.	Student Activity Book pages 219–220	In today's activities, the students are involved in discussion as they
① Teaching the Lesson A1: Explain how to rename and ungroup fractions. A2: Review and classify the various ways to find a common denominator.	Numbered index cards 1–20 Grid paper Rulers Colored pencils Math Journals	▶ explain the steps in calculating a difference using unlike fractions ▶ summarize strategies for determining the least common denominator
② Extending the Lesson ▶ Differentiated Instruction	Homework and Remembering pages 129–130	
③ Homework and Cumulative Review		

Quick Practice

🕐 **5 MINUTES**   **Goal:** Determine common denominators.

Common Denominator Parade Send six students to the board. Ask each student to write, but not complete, an addition equation with two fractions. The only requirement is that no fraction can contain a number larger than 10. In turn, each person at the board points to his or her equation and says, "Name the least common denominator." At a signal, the class responds with the answer.

Teaching the Lesson

The Puzzled Penguin

 25 MINUTES

Goal: Explain how to rename and ungroup fractions.

Materials: Student Activity Book page 219

✔ **NCTM Standards:**
Number and Operations
Problem Solving
Communication

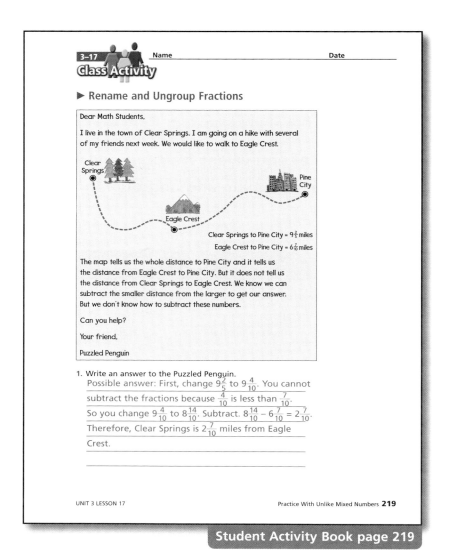

Student Activity Book page 219

Teaching Note

What to Expect from Students

This problem requires both renaming and ungrouping. First students must change $9\frac{2}{5}$ to $9\frac{4}{10}$. Then they must change $9\frac{4}{10}$ to $8\frac{14}{10}$ so that they can subtract $\frac{7}{10}$.

The correct answer is $2\frac{7}{10}$ miles.

▶ Rename and Ungroup Fractions WHOLE CLASS

Direct students' attention to the Puzzled Penguin letter on Student Activity Book page 219 and read it together. Be sure everyone understands the basic problem. Have the students write a reply to the penguin.

Ask a few volunteers to read their letters to the class. The rest of the class should listen carefully for:

● steps that are explained clearly

● steps that are left out

● ideas that are still unclear

Invite the students to ask questions or make suggestions for clarifying the explanation. You may want to collect the letters for students' portfolios or for parent conferences.

Activity 2

Review the Common Denominator

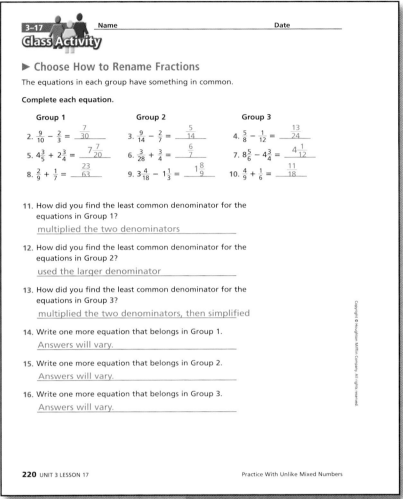

3-17
Class Activity

Name _____ Date _____

▶ **Choose How to Rename Fractions**

The equations in each group have something in common.

Complete each equation.

Group 1	Group 2	Group 3
2. $\frac{9}{10} - \frac{2}{3} = \frac{7}{30}$	3. $\frac{9}{14} - \frac{2}{7} = \frac{5}{14}$	4. $\frac{5}{8} - \frac{1}{12} = \frac{13}{24}$
5. $4\frac{3}{5} + 2\frac{3}{4} = 7\frac{7}{20}$	6. $\frac{3}{28} + \frac{3}{4} = \frac{6}{7}$	7. $8\frac{5}{6} - 4\frac{3}{4} = 4\frac{1}{12}$
8. $\frac{2}{9} + \frac{1}{7} = \frac{23}{63}$	9. $3\frac{4}{18} - 1\frac{1}{3} = 1\frac{8}{9}$	10. $\frac{4}{9} + \frac{1}{6} = \frac{11}{18}$

11. How did you find the least common denominator for the equations in Group 1?

multiplied the two denominators

12. How did you find the least common denominator for the equations in Group 2?

used the larger denominator

13. How did you find the least common denominator for the equations in Group 3?

multiplied the two denominators, then simplified

14. Write one more equation that belongs in Group 1.

Answers will vary.

15. Write one more equation that belongs in Group 2.

Answers will vary.

16. Write one more equation that belongs in Group 3.

Answers will vary.

220 UNIT 3 LESSON 17   Practice With Unlike Mixed Numbers

Student Activity Book page 220

 25 MINUTES

Goal: Review and classify the various ways to find a common denominator.

Materials: Student Activity Book page 220

 NCTM Standards:
Number and Operations
Communication

▶ Choose How to Rename Fractions WHOLE CLASS

Have students work alone to complete exercises 2–10 on Student Activity Book page 220. Then discuss their answers to questions 11, 12, and 13 as a class. Allow students to explain in their own words how they found a common denominator for the fractions in each group. Encourage other students to ask questions if an explanation is unclear to them.

Three basic situations are represented here:

Group 1: The two denominators must be multiplied together to produce a new denominator for both fractions. The specific denominators in this group are 30, 20, and 63.

Group 2: One denominator is a factor of the other, so we can use the larger denominator as the common denominator. The specific denominators in this group are 14, 28, and 18.

Activity continued ▶

① Teaching the Lesson (continued)

Activity 2

Group 3: Neither denominator is a factor of the other, but we can still find a denominator that is smaller than the one produced by multiplying the two denominators together. The specific denominators in this group are 24, 12, and 18.

Ask students,

● **Which method can you always use to find a common denominator?** the first method

● **Why don't we always use it?** It can produce large numbers that are hard to work with. We usually look for the smallest denominator, or the least common denominator.

Have students work on their own to complete questions 14–16. Invite a couple of students to work at the board. Ask the others to check the equations on the board and to explain whether they agree with the responses.

If students still need practice finding common denominators, you might ask two students to call out a number between 1 and 20, for example, 3 and 12. Write fractions on the board with these numbers as denominators, for example, $\frac{2}{3}$ and $\frac{1}{12}$. Invite students to explain how to find a common denominator. Others can suggest alternatives if appropriate.

② Extending the Lesson

Intervention
for students having difficulty

PAIRS

How Far Is It?

Materials: ruler

Each student draws a triangle on a piece of paper. Each partner first uses a ruler to measure the length of each side in inches and fractions of an inch and then adds the three lengths to find the perimeter of the triangle. Students should check their partner's work by adding. Students can also check by adding on, on the ruler.

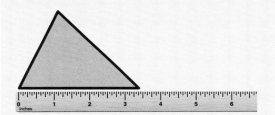

On Level
for students having success

PAIRS

Add Unlike Fractions

Materials: numbered index cards 1–20

One partner chooses four number cards and arranges them to make two fractions. Both partners find a common denominator and add the fractions. They check their work by comparing answers and award themselves 1 point for each correct addition. The first person to reach 5 points wins.

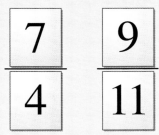

Challenge
for students seeking a challenge

INDIVIDUALS

Fraction Designs

Materials: grid paper, colored pencils

On grid paper, students draw a design that meets these criteria:

$\frac{1}{4}$ red

$\frac{1}{5}$ blue

$\frac{1}{6}$ yellow

$\frac{1}{7}$ green

and the rest purple.

Students share their designs with classmates.

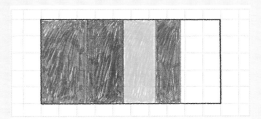

 Math Writing Prompt

Intervention

Draw a Picture

Draw a picture that helps you find a common denominator for $\frac{1}{2}$ and $\frac{1}{9}$. Explain what your picture shows.

 Math Writing Prompt

On Level

Investigate Mathematics

Show two ways to find a common denominator for $\frac{1}{2}$ and $\frac{1}{9}$.

 Math Writing Prompt

Challenge

Prove It

No two unlike fractions can have a common denominator of 31. Do you agree or disagree? Explain your reasoning.

③ Homework and Cumulative Review

Homework **Goal:** Additional Practice

✓ Include students' work for page 129 as part of their portfolios.

Remembering **Goal:** Cumulative Review

This Remembering activity is appropriate anytime after today's lesson.

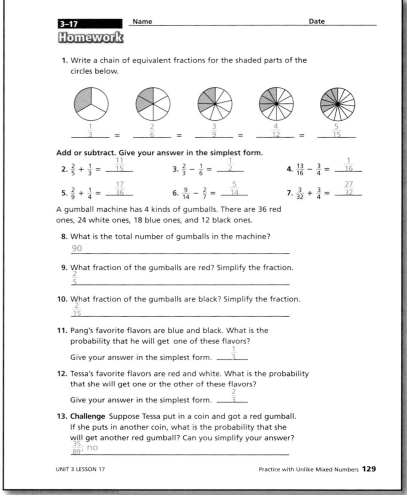

3-17 Name _____ Date _____
Homework

1. Write a chain of equivalent fractions for the shaded parts of the circles below.

$\frac{1}{3}$ = $\frac{2}{6}$ = $\frac{3}{9}$ = $\frac{4}{12}$ = $\frac{5}{15}$

Add or subtract. Give your answer in the simplest form.

2. $\frac{2}{5} + \frac{1}{3} = \frac{11}{15}$ 3. $\frac{2}{3} - \frac{1}{6} = \frac{1}{2}$ 4. $\frac{13}{16} - \frac{3}{4} = \frac{1}{16}$

5. $\frac{2}{9} + \frac{1}{4} = \frac{17}{36}$ 6. $\frac{9}{14} - \frac{2}{7} = \frac{5}{14}$ 7. $\frac{3}{32} + \frac{3}{4} = \frac{27}{32}$

A gumball machine has 4 kinds of gumballs. There are 36 red ones, 24 white ones, 18 blue ones, and 12 black ones.

8. What is the total number of gumballs in the machine?
90

9. What fraction of the gumballs are red? Simplify the fraction.
$\frac{2}{5}$

10. What fraction of the gumballs are black? Simplify the fraction.
$\frac{2}{15}$

11. Pang's favorite flavors are blue and black. What is the probability that he will get one of these flavors?
Give your answer in the simplest form. $\frac{1}{3}$

12. Tessa's favorite flavors are red and white. What is the probability that she will get one or the other of these flavors?
Give your answer in the simplest form. $\frac{2}{3}$

13. **Challenge** Suppose Tessa put in a coin and got a red gumball. If she puts in another coin, what is the probability that she will get another red gumball? Can you simplify your answer? $\frac{35}{89}$; no

UNIT 3 LESSON 17   Practice with Unlike Mixed Numbers **129**

Homework and Remembering page 129

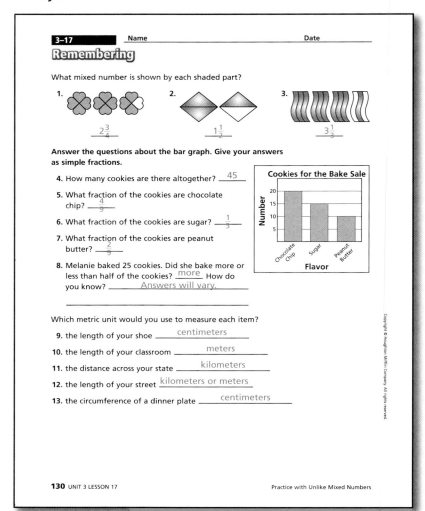

3-17 Name _____ Date _____
Remembering

What mixed number is shown by each shaded part?

1.   2.   3.
$2\frac{3}{4}$ $1\frac{1}{2}$ $3\frac{1}{3}$

Answer the questions about the bar graph. Give your answers as simple fractions.

4. How many cookies are there altogether? 45

5. What fraction of the cookies are chocolate chip? $\frac{4}{9}$

6. What fraction of the cookies are sugar? $\frac{1}{3}$

7. What fraction of the cookies are peanut butter? $\frac{2}{9}$

8. Melanie baked 25 cookies. Did she bake more or less than half of the cookies? more How do you know? Answers will vary.

Cookies for the Bake Sale

Which metric unit would you use to measure each item?

9. the length of your shoe centimeters

10. the length of your classroom meters

11. the distance across your state kilometers

12. the length of your street kilometers or meters

13. the circumference of a dinner plate centimeters

130 UNIT 3 LESSON 17   Practice with Unlike Mixed Numbers

Homework and Remembering page 130

Home or School Activity

 Sports Connection

Shots Made Fractions can be used to track statistics in sports. You can track how many free throws a player makes in basketball, how many pitches a player hits in baseball, how many shots a player scores in hockey. Have students try an activity, such as shooting baskets or throwing beanbags at a target, and have them record their success rate as a fraction. Students can write a short report using fractions to compare their results in a meaningful way.

Unit Review and Test

Lesson Objective

- **Assess student progress on unit objectives.**

The Day at a Glance

Today's Goals	Materials
① Assessing the Unit ▶ Assess student progress on unit objectives. ▶ Use activities from unit lessons to reteach content. **② Extending the Assessment** ▶ Use remediation for common errors. There is no homework assignment on a test day.	Unit 3 Test, Student Activity Book pages 221–222 Unit 3 Test, Form A or B, Assessment Guide (optional) Unit 3 Performance Assessment, Assessment Guide (optional)

 Class Management

Review and Test Day You may want to choose a quiet game or other activity (reading a book or working on homework for another subject) for students who finish early.

① Assessing the Unit

Assess Unit Objectives

45 MINUTES (more if schedule permits)

Goal: Assess student progress on unit objectives.

Materials: Student Activity Book pages 221–222

▶ Review and Assessment

If your students are ready for assessment on the unit objectives, you may use either the test on the Student Activity Book pages or one of the forms of the Unit 3 Test in the Assessment Guide to assess student progress.

If you feel that students need some review first, you may use the test on the Student Activity Book pages as a review of unit content, and then use one of the forms of the Unit 3 Test in the Assessment Guide to assess student progress.

To assign a numerical score for all of these test forms, use 10 points for each question.

You may also choose to use the Unit 3 Performance Assessment. Scoring for that assessment can be found in its rubric in the Assessment Guide.

▶ Reteaching Resources

The chart lists the test items, the unit objectives they cover, and the lesson activities in which the objective is covered in this unit. You may revisit these activities with students who do not show mastery of the objectives.

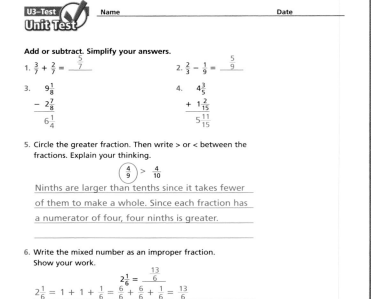

Student Activity Book page 221

Unit Test Items	Unit Objectives Tested	Activities to Use for Reteaching
1–4	**3.1** Add and subtract fractions and mixed numbers with like and unlike denominators.	Lesson 1, Activity 1 Lesson 7, Activity 2 Lesson 8, Activity 2 Lesson 15, Activity 1 Lesson 16, Activity 1 Lesson 17, Activity 2
5–6	**3.2** Write and compare fractions and mixed numbers.	Lesson 2, Activity 1 Lesson 6, Activity 1 Lesson 9, Activity 1
7	**3.3** Relate fractions and wholes.	Lesson 4, Activity 1 Lesson 5, Activity 1

Name _____ **Date** _____

7. What fraction of the whole is the shaded triangle?

$\frac{1}{9}$

8. Circle the fraction that is equivalent to $\frac{9}{10}$. Show your work.

$\frac{32}{40}$ $\frac{81}{100}$ $\boxed{\frac{36}{40}}$

$\frac{32 \div 4}{40 \div 4} = \frac{8}{10}$ $\frac{36 \div 4}{40 \div 4} = \frac{9}{10}$

Solve. Simplify your answer.   *Show your work.*

9. Kendra has 6 red marbles and 2 blue marbles in a bag. She reaches in and chooses one without looking. What is the probability that it is a blue marble?

$\frac{1}{4}$

10. **Extended Response** Terry worked in the garden for $\frac{3}{4}$ hour. Peter worked in the garden for $\frac{1}{6}$ hour more than Terry. How many hours did they work in the garden altogether?

First calculate how long Peter has worked.

Add both fractions together. $\frac{3}{4} + \frac{1}{6} = \frac{11}{12}$

Peter has worked $\frac{11}{12}$ hour. Now add

these two together to calculate the total

number of hours they worked in the garden

altogether. $\frac{3}{4} + \frac{11}{12} = 1\frac{2}{3}$

Together, they have worked $1\frac{2}{3}$ hours in the

garden.

222 UNIT 3 TEST

Student Activity Book page 222

Unit Test Items	Unit Objectives Tested	Activities to Use for Reteaching
8	**3.4** Find equivalent fractions.	Lesson 11, Activity 1 Lesson 12, Activity 2 Lesson 13, Activity 2
9	**3.5** Express the probability of an event as a fraction.	Lesson 14, Activity 1
10	**3.6** Solve problems involving fractions.	Lesson 3, Activity 1 Lesson 5, Activity 2 Lesson 8, Activity 1 Lesson 9, Activity 2 Lesson 10, Activity 2 Lesson 14, Activity 2 Lesson 16, Activity 2

▶ Assessment Resources

Free Response Tests
Unit 3 Test Student Activity Book, pages 221–222
Unit 3 Test, Form A, Assessment Guide

Extended Response Item
The last item in the Student Activity Book test and in the Form A test will require an extended response as an answer.

Multiple Choice Test
Unit 3 Test, Form B, Assessment Guide

Performance Assessment
Unit 3 Performance Assessment, Assessment Guide
Unit 3 Performance Assessment Rubric, Assessment Guide

▶ Portfolio Assessment

Teacher-selected Items for Student Portfolios:

- Homework, Lessons 3, 6, 9, 11, 13, 14, 15, 16, and 17

- Class Activity work, Lessons 3, 8, 10, 15, and 17

Student-selected Items for Student Portfolios:

- Favorite Home or School Activity

- Best Writing Prompt

Unit Objective 3.1

Add and subtract fractions and mixed numbers with like and unlike denominators.

Common Error: Ungroups incorrectly.

When ungrouping is necessary for a subtraction, students may forget to add the fractional part of the mixed number to the ungrouped whole.

Remediation Encourage students who are experiencing difficulty to write out all of the steps. For example, when ungrouping $2\frac{1}{4}$, write $2\frac{1}{4} = 1 + \frac{4}{4} + \frac{1}{4} = 1 + \frac{5}{4}$. They can also think of ungrouping in terms of money. Two one-dollar bills and one quarter is the same amount of money as 1 one-dollar bill and 5 quarters.

Unit Objective 3.2

Write and compare fractions and mixed numbers.

Common Error: Misidentifies the greater fraction.

Some students may think the greater denominator indicates the greater fraction.

Remediation Remind students that the <u>d</u>enominator tells the number of <u>d</u>ivisions of the whole. If the same whole is divided into more parts, each part must be smaller. Talk about sharing a pizza. Ask students which piece will be bigger—the one they will get if the pizza is shared equally by 4 friends, or the one they will get if the pizza is shared equally by three friends.

Unit Objective 3.3

Relate fractions and wholes.

Common Error: Writes an incorrect denominator.

Students may have trouble deciding into how many parts the whole has been divided.

Remediation Draw a square divided into four smaller squares on the board and shade one of the smaller squares. Write $\frac{part}{whole}$ beside the picture. Ask students how many parts are shaded and how many parts are not. Then ask how many parts make up the whole. Ask why it doesn't make sense to say that the picture represents $\frac{1}{3}$.

Unit Objective 3.4

Find equivalent fractions.

Common Error: Has difficulty determining equivalence.

Some students find it difficult to compare fractions for equivalence.

Remediation Encourage students to look for the relationship between the numerators and compare it to the relationship between the denominators. Write $\frac{2}{3} \longrightarrow \frac{4}{12}$ on the board. Ask students what the 2 on the left has been multiplied by to get 4 and what the 3 on the left has been multiplied by to get 12. Since the answers are different, the fractions are not equivalent.

Unit Objective 3.5

Express the probability of an event as a fraction.

Common Error: Records probability incorrectly.

Students may be confused about what each part of the fraction represents when it describes a probability.

Remediation Discuss the meaning of the numerator as number of favorable outcomes and the denominator as total number of outcomes with the class. To reinforce the ideas, roll a number cube and ask students to name the possible outcomes. Write 6 for the denominator in a probability fraction. Then ask about the number of favorable outcomes for an event, such as rolling a 1 or rolling an even number. Record the appropriate number in the numerator.

Unit Objective 3.6

Solve problems involving fractions.

Common Error: Forgets to simplify the answer.

Some students may not remember to write their answers in simplest form.

Remediation Remind students that answers are often easier to understand when presented in simplest form. This may involve regrouping or finding the simplest equivalent fraction, or both. For example, the answer $\frac{20}{12}$ hours can be regrouped to $1\frac{8}{12}$ hours, then further simplified to $1\frac{2}{3}$ hours.

Volume, Capacity, and Weight

IN THIS UNIT, students develop some important relationships in measurement. They begin by using what they know about length and area to develop a formula for volume. Then students change the length or the area of a figure and predict how the volume will change.

Later in the unit, students compare volume and capacity, and mass and weight. Activities in this unit provide students with opportunities to build familiarity with both metric and customary units of measure.

Planning Unit C Unit Pacing: 7–11 days

Lesson Title	Lesson Resources	Materials and Manipulatives	
		Math Expressions	**Other**
1 Cubic Units and Volume	Family Letter Student Activity Book pages 223–226 Homework and Remembering pages 131–132		Centimeter or inch cubes or one large demonstration cube, centimeter cubes (connecting), or one large demonstration cube, meter sticks or tape measures, Math Journals
2 Relate Length, Area, and Volume	Student Activity Book pages 227–230 Homework and Remembering pages 133–134	Centimeter-Grid Paper (Copymaster M19)	Connecting cubes, Math Journals
3 Measures of Capacity	Student Activity Book pages 231–232 Homework and Remembering pages 135–136		Containers and boxes, customary and metric measuring cups, teaspoons, tablespoons, variety of containers, Math Journals
4 Measures of Mass and Weight	Student Activity Book pages 233–234 Homework and Remembering pages 137–138		Balance scale (optional), classroom objects (optional), Math Journals
✓ Unit C Review and Test	Student Activity Book pages 235–236 Assessment Guide		

Unit C Assessment

✓ Unit Objectives Tested	Unit Test Items	Lessons
C.1 Find the volume of a rectangular prism.	1–5, 9	1, 2
C.2 Solve problems involving capacity, mass, and weight.	6–8, 10	3, 4

Formal Assessment	Informal Assessment	Review Opportunities
Open or Free Response Tests • Unit Review and Test (Student Activity Book pages 235–236, Teacher's Guide pages 505–508) • Unit C Test Form A (Assessment Guide) • Unit C Open Response Test (Test Generator) • Test Bank Items for Unit C (Test Generator) **Multiple Choice Tests** • Unit C Test Form B (Assessment Guide) • Unit C Multiple Choice Test (Test Generator) • Test Bank Items for Unit C (Test Generator) **Performance Tasks** • Unit C Performance Assessment (Assessment Guide) • Unit C Performance Assessment (Test Generator)	**Ongoing Assessment** • In every Teacher's Guide lesson **Performance Assessment** • Class discussions • Small-group work • Individual work on teacher-selected tasks **Portfolios** • See Unit C Review and Test for suggestions for selecting items for portfolios. • Some Homework pages are noted as suitable for portfolio inclusion.	**Homework and Remembering** • Homework pages provide review of recently taught topics. • Remembering pages provide cumulative review. **Teacher's Guide** • Unit Review and Test (page 505) **Teacher's Resource Book** • Problem Bank **Test Generator CD-ROM** • Test Bank Items can be used to create custom review sheets.

Unit C Teaching Resources

Differentiated Instruction

Reaching All Learners

Extra Help
Lesson 1, page 481

Advanced Learners
Lesson 2, page 487

Lesson 4, page 502

Individualizing Instruction

Activities
- Intervention (in every lesson)
- On Level (in every lesson)
- Challenge (in every lesson)

Math Writing Prompts
- Intervention (in every lesson)
- On Level (in every lesson)
- Challenge (in every lesson)

Cross-Curricular Links • Home or School Activities

 Multicultural Connection
Recipe Research (Lesson 3, page 498)

 Physical Education Connection
Jumping Jacks (Lesson 2, page 492)

 Science Connection
Birth Weights (Lesson 4, page 504)

Teaching Unit C

Putting Research into Practice for Unit C

From Current Research: Concepts of Volume

Many students never learn about volume because they do not make it past plane geometry. Those who do often reach calculus by a head-long rush that leaves little or no time for the kind of geometrical thinking on which calculus thrives. Calculus is not the time when students should be doing their first serious thinking about geometry. Rather it should be the culmination of years of consideration of increasingly sophisticated geometrical topics. When a student finally sees the full justification of the formula for the volume of a cone or a sphere, it should be a peak experience, fulfilling a promise implicit in all the experiences he or she has had with cones and spheres all the way through school, beginning in kindergarten.

Froebel's young students spent a great deal of time pouring water and sifting sand. Differently-shaped containers held different amounts, so a student would gradually learn common relationships without even thinking of writing them down. For example, how many conical cups can be filled from the water in a cylindrical cup with the same height and the same base? With a rack of such cups, any student can perform the experiment. The cylinder fills three cups.

We can test this over and over again with different heights and different circular tops. Only later, after the student is familiar with the language of fractions, need this relationship be stated in terms of one volume being one-third of another. Still later, that relationship can be expressed by a formula: the volume of the cone is one-third the area of the base multiplied by the height.

By this time, that relationship should already have been observed in other shapes. Three square-based pyramids can be filled with the sand from one square prism of the same base and height. Even if the base is irregular, this relationship is true. We don't even have to have the center of the cone over the center of the base, assuming that the base even has a center! All this understanding can take place before the student has even seen a fraction, let alone a number like π.

Banchoff, Thomas F. "Dimension." *On the Shoulders of Giants: New Approaches to Numeracy.* Ed. Lynn Arthur Steen. Mathematical Sciences Education Board. National Research Council. Washington: National Academy Press, 1990. 14.

Other Useful References: Volume, Capacity, and Weight

Ferrer, Bellasanta B., Bobbie Hunter, Kathryn C. Irwin, Maureen J. Sheldon, Charles S. Thompson, and Catherine P. Vistro-Yu. "By the Unit or Square Unit?" *Mathematics Teaching in the Middle School* 7.3 (Nov. 2001).

Learning Math: Geometry. Annenberg/CPB Learner.org. 1997–2004. <www.learner.org/resources/series167.html>.

Learning Math: Measurement. Annenberg/CPB Learner.org. 1997–2004. <www.learner.org/resources/series184.html>.

National Council of Teachers of Mathematics. *Learning and Teaching Measurement* (NCTM 2003 Yearbook). Ed. Douglas H. Clements. Reston: NCTM, 2003.

National Council of Teachers of Mathematics. *Mathematics Teaching in the Middle School* (Focus Issue: Measurement) 9.8 (Apr. 2004).

National Council of Teachers of Mathematics. *Principles and Standards for School Mathematics.* Reston: NCTM, 2000.

Math Background

Volume and Capacity

Students begin this unit by examining cubes and arranging them in layers to create rectangular prisms. By doing this, students internalize a clear concept of volume that they can draw on when they are asked to develop a formula for volume. $V = l \times w \times h$ becomes a meaningful statement for them.

While volume is a measure of the amount of space an object takes up, capacity is a measure of how much a container can hold. Volume is measured in cubic centimeters, cubic meters, cubic inches, and so on. Capacity is usually measured in "liquid" units, such as liters, gallons, and ounces.

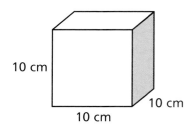

The volume of this prism is 1000 cu cm.

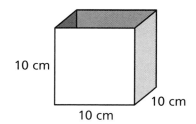

The capacity of this container is 1 L.

Weight and Mass

Because we most often talk about the weight or mass of objects on the surface of Earth, we often use the two terms interchangeably. In fact, they refer to different properties. Mass is a measure of the amount of "stuff" in an object. The mass of an object is the same on the moon as it is on Earth, because the amount of "stuff" in the object does not change. Weight is a measure of the pressure an object exerts downward because of gravity. Your weight is less on the moon than it is on Earth, because there is less gravity on the moon's surface than there is on Earth's surface. Mass is always measured on a balance, where one object is compared to a known mass. Weight can be measured on a scale with a spring, such as a common bathroom scale. On Earth, though, an object with a mass of one pound will also have a weight of one pound.

It is generally accepted that students should learn to work with both metric and customary measures. In real life both are used. Also, both reinforce different number sense and operation skills. While working with metric units builds facility with decimals and powers of 10, working with customary units can involve a deeper understanding of fractions. Both types of measures are used in this unit.

Cubic Units and Volume

Vocabulary

face
edge
vertex
volume
cubic unit
rectangular prism

Lesson Objectives

- Visualize the cubic units contained in a cube or solid rectangular figure.
- Use a formula to calculate the volume of a rectangular prism.

The Day at a Glance

Today's Goals	Materials	📱 Math Talk
1 Teaching the Lesson **A1:** Identify the parts of a cube. **A2:** Explore the concept of volume as cubic units. **A3:** Develop a formula for calculating volume and use it to solve problems. **2 Extending the Lesson** ▶ Differentiated Instruction **3 Homework and Cumulative Review**	Centimeter or inch cubes, or one large demonstration cube Student Activity Book pages 223–226 Centimeter cubes (connecting) Meter sticks or tape measures Homework and Remembering pages 131–132 Math Journals Family Letter	In today's activities, the students are involved in discussion as they ▶ describe the attributes of a cube ▶ measure and calculate volume ▶ Solve and Discuss problems involving volume

Teaching the Lesson

Attributes of a Cube

 15 MINUTES

Goal: Identify the parts of a cube.

Materials: centimeter or inch cubes (1 per student) or 1 large demonstration cube, Student Activity Book page 223

✔ **NCTM Standards:**
Geometry
Measurement
Communication

▶ Describe a Cube [WHOLE CLASS]

Distribute the centimeter or inch cubes or display a demonstration cube.

● **Name some objects you use that are cubes.** Possible answers: number cubes for board games, ice cubes (not always cube-shaped), sugar cubes, stock cubes for soup, caramels

Explain that the sides of a cube are called *faces*.

● **What is the shape of each face of a cube?** square

● **Are all the faces congruent?** yes

● **How do you know?** They are all square and they all have the same side length.

Discuss exercises 1 and 2 on Student Activity Book page 223 as a class. If students have difficulty recognizing the number of faces a cube has, have them recall any number cubes they may have used while playing board games, and describe the faces of those cubes.

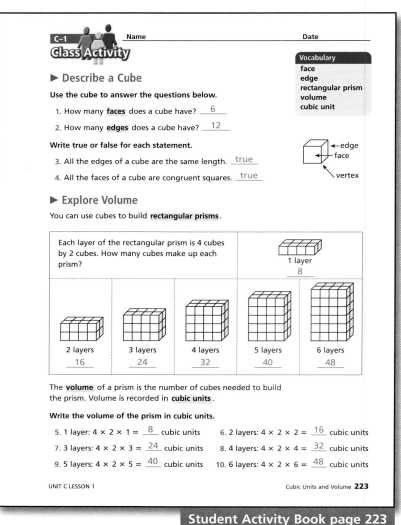

Student Activity Book page 223

● **What numbers are on the faces of a number cube for a board game?** 1 to 6

● **So how many faces does a cube have?** 6

Ask students to complete exercises 3–10.

Teaching Note

Math Background Remind students that a square is a special kind of rectangle. Then point out that a cube is a special kind of rectangular prism—all of the edges of a cube are the same length.

Visualize Volume

 20 MINUTES

Goal: Explore the concept of volume as cubic units.

Materials: Student Activity Book page 223, centimeter or inch cubes

 NCTM Standards:
Geometry
Measurement

▶ Explore Volume WHOLE CLASS

Ask the students to describe how they can figure out the amount of space inside a box. Encourage them to carry the discussion as far as they can and, if possible, include a description of how to calculate the amount of space. If necessary, lead the students to understand that the idea of measuring the amount of space inside a box is the same as finding the volume of that box. See a sample of classroom dialogue in the Math Talk in Action below. Volume is stated in cubic units because volume measures the number of unit cubes that will fit in the box.

 Math Talk in Action

How can you find the number of unit cubes that will fit in a box?

Lilah: You can fill the box and count them.

What if you don't have enough unit cubes to fill the box?

Lilah: You can make a layer of cubes to cover the bottom of the box. Then you need to find the number of layers.

Percy: You can stack some cubes to find how many layers you need.

Lilah: Right. Then you multiply the cubes in a layer by the number of layers.

Cubic Units Have students look at the rectangular prisms on Student Activity Book page 223. Ask all of the class members to look at each prism and determine its volume by counting individual cubes. Remind students to include the label *cubic units* when they tell the volume of each prism.

1 layer: $4 \times 2 \times 1 = 8$ cu units
2 layers: $4 \times 2 \times 2 = 16$ cu units
3 layers: $4 \times 2 \times 3 = 24$ cu units
4 layers: $4 \times 2 \times 4 = 32$ cu units
5 layers: $4 \times 2 \times 5 = 40$ cu units
6 layers: $4 \times 2 \times 6 = 48$ cu units

Invite students to imagine adding one layer to the six-layer prism, and to name the volume of that prism (56 cubic units). Remind students that whenever they find volume, they must include the word *cubic* or the symbol *cu* as part of their answer. Have students complete exercises 6–11.

Differentiated Instruction

Extra Help Distribute 25 cubes (either inch or centimeter) to students who have difficulty understanding the concept of volume. Invite the students to use the cubes to duplicate the one-layer, two-layer, and three-layer prisms shown on Student Activity Book page 223.

Ongoing Assessment

Ask students to calculate the total number of cubes. How many cubes are in:

▶ 6 layers of 2 by 4 rectangles?

▶ 10 layers of 3 by 3 rectangles?

▶ 9 layers of 10 by 10 rectangles?

① Teaching the Lesson (continued)

Activity 3

Solve Volume Problems

 25 MINUTES

Goal: Develop a formula for calculating volume and use it to solve problems.

Materials: Student Activity Book page 224

 NCTM Standards:
Geometry
Measurement

C-1
Class Activity

Name _____ Date _____

▶ **Develop a Formula**

11. What is the volume of this rectangular prism?
    30 cu cm

12. Write a formula for finding the volume of any rectangular prism.
    Volume = length × width × height or l × w × h

3 cm, 5 cm, 2 cm (rectangular prism diagram)

▶ **Share Solutions**

Solve.

13. A box shaped like a rectangular prism is 4 dm long, 2 dm wide, and 3 dm tall. What is the volume of the box?
    24 cu dm

14. When closed, the cargo area of a truck measures 3 m long by 2 m wide by 1 m deep. How many cubic meters of cargo will fit in the closed area?
    6 cu m

15. A flower box is 3 feet long, 2 feet wide, and ½ foot deep. How many cubic feet of dirt can it hold?
    3 cu ft

16. Cubes of fudge are arranged in 2 layers on a tray. Each layer is 8 cubes long and 6 cubes wide. How many cubes of fudge are on the tray?
    96 cubes

17. Todd used 8 small cubes and glue to build the cube shown at the right. Then he painted the entire cube red. After the paint dried, Todd broke the cube apart into the 8 smaller cubes he started with. How many faces of the 8 smaller cubes are *not* painted red?
    24 faces

224 UNIT C LESSON 1   Cubic Units and Volume

Student Activity Book page 224

▶ **Develop a Formula** [INDIVIDUALS]

Help students see that to find volume, they first need to find area, then multiply area by height.

After students complete exercise 11.

● How do you find the area of a rectangle? multiply length by width

---

● How do you find the volume of a rectangular prism? multiply length by width and then by height

● How is finding volume different from finding area? Possible answers: use three numbers to calculate volume, but only two to calculate area; measure volume in cubic units and area in square units; volume is a measurement for a three-dimensional figure and area is a measurement for a two-dimensional figure

For exercise 12, have students write a formula for finding the volume of a rectangular prism, then share their completed formulas by writing them on the board. Accept any formula that multiplies the length and the width and the height. If the traditional formula does not appear on the board, you may want to introduce it now: $V = l \times w \times h$ or $V = lwh$.

▶ **Share Solutions** [WHOLE CLASS]

123 Use Solve and Discuss for exercises 13–17, emphasizing for each problem the idea that volume is always given in cubic units. Invite a few students to work at the board while others work at their desks. Two or three students give their solutions and explain their thinking. Encourage other students to listen carefully and ask questions. Classroom discussions may include:

● For exercise 13: $4 \times 2 \times 3 = 24$ cu dm: The bottom layer is 4×2 or 8 cu dm, and there are 3 layers, so $8 \times 3 = 24$ cu dm:

● For exercise 14: $3 \times 2 \times 1 = 6$ cu m: The cargo area has only one layer.

● For exercise 15: $3 \times 2 \times \frac{1}{2} = 3$ cu ft of dirt: Measurements need not be whole numbers, and answers may not be whole numbers.

● For exercise 16: $8 \times 6 \times 2 = 96$ cubes: The bottom layer is 8×6 or 48 cubes, and there are 2 layers.

● For exercise 17: 24 faces are not painted red: The 8 individual cubes each have 6 faces, so there are 48 faces altogether. After the larger cube was assembled and painted, paint covered 24 of those faces, so 48 faces − 24 painted faces = 24 unpainted faces.

② Extending the Lesson

Differentiated Instruction
Activities for Individualizing

Intervention
for students having difficulty

PAIRS

Different Dimensions

Materials: 36 centimeter cubes (connnecting)

Students build different boxes (rectangular prisms), and record the dimensions and volumes.

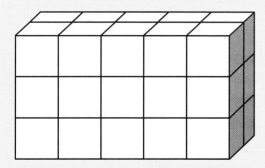

5 by 3 by 2
30 cubic centimeters

On Level
for students having success

PAIRS

Different Dimensions

Materials: 36 centimeter cubes (connnecting)

Students show how to build at least two different boxes, each having a volume of 36 cu cm.

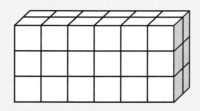

6 by 3 by 2

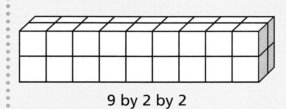

9 by 2 by 2

Challenge
for students seeking a challenge

SMALL GROUPS

Estimate Volume

Materials: meter sticks or tape measures

Students estimate the dimensions of the classroom in meters and record their estimates. They can use their estimates to calculate the volume. Students then measure the dimensions of the classroom to the nearest meter, and compare the results with their estimates.

> *We think the classroom is about 5 meters by 10 meters by 2 meters high.*
> *The volume is 5 x 10 x 2 = 100 cu m*

 Math Writing Prompt

Intervention

Explain Your Thinking
If you turn an object upside down or on its side, does its volume change? Explain your answer.

 Math Writing Prompt

On Level

Summarize
In your own words, describe how centimeters, decimeters, and meters are related and how cubic centimeters, cubic decimeters, and cubic meters are related.

 Math Writing Prompt

Challenge

Solve a Problem
A box measures 10 cm on each side. How many cubic centimeters of paper are needed to cover all the faces of the box?

③ Homework and Cumulative Review

C–1

Homework **Goal:** Additional Practice

✔ For homework, students calculate volume to solve word problems.

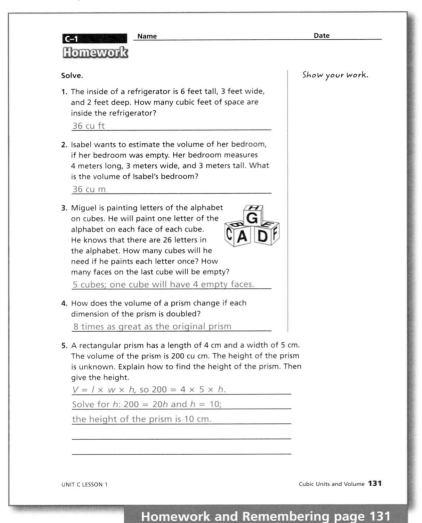

C–1

Homework

Name _____ Date _____

Solve.

Show your work.

1. The inside of a refrigerator is 6 feet tall, 3 feet wide, and 2 feet deep. How many cubic feet of space are inside the refrigerator?
   36 cu ft

2. Isabel wants to estimate the volume of her bedroom, if her bedroom was empty. Her bedroom measures 4 meters long, 3 meters wide, and 3 meters tall. What is the volume of Isabel's bedroom?
   36 cu m

3. Miguel is painting letters of the alphabet on cubes. He will paint one letter of the alphabet on each face of each cube. He knows that there are 26 letters in the alphabet. How many cubes will he need if he paints each letter once? How many faces on the last cube will be empty?
   5 cubes; one cube will have 4 empty faces.

4. How does the volume of a prism change if each dimension of the prism is doubled?
   8 times as great as the original prism

5. A rectangular prism has a length of 4 cm and a width of 5 cm. The volume of the prism is 200 cu cm. The height of the prism is unknown. Explain how to find the height of the prism. Then give the height.
   $V = l \times w \times h$, so $200 = 4 \times 5 \times h$.
   Solve for h: $200 = 20h$ and $h = 10$;
   the height of the prism is 10 cm.

UNIT C LESSON 1   Cubic Units and Volume **131**

Homework and Remembering page 131

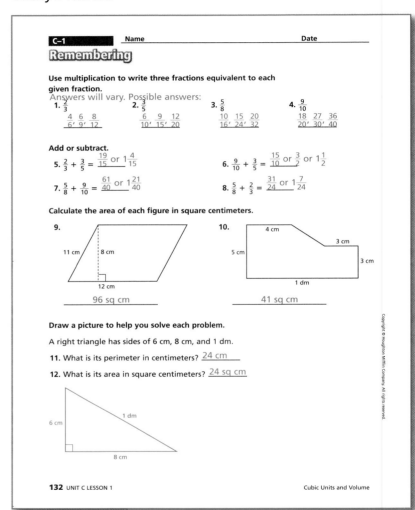

C–1

Remembering **Goal:** Cumulative Review

This Remembering activity is appropriate anytime after today's lesson.

C–1

Remembering

Name _____ Date _____

Use multiplication to write three fractions equivalent to each given fraction.
Answers will vary. Possible answers:

1. $\frac{2}{3}$ $\frac{4}{6}, \frac{6}{9}, \frac{8}{12}$

2. $\frac{3}{5}$ $\frac{6}{10}, \frac{9}{15}, \frac{12}{20}$

3. $\frac{5}{8}$ $\frac{10}{16}, \frac{15}{24}, \frac{20}{32}$

4. $\frac{9}{10}$ $\frac{18}{20}, \frac{27}{30}, \frac{36}{40}$

Add or subtract.

5. $\frac{2}{3} + \frac{3}{5} = \frac{19}{15}$ or $1\frac{4}{15}$

6. $\frac{9}{10} + \frac{3}{5} = \frac{15}{10}$ or $\frac{3}{2}$ or $1\frac{1}{2}$

7. $\frac{5}{8} + \frac{9}{10} = \frac{61}{40}$ or $1\frac{21}{40}$

8. $\frac{5}{8} + \frac{2}{3} = \frac{31}{24}$ or $1\frac{7}{24}$

Calculate the area of each figure in square centimeters.

9.
11 cm   8 cm
12 cm
96 sq cm

10.
4 cm
3 cm
5 cm
3 cm
1 dm
41 sq cm

Draw a picture to help you solve each problem.

A right triangle has sides of 6 cm, 8 cm, and 1 dm.

11. What is its perimeter in centimeters? 24 cm

12. What is its area in square centimeters? 24 sq cm

6 cm   1 dm
8 cm

132 UNIT C LESSON 1   Cubic Units and Volume

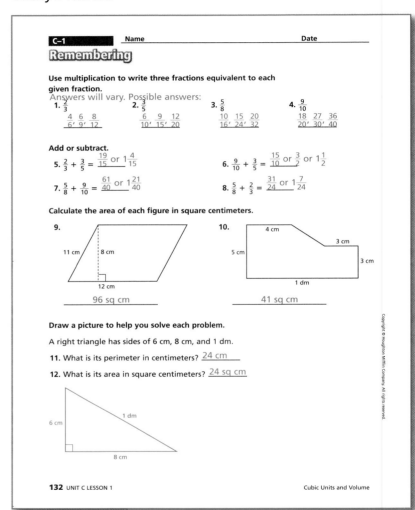

Homework and Remembering page 132

Home and School Connection

Family Letter Have children take home the Family Letter on Student Activity Book page 225. This letter explains how the concepts of volume, capacity, and weight are developed in *Math Expressions*. It gives parents and guardians a better understanding of the learning that goes on in math class and creates a bridge between school and home. A Spanish translation of this letter is on the following page in the Student Activity Book.

Student Activity Book page 225

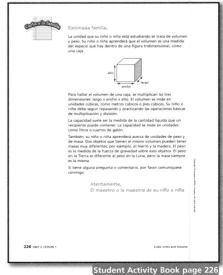

Student Activity Book page 226

Relate Length, Area, and Volume

Lesson Objectives

- **Identify whether a situation involves measuring length, area, or volume.**
- **Examine and apply relationships among figures measured in one dimension, two dimensions, and three dimensions.**

Vocabulary

one-dimensional
two-dimensional
three-dimensional

The Day at a Glance

Today's Goals	Materials	123 Math Talk
1 Teaching the Lesson **A1:** Identify whether a situation involves measuring length, area, or volume. **A2:** Calculate the length of a missing edge of a figure given the volume and other dimensions. **A3:** Discover how area and volume increase when dimensions increase. **2 Extending the Lesson** ▶ Going Further: Estimate to Solve Problems ▶ Differentiated Instruction **3 Homework and Cumulative Review**	Student Activity Book pages 227–230 Centimeter-Grid Paper (Copymaster M19) Connecting cubes Homework and Remembering pages 133–134 Math Journals	In today's activities, the students are involved in discussion as they ▶ examine relationships among length, area, and volume ▶ investigate how area and volume change when dimensions change

Teaching the Lesson

Applications of Length, Area, and Volume

 20 MINUTES

Goal: Identify whether a situation involves measuring length, area, or volume.

Materials: Student Activity Book page 227

✔ **NCTM Standards:**
Geometry
Measurement
Connection

▶ Compare Length, Area, and Volume

WHOLE CLASS

Ask the students to define the terms *one-dimensional*, *two-dimensional,* and *three-dimensional* using words and pictures. Together, read the definitions at the top of Student Activity Book page 227 and discuss how the terms relate to length, area, and volume.

To prepare students to do exercises 1–8, you might ask:

- How many length measurements do you need to find the area of a rectangle? 2; length and width

- How many length measurements do you need to find the volume of a box or rectangular prism? 3; length, width, and height

Invite students to suggest an appropriate unit of measure (either in customary or metric measurements) for each situation. Encourage students to discuss how they got their answers. See a sample of a classroom dialogue in the Math Talk in Action below.

 Math Talk in Action

What kind of figure has one dimension?

Eartha: a line or line segment

How do you describe the size of something that has one dimension?

Daniel: You can tell how long it is.

What kind of figure has two dimensions?

Eartha: any kind of quadrilateral

Daniel: Triangles too. Anything that's flat.

C-2   Name   Date

Class Activity

Vocabulary
Length   one-dimensional
Area   two-dimensional
Volume   three-dimensional

▶ **Compare Length, Area, and Volume**

Length tells how wide, tall, or long something is. Finding length requires one measurement. Length is **one-dimensional**.

Area tells how much surface a figure covers. Finding area requires two length measurements. Area is **two-dimensional**.

Volume tells how much space is inside an object. Finding volume requires three length measurements. Volume is **three-dimensional**.

Length   ⊢——⊣ 1 cm

Area   ▢ 1 cm / 1 cm

Volume   ⬛ 1 cm / 1 cm / 1 cm

Tell if you need to measure for length, area, or volume. Then, write the number of measurements you need to make.

1. How much water is in a swimming pool? volume; 3

2. How tall are you? length; 1

3. How much carpet is needed for a floor? area; 2

4. How far is it from a doorknob to the floor? length; 1

5. How much sand is in a sandbox? volume; 3

6. How much wallpaper is needed for a room? area; 2

7. How long is a string? length; 1

8. How much space is there inside a refrigerator? volume; 3

UNIT C LESSON 2   Relate Length, Area, and Volume **227**

Student Activity Book page 227

How do you describe the size of something that has two dimensions?

Daniel: Tell how much surface it covers.

Eartha: That's the area. You tell the size in square units.

Daniel: To measure it, you have to measure both dimensions.

What kind of figure has three dimensions?

Eartha: a box or a ball

Daniel: any real object, actually

How do you describe the size of something that has three dimensions?

Daniel: Tell how much space it takes up.

Eartha: That's the volume.

Daniel: You tell the size in cubic units and measure three dimensions.

Find an Unknown Edge

 20 MINUTES

Goal: Calculate the length of a missing edge of a figure given the volume and other dimensions.

Materials: Student Activity Book page 228

 NCTM Standards:
Geometry
Measurement
Algebra

▶ Cubic Relationships WHOLE CLASS

Have students complete exercises 9–14. Invite them to explain how they calculated each answer, and if necessary, remind them to include the appropriate unit labels in their answers (square units for area, cubic units for volume). As students share their explanations, write the appropriate equation on the board to help them become familiar with simple algebraic expressions.

```
 9. A = 3 x 3 = 9 sq cm
10. V = 3 x 3 x 3 = 27 cu cm

11. e x e x e = 8, so e = 2 m
12. A = 2 x 2 = 4 sq m

13. e x e = 16, so e = 4 in.
14. V = 4 x 4 x 4 = 64 cu in.
```

Ask students to complete exercises 15–18 and to share their ideas.

Student Activity Book page 228

Differentiated Instruction

Advanced Learners The factors of 24 include 1, 2, 3, 4, 6, 8, 12, and 24. Since two opposite faces of the prism are squares, one of the factors represents the length of the sides of the squares. Students will most likely use guess and check to discover that the dimensions are 2 in. by 2 in. by 6 in.

Ongoing Assessment

Ask:

▶ How do you know whether to solve a problem for length? area? volume?

▶ Why should you always include the units in your answers to these problems?

Teaching the Lesson (continued)

Activity 3

Change Dimensions

 20 MINUTES

Goal: Discover how area and volume increase when dimensions increase.

Materials: Centimeter-Grid Paper (Copymaster M19), Student Activity Book page 229

✔ **NCTM Standards:**
Geometry
Measurement
Algebra

► Double One Dimension of a Figure

| INDIVIDUALS |

Have students draw a 1-by-3 rectangle on grid paper. Ask them to keep doubling the length of the 1-cm side and have them record what happens to the area. Record the results in a table on the board.

	Area
1-by-3	3 sq cm
2-by-3	6 sq cm
4-by-3	12 sq cm
8-by-3	24 sq cm

● What happens to the area when you double one dimension? *You double the area.*

► Double Two Dimensions of a Figure

| INDIVIDUALS |

Ask students to complete exercise 19 independently and explain their conclusions.

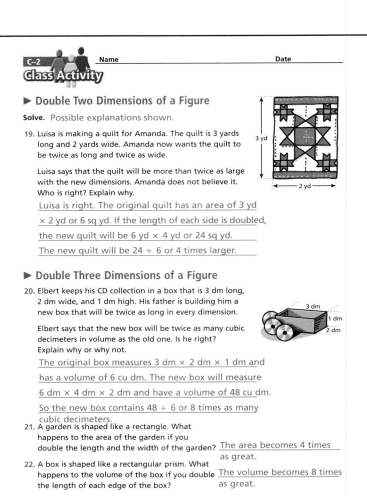

C–2 **Class Activity**   Name _____ Date _____

► **Double Two Dimensions of a Figure**

Solve. Possible explanations shown.

19. Luisa is making a quilt for Amanda. The quilt is 3 yards long and 2 yards wide. Amanda now wants the quilt to be twice as long and twice as wide.

   Luisa says that the quilt will be more than twice as large with the new dimensions. Amanda does not believe it. Who is right? Explain why.

   Luisa is right. The original quilt has an area of 3 yd × 2 yd or 6 sq yd. If the length of each side is doubled, the new quilt will be 6 yd × 4 yd or 24 sq yd. The new quilt will be 24 ÷ 6 or 4 times larger.

► **Double Three Dimensions of a Figure**

20. Elbert keeps his CD collection in a box that is 3 dm long, 2 dm wide, and 1 dm high. His father is building him a new box that will be twice as long in every dimension.

   Elbert says that the new box will be twice as many cubic decimeters in volume as the old one. Is he right? Explain why or why not.

   The original box measures 3 dm × 2 dm × 1 dm and has a volume of 6 cu dm. The new box will measure 6 dm × 4 dm × 2 dm and have a volume of 48 cu dm. So the new box contains 48 ÷ 6 or 8 times as many cubic decimeters.

21. A garden is shaped like a rectangle. What happens to the area of the garden if you double the length and the width of the garden? The area becomes 4 times as great.

22. A box is shaped like a rectangular prism. What happens to the volume of the box if you double the length of each edge of the box? The volume becomes 8 times as great.

UNIT C LESSON 2   Relate Length, Area, and Volume **229**

Student Activity Book page 229

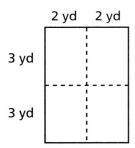

Doubling the length of each side of the quilt will make the area of the quilt four times as large. Students can see this relationship easily if they draw a picture like the one shown above. The first design was 6 square yards in area. The final design is 24 square yards in area.

▶ Double Three Dimensions of a Figure

WHOLE CLASS

Have the class read exercise 20 on Student Activity Book page 229 and solve it together. Doubling the length of the sides will result in the volume being eight times greater, or 48 cubic decimeters instead of 6 cubic decimeters.

Encourage the class to try to visualize the situation: the bottom layer of the new box will be four times as large (just as the quilt in the previous problem became four times as large), and the new box will have two layers because it will be twice as tall. So, four times as large and two times as tall is the same as $4 \times 2 = 8$.

Sketch a 1-by-1-by-1 box on the board. Ask questions as you complete a table to show what happens as you double the length of one side.

Side	Side	Side	Volume
1	1	1	1 cu cm
2	1	1	2 cu cm
4	1	1	4 cu cm
8	1	1	8 cu cm

● What happens to the volume when you double the length of one side? It doubles.

Repeat the activity by doubling the length of two of the sides.

Side	Side	Side	Volume
1	1	1	1 cu cm
2	2	1	4 cu cm
4	4	1	16 cu cm
8	8	1	64 cu cm

● What happens to the volume when you double two dimensions? It becomes four times as large.

Invite students to complete exercises 21 and 22 on Student Activity Book page 229.

Formulate a Generalization Ask the class to state a generalization related to the doubling they just discovered. Help them relate the generalization to the number of dimensions in a figure. For example:

● Length is one-dimensional. If we double it, it becomes two times as long.

● Area is two-dimensional. If we double each length, we have $2 \times 2 = 4$. It becomes four times as large.

● Volume is three-dimensional. If we double each length, we have $2 \times 2 \times 2 = 8$. It becomes eight times as large.

● The factor 2 (the double) occurs once, twice, or three times, depending on whether the shape has one dimension, two dimensions, or three dimensions.

Teaching Note

Math Background Some students may be familiar with exponents. Exponents tell the number of factors in a product of equal numbers. So 4^2 is another way to write 4×4, and 4^3 is another way to write $4 \times 4 \times 4$.

The standard way to write the symbols for area and volume units is to use exponents. So 10 sq cm is written as 10 cm^2 and 10 cu cm is written as 10 cm^3. The exponent is equal to the number of dimensions of the figure being measured.

② Extending the Lesson

Going Further: Estimate to Solve Problems

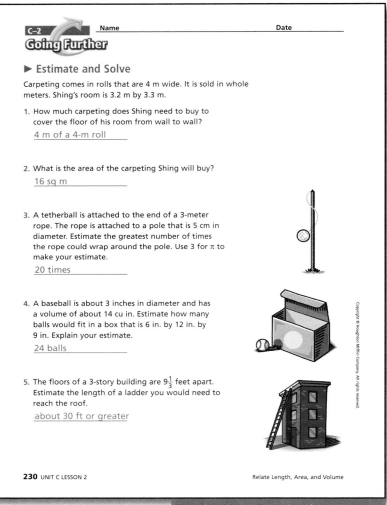

Student Activity Book page 230

▶ **Estimate and Solve** WHOLE CLASS

Discuss when an overestimate or underestimate is reasonable to solve a problem. For example:

● If 13 students travel in cars with 4 students in each car, how many cars do they need? The closest estimate is 3 cars, but then 1 student would be left behind. So they would need 4 cars.

● If the ceiling of a room is $9\frac{1}{2}$ feet high, how many 2-foot-high boxes can you stack in the room? We might estimate 10 ÷ 2 = 5 boxes, but that won't work because only 4 boxes will fit.

Use Solve and Discuss to complete exercises 1–5. Have the students read exercise 1.

● Estimate the area of Shing's room.
about 3 × 3 = 9 sq m

● Is the actual area greater or less than 9 sq m? Why? greater; each side is greater than 3.

● Is this a good estimate for buying the carpet? Why? No; the carpet has to be wider and longer than 3 m.

Have students solve the word problem.

For exercise 3, you might ask, "If the real value of π is greater than 3, will your estimate be greater than or less than the actual answer?" Less than

In exercise 4, the volume of the baseball is extra information. Students should see that they need to use the diameter to figure out how many balls fit along each dimension of the box. Dividing the volume of the box by the volume of the baseball gives an inaccurate answer because the balls cannot be packed tightly like cubes.

In exercise 5, discuss why an exact answer of 28 feet is not a good estimate. The ladder has to lean against the wall and needs to be longer than 28 feet to reach the roof.

Intervention
for students having difficulty

`PAIRS`

Build Boxes

Materials: connecting cubes

Students make a rectangular layer of cubes and record the volume of the layer. They add at least three more layers, one at a time, and record the number of layers and the volume of each new box.

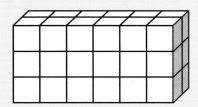

1 layer	2 × 6 = 12 cubes
2 layers	2 × 12 = 24 cubes
3 layers	3 × 12 = 36 cubes
4 layers	

On Level
for students having success

`PAIRS`

Square Areas That Grow

Materials: Centimeter-Grid Paper (Copymaster M19)

Students begin with a 1-by-1 square in the upper left corner of the grid. They draw new squares, increasing both dimensions by 1 each time.

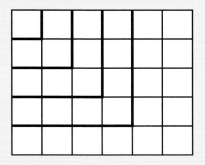

They make a table to record the growth in area and look for a pattern in the number of new square units added each time.

Square	Area	Increase in area
1-by-1	1	
2-by-2	4	3
3-by-3	9	5
4-by-4	16	7
5-by-5		

Challenge
for students seeking a challenge

`PAIRS`

Clap Hands

Present this problem to your students.

To set a world record for hand clapping, you'd need to clap at least 160 times a minute for two days, and be heard from a distance of 120 yards. Make an estimate of how many times you would clap in two days.

> Two days is 48 hours and there are 60 minutes in an hour. That's about 50 × 60 = 3,000 minutes.
>
> 3,000 × 160 = 480,000
>
> So you'd have to clap about 500,000 times.

 Math Writing Prompt

Intervention

Explain Your Thinking
Explain how to measure and find the volume of a rectangular box.

 Math Writing Prompt

On Level

Draw a Picture
Sketch a picture of a box with a volume of 100 cu cm. Label the dimensions. Explain how you know the volume is correct.

 Math Writing Prompt

Challenge

Use Reasoning
Explain how the volume of a triangular prism is related to the volume of a rectangular prism with the same base, height, and length.

③ Homework and Cumulative Review

C–2 Homework **Goal:** Additional Practice

✓ Include students' work for page 133 as part of their portfolios.

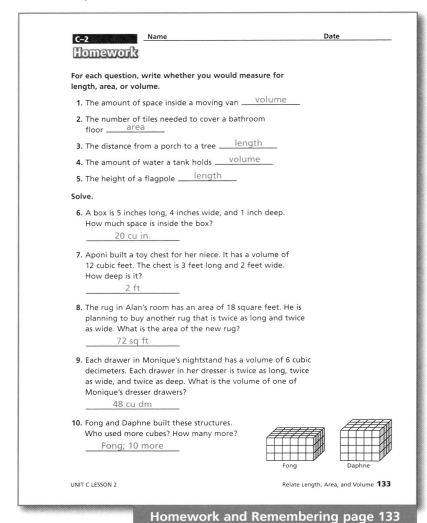

C–2 Homework

Name _____ Date _____

For each question, write whether you would measure for length, area, or volume.

1. The amount of space inside a moving van ___volume___

2. The number of tiles needed to cover a bathroom floor ___area___

3. The distance from a porch to a tree ___length___

4. The amount of water a tank holds ___volume___

5. The height of a flagpole ___length___

Solve.

6. A box is 5 inches long, 4 inches wide, and 1 inch deep. How much space is inside the box?
___20 cu in.___

7. Aponi built a toy chest for her niece. It has a volume of 12 cubic feet. The chest is 3 feet long and 2 feet wide. How deep is it?
___2 ft___

8. The rug in Alan's room has an area of 18 square feet. He is planning to buy another rug that is twice as long and twice as wide. What is the area of the new rug?
___72 sq ft___

9. Each drawer in Monique's nightstand has a volume of 6 cubic decimeters. Each drawer in her dresser is twice as long, twice as wide, and twice as deep. What is the volume of one of Monique's dresser drawers?
___48 cu dm___

10. Fong and Daphne built these structures. Who used more cubes? How many more?
___Fong; 10 more___

Fong   Daphne

UNIT C LESSON 2   Relate Length, Area, and Volume **133**

Homework and Remembering page 133

C–2 Remembering **Goal:** Cumulative Review

This Remembering activity is appropriate anytime after today's lesson.

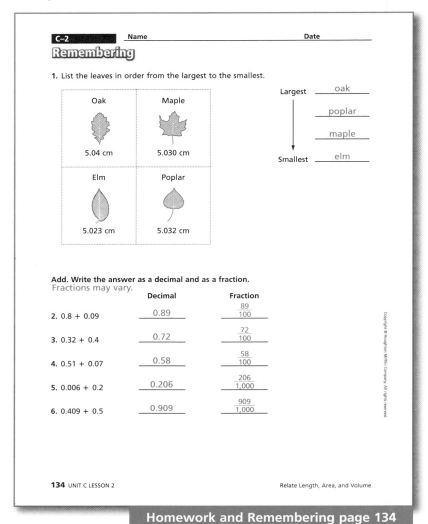

C–2 Remembering

Name _____ Date _____

1. List the leaves in order from the largest to the smallest.

Oak	Maple
5.04 cm	5.030 cm
Elm	Poplar
5.023 cm	5.032 cm

Largest ___oak___
↓ ___poplar___
___maple___
Smallest ___elm___

Add. Write the answer as a decimal and as a fraction.
Fractions may vary.

	Decimal	Fraction
2. 0.8 + 0.09	0.89	$\frac{89}{100}$
3. 0.32 + 0.4	0.72	$\frac{72}{100}$
4. 0.51 + 0.07	0.58	$\frac{58}{100}$
5. 0.006 + 0.2	0.206	$\frac{206}{1,000}$
6. 0.409 + 0.5	0.909	$\frac{909}{1,000}$

134 UNIT C LESSON 2   Relate Length, Area, and Volume

Homework and Remembering page 134

Home or School Activity

 Physical Education Connection

Jumping Jacks Predict how many jumping jacks you can do in one minute. Check your prediction. Make a table showing how many jumping jacks you can do in 2 minutes, 3 minutes, 4 minutes, and 5 minutes.

Measures of Capacity

Vocabulary

capacity
liter
kiloliter
milliliter
cup
pint
quart
gallon

Lesson Objectives

● Explore the relationship among metric and among customary units of capacity.

● Solve problems involving metric and customary measures of capacity.

The Day at a Glance

Today's Goals	Materials	123 Math Talk
① Teaching the Lesson **A1:** Compare volume and capacity. **A2:** Convert among metric units of capacity. **A3:** Convert among customary units of capacity. **② Extending the Lesson** ► Differentiated Instruction **③ Homework and Cumulative Review**	Containers and boxes Student Activity Book pages 231–232 Customary and metric measuring cups Teaspoons Tablespoons Homework and Remembering pages 135–136 Math Journals	In today's activities, the students are involved in discussion as they ► compare the uses for and units of volume and capacity ► describe the numerical relationship between metric units of capacity ► Solve and Discuss real-world capacity problems

① Teaching the Lesson

Volume and Capacity

 10 MINUTES

Goal: Compare volume and capacity.

Materials: containers and boxes

 NCTM Standards:
Measurement
Communication

▶ Compare and Contrast Volume and Capacity WHOLE CLASS

In the two previous lessons, students explored volume and learned that it was a measure of the amount of space occupied by a geometric solid. To contrast volume

with capacity, display a container that is usually associated with liquids, such as a cup or a milk jug, and a box. Write the terms volume and capacity on the board and explain that although both terms in a general way can refer to the amount of space inside an object, volume is a "dry" measure and capacity is a "wet," or liquid, measure.

● Name containers that are commonly used for liquid capacity. Possible answers: milk jug, juice box, water bottle

● Name items you might measure with volume units. Possible answers: a packing box, storage space, a refrigerator, trunk space in a car, cargo space in a truck

Metric Measures of Capacity

 20 MINUTES

Goal: Convert among metric units of capacity.

Materials: Student Activity Book page 231

 NCTM Standards:
Geometry
Measurement

▶ Decimals and Capacity WHOLE CLASS

Write the number 1,000 on the board.

● What is 1,000 ÷ 10? 100

Write 100 underneath 1,000, and continue to divide by 10.

● What is 100 ÷ 10? 10

● What is 10 ÷ 10? 1

● What is 1 ÷ 10? 0.1

● What is 0.1 ÷ 10? 0.01

● What is 0.01 ÷ 10? 0.001

Continue recording on the board.

$$1000 \div 10 = 100$$
$$100 \div 10 = 10$$
$$10 \div 10 = 1$$
$$1 \div 10 = 0.1$$
$$0.1 \div 10 = 0.01$$
$$0.01 \div 10 = 0.001$$

Remind students that these decimal relationships are the basis for the relationships among all metric units of measurement. Together, discuss what students recall about metric prefixes from their work with length.

Read aloud the introductory material on Student Activity Book page 231, or read it together. To work with metric units of capacity, students need to understand the relationships shared by the units, especially liters, kiloliters, and milliliters. Have students study the table.

● Is a kiloliter to the left of a liter, or to the right of a liter? to the left

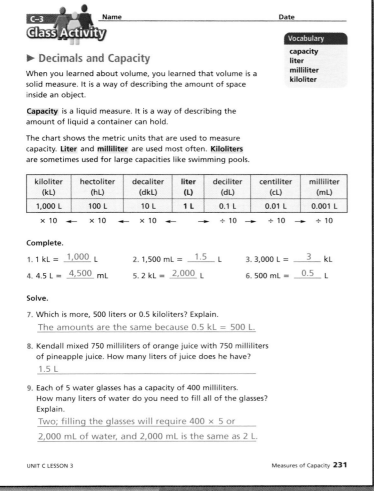

Student Activity Book page 231

- Which is greater, a kiloliter or a liter? kiloliter

- A kiloliter is 1,000 times as great as a liter. Explain how the table shows this. To change liters to kiloliters, you must multiply by 10, by 10, and then by 10 again; 10 x 10 x 10 = 1,000.

- Is a milliliter to the left of a liter, or to the right of a liter? to the right

- Which is smaller, a milliliter or a liter? milliliter

- A milliliter is 1,000 times as small as a liter. Explain how the table shows this. To change liters to milliliters, you must divide by 10, by another 10, and then by 10 again; dividing by 10 three times is the same as dividing by 10 x 10 x 10 or by 1,000.

- Describe the mathematical relationship shared by all of the units in the table. Any unit is 10 times as great as the unit immediately to its right, and 10 times as small as the unit immediately to its left.

Have the class work cooperatively to discuss and complete exercises 1–6. Challenge students to decide the answers using only mental math. Then use Solve and Discuss for exercises 7–9.

 Math Talk in Action

What metric prefixes are related to each number in the chart?

Enrique: The number 1,000 is kilo-, like in kilometers.

Lauren: And 0.01 and 0.001 are centi- and milli-, like in centimeters and millimeters.

What metric prefixes are related to ten and one tenth? Think about the word *decimal*.

Lauren: A decimeter is a length, but is it 10 m or 0.1 m?

Tao: Deci- ends in *i* like centi- and milli-, so I think it's less than 1. So a decimeter is 0.1 m.

Enrique: Then 10 m is a decameter.

Does anyone remember what 100 meters is? There's an area measure called a hectare.

Lauren: A hectameter?

Enrique: I think it's hect-OH-meter, like kil-OH-meter.

Teaching Note

Math Background The metric system has simple and elegant relationships between length, volume, capacity, and even mass. A cubic decimeter of water is exactly equivalent to one liter and has a mass of one kilogram. A cubic centimeter of water is equivalent to one milliliter and has a mass of one gram.

 Ongoing Assessment

Ask students what metric unit might best be used for different liquid amounts.

▶ What unit would you use to measure gasoline for a car? drops of liquid medicine? water falling over Niagara Falls?

Activity 3

Customary Measures of Capacity

 20 MINUTES

Goal: Convert among customary units of capacity.

Materials: Student Book Activity page 232

 NCTM Standards:
Measurement
Number and Operations

▶ **Fractions and Capacity** [SMALL GROUPS]

Students may find it more difficult to convert within the customary system than within the metric system. For example, to change one metric unit to another, a student needs only to multiply or divide by multiples of 10, often using mental math. Changing customary units is more involved. For example, a typical way to

determine the number of pints in 1 gallon is to think that since 2 pints = 1 quart and 4 quarts = 1 gallon, the number of pints in 1 gallon is 2 × 4 or 8.

Read aloud the introductory material on Student Activity Book page 232, or read it together. Encourage students to discuss the different relationships shown in the table. To help them practice applying the relationships, you might choose to write the following exercises on the board, and others like then, then have students work collectively or in small groups to discuss and decide the answers.

4 pints = ___8___ cups

6 pints = ___3___ quarts

8 quarts = ___2___ gallons

1 gallon = ___16___ cups

Use Solve and Discuss for exercises 10–15. Encourage students to use the table to help decide the answers and to commit the relationships shown in the table to memory.

Teaching Note

Math Background The metric system was developed in the 17th and 18th centuries to establish a simple, easily used system of weights and measures that would be universally acceptable to the countries of the world. The metric system is built on a foundation of seven basic units, and all other units are derived from them.

The United States is the only industrialized country in the world that does not use the metric system as its predominant system of measurement.

C-3
Class Activity

Name _____ Date _____

▶ **Fractions and Capacity**

In the United States we measure in customary units.

Vocabulary
gallon
quart
pint
cup

Customary Units of Capacity					
1 pint (pt)	=	2 cups (c)	1 gallon (gal)	=	4 quarts
1 quart (qt)	=	2 pints	1 gallon (gal)	=	8 pints
1 quart (qt)	=	4 cups	1 gallon (gal)	=	16 cups

Answer with a fraction in simplest form.

10. What fraction of 1 **gallon** is 3 quarts?
$\frac{3}{4}$

11. What fraction of 1 **quart** is 1 **pint**?
$\frac{1}{2}$

12. What fraction of 1 quart is 1 **cup**?
$\frac{1}{4}$

13. What fraction of 1 gallon is 1 pint?
$\frac{1}{8}$

Solve. Write your answers in simplest form.

14. A muffin recipe requires $2\frac{3}{4}$ cups of milk. What amount of milk do you need to make double the number of muffins?
$5\frac{1}{2}$ cups

15. A recipe requires $\frac{3}{4}$ of a cup of water. Farha has a measuring cup that measures only ounces, but she knows that 8 ounces is 1 cup. How many ounces of water will she add to the mixture? Explain.
6 ounces; 8 ounces divided into 4 equal parts is
2 ounces; 3 × 2 is 6 ounces.

232 UNIT C LESSON 3

Measures of Capacity

Student Activity Book page 232

② Extending the Lesson

Intervention
for students having difficulty

`PAIRS`

Estimate Liquids

Materials: customary and metric measuring cups, teaspoons, tablespoons, variety of containers

Students estimate the number of milliliters in a cup and check their estimate. They repeat by estimating the number of milliliters in a teaspoon, a tablespoon, and any small containers in the classroom. They check their estimates with a metric measuring cup.

A tablespoon holds about 15 mL.

On Level
for students having success

`PAIRS`

Leaky Faucets

A faucet that leaks 30 drops in a minute can waste 10 liters of water in a day. Students make a table to show the total amount of water wasted after each day for a week. They write an equation to show the amount wasted, *W*, in days (*d*). Students then decide how long it will take for a kiloliter of water to leak from the faucet.

Day	Leakage
1	10L
2	20L
3	30L
4	40L
5	50L
6	60L
7	70L

$W = 10 \times d$
1 kL is 1,000 L
$1,000 = 10 \times d$
d must be 100. It would take 100 days to waste 1 kiloliter.

Challenge
for students seeking a challenge

`SMALL GROUPS`

Gasoline Consumption

Pose the following word problem:

A car traveling at 60 miles per hour uses 2 gallons of gasoline in one hour. How far can the car travel on one gallon of gasoline?
Students make a table to show gasoline used and distance traveled each hour of a five-hour trip.

Hour	Distance	Gallons used
1	60 mi	2 gal
2	120 mi	4 gal
3	180 mi	6 gal

Students find how far the car travels on one gallon of gas and write an equation relating gallons, *g*, to distance, *d*.

The car travels 30 miles on one gallon.
$d = 30 \times g$

 Math Writing Prompt

Intervention

Show What You Know
List some items that you can measure by volume and others you can measure by capacity.

 Math Writing Prompt

On Level

Change Units
Use an example to explain how to change a capacity in milliliters to liters. Use another example to explain how to change a capacity in kiloliters to liters.

 Math Writing Prompt

Challenge

Solve a Problem
How can you pour exactly 4 L of water into a large bucket if you have only a 5-liter container and a 3-liter container?

 Homework and Cumulative Review

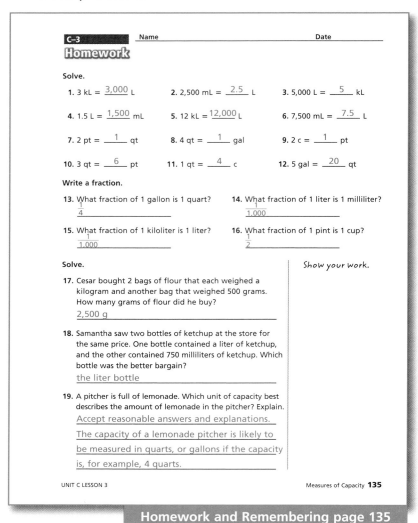

Homework Goal: Additional Practice

For homework, students convert among metric and among customary units of capacity to solve word problems.

Remembering Goal: Cumulative Review

This Remembering activity is appropriate anytime after today's lesson.

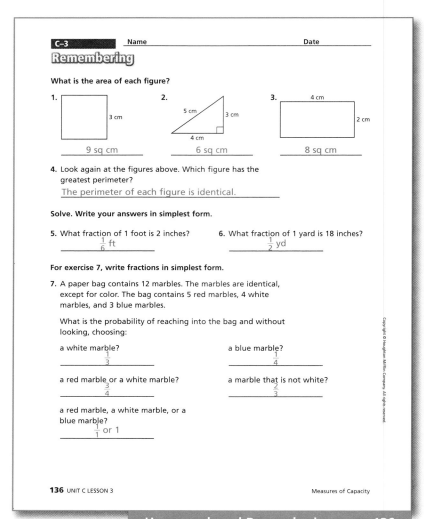

Homework and Remembering page 135

Homework and Remembering page 136

Home or School Activity

 Multicultural Connection

Recipe Research Find a recipe for a dish that comes from a culture different from your own. List all the capacity units and amounts that are used in the recipe.

MINI UNIT C
LESSON
4

Measures of Mass and Weight

Lesson Objectives

- Explore the relationships among metric units of mass and among customary units of weight.

- Solve problems involving metric measures of mass and customary measures of weight.

Vocabulary

mass
kilogram
gram
milligram
ounce
pound
ton

The Day at a Glance

Today's Goals	Materials	123 Math Talk
① Teaching the Lesson **A1:** Discuss the similarities and differences between mass and weight. **A2:** Convert among metric units of mass. **A3:** Convert among customary units of weight. **② Extending the Lesson** ▶ Differentiated Instruction **③ Homework and Cumulative Review**	Balance scale and classroom objects (optional) Student Activity Book pages 223–234 Homework and Remembering pages 137–138 Math Journals	In today's activities, the students are involved in discussion as they ▶ compare the uses for and units of mass and weight ▶ describe how to convert among metric units of mass ▶ explain how to simplify fractions ▶ Solve and Discuss real-world problems involving mass and weight

Teaching the Lesson

Measures of Mass and Weight

 20 MINUTES

Goal: Discuss the similarities and differences between mass and weight.

Materials: balance scale and classroom objects (optional)

✔ **NCTM Standards:**
Measurement
Communication

► Compare and Contrast Measures of Mass and Weight WHOLE CLASS

Although the terms mass and weight are sometimes used interchangeably, the terms do not have the same meaning. Use the following example to help students understand the difference.

- Suppose your weight on Earth is 60 pounds. Because the force of gravity on the moon is only $\frac{1}{6}$ as much as the force of gravity on Earth, your weight on the moon would be $\frac{1}{6}$ of your weight on Earth. If you could go to the moon and stand on a scale, how much would you weigh? $\frac{1}{6}$ of 60 pounds or 10 pounds

You might ask students for the weight of a 60-pound person on other planets with these approximate forces of gravity compared with Earth.

Mercury or Mars $\frac{1}{3}$

Jupiter $2\frac{1}{2}$ times

Pluto $\frac{1}{25}$

Then ask what the mass would be on each planet. 60 pounds.

Explain that a mass of 60 pounds is still 60 pounds on the moon, because the amount of matter doesn't change by traveling to the moon. Your body is made up of an amount of material. This amount is your mass; it is the same whether you are on Earth or on the moon. In other words, you are the same mass in each place. But your weight is different.

 Alternate Approach

Balance Scale Have students compare some classroom objects for weight (or mass). They can use a box of pencils, a tape dispenser, a stapler, scissors, and so on. Ask them to order the objects from lightest to heaviest. Then have them check their predictions using a balance scale. Have them continue checking and comparing until they get all the objects in the correct order.

Teaching Note

Math Background Mass is a difficult concept to define for students. Sir Isaac Newton (1642–1727) defined mass as the quantity of matter. Students may then ask, "What is matter?" This would involve a discussion of the concept of density. Two objects of exactly the same volume may have different masses because the matter or "stuff" in one object is more densely packed than in the other—like packing more stuff in a suitcase of the same size.

Weight depends on the pull of gravity, the concept for which Newton is most famous. In the customary system, pounds are used to measure both weight and mass, so you have to specify what you are measuring. A mass of 60 pounds on the moon has a weight of 10 pounds. The metric unit of weight is the newton (N), named after the famous Sir Isaac, of course. A mass of 1 kg weighs 9.8 newtons on Earth or about 1.6 newtons on the moon.

Metric Measures of Mass

 20 MINUTES

Goal: Convert among metric units of mass.

Materials: Student Activity Book page 233

 NCTM Standard:
Measurement

C-4
Class Activity

Name _____ Date _____

Vocabulary
mass
kilogram
gram
milligram

▶ **Decimals and Mass**

Mass is the amount of matter in an object. Heavier objects have more mass. This table shows the metric units that we use to measure mass. We use **kilogram**, **gram**, and **milligram** most often.

kilogram (kg)	hectogram (hg)	decagram (dkg)	**gram (g)**	decigram (dg)	centigram (cg)	milligram (mg)
1,000 g	100 g	10 g	**1**	0.1 g	0.01 g	0.001 g

× 10 ← × 10 ← × 10 ← → ÷ 10 → ÷ 10 → ÷ 10

Complete.

1. 1 kg = __1,000__ g   2. 500 mg = __0.5__ g   3. 2,000 g = __2__ kg

4. 2.5 g = __2,500__ mg   5. 4 kg = __4,000__ g   6. 5,000 mg = __5__ g

Solve.

7. Hiro has 5 kg of potatoes and 2 kg of onions. He plans to use 3 kg of potatoes and 0.5 kg of onions for a recipe. How many kilograms of each will not be used?
   2 kg of potatoes and 1.5 kg of onions

8. Javier estimates there are 2.5 kg of books in his book bag. Mavis estimates there are 1,500 g of books in her book bag. If the estimates are reasonable, who is carrying the heavier bag? Explain.
   Javier; 1,500 g is the same as 1.5 kg; 2.5 is greater than 1.5

9. A United States nickel has a mass of 5 g. A cloth bag contains 1 kg of nickels. About how many nickels are in the bag? Explain.
   about 200; 1 kg = 1,000 g and 1,000 ÷ 5 = 200

UNIT C LESSON 4   Measures of Mass and Weight **233**

Student Activity Book page 233

▶ **Decimals and Mass** [WHOLE CLASS]

Read aloud the introductory material on Student Activity Book page 233, or read it together. Invite students to discuss the table.

● How do the prefixes of the units compare with the prefixes of the units of capacity in the previous lesson? They are the same prefixes.

Review how to use the table to help to change units of mass. For example, to change from a larger unit (such as kilograms) to a smaller unit (such as grams), you need to multiply the number of kilograms by 10, by 10, and by 10 again. It is helpful for students to recall that multiplying a number by 10, by 10, and by 10 again is the same as multiplying that number by $10 \times 10 \times 10$, or 1,000. Multiplying a number by 1,000 is the same as moving the decimal point 3 places to the right.

● Describe how to change milligrams to grams. Divide the number of milligrams by 1,000, or move the decimal point 3 places to the left.

Have the students work together to discuss and complete exercises 1–6. Challenge students to use only mental math. Then use Solve and Discuss for exercises 7–9.

Teaching Note

Math Background A *tonne*, sometimes called a metric ton, is 1,000 kg. It is equivalent to about 2,200 pounds. A lowercase "t" is the symbol for tonne. 1,000 L, or 1 kL, of water has a mass of one tonne.

 Ongoing Assessment

Ask students what metric unit is best used to measure different objects.

▶ What would you use to measure the mass of a strawberry? a pumpkin? a drop of water?

Activity 3

Customary Measures of Weight

 20 MINUTES

Goal: Convert among customary units of weight.

Materials: Student Activity Book page 234

✓ **NCTM Standards:**
Measurement
Number and Operations

▶ Fractions and Weight [WHOLE CLASS]

Write the words *ounces*, *pounds*, and *tons* in a horizontal row on the board. Remind students that these units are the customary, or common, units we use to measure weight. Then invite volunteers to write, in the appropriate column, an object whose weight is likely to be measured with that unit. For example, you might measure a coin in ounces, a textbook in pounds, and an automobile in tons.

During this activity, students will work with fractions and must write fractions and mixed numbers in simplest form. Prior to completing the activity, you might choose to review how to simplify fractions.

● What operation do we use to change a fraction to simplest form? division

● How do we use division to change a fraction to simplest form? Divide the numerator and the denominator of a fraction by the same number.

● Whenever possible, what number should you choose to divide by whenever you change a fraction to simplest form? the greatest common factor (or greatest common divisor) of the numerator and of the denominator

Teaching Note

Language and Vocabulary The term *ounce* has two meanings, one for capacity and one for weight or mass. To avoid confusion, sometimes the capacity unit is referred to as a *fluid ounce*. The weight measure was once called an *ounce avoirdupois*, the system of weights in which 16 ounces equals 1 pound. An older system used the *ounce troy*, which had 12 ounces in a pound. This system is still in use today by goldsmiths and jewelers.

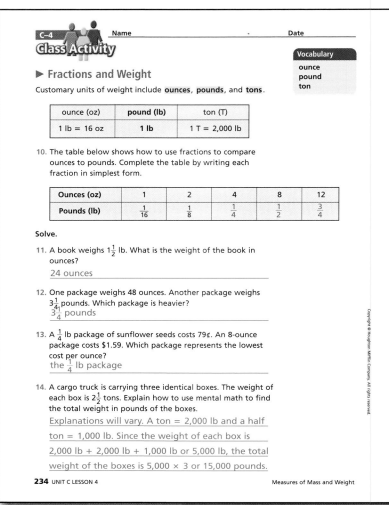

Student Activity Book page 234

Use Solve and Discuss for exercises 10–14. As students work, encourage them to memorize the equivalent units that are presented in the lesson.

1 pound = 16 ounces

1 ton = 2,000 pounds

Differentiated Instruction

Advanced Learners Point out that in the customary measurement system, a standard ton is equal to 2,000 pounds and is also called a short ton. Students may enjoy the challenge of discovering what a long ton is, and sharing their findings with their classmates. (A long ton = 2,240 pounds and is occasionally used to measure the displacement of ships.)

② Extending the Lesson

Intervention
for students having difficulty
PAIRS

Balancing Act

On the board, draw a diagram showing two weights balanced on a scale.

Students copy the diagram and write a weight on one side of the scale in milligrams, grams, kilograms, ounces, pounds, or tons. They trade with a partner who writes a weight that will balance the scale, but uses a different unit in the same system. Students should include examples that use whole numbers, fractions, and decimals.

Possible answers:

2,000 mg	2 g
5 g	0.005 kg
1,000 lb	$\frac{1}{2}$T
4 oz	$\frac{1}{4}$lb

On Level
for students having success
PAIRS

Changing Units

Tell students that 1 kilogram is equal to about 2.2 pounds. Students make a table that shows how to convert kilograms to pounds.

Kilograms	Pounds
1	2.2
2	4.4
3	6.6
4	8.8

Students then write a general equation relating weight in pounds (p) to kilograms (k).

$$k = 2.2 \times p$$

Students investigate other conversions between measurement systems, such as ounces to grams.

Challenge
for students seeking a challenge
PAIRS

Relate Age and Weight

Tell students that a certain 54-pound child gains 7 pounds per year from age 7 to age 12. Students make a table to show the child's age and weight each year.

Age (years)	Weight (pounds)
7	54
8	61
9	68
10	75
11	82
12	89

Students write an equation that shows weight, w, at age y in years.

$$w = 7 \times y + 5$$

 Math Writing Prompt

Intervention
Investigate Mathematics
Explain how to calculate how many ounces are in 1 ton.

 Math Writing Prompt

On Level
Explain Your Thinking
Explain why astronauts in space are said to be "weightless," while their mass remains the same as on Earth.

 Math Writing Prompt

Challenge
Use Appropriate Units
Write about some animals you might weigh in ounces, pounds, or tons. Include an estimate of how much each animal might weigh.

 **Homework and Cumulative Review**

Homework **Goal:** Additional Practice

✓ For homework, students convert among metric and among customary units of mass and weight to solve word problems.

Remembering **Goal:** Cumulative Review

This Remembering activity is appropriate anytime after today's lesson.

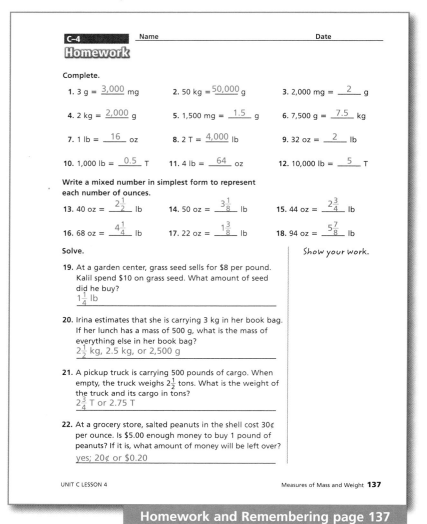

Homework and Remembering page 137

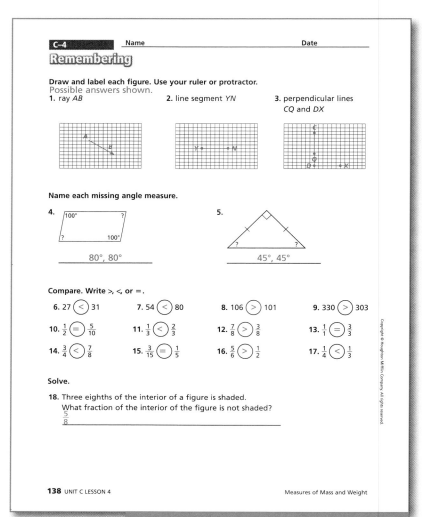

Homework and Remembering page 138

Home or School Activity

 Science Connection

Birth Weights The average human baby weighs 7 pounds 5 ounces at birth. Use science books, encyclopedias, or the Internet to research the average birth weights of various animals. Show your information in a table organized from least to greatest weight.

Unit Review and Test

Lesson Objective

● **Assess student progress on unit objectives.**

The Day at a Glance

Today's Goals	Materials
1 Assessing the Unit ▶ Assess student progress on unit objectives. ▶ Use activities from unit lessons to reteach content. **2 Extending the Assessment** ▶ Use remediation for common errors. There is no homework assignment on a test day.	Unit C Test, Student Activity Book pages 235–236 Unit C Test, Form A or B, Assessment Guide (optional) Unit C Performance Assessment, Assessment Guide (optional)

 Class Management

Review and Test Day You may want to choose a quiet game or other activity (reading a book or working on homework for another subject) for students who finish early.

Assessing the Unit

Assess Unit Objectives

🕐 **45 MINUTES (more if schedule permits)**

Goal: Assess student progress on unit objectives.

Materials: Student Activity Book pages 235–236; Assessment Guide (optional)

▶ Review and Assessment

If your students are ready for assessment on the unit objectives, you may use either the test on the Student Activity Book pages or one of the forms of the Unit C Test in the Assessment Guide to assess student progress.

If you feel that students need some review first, you may use the test on the Student Activity Book pages as a review of unit content, and then use one of the forms of the Unit C Test in the Assessment Guide to assess student progress.

To assign a numerical score for all of these test forms, use 10 points for each question.

You may also choose to use the Unit C Performance Assessment. Scoring for that assessment can be found in its rubric in the Assessment Guide.

▶ Reteaching Resources

The chart lists the test items, the unit objectives they cover, and the lesson activities in which the objective is covered in this unit. You may revisit these activities with students who do not show mastery of the objectives.

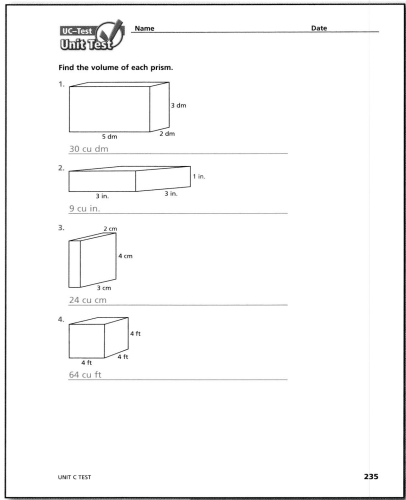

Student Activity Book page 235

Unit Test Items	Unit Objectives Tested	Activities to Use for Reteaching
1–5, 9	**C.1** Find the volume of a rectangular prism.	Lesson 1, Activity 2 Lesson 2, Activity 2
6–8, 10	**C.2** Solve problems involving capacity, mass, and weight.	Lesson 3, Activity 1 Lesson 3, Activity 2 Lesson 4, Activity 1 Lesson 4, Activity 2

Name _____ **Date** _____

Solve.   *Show your work.*

5. A box top is 24 sq cm in area. The volume of the box is 240 cu cm. What is the height of the box?

   10 cm

6. Cardiss made a punch with 1,500 mL of ginger ale and 600 mL of cranberry juice. How many liters of punch did Cardiss make?

   2.1 L

7. A recipe for one batch of muffins requires $1\frac{1}{3}$ cups of flour. Kazuo has $1\frac{1}{2}$ cups of flour. Is that enough flour to make the recipe?

   Yes; $\frac{1}{3}$ is less than $\frac{1}{2}$.

8. Pauline has 3 kg of potatoes and 3 kg of meat. She plans to use 1.5 kg of potatoes and 500 g of meat to make a stew. How many grams of each will not be used?

   1,500 g of potatoes and 2,500 g of meat will not be used.

9. A refrigerator is 3 ft wide, 2 ft deep, and 6 ft high. How much floor space will it cover?

   It will cover 6 sq ft.

10. **Extended Response** One package weighs 36 ounces. Another package weighs $2\frac{3}{4}$ pounds. Which package is heavier? Explain your answer.

    36 ounces is equivalent to 2 pounds 4 ounces.

    4 ounces is less than half a pound so the

    package that weighs $2\frac{3}{4}$ pounds is heavier.

236 UNIT C TEST

Student Activity Book page 236

▶ Assessment Resources

Free Response Tests
Unit C Test, Student Activity Book pages 235–236
Unit C Test, Form A, Assessment Guide

Extended Response Item
The last item in the Student Activity Book test and in the Form A test will require an extended response as an answer.

Multiple Choice Test
Unit C Test, Form B, Assessment Guide

Performance Assessment
Unit C Performance Assessment, Assessment Guide
Unit C Performance Assessment Rubric, Assessment Guide

▶ Portfolio Assessment

Teacher-selected Items for Student Portfolios:

- Homework, Lesson 2
- Class Activity work, Lessons 3 and 4

Student-selected Items for Student Portfolios:

- Favorite Home or School Activity
- Best Writing Prompt

② Extending the Assessment

Unit Objective C.1

Find the volume of a rectangular prism.

Common Error: Doesn't Label the Answer

In writing answers to problems, students may not include a unit of measure with their numerical answers.

Remediation Point out that a measurement problem usually requires a unit of measure with the answer. Emphasize that it is important to look back at the problem to see what unit of measure is needed for the label. Remind students that answers must show the units used. For example an answer of 3 might mean 3 cm or 3 cu cm. This is especially important if dimensions are given in different units.

Common Error: Has Difficulty Visualizing Three-Dimensional Objects

Some students may have difficulty looking at a two-dimensional picture of a rectangular prism and visualizing the three-dimensional object that the picture represents.

Remediation Provide students with actual rectangular prisms, such as books or small boxes, and encourage them to look for pictures of these prisms. Point out that the objects are often drawn from slightly above, rather than from straight on, so the top and sides are visible. Also, give students practice using cubes to build a variety of solid figures.

Unit Objective C.2

Solve problems involving capacity, mass, and weight.

Common Error: Doesn't Use the Correct Units

Some students do not remember to check for units used in their calculations and answers.

Remediation Remind students that answers must show the correct units. They should ensure the same units are used before adding or multiplying. For example, to calculate volume when given dimensions in centimeters and decimeters, students must convert some measures so all of them are in the same units.

The answer should also be stated using the correct units. For example, students might write an answer of 12 cm when the unit should be cubic centimeters. Encourage students to state the given units, and the units that they will use for answers.

Common Error: Labels Answers Incorrectly

In writing the answers to volume questions, students may not label the answers in cubic units.

Remediation Emphasize that it is important to look back at the problem to see what unit of measure is needed for the label. Remind students that answers must show the units used. For example an answer of 3 might mean 3 cm or 3 dm. This is especially important if dimensions

are given in different units. Remind students to label volume computations as cubic units.

Common Error: Confuses Area and Volume

Some students may confuse area and volume when choosing a unit.

Remediation Demonstrate that determining the area of a plane figure requires two factors—length and width.

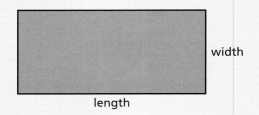

width

length

Demonstrate that determining the volume of a solid figure requires three factors—length, width, and height.

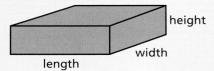

height

length   width

Common Error: Uses an Incorrect Formula

Some students may fail to apply the correct formula when solving a word problem. For example, a student may assume an area problem to be a volume problem, and vice versa.

Remediation Encourage students to draw a picture to represent the problem, and then use their drawing to determine if they need to find the area or volume.

Glossary

Glossary

acre A measure of land area. An acre is equal to 4,840 square yards.

acute angle An angle whose measure is less than 90°.

acute triangle A triangle with three acute angles.

addend One of two or more numbers added together to find a sum.

Example:

add on Find the difference between two numbers by adding to the smaller number to get the greater number.

angle A figure formed by two rays with a common endpoint.

area The amount of surface covered or enclosed by a figure.

array An arrangement of objects, symbols, or numbers in rows and columns.

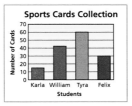

Associative Property of Addition Grouping the addends in different ways does not change the sum.

Example: 3 + (5 + 7) = 15
(3 + 5) + 7 = 15

Associative Property of Multiplication Grouping the factors in different ways does not change the product.

Example: 3 × (5 × 7) = 105
(3 × 5) × 7 = 105

bar graph A graph that uses bars to show data.

Sports Cards Collection

(bar graph: Number of Cards vs. Students — Karla, William, Tyra, Felix)

Glossary (Continued)

base For a triangle or parallelogram, a base is any side. For a trapezoid, a base is either of the parallel sides. For a prism, a base is one of the congruent parallel faces. For a pyramid, the base is the face that does not touch the vertex of the pyramid.

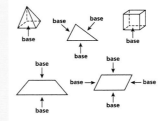

billion One thousand million.

billionth One thousandth of a millionth.

capacity A measure of how much a container can hold.

Celsius The metric temperature scale.

centimeter A unit of measure in the metric system that equals one hundredth of a meter. 1 cm = 0.01 m

change minus A change situation that can be represented by subtraction. In a change minus situation, the starting number, the change, or the result will be unknown.

Example:

Unknown Start	Unknown Change	Unknown Result
$n - 2 = 3$	$5 - n = 3$	$5 - 2 = n$

change plus A change situation that can be represented by addition. In a change plus situation, the starting number, the change, or the result will be unknown.

Example:

Unknown Start	Unknown Change	Unknown Result
$n + 2 = 5$	$3 + n = 5$	$3 + 2 = n$

circle A plane figure that forms a closed path so that all the points on the path are the same distance from a point called the center.

(circle with center point)

circle graph A graph that uses parts of a circle to show data.

Zak's Book Collection

(circle graph with sections: Humor, Fantasy, Mystery, Adventure)

circumference The distance around a circle.

collection situations Situations that involve putting together (joining) or taking apart (separating) groups.

---

column A part of a table or array that contains items arranged vertically.

combination An arrangement of elements.

common denominator A common multiple of two or more denominators.

Example: 6 could be used as a common denominator for $\frac{1}{2}$ and $\frac{1}{3}$.
$\frac{1}{2} = \frac{3}{6}$ $\frac{1}{3} = \frac{2}{6}$

Commutative Property of Addition The order of addends does not change the sum.

Example: 3 + 8 = 11
8 + 3 = 11

Commutative Property of Multiplication The order of factors does not change the product.

Example: 3 × 8 = 24
8 × 3 = 24

comparison situation A situation in which two amounts are compared to find which is more, which is less, and how much more or less.

complementary angles Angles having a sum of 90°.

complex figure A figure made by combining simple geometric figures like rectangles and triangles.

(L-shaped figure)

composite number A number greater than 1 that has more than one factor pair. Examples of composite numbers are 4, 15, and 45. The factor pairs of 4 are: 1 and 4, 2 and 2.

congruent Exactly the same size and shape.

Example: Triangles *ABC* and *PQR* are congruent.

counterexample An example that proves that a general statement is false.

cubic centimeter A metric unit for measuring volume. It is the volume of a cube with one-centimeter edges.

cubic meter A metric unit for measuring volume. It is the volume of a cube with one-meter edges.

cubic unit A unit of volume equal to the volume of a cube with all edges one unit long.

Example: Cubic centimeters and cubic inches are cubic units.

cup A U.S. customary unit of capacity equal to half a pint.

Glossary (Continued)

data A collection of information.

decimeter A unit of measure in the metric system that equals one tenth of a meter. 1 dm = 0.1 m

degree A unit for measuring angles. Also a unit for measuring temperature. (See Celsius and Fahrenheit.)

denominator The number below the bar in a fraction.

Example: $\frac{3}{4}$ ← denominator

diagonal A line segment connecting two vertices that are not next to each other.

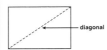
(rectangle with diagonal)

diameter A line segment from one point on a circle to an other through the center. Also the length of that segment.

difference The result of a subtraction.

Example: 54 − 37 = 17 ← **difference**

digit Any of the symbols 0, 1, 2, 3, 4, 5, 6, 7, 8, or 9.

dimension The height, length, or width.

Examples:

A line segment has only length, so it has *one* dimension.

A rectangle has length and width, so it has *two* dimensions.

A cube has length, width, and height, so it has *three* dimensions.

Distributive Property You can multiply a sum by a number, or multiply each addend by the number and add the products; the result is the same.

Example:

3 × (2 + 4) = (3 × 2) + (3 × 4)
3 × 6   =   6   +   12
18   =   18

dot array An arrangement of dots in rows and columns.

double bar graph A graph that uses pairs of bars drawn next to each other to compare data.

Rainy Days

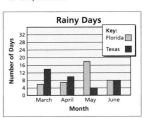

(double bar graph: Number of Days vs. Month — March, April, May, June; Key: Florida, Texas)

Glossary (Continued)

E

edge A line segment that forms a side of a two-dimensional figure or the part of a three-dimensional figure where two faces meet.

elapsed time The amount of time that passes from the start of an event to its end.

equal groups Having the same number of objects in more than one group.

equation A statement that two expressions are equal. An equation always has an equals sign.
Example: 32 + 35 = 67

equilateral Having all equal sides.
Example: An equilateral triangle

equivalent Representing the same number.

equivalent fractions Two or more fractions that represent the same number.

estimate Find about how many or how much. A reasonable guess about a measurement or answer.

example A specific instance that demonstrates a general statement.

expanded form A way of writing a number that shows the value of each of its digits.
Example: Expanded form of 835:
800 + 30 + 5
8 hundreds + 3 tens + 5 ones

expression A combination of one or more numbers, variables, or numbers and variables with one or more operations.
Examples: 4
6x
6x − 5
7 + 4

F

face A flat surface of a three-dimensional figure.

factor One of two or more numbers multiplied together to make a product.
Example:

Fahrenheit The temperature scale used in the United States.

foot A U.S. customary unit of length equal to 12 inches.

function A consistent relationship between two sets of numbers. Each number in one of the sets is paired with exactly one number in the other set.
Example: The relationship between yards and feet.

Yards	1	2	3	4	5	6	7
Feet	3	6	9	12	15	18	21

Glossary (Continued)

G

gallon A U.S. customary unit of capacity equal to 4 quarts.

gram The basic unit of mass in the metric system.

greater than (>) A symbol used when comparing two numbers. The greater number is given first.
Example: 33 > 17
33 is greater than 17.

greatest Largest.

H

half turn A 180° rotation.

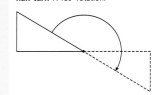

height The perpendicular distance from a base of a figure to the highest point.

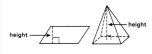

hexagon A six-sided polygon.

histogram A graph in which bars are used to display how frequently data occurs in different intervals.

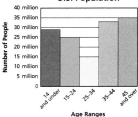
U.S. Population

I

Identity Property of Multiplication The product of 1 and any number equals that number.
Example: 10 × 1 = 10

improper fraction A fraction whose numerator is greater than or equal to the denominator.
Example: $\frac{3}{2}$

inch A U.S. customary unit of length.

inequality A statement that two expressions are not equal.
Examples: 2 < 5
4 + 5 > 12 − 8

---

inverse operations Opposite or reverse operations that undo each other. Addition and subtraction are inverse operations. Multiplication and division are inverse operations.
Examples: 4 + 6 = 10, so 10 − 6 = 4
3 × 9 = 27, so 27 ÷ 9 = 3

isosceles trapezoid A trapezoid with a pair of opposite congruent sides.

isosceles triangle A triangle with at least two equal sides.

K

kilogram A unit of mass in the metric system that equals one thousand grams. 1 kg = 1,000 g

kiloliter A unit of capacity in the metric system that equals one thousand liters. 1 kL = 1,000 L

kilometer A unit of length in the metric system that equals one thousand meters. 1 km = 1,000 m

L

leading A comparing sentence containing language that suggests which operation to use to solve the problem.
Example: John's age is 3 more than Jessica's. If Jessica is 9, how old is John?

least Smallest.

least common denominator The least common multiple of two denominators.
Example: 6 is the least common denominator of $\frac{1}{2}$ and $\frac{1}{3}$.

length The measure of a line segment, or of one side or edge of a figure.

less than (<) A symbol used when comparing two numbers. The smaller number is given first.
Example: 54 < 78
54 is less than 78.

line A straight path that goes on forever in opposite directions.
Example: line AB

line graph A graph that uses connected line segments to show changes in data.

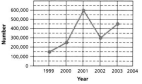
Deer Population in Midland Park

Glossary (Continued)

line of symmetry A line that divides a figure into two congruent parts that are mirror images.

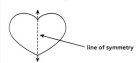
line of symmetry

line segment Part of a line that has two endpoints.

line symmetry A figure has line symmetry if it can be folded along a line to create two halves that match exactly.

liter The basic unit of capacity in the metric system.

M

mass The measure of the amount of matter in an object.

median The middle number in a set of ordered numbers. For an even number of numbers, the median is the average of the two middle numbers.
Examples: 13 26 34 47 52
The median for this set is 34.
8 8 12 14 20 21
The median for this set is
(12 + 14) ÷ 2 = 13.

meter The basic unit of length in the metric system.

milligram A unit of mass in the metric system that equals one thousandth of a gram. 1 mg = 0.001 g

milliliter A unit of capacity in the metric system that equals one thousandth of a liter. 1 mL = 0.001 L

millimeter A unit of length in the metric system that equals one thousandth of a meter. 1 mm = 0.001 m

misleading A comparing sentence containing language that may trick you into doing the wrong operation.
Example: John's age is 3 *more* than Jessica's. If John is 12, how old is Jessica?

mixed number A number represented by a whole number and a fraction that is less than 1.
Example: $4\frac{2}{3}$

mode The number that appears most frequently in a set of numbers.
Example: 2, 4, 4, 4, 5, 7, 7
4 is the mode in this set of numbers.

multiplication table A table that shows the product of each pair of numbers in the left column and top row.

multiplier The factor used to multiply the numerator and denominator to create an equivalent fraction.
Example: A multiplier of 3 changes $\frac{2}{3}$ to $\frac{6}{9}$.

N

non-unit fraction A fraction with a numerator greater than 1.
Examples: $\frac{3}{4}$ or $\frac{4}{8}$.

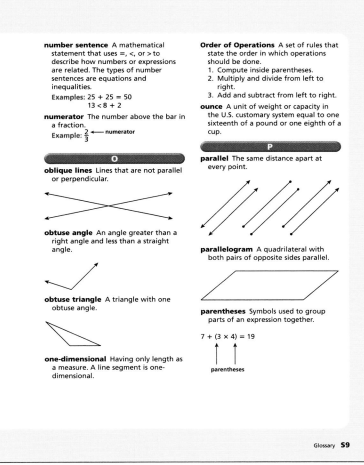

number sentence A mathematical statement that uses =, <, or > to describe how numbers or expressions are related. The types of number sentences are equations and inequalities.

Examples: 25 + 25 = 50
13 < 8 + 2

numerator The number above the bar in a fraction.

Example: $\frac{2}{3}$ ← numerator

O

oblique lines Lines that are not parallel or perpendicular.

obtuse angle An angle greater than a right angle and less than a straight angle.

obtuse triangle A triangle with one obtuse angle.

one-dimensional Having only length as a measure. A line segment is one-dimensional.

Order of Operations A set of rules that state the order in which operations should be done.
1. Compute inside parentheses.
2. Multiply and divide from left to right.
3. Add and subtract from left to right.

ounce A unit of weight or capacity in the U.S. customary system equal to one sixteenth of a pound or one eighth of a cup.

P

parallel The same distance apart at every point.

parallelogram A quadrilateral with both pairs of opposite sides parallel.

parentheses Symbols used to group parts of an expression together.

7 + (3 × 4) = 19
↑   ↑
parentheses

Glossary (Continued)

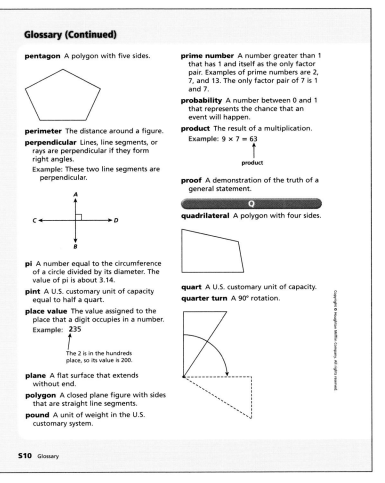

pentagon A polygon with five sides.

perimeter The distance around a figure.

perpendicular Lines, line segments, or rays are perpendicular if they form right angles.

Example: These two line segments are perpendicular.

pi A number equal to the circumference of a circle divided by its diameter. The value of pi is about 3.14.

pint A U.S. customary unit of capacity equal to half a quart.

place value The value assigned to the place that a digit occupies in a number.

Example: 235

The 2 is in the hundreds place, so its value is 200.

plane A flat surface that extends without end.

polygon A closed plane figure with sides that are straight line segments.

pound A unit of weight in the U.S. customary system.

prime number A number greater than 1 that has 1 and itself as the only factor pair. Examples of prime numbers are 2, 7, and 13. The only factor pair of 7 is 1 and 7.

probability A number between 0 and 1 that represents the chance that an event will happen.

product The result of a multiplication.

Example: 9 × 7 = 63
product

proof A demonstration of the truth of a general statement.

Q

quadrilateral A polygon with four sides.

quart A U.S. customary unit of capacity.

quarter turn A 90° rotation.

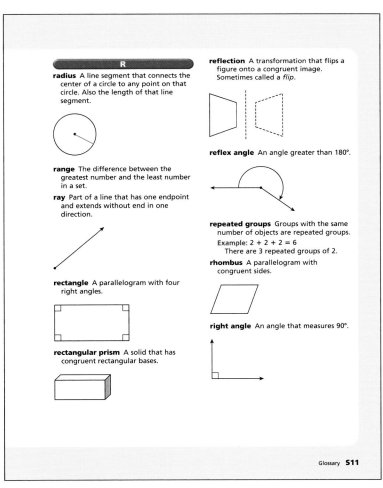

R

radius A line segment that connects the center of a circle to any point on that circle. Also the length of that line segment.

range The difference between the greatest number and the least number in a set.

ray Part of a line that has one endpoint and extends without end in one direction.

rectangle A parallelogram with four right angles.

rectangular prism A solid that has congruent rectangular bases.

reflection A transformation that flips a figure onto a congruent image. Sometimes called a *flip*.

reflex angle An angle greater than 180°.

repeated groups Groups with the same number of objects are repeated groups.

Example: 2 + 2 + 2 = 6
There are 3 repeated groups of 2.

rhombus A parallelogram with congruent sides.

right angle An angle that measures 90°.

Glossary (Continued)

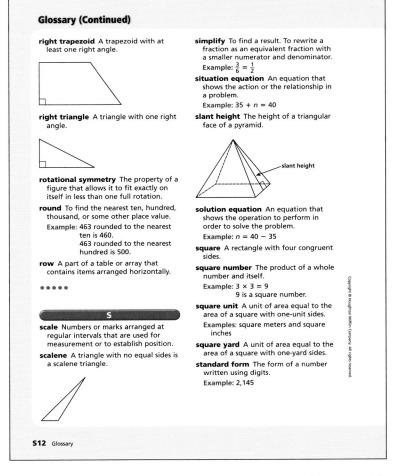

right trapezoid A trapezoid with at least one right angle.

right triangle A triangle with one right angle.

rotational symmetry The property of a figure that allows it to fit exactly on itself in less than one full rotation.

round To find the nearest ten, hundred, thousand, or some other place value.

Example: 463 rounded to the nearest ten is 460.
463 rounded to the nearest hundred is 500.

row A part of a table or array that contains items arranged horizontally.

• • • • •

S

scale Numbers or marks arranged at regular intervals that are used for measurement or to establish position.

scalene A triangle with no equal sides is a scalene triangle.

simplify To find a result. To rewrite a fraction as an equivalent fraction with a smaller numerator and denominator.

Example: $\frac{3}{6} = \frac{1}{2}$

situation equation An equation that shows the action or the relationship in a problem.

Example: 35 + n = 40

slant height The height of a triangular face of a pyramid.

slant height

solution equation An equation that shows the operation to perform in order to solve the problem.

Example: n = 40 − 35

square A rectangle with four congruent sides.

square number The product of a whole number and itself.

Example: 3 × 3 = 9
9 is a square number.

square unit A unit of area equal to the area of a square with one-unit sides.

Examples: square meters and square inches

square yard A unit of area equal to the area of a square with one-yard sides.

standard form The form of a number written using digits.

Example: 2,145

straight angle An angle of 180°.

sum The result of an addition.
Example:

$$53 + 26 = 79$$

addend   addend   sum

supplementary angles Angles having a sum of 180°.

table Data arranged in rows and columns.

three-dimensional Having length measurements in three directions, perpendicular to each other.

ton A unit of weight or mass that equals 2,000 pounds.

tonne A metric unit of mass that equals 1,000 kilograms.

translation A transformation that moves a figure along a straight line without turning or flipping. Sometimes called a *slide*.

trapezoid A quadrilateral with one pair of parallel sides.

triangle A polygon with three sides.

two-dimensional Having length measurements in two directions, perpendicular to each other.

ungroup Rewrite a mixed number with a different whole number and fraction part.
Example: $4\frac{2}{3} = 3\frac{5}{3}$

unit A standard of measurement.
Examples: Centimeters, pounds, inches, and so on.

unit fraction A fraction with a numerator of 1.
Examples: $\frac{1}{2}$ and $\frac{1}{10}$

unsimplify Rewrite a fraction as an equivalent fraction with a greater numerator and denominator.
Examples: $\frac{1}{2} = \frac{3}{6}$

Glossary (Continued)

variable A letter or symbol that represents a number in an expression.

vertex A point that is shared by two arms of an angle, two sides of a polygon, or edges of a solid figure. The point of a cone.

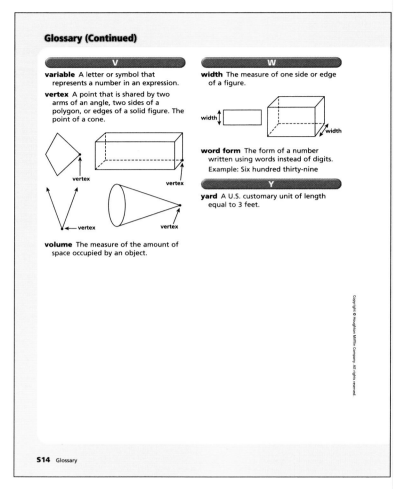

vertex   vertex   vertex   vertex

volume The measure of the amount of space occupied by an object.

width The measure of one side or edge of a figure.

width   width

word form The form of a number written using words instead of digits.
Example: Six hundred thirty-nine

yard A U.S. customary unit of length equal to 3 feet.

Index

Index (Continued)

Index (Continued)

Index (Continued)